eating
out in
pubs

The 2010 ... over
550 pubs. ... n the
guide is th ... n the style
of cookin ... to the
next, our ... n and
every pub ...
Cooking i ... eights,
and there is an enormous amount of choice now available to diners. Some pubs proudly take the organic route with the support of small local suppliers, while others focus more on regional specialities and long-established local recipes. Some serve creative, contemporary cooking with more of an international flavour, but equally, there are plenty offering traditional British favourites too.

If you're having trouble choosing where to go, the descriptive texts give an insight into the individual character of each pub, highlighting what we found to be most memorable and charming, and the accompanying pictures reveal a little bit more of their personality.

Some of these pubs serve their food by the fireplace in the bar; others may have a more formal dining room, but whatever their style, they all have one thing in common: carefully prepared, flavoursome food made from fresh, quality ingredients.

Readers of the Michelin guide Eating out in Pubs write thousands of letters and emails to us every year, praising or criticising current entries or recommending new entries. Please keep these coming and help us to make the next edition even better.

contents

Contents

SCOTLAND
NORTHERN IRELAND
IRELAND
REPUBLIC OF IRELAND
ISLE OF MAN
NORTH EAST
YORKSHIRE & THE HUMBER
NORTH WEST
EAST
ENGLAND
WALES
WEST MIDLANDS
SOUTH WEST
SOUTH
ISLE OF WIGHT
CHANNEL ISLANDS

ENGLAND

COUNTRY OR REGION & COUNTY NAMES

ONE OF OUR FAVOURITE SELECTIONS

TOWN/VILLAGE NAME

NAME, ADDRESS, TELEPHONE, E-MAIL AND WEBSITE OF THE ESTABLISHMENT

ENTRY NUMBER

Each pub or inn has its own entry number.

This number appears on the regional map at the start of each section to show the location of the establishment.

COLOURED PAGE BORDER

- Introduction
- East Midlands
- East of England
- London
- North East
- North West
- South East
- South West
- West Midlands
- Yorkshire & The Humber
- Scotland
- Wales
- Northern Ireland
- Republic of Ireland

England • East of England • Cambridgeshi

Hemingford Grey

The Cock

9

47 High St, Hemingford Grey PE28 9BJ

Tel.: (01480)463609 – Fax: (01480)461747

e-mail: cock@cambscuisine.com **Website:** www.cambscuisine.com

VISA

Buntingford Highwayman IPA, Wolf Golden Jackal, Oldershaw Harrowby Pale, Great Oakley Gobble

Set among thatched houses in the more traditional end of the village, this 17C country pub is run by a very experienced team. Outside you'll come across two doors – one marked 'Pub', the other, 'Restaurant' – the first leading to a split-level bar, the second, to a spacious L-shaped dining room. There's a homely feel about the place, with warm fabrics and comfy seating on display in the bar, and soft, dark hues and attractively papered walls in the dining room. In winter, the best seats in the house are beside the fire, while in summer the most pleasant are near the French windows, looking out into the garden. Cooking rests firmly on the tried and tested side of things, with good value set price lunches; classic pub staples such as lamb shank and belly pork; daily changing fish specials; and a tempting sausage board. The latter, an appealing mix and match menu offering several varieties of homemade sausage, mashed potato and sauces.

Closing times
Closed 26 December

Prices
Meals: £ 15 (weekday lunch) and à la carte £ 20/31

Typical Dishes
Lobster & crayfish risotto
Roast lamb shoulder
Pear & almond tart

5 mi southeast of Huntingdon by A 1198 off A 14. Parking.

58

HOW TO FIND A PUB

There are 3 ways to search for a pub in this guide:
- use the regional maps that precede each section of the guide
- use the alphabetical list of pubs at the end of the guide or
- use the alphabetical list of place names also at the end of the guide

PUBS WITH BEDROOMS

For easy reference, those pubs that offer accommodation are highlighted. in blue This theme is continued on the regional maps that precede each section of the guide.

Horningsea

10 **Crown and Punchbowl**

High St, Horningsea CB25 9JG
Tel.: (01223)860643 – Fax: (01223)441814
e-mail: info@thecrownandpunchbowl.co.uk
Website: www.thecrownandpunchbowl.co.uk

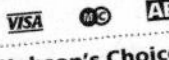

Hobson's Choice

This is more of a place for dining than drinking – as despite the fact that it's a pub, there's no real bar, just a very small counter and seating area. Service is fairly formal but there's a homely atmosphere about the place, with its wooden beams, simple furniture, assortment of framed sketches, and pleasant conservatory, terrace and gardens. To kick things off you'll be brought a board of olives and ciabatta, and to finish, homemade fudge. In between, you'll find a real mix of dishes: some British, others European; some classic – such as pie of the day or homemade burgers – some with a more ambitious edge – such as venison steak with parsnip purée or confit leg of pheasant with chestnut mash. There's a daily fish board which could include halibut with beetroot and bouillabaisse sauce, or sea bream with clam chowder and crab ravioli; as well as a tasty mix and match sausage menu. Bedrooms are simple, tidy and handy for the airport.

Closing times
Closed 26-30 December, Sunday dinner and bank holiday Monday dinner

Prices
Meals: £ 15 (lunch) and à la carte £ 24/33
5 rooms: £ 75/95

Typical Dishes
Scallops with noodles
Fillet of beef
Sticky toffee pudding

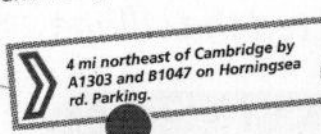

4 mi northeast of Cambridge by A1303 and B1047 on Horningsea rd. Parking.

England • East of England • Cambridgeshire

59

SYMBOLS

Meals served in the garden or on the terrace

A particularly interesting wine list

No dogs allowed

Visa accepted

American Express accepted

Diners Club accepted

MasterCard accepted

REAL ALES SERVED

A listing to indicate the number and variety of regular and guest cask beers usually served.

CLOSING TIMES PRICES ROOMS

Approximate range of prices for a three-course meal, plus information on booking and annual closures.

Some inns offering accommodation may close in mid-afternoon and only allow guests to check in during evening hours. If in doubt, phone ahead.

Room prices range from the lowest-priced single to the most expensive double or twin.

The cup and saucer symbol and price relate to breakfast; if no symbol is shown, assume it is included in the price of the room.

Prices are given in £ sterling, except for the Republic of Ireland where €uro are quoted.

HOW TO GET THERE

Directions and driving distances from nearby towns, and indication of parking facilities and any other information that might help you get your bearings.

THE BLACKBOARD

An example of a typical starter, main course and dessert, chosen by the chef.

Whilst there's no guarantee that these dishes will be available, they should provide you with an idea of the style of the cuisine.

The Pub of the year

Despite all the recent doom and gloom, people continue to love to eat out, and where better than at their local inn, in the heart of the community? Our team of impartial inspectors have travelled Britain and Ireland to find pubs worthy of inclusion in this year's Guide. Each has naturally been chosen for the quality of its food. But what merits the title Pub of the Year?
Location is important, as is a warm welcome. An impressive wine list helps, as do professional service and a relaxed atmosphere. Over and above these things, however, is the star quality which makes this pub extra special; that indefinable ingredient which people will travel long distances to experience and which keeps them coming back, time and again.

The Location

This pretty thatched pub is situated in a secluded hamlet just off the A361, in an area known for its hunting, fishing and shooting, and not far from either the beautiful beaches of North Devon or the foothills of Exmoor. Dating from the 13C, it was originally three cottages; built to house the masons as they constructed the village church of St Peter's.
It has undergone few modifications in its long life and retains an abundance of rural charm.

The Pub

Part of this pub's appeal is that it is still the village local, and as you enter into its cosy, low beamed bar you'll often find regulars with their dogs and guns sat next to the huge fireplace, sinking pints and shooting the breeze with walkers fresh from the hills. Move through to the tasteful little lounge for an aperitif, before taking your seat in the bright rear dining room with its exquisite celestial ceiling mural and fine views over the rolling hills towards Exmoor.

The Chef

Having spent 12 years as Michel Roux's Head Chef at the three Michelin-starred Waterside Inn, Bray-on-Thames, chef-owner Mark Dodson's grounding is about as impressive as it gets. When the lure of country life proved too strong, Mark and his wife Sarah – who heads the charming front of house team – relocated to Devon with their three girls; achieving a Michelin star for the pub a year later.

The Food

Given his background, it comes as no surprise that Mark's cooking leans towards the classics, and he creates sophisticated French and British dishes with an understated modern edge. Produce is sourced from local farmers and growers, with the emphasis firmly on quality, and dishes are attractively presented and deliciously fresh with precise, balanced flavours that show a real understanding of ingredients.

Rustic, characterful and quintessentially British, our Pub of the Year for 2010 is…

The Masons Arms

Knowstone, Devon, EX36 4RY

Tel: (01398) 341 231

e-mail: *dodsonmasonsarms@aol.com* – **website** *: www.masonsarmsdevon.co.uk*

see page 397 for more details

All the pubs in this guide have been selected for the quality of their cooking. However, we feel that several of them deserve additional consideration as they boast at least one extra quality which makes them particularly special.

It may be the delightful setting, the charm and character of the pub, the general atmosphere, the pleasant service, the overall value for money or the exceptional cooking. To distinguish these pubs, we point them out with our "Inspectors' favourites" Bibendum stamp.

We are sure you will enjoy these pubs as much as we have.

ENGLAND

EAST MIDLANDS

EAST OF ENGLAND

LONDON

NORTH EAST

NORTH WEST

SOUTH EAST

Beer in the U.K. and Ireland

It's easy to think of beer as just bitter or lager. But that doesn't tell half the story. Between the two there's a whole range of styles and tastes, including pale ales, beers flavoured with spices, fruits and herbs, and wheat beers. It's all down to the skill of the brewer who'll juggle art, craft and a modicum of science to create the perfect pint.

Grist and wort may sound like medieval hangover cures, but they're actually crucial to the brewing process. Malted barley is crushed into grist, a coarse powder which is mashed with hot water in a large vessel called a mash tun. Depending on what sort of recipe's required, the brewer will add different cereals at this stage, such as darker malt for stout. The malt's natural sugars dissolve and the result is wort: a sweet brown liquid, which is boiled with hops in large coppers. Then comes the most important process of all: fermentation, when the hopped wort is cooled and run into fermentation vessels. The final addition is yeast, which converts the natural sugars into alcohol, carbon dioxide and a host of subtle flavours.

Finally, a beer has to be conditioned before it leaves the brewery, and in the case of cask conditioned real ales, the beer goes directly into the cask, barrel or bottle. The yeast is still active in there, fermenting the beer for a second time, often in a pub cellar. All the time there's a delicate process going on as the beer is vulnerable to attack from micro-biological organisms. But as long as the publican cares about his beer, you should get a tasty, full-flavoured pint.

Beer's as natural a product as you can get. This is what's in your pint:

Barley
It's the main ingredient in beer and rich in starch. Malted before brewing to begin the release of sugars.

Hops
Contain resins and essential oils, and used at varying times to give beer its distinctive flavour. Early on they add bitterness, later on they provide a spicy or citrus zest.

Yeast
Converts the sugars from the barley into alcohol and carbon dioxide during fermentation. It produces compounds that affect the flavour of the beer.

Water
Burton and Tadcaster have excellent local water, and that's why they became great ale brewing centres. Meanwhile, the water of London and Dublin is just right for the production of stouts and porters.

Real quality

The modern taste for real ale took off over thirty years ago when it looked like the lager industry was in the process of killing off traditional "warm ale". There are several styles, but the most popular in England and Wales is bitter, which boasts a seemingly inexhaustible variety of appearance, scent and flavour. You can have your bitter gold or copper of colour, hoppy or malty of aroma, dry or sweet of flavour (sweet flavoured bitter? This is where the term "bitter" is at its loosest). Sometimes it has a creamy head; sometimes no head at all. Typically, go to a Yorkshire pub for the former, a London pub for the latter.

Mild developed its popularity in Wales and the north west of England in Victorian times. Often dark, it's a weaker alternative to bitter, with a sweetish taste based on its hop characteristics. In Scotland, the near equivalent of bitter is heavy, and the most popular draught ales are known as 80 shilling (export) or 70 shilling (special). And, yes, they have a heavy quality to them, though 60 shilling ale – or Light – is akin to English mild.
Full-bodied and rich, stouts (and their rarer porter relatives) are almost a meal in themselves. They're famously black in colour with hints of chocolate and caramel, but it's the highly roasted yeast flavour that leaves the strong after taste.

A vision of England sweeps across a range of historic buildings, monuments and rolling landscapes. This image, taking in wild natural borders extending from the rugged splendour of Cornwall's cliffs to pounding Northumbrian shores, seeks parity with a newer picture of Albion: redefined cities and towns whose industrial past is being reshaped by a shiny, steel-and-glass, interactive reality. The country's geographical bones and bumps are a reassuring constant: the windswept moors of the south west and the craggy peaks of the Pennines, the summery orchards of the Kentish Weald, the "flat earth" constancy of East Anglian skies and the mirrored calm of Cumbria's lakes. The pubs of England have made good use of the land's natural bounty over the past decade; streamlined establishments have stripped out the soggy carpets and soggier menus and replaced them with crisp décor and fresh, inventive cooking. England's multi-ethnic culture has borne fruit in the kitchens of your local…

61
41

An area that combines the grace of a bygone age with the speed of the 21C. To the east (Chatsworth House, Haddon Hall and Burghley House) is where Pride and Prejudice came to life, while Silverstone to the south hosts the Grand Prix. Market towns are dotted all around: Spalding's cultivation of tulips rivals that of Holland, Oakham boasts its stunning Castle and Great Hall, and the legendary "Boston Stump" oversees the bustle of a 450 year-old market. The brooding beauty of the Peak District makes it the second most visited National Park in the world. Izaac Walton popularised the river Dove's trout-filled waters in "The Compleat Angler" and its surrounding hills are a rambler's dream, as are the wildlife habitats of the National Forest and the wind-swept acres of the pancake-flat fens. Above it all looms Lincoln Cathedral's ancient spire, while in the pubs, local ale – typically brewed in Bakewell, Dovedale or Rutland – slips down a treat alongside the ubiquitous Melton Mowbray pie.

Yorkshire & the Humber
North West
EAST
West Midlands
South East
Oldham
Holmfirth
Barnsley
Wigan
MANCHESTER
Leigh
Ashton-under-Lyne
Conisbrough
Doncaster
Glossop
Stocksbridge
Peak District
Rotherham
Altrincham
Hyde
Stockport
SHEFFIELD
Bawtry
High Peak
Maltby
Castleton
Knutsford
Whaley Bridge
Chapel-en-le-Frith
National
Dronfield
Worksop
Northwich
Macclesfield
Buxton
Baslow
Staveley
Chatsworth House
Chesterfield
Middlewich
Congleton
Bakewell
Park
Sandbach
Little Moreton Hall
Clay Cross
Hardwick Hall
Tuxford
Crewe
Kidsgrove
Leek
Matlock
Alfreton
Mansfield
Newark-on-Trent
Sutton-in-Ashfield
DERBY
Southwell
Ripley
Heanor
Hucknall
Ashbourne
Belper
R. Trent
Audlem
STOKE-ON-TRENT
NOTTINGHAM
Ilkeston
Market Drayton
Stone
Derby
Bingham
Uttoxeter
West Bridgford
Eccleshall
Sudbury
Long Eaton
Burton-upon-Trent
Stafford
Abbots Bromley
Rempstone
Newport
Rugeley
Shepshed
Loughborough
Swadlincote
STAFFORD
Ashby de la Zouch
Cannock
Gailey
Coalville
Brownhills
Lichfield
LEICESTER
Walsall
Tamworth
LEICESTER
WOLVERHAMPTON
Sutton Coldfield
Oadby
Atherstone
Hinckley
Dudley
BIRMINGHAM
Nuneaton
Market Harborough
Stourbridge
Halesowen
Bedworth
Lutterworth
Kidderminster
Solihull
Husbands Bosworth
Bewdley
COVENTRY
Rugby
Rothwell
Stourport
Bromsgrove
Kenilworth
WARWICK
NORTHAM
Redditch
Royal Leamington Spa
Wellingborough
Droitwich
Henley
Warwick
Daventry
Worcester
Alcester
Southam
WORCESTER
Stratford-upon-Avon
Great Malvern
Pershore
Evesham
Ettington
Towcester
Upton
Chipping Campden
Shipston-on-Stour
Banbury
Wolverton
Broadway
Tewkesbury
Moreton
Brackley
Milton Keynes
Winchcombe
Stow-on-the-Wold
Chipping Norton
Buckingham
Bletchley
Gloucester
Cheltenham
OXFORD
Bicester

MIDLANDS
East of England
Scunthorpe
Grimsby
Cleethorpes
Immingham Dock
Immingham
Kilnsea
Spurn Head
Rotterdam
Zeebrugge
Brigg
Humberside
Caistor
Gainsborough
Market Rasen
Louth
Mablethorpe
Sutton-on-Sea
Wragby
Alford
Lincoln
Horncastle
Partney
Woodhall Spa
Spilsby
Skegness
L I N C O L N
Sleaford
Grantham
Boston
Hunstanton
Wells-next-the-Sea
The Wash
Donington
Sutterton
Sandringham House
Fakenham
Holbeach
Long Sutton
Mowbray
Bourne
Spalding
King's Lynn
R U T L A N D
N O R F
Oakham
Stamford
Crowland
Wisbech
East Dereham
Eye
Outwell
Swaffham
Guyhirn
Stradsett
Peterborough
Downham Market
Watton
Corby
Whittlesey
March
Mundford
Weldon
Oundle
Chatteris
Ramsey
Littleport
Brandon
Kettering
Thetford
C A M B R I D G E
Thrapston
Ely
Huntingdon
Earith
Soham
Higham Ferrers
St. Ives
Rushden
Godmanchester
Ixworth
NORTHAMPTON
St. Neots
Newmarket
Bury St. Ed
BEDFORD
Eltisley
Stowmarket
Cambridge
Sandy
Potton
S U F F
Newport Pagnell
Bedford
Haverhill
Lavenham
Biggleswade
Clare
IPSW
Ampthill
Shefford
Saffron Walden
Sudbury
Royston
Woburn Abbey
Letchworth
Baldock
Leighton Buzzard
Hitchin
Buntingford
Finchingfield
Halstead
Stour
Luton

1 The Devonshire Arms

Devonshire Square,
Beeley DE4 2NR
Tel.: (01629)733259 – Fax: (01629)734542
e-mail: enquiries@devonshirebeeley.co.uk **Website:** www.devonshirebeeley.co.uk

Chatsworth Gold, Thornbridge Jaipur, Hartington, Black Sheep, Old Peculiar

Part of the famous Chatsworth estate, this historic stone inn has two distinct parts to it: one side is decidedly rural in character, typified by its low ceilings, oak beams and inglenook fireplace, while, by contrast, light streams in through the floor to ceiling windows in the brightly furnished, modern extension. Upstairs, stylish contemporary bedrooms complete the picture. Far from typical pub rooms, they have been styled by the Duchess of Devonshire and are named after the nearby Dales. Food is also far from typical, and although classics like bangers and mash and prawn cocktail are on the menu, other dishes offered might include confit duck terrine, warm salad of wood pigeon or lobster, with most of the fresh, seasonal ingredients coming from local sources and from the estate itself. Wine lovers are also well-catered for with an impressive wine list containing over 300 bins, housed in a glass-fronted cave.

Closing times
Open daily

Prices
Meals: à la carte £ 22/40
8 rooms: £ 82/182

Typical Dishes
Goat's cheese salad
Wood pigeon
Lemon tart

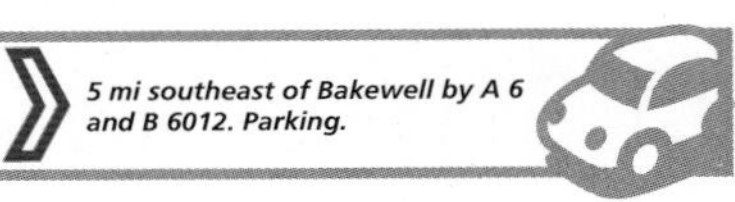

5 mi southeast of Bakewell by A 6 and B 6012. Parking.

2 The Druid Inn

Main St,
Birchover DE4 2BL
Tel.: (01629)650302
e-mail: thedruidinn@hotmail.co.uk **Website:** www.thedruidinn.co.uk

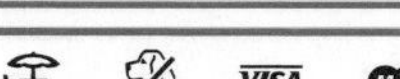

 **Druid Ale, Hairy Helmet, Dovedale**

Many local legends relate to Druid activity in the Birchover area, not least the nearby Nine Ladies stone circle, where Druids would gather to celebrate the summer solstice. You're unlikely to bump into anyone dressed in white robes and chanting Celtic poetry at this pub, however, as it's considerably more famed for its food than for any spiritual inclinations. Worship instead at the table of the Thompson brothers, who work together in the kitchen to produce tasty, wholesome food, including dishes for two to share, a selection of pies and popular sandwiches on homemade bread; favourites such as shepherd's pie or sausage and mash, as well as more restaurant-style dishes, maybe baked monkfish tail, tomato, chorizo and butterbean stew. Wash down your food with a pint of local Druid Ale – you can sit in the more rustic bar area or head down the few steps to the airy, modern dining room with its open plan kitchen.

Closing times
Closed 25 December and Sunday dinner

Prices
Meals: £ 14 (weekdays) and à la carte £ 25/38

Typical Dishes
Crab cocktail
Rump of lamb confit
White chocolate orange cheesecake

7½ mi northwest of Matlock by A 6 and 5 ½ mi from Bakewell. Parking.

England • East Midlands • Derbyshire

3 The Chequers Inn

Froggatt Edge,
Hope Valley S32 3ZJ

Tel.: (01433)630231 – Fax: (01433)631072

e-mail: info@chequers-froggatt.com **Website:** www.chequers-froggatt.com

VISA MC AE

Kelham Island Easy Rider, Black Sheep Bitter, Greene King IPA

On the eastern edge of the Peak District National park, in the heart of the Derbyshire countryside, this traditional 16C country inn is ideally set for nourishment and refreshment before or after a hike, and even has a direct path from its pretty woodland garden right up to the glorious views at Froggatt Edge. Beware when leaving by the front door, however, as the main road is right outside. Inside, clocks and farm implements decorate the walls, there's a large room with a bar, and a quieter, cosier room on the other side of the hall. Menus are chalked up on blackboards, and you place your order at the bar – satisfying favourites such as sausage and mash and pot roasted lamb shank will recharge your batteries, and – named after the nearby market town – Bakewell pudding and custard makes a fitting dessert. Weary walkers staying the night will find bedrooms comfortable – go for one at the back to avoid noise from passing traffic.

Closing times

Closed 25 December

Prices

Meals: à la carte £ 20/27

5 rooms: £ 75/95

Typical Dishes

Belly pork
Breast of duck
Chocolate brownie

Situated on the edge of the village. Parking.

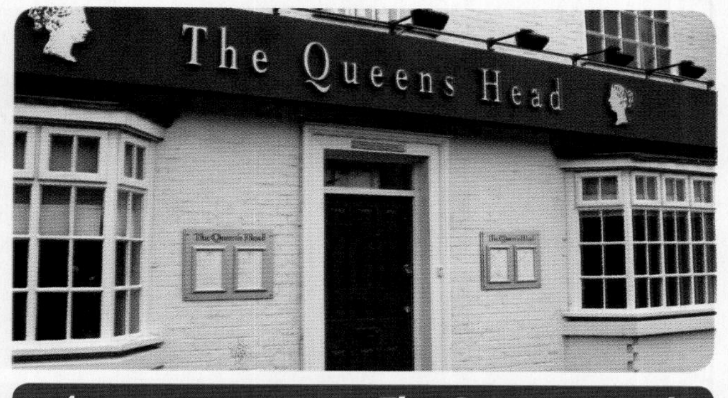

4 The Queen's Head

2 Long St,
Belton LE12 9TP

Tel.: (01530)222359 – Fax: (01530)224860
e-mail: liam@maverickvenues.com **Website:** www.thequeenshead.org

 **Queen's Special, Marston's Pedigree, Beaver Bitter**

A pub of two halves: turn right for the cool lounge and bar, all calming creams, comfy chocolate leather furniture, sleek lines and pale wood, or turn left to dine more formally in the stylishly stark, two-roomed restaurant. There are various seasonally-evolving menus from which to choose, with dishes all proudly made from local produce: lunch might mean a sandwich, steak or fish and chips, whilst more elaborate evening offerings could include roast squab pigeon, with potato and foie gras terrine; pan-fried halibut or roast pheasant. The daily-changing set menu is a well-priced alternative and also proving popular are the 'bring your own wine' evenings held on the first Wednesday of every month. For larger parties there's a separate function room, for al fresco dining there's a covered deck and for sleeping it all off there are bright, individually furnished contemporary bedrooms, which come in varying shapes and sizes.

Closing times
Closed 25 December and Sunday dinner

Prices
Meals: £ 16/23
and à la carte £ 23/35
6 rooms: £ 65/110

Typical Dishes
Seared fillet of red mullet
Fillet of local beef
Vanilla panna cotta

6 mi west of Loughborough by A 6 on B 5234; on the Diseworth/ Breedon rd. Parking.

5 The Three Horseshoes Inn

Main St,
Breedon-on-the-Hill DE73 8AN
Tel.: (01332)695129
e-mail: ian@thehorseshoes.com **Website:** www.thehorseshoes.com

 **Marston Pedigree**

Call in here if you have a sweet tooth, for a one-man chocolate shop has opened up out the back, as well as a deli selling local produce such as biscuits, preserves and traditional sweets. If it's a meal you're after, head inside to where logs burn in the fireplace, candles cast a welcoming glow and various artefacts and pictures tell their stories. Cooking may have international touches, but this is fundamentally simple, honest food, with no unnecessary garnishes; just bold flavours from locally sourced, seasonal produce. Choose from dishes such as beef, mushroom and red wine casserole or pheasant with Savoy cabbage and whisky; homemade desserts might include treacle oat tart or bread and butter pudding. Drinks are as well thought out as the venue and the menu – but mind you don't get rowdy after too much malt of the month; it hasn't held prisoners since 1885, but you never know when the village lock up might be brought back into use.

Closing times
Closed 25-26 December, 1 January and Sunday dinner

Prices
Meals: à la carte £ 18/33

Typical Dishes
Chicken & spinach pancake
Beef & mushroom suet pudding
Chocolate whisky trifle

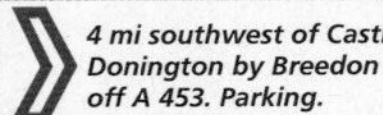

4 mi southwest of Castle Donington by Breedon rd off A 453. Parking.

6 The Joiners

Church Walk,
Bruntingthorpe LE17 5QH
Tel.: (0116)2478258
e-mail: enquiries@joinersarms.co.uk **Website:** www.thejoinersarms.co.uk

 **Greene King, Timothy Taylor**

You can't help but feel that the locals had a part to play in the naming of this pub, which originally started life as the Joiners Arms and has since been affectionately renamed 'The Joiners'. Set in a small rural village, this neat and tidy whitewashed building dates back to the 17C and boasts characterful wood floors, low beams and a small pine fitted bar. Run by an enthusiastic husband and wife team, it's more of a dining pub than a place for a casual drink; although the group of regulars crowded round the bar would probably tell you otherwise. The majority of tables are left set for dining and the casually dressed team are always welcoming. Menus display a mix of refined pub classics and more brasserie-style dishes, all cooked and presented in a straightforward yet effective manner. There's a good value set lunch on offer, as well as a fairly-priced à la carte, accompanied by a wide selection of interesting wines by the glass.

Closing times
Closed 25-26 December, 1 January, Sunday dinner, Monday, bank holidays

Booking essential

Prices
Meals: £ 14 (weekdays) and à la carte £ 21/28

Typical Dishes
Duck fat toast
Sea bass & crab ravioli
Lime tart & chocolate sorbet

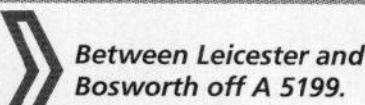
Between Leicester and Husbands Bosworth off A 5199.

7 **Red Lion Inn**

2 Red Lion St,
Stathern LE14 4HS
Tel.: (01949)860868 – Fax: (01949)861579
e-mail: info@theredlioninn.co.uk **Website:** www.theredlioninn.co.uk

Inspectors' favourites

VISA MC

Red Lion Ale, Brewsters Hop Head, Fuller's London Pride, Oldershaw's Caskade, Grainstore Triple B, Greene King IPA

Set in the centre of the village, this spacious whitewashed pub is very much a part of the local community, and while it maintains a healthy drinking trade, it's the food here that's the main attraction. As you walk past its allotment, a blackboard informs you of the latest produce to be planted and picked – and it's this seasonal variation that guides the menus. Inside, there's a rustic stone-floored bar with an open fire, and two characterful wood furnished dining rooms boasting rich fabrics and objets d'art; one of them linen-laid. Menus arrive with a map of suppliers' locations on the back and it's reassuring that they don't stray too far from the doorstep; you'll find sausages from the village butcher, game from the Belvoir estates, cheese from the nearby dairies and fruit from the local farms and hedgerows. Cooking is straightforward and unfussy, resulting in refined pub classics with the odd local or international twist.

Closing times

Closed Sunday dinner

Booking essential

Prices

Meals: £ 16/18
and à la carte £ 19/32

Typical Dishes

Stilton stuffed mushroom

Braised blade of beef

Chocolate & toffee tart

8 mi north of Melton Mowbray by A 607. Parking.

8 The Bakers Arms

Main St,
Thorpe Langton LE16 7TS
Tel.: (01858)545201 – Fax: (01858)545924
Website: www.thebakersarms.co.uk

Langton Brewery Baker's Dozen

If you're looking for character, this thatched, yellow-washed pub in the small village of Thorpe Langton has plenty. It may be deceptively large but the low beamed ceilings, fitted bar and pleasing array of rustic dressers, old scrubbed tables and wooden chairs, ensure that it's cosy and welcoming. The food here is constantly evolving depending on the produce that's available and the large blackboard menu changes not only daily but between – and even during – services. You'll find plenty of pub classics on offer here and reliable combinations; your chicken will come with avocado, your lamb with pea mash and your lemon sole with parsley butter. Thursdays are fish nights, so alongside the usual selection, you'll find an extra list of seafood dishes. If you've got room, there are desserts to take you back to your childhood; including maybe vanilla ice cream with chocolate sauce, a fresh fruit sundae or good old sticky toffee pudding.

Closing times

Closed first week in January, Tuesday-Friday lunch, Sunday dinner and Monday

Booking essential

Prices

Meals: à la carte £ 20/35

Typical Dishes

Pan fried scallops
Duck confit
Sticky toffee pudding

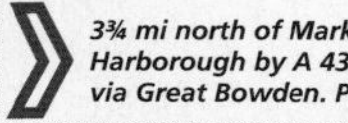

3¾ mi north of Market Harborough by A 4304 via Great Bowden. Parking.

9 The Blue Bell Inn

1 Main Rd,
Belchford LN9 6LQ
Tel.: (01507)533602

 **Black Sheep and weekly changing local ale**

This whitewashed pub is situated in a tiny village between Louth and Horncastle in the heart of the Lincolnshire Wolds and is a popular destination for walkers following the Viking Way, a footpath stretching from the Humber Bridge to Rutland. You can't miss the big blue bell which hangs outside the pub, however, when you delve deeper into it, nobody really knows why it is there, since the pub was originally named after the bluebell flower. It is very much a traditional pub, carpeted throughout, with wooden beams, a typical black wood bar and a friendly, old-fashioned feel. There are old-style armchairs in the cosy bar and linen-clad tables in the similarly styled dining room. It is run by a young couple – Darren and Shona – she manages, whilst he cooks. Dishes are listed on numerous small blackboards on the wall above the fire in the bar and include sandwiches and old pub favourites, alongside more ambitious creations.

Closing times
Closed 25 December, 1 January, 2nd and 3rd weeks in January, Sunday dinner and Monday

Prices
Meals: à la carte £ 14/28

Typical Dishes
Smoked Arbroath haddock
Fillet of Lincolnshire ostrich
Summer pudding

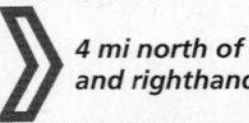

4 mi north of Horncastle by A 153 and righthand turn east. Parking.

10 Gregory Arms

The Drift,
Harlaxton NG32 1AD
Tel.: (01476)577076
e-mail: info@thegregory.co.uk **Website:** www.thegregory.co.uk

 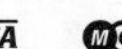

 **Deuchars, Theakstons**

This pub has been part of the local community since the 19C, when workers from the Gregory family's Estate – which covered most of Harlaxton – made it their favourite haunt. Later it was relocated by the Squire to its present spot, where it took responsibility for the delivery of coal from the canal boats at the nearby wharf; it's believed that the weighbridge still lies under the current property. Don't be put off by the busy road running past the front door, as it's definitely worth taking a look inside; the pub was taken over in 2009 by the owners of The Chequers at nearby Woolsthorpe-by-Belvoir, and chances are, if you're fond of a meal there, then you'll probably enjoy one at its sister pub too. The menu offers a selection of pub classics; perhaps fish and chips, a homemade pie or a rib-eye steak; there are sandwiches at lunchtime, and old fashioned puds like those of the sticky toffee or bread and butter variety for afters.

Closing times

Closed 25-26 December dinner, 1 January dinner and Sunday dinner

Prices

Meals: à la carte £ 20/30

Typical Dishes

Oriental beef salad
Chargrilled rib of pork
Warm chocolate tart

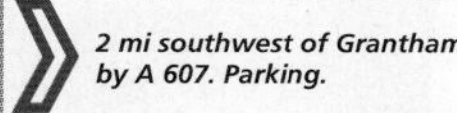
2 mi southwest of Grantham by A 607. Parking.

11 Wig & Mitre

30-32 Steep Hill,
Lincoln LN2 1LU
Tel.: (01522)535190 – Fax: (01522)532402
e-mail: email@wigandmitre.com **Website:** www.wigandmitre.com

Black Sheep, Batemans XB Best Bitter

This pub stands between the castle, which is still used as a court – hence the wig – and the cathedral – hence the bishop's mitre. Open all year round and serving food all day, the owners also run the adjacent wine shop and each dish on the à la carte has a wine recommendation, with even Krug champagne being sold by the glass. Part 14C, part 16C and part 20C extension, the Wig and Mitre is certainly a unique building. Downstairs, there's a small cosy bar with scrubbed tables at the front and lounge style seating at the rear, while upstairs there's another small bar, two smaller period dining rooms, plus a light and airy beamed restaurant with pictures of old judges on the walls. The same menus are served upstairs and down and might include smoked salmon and scrambled eggs for breakfast, sandwiches and other light meals at lunch, with perhaps a caviar starter, followed by steak or duck breast in the evening.

Closing times
Open daily
Prices
Meals: £ 15/20
and à la carte £ 21/46

Typical Dishes
Goat's cheese & asparagus salad
Broccoli Vignotte
Dark chocolate torte

Close to the Cathedral. Lincoln Castle car parks adjacent.

12 The Black Horse Inn

Magna Mile,
Ludford LN8 6AJ
Tel.: (01507)313645 – Fax: (01507)313645
e-mail: reedannam@aol.com

   VISA

 **Batemans XB, Lincoln Red Tom Woods, Rich Ruby Milestone, Village Life Fugglestone**

This 18C pub may not have the most handsome of exteriors, but it matters not a jot, for it's the cooking which entices here. This is tasty, honest food, freshly made from seasonal, local ingredients, with main courses such as steak, fish pie or oxtail with parsnip mash, as well as some interesting vegetarian options, and plenty of comforting nursery puddings like rice pudding or jam roly poly and custard. Although they hail from Lancashire, the husband and wife owners are seriously banging the drum for Lincolnshire produce and, apart from the walnuts – which come direct from her parents' garden in France – everything else is proudly local, including the famous Lincolnshire Poacher cheese. The pub is divided into three rooms and, like the food, has a certain earthiness about it with open fires, simple wooden tables and understated, homely décor livened up by horse prints from nearby Market Rasen and models of Lancaster bombers.

Closing times

Closed 2 weeks in January, Sunday dinner and Monday

Prices

Meals: à la carte £ 16/27

Typical Dishes

Local smoked eel salad
Braised wild rabbit
Walnut tart

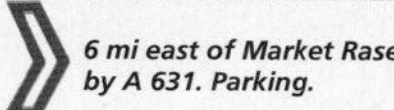

6 mi east of Market Rasen by A 631. Parking.

13 The Bustard Inn

44 Main St,
South Rauceby NG34 8QG
Tel.: (01529)488250
e-mail: info@thebustardinn.co.uk **Website:** www.thebustardinn.co.uk

   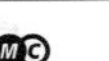 AE

Cheeky Bustard, Bateman's GHA and one weekly changing guest beer

Set in a peaceful hamlet, this Grade II listed building dates back to 1860. Sharing its name with only one other pub in the UK, it's so called because legend has it that the last Great Bustard alive in England was shot just behind the pub. Having undergone a sympathetic restoration, it retains much of its period charm: the characterful flag-floored bar boasts an oak counter and stone fireplace, while the beamed restaurant displays exposed stone walls, tiled floors and wrought iron work, along with ash tables and tapestry chairs. In the former, you'll find an appealing blackboard menu of seasonal dishes such as artichoke tempura or corned beef hash; in the latter, a more structured menu which might include gravadlax or slow roast pork belly, finished off with classical puddings and freshly churned sorbet. Some unusual wines provide a great accompaniment for your meal, while the well-kept ales taste especially good outside in the sun.

Closing times

Closed 1 January, Sunday dinner and Monday

Prices

Meals: £ 15 (lunch) and à la carte £ 20/40

Typical Dishes

Parma ham & goats' cheese salad
Beef Wellington
Sticky toffee pudding

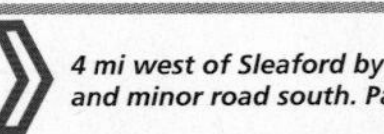

4 mi west of Sleaford by A 17 and minor road south. Parking.

14 The Ship Inn

154 Reservoir Rd,
Surfleet Seas End PE11 4DH
Tel.: (01775)680547 – Fax: (01775)680541
e-mail: shipsurf@hotmail.com **Website:** www.shipinnsurfleet.com

   MC

 **Greene King IPA and other guest beers**

The area of Lincolnshire east of the A1 is hardly known as a gastronomic haven, making The Ship Inn something of a culinary lighthouse. The chef works closely with local producers to source quality ingredients and serves up good old fashioned pub food, so expect the likes of sausage and mash or leek and potato pie, with homemade, old school desserts such as apple and blackberry crumble. From outside, this big square block looks little like a pub, but inside it's spacious, with lots of room in the bar for the locals, and plenty of space for diners too. The full-length windows in the first floor restaurant afford excellent views of the jetty and the fens beyond and the upstairs terrace is a welcoming sight when the temperature begins to climb. Take full advantage of your trip by joining the Pie Club, membership of which grants discounts on pie meals as well as the gift of a pie on your birthday. Bedrooms are large and plainly furnished.

Closing times
Open daily

Prices
Meals: à la carte £ 15/30
4 rooms: £ 45/65

Typical Dishes
Home-cured salmon
Stuffed chicken & lemon sausage
Apple Bakewell tart

4 mi north of Spalding by A 16. Parking.

15 The Chequers

Main Street,
Woolsthorpe-by-Belvoir NG32 1LU

Tel.: (01476)870701

e-mail: justinnabar@yahoo.co.uk **Website:** www.chequersinn.net

Two guest beers such as Youngs, Woodforde's Wherry

The Chequers still has the feel of a village pub: locals sit supping real ale on their stools at the bar and the fixtures for matches on the adjacent cricket pitch hang by the front door, while framed menus from famous restaurants and cruise liners, and the framed Mouton Rothschild labels are a clue to the owners' passion for good food and drink. Made with locally sourced ingredients wherever possible, cooking is simple yet modern, and menus might include classics such as sausage and mash or Stilton pork pie, or for the more adventurous, dishes like clam, squid and salmon risotto or roast rabbit leg. Close to the famous castle in the Vale of Belvoir, this part-17C pub has several areas in which to dine; sit at one of the long tables in the bar or try the more intimate dining room - the cosiest seat in the house is the leather banquette next to the wood burning stove. Four bedrooms are situated next door in the converted stable block.

Closing times

Closed 25-26 December dinner and 1 January dinner

Prices

Meals: £ 15/17
and à la carte £ 21/33

4 rooms: £ 49/59

Typical Dishes

Pan-fried scallops
Roast rump of beef
Yorkshire curd cheesecake

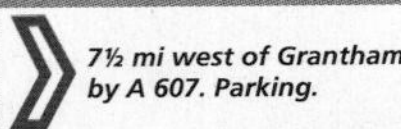

7½ mi west of Grantham by A 607. Parking.

16 The Collyweston Slater

87-89 Main Road,
Collyweston PE9 3PQ
Tel.: (01780)444288 – Fax: (01780)444270
e-mail: info@collywestonslater.co.uk **Website:** www.collywestonslater.co.uk

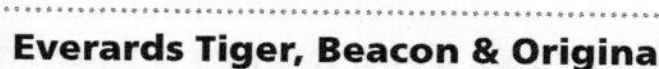

Everards Tiger, Beacon & Original

This stone-built pub successfully combines contemporary décor and furnishings with rural charm and a relaxed atmosphere. Featuring high-backed leather chairs and chunky pine tables, the restaurant feels light and fresh, while the bar area with its tub chairs and welcoming wood burner is more cosy. There's always a way to build up your appetite, be it at one of the monthly quiz or jazz nights, or from playing giant Jenga or Connect 4 in the garden and listening to the gentle 'chink' of petanque balls ringing through the air. The bar menu offers pub favourites such as burger and ploughman's, as well as featuring sandwich and pie sections, while the seasonal à la carte offers dishes with influences from further afield, such as pan-fried salmon with Vietnamese vegetables or roast monkfish with ratatouille ravioli. Bedrooms are comfortable, stylish and well-priced; popular with passing business travellers, as well as those here for pleasure.

Closing times
Open daily

Prices
Meals: à la carte £ 15/25
5 rooms: £ 60/120

Typical Dishes
Pan-fried scallops
Roast rib-eye steak
Sticky toffee pudding

3 mi southwest of Stamford by A 43. Parking.

17 The Falcon Inn

Fotheringhay,
Oundle PE8 5HZ

Tel.: (01832)226254 – Fax: (01832)226046
e-mail: info@thefalcon-inn.co.uk **Website:** www.thefalcon-inn.co.uk

VISA MC AE

Fools Nook, IPA & Regular and changing guest beers

In the pretty village of Fotheringhay – the birthplace of Richard III and deathplace of Mary Queen of Scots – under the shadow of a large church, sits the attractive ivy-clad Falcon Inn. It boasts a neat garden and small paved terrace for al fresco dining and a pleasant beamed, wood-furnished bar – with an unusual display of 15C bell clappers. If you're looking for the regulars, they'll be in the small tap bar playing darts and drinking real ales; while the diners will be found in the conservatory restaurant with its wicker chairs, formally laid tables and pleasant garden outlook. Good-sized menus include unusual combinations and some interesting modern takes on traditional dishes; you might find purple sprouting broccoli in your stilton soup, red pepper and dandelion dressing on your crab, pear chutney with your pork rillette or polenta next to your fillet steak. For private parties the Cottage room annexe provides a pleasant space.

Closing times
Open daily

Prices
Meals: à la carte £ 25/40

Typical Dishes
Salad of roasted butternut squash
Fillet of sea bream
Sticky toffee pudding

3 ¾ mi north of Oundle by A 427 off A 605. Parking.

18 Caunton Beck

Main St,
Caunton NG23 6AB
Tel.: (01636)636793 – Fax: (01636)636828
e-mail: email@cauntonbeck.com **Website:** www.wigandmitre.com

 **Marston's Pedigree, Batemans GHA Pale Ale, Castle Rock Harvest Pale Ale**

Ducks breed on the banks of the Beck, which runs behind this pretty brick pub, and if you approach from the north, you'll make a splash through a ford on you way into the village. There's been a pub at this site for over 300 years, at one point in a state of semi-ruin, but these days, it's modern, welcoming, well-run, and popular with the locals, who enjoy sampling the cask ales. Like its sister pub, the Wig and Mitre, it opens from 8 a.m., and it's a particularly popular destination for breakfast at weekends. The menu offers mostly classic dishes; maybe steak and ale pie, lamb chop or sausage and mash, and daily specials and set menus are chalked up on a blackboard. The restaurant boasts period furniture, beamed ceilings and decorative antique cartoons, but don't dismiss a meal in the stone-floored bar, especially if you're after something lighter. In better weather, try the large front terrace with its colourful flower baskets.

Closing times
Open daily

Prices
Meals: £ 15 and à la carte £ 24/38

Typical Dishes
Breast of pigeon
Toulouse sausage
Chilled lemon & elderflower posset

7 mi northwest of Newark by A 616, 6 mi past the sugar beet factory. Parking.

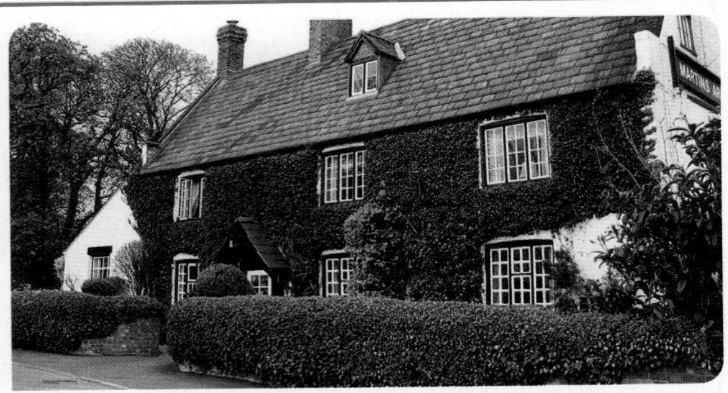

19 The Martins Arms

School Lane,
Colston Bassett NG12 3FD
Tel.: (01949)81361 – Fax: (01949)81039
Website: www.themartinsarms.co.uk

   AE

Bass, Jennings Cumberland, Greene King IPA, Pedigree, Timothy Taylor Landlord, Woodforde's Wherry, Oxford Gold Organic

Warm, welcoming and well run, The Martins Arms has the sort of appearance and atmosphere you'd like to expect from a village pub. Its white façade wears a cloak of creepers, while inside, the traditional décor takes in copper, brass and carpet; plus several pieces of furniture rescued from the village manor house, including a fine Jacobean fireplace. If it's a cosy corner you're after, try the candlelit snug, or for more formal service and surroundings, head for the dining room. With an appealing mix of the traditional and the more modern, the menus contain something for everyone. The owner is a keen hunter, so expect some local game; other choices might range from Ploughman's with Colston Bassett Stilton on the bar menu, to duck liver and foie gras parfait on the à la carte. The large, neatly lawned garden provides a pleasant setting for al fresco dining should the sun decide to spread its love as far north as Nottinghamshire.

Closing times

Closed dinner 25 and 31 December and Sunday dinner

Prices

Meals: £ 16 (lunch) and à la carte £ 20/30

Typical Dishes

Goat's cheese & beetroot

Roast halibut fillet

White chocolate panna cotta

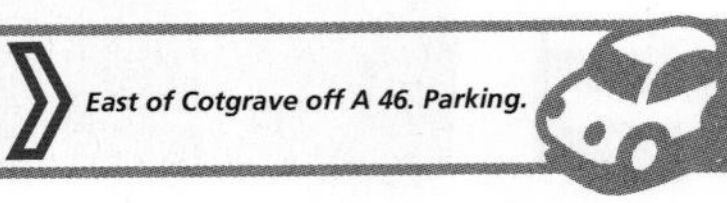

20 Waggon and Horses

The Turnpike,
Mansfield Rd, Halam NG22 8AE
Tel.: (01636)813109 – Fax: (01636)816228
e-mail: info@thewaggonathalam.co.uk **Website:** www.thewaggonathalam.co.uk

 **Thwaites Lancaster Bomber and Wainwrights**

A simple facelift has left this small, cosy pub light, bright and up-to-date. The walls have been re-painted a pleasant shade of green, which contrasts well with the striking modern flower displays on the bar, while in place of the old cricket prints there is now a fresh floral theme. The daily blackboard menu features local meat – such as pan-fried pheasant, slow cooked lamb or pork in a kale and apple hotpot – and lots of fish, which arrives regularly from Grimsby: maybe grilled halibut steak, whole lemon sole or monkfish with creamy mussels. Main dishes are automatically accompanied by a bamboo steamer of fresh vegetables from the fields close by, for which there is commendably no charge. Another pleasant gesture from chef-owner Roy Wood is knocking a couple of pounds off the already good value set lunch menu for the local senior citizens: you could say it's like Christmas every day, well from Tuesday through to Sunday anyway.

Closing times
Closed first week in January, Sunday dinner and Monday

Prices
Meals: £ 15 and à la carte £ 20/40

Typical Dishes
Ham hock terrine
Nottinghamshire pie
Rice pudding & jam

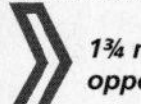
1¾ mi west of Southwell, opposite the school. Parking.

21 The Reindeer Inn

Main Street,
Hoveringham NG14 7JR
Tel.: (0115)9663629
Website: www.thereindeerinn.com

Inspectors' favourites

  MC

 **Caythorpe Stout Fellow, Castle Rock Harvest Pale, Blue Monkey Original, Youngs Bitter**

Hidden away in a pretty village close to the river, this pub offers pleasant views over the local cricket pitch, so be sure to arrive early on match days if you want to secure a spot outside. Its exterior may appear modest but inside it's full of charm. There's a small cushion-filled bar with a welcoming open fire and array of beer pump clips hanging from the ceiling, as well as a more formal dining room with high-backed chairs. The cooking here displays a strong classical base, featuring dishes such as honey-roast pig's cheeks, braised oxtail pie or chicken confit; followed by chocolate mousse or traditional bread pudding. The set price lunch offers excellent value and the à la carte sees selected dishes reduced to half price midweek. Sundays are bangers and mash nights – you pay by the sausage – and every first Friday there's a fish and lobster evening; other events include Greek nights, Mediterranean barbeques and fine food evenings.

Closing times

Closed 2 weeks mid May, Sunday dinner, Monday, and Tuesday lunch

Prices

Meals: £ 7 (lunch) and à la carte £ 19/29

Typical Dishes

Scallop & leek gratin
Rib of Nottinghamshire beef
Butterscotch pavlova

 *5 mi south of Southwell by A 612. Parking.* 

22 Cock and Hoop

29-31 High Pavement,
Nottingham NG1 1HE
Tel.: (0115)8523231 – Fax: (0115)8523223
e-mail: cockandhoop@lacemarkethotel.co.uk **Website:** www.cockandhoop.co.uk

Pedigree, Cock and Hoop, Amber Ale

Situated opposite the Galleries of Justice in the redeveloped Lace Market quarter, and owned by the next door Lace Market Hotel, this comfortable, characterful, well-run pub is popular with hotel guests and locals alike. The attractive building dates back to 1765 and its interior is fittingly charming, with mullioned windows, wood panelled walls, open fire and a vaulted ceiling; the zinc-topped bar complete with hand pumps for real ale; softly lit and lined with assorted black and white photos. Printed and blackboard menus offer sandwiches plus all the traditional pub favourites in satisfying portions, like steak and kidney pie or sausage and mash; to follow you might find rhubarb crumble, lemon curd tart or sticky toffee pudding. Make sure that you mind your table manners – not just because this is a well-heeled sort of a place, but because there are some old prison cells in the cellar which could probably be put to good use.

Closing times
Open daily

Prices
Meals: à la carte £ 17/22

Typical Dishes
Chicken liver parfait
Honey glazed ham
Eton mess with stewed plums

Adjacent to Lace Market Hotel. Fletchergate car park and free on-street parking in offpeak hours.

23 Exeter Arms

28 Main St,
Barrowden LE15 8EQ
Tel.: (01572)747247 – Fax: (01572)747247
e-mail: info@exeterarms.com **Website:** www.exeterarms.com

 **Beech, Hopgear, Black Five Porter**

If you like your real ales then the Exeter Arms is the pub for you, as behind the main building, in what was the old barn, you'll find its very own micro-brewery – which supplies the pub exclusively. Set in the sleepy village of Barrowden, this traditional sandstone pub is just what a pub should be, boasting pleasant views from its front terrace across to the green and duck pond, and a simple interior with yellow walls, small bar and a mix of old wood tables and chairs. Framed pictures and photographs adorn the walls, displaying images of the local area and telling the story of the pub's past. The same menu is served throughout, so you can choose to stay in the open-fired bar or move to the more formal dining room with its exposed stone walls. Cooking is traditional and straightforward, offering well-priced classical combinations, delivered by the friendly, efficient owner. Cottage-style bedrooms offer pond and countryside views.

Closing times
Closed Sunday dinner and Monday

Prices
Meals: £ 17 and à la carte £ 19/22

3 rooms: £ 50/79

Typical Dishes
Prawns & smoked salmon
Lamb shank
Strawberry profiteroles

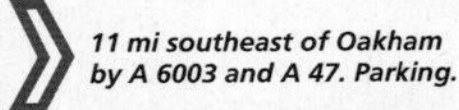

11 mi southeast of Oakham by A 6003 and A 47. Parking.

24 The Olive Branch & Beech House

Main St,
Clipsham LE15 7SH
Tel.: (01780)410355 – Fax: (01780)410000
e-mail: info@theolivebranchpub.com **Website:** www.theolivebranchpub.com

 **Grainstore Olive Oil, Brewsters Decadence, Batemans XXXB**

Very much at the heart of the community, locals are to be found at the bar of The Olive Branch sampling the real ales and soaking up the friendly atmosphere, while the shelves full of cookery books above the church pew seating will also give any newcomers a clue to the pub's gastronomic bent. Their provenance detailed on the menu, dishes might include cottage pie, langoustine ravioli or venison casserole; the kitchen here confident enough to keep things simple and let the quality ingredients speak for themselves. Don't leave without dessert; they are a speciality and definitely worth leaving room for. Six bedrooms in the delightful building across the road have equally delicious-sounding names and every extra has been thought of from homemade biscuits to a DVD player, magazines and books. Breakfast by the fire is also a treat, with freshly squeezed orange juice, and homemade everything, including the fruit compotes and the brown sauce.

Closing times

Closed 25 December dinner, 31 December lunch and 1 January

Booking essential

Prices

Meals: £ 20/25 and à la carte £ 26/38

6 rooms: £ 85/170

Typical Dishes

Potted shrip & prawn terrine

Honey roast Gressingham duck breast

Carrot cake

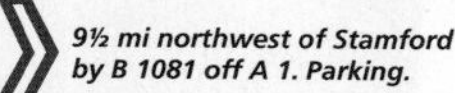

9½ mi northwest of Stamford by B 1081 off A 1. Parking.

25 Finch's Arms

Ketton Rd,
Hambleton LE15 8TL
Tel.: (01572)756575 – Fax: (01572)771142
e-mail: info@finchsarms.co.uk **Website:** www.finchsarms.co.uk

VISA MC AE

Black Sheep, Abbot Ale, IPA

With its light sandstone walls and dark slate roof, this attractive 17C building is the very essence of a traditional country pub in outward appearance. Inside, however, it offers much more than this. True, you'll find the regulars drinking in a characterful bar area among rustic beams and flag floors but, next door, the other rooms take on a surprisingly Mediterranean feel, displaying round stone topped tables and rattan chairs. Continue through yet further and to the rear of the pub you'll find its biggest draw: a large paved, wood-furnished terrace, boasting beautiful views out across Rutland Water. You can eat in any of the rooms, choosing from a list which displays both classic and modern British dishes, but when the weather's warm, the terrace is definitely the place to be – to sit, linger over your meal and watch the world go by. In pleasant contrast to the exterior, bedrooms are smart, contemporary and exceedingly stylish.

Closing times
Open daily

Prices
Meals: £ 15/19
and à la carte £ 20/30

6 rooms: £ 95/150

Typical Dishes
Grilled mozzarella salad
Pan-fried duck breast
Blood orange parfait

3 mi east of Oakham by A 606. Parking.

26 Old White Hart

51 Main Street,
Lyddington LE15 9LR
Tel.: (01572)821703 – Fax: (01572)821965
e-mail: mail@oldwhitehart.co.uk **Website:** www.oldwhitehart.co.uk

Greene King - Abbot and IPA, Timothy Taylor Golden Best

If you're looking for somewhere that ticks all the boxes, then this is it. A 17C former coaching inn set in the pleasant village of Lyddington, this pub boasts a neat garden, canopy-covered terrace and petanque pitches outside; and several cosy open-fired rooms crammed full of old pictures, ornaments and objets d'art on the inside. In keeping with the place, the monthly changing menu offers a selection of traditional pub dishes, cooked and served in a simple, unfussy manner. You might find roast loin of lamb, toad in the hole or pan-fried calves liver, followed by lemon meringue pie, sticky toffee pudding or crumble of the day. If you fancy a bit of light competition, book yourself in for one of the regular petanque evenings, where you get plenty of game play before settling down to dinner. If you still have time to spare, stay in one of the stylish, modern bedrooms – the best has a spiral staircase leading to a private jacuzzi.

Closing times

Closed 25 December and Sunday dinner (September-April)

Prices

Meals: £ 14 and à la carte £ 22/30

10 rooms: £ 60/95

Typical Dishes

Goose liver parfait
Roast rack of lamb
Bread & butter pudding

1½ mi south of Uppingham off A 6003; by the village green. Parking.

England • East Midlands • Rutland

Wide lowland landscapes and huge skies, timber-framed houses, a frowning North Sea canvas: these are the abiding images of England's east. This region has its roots embedded in the earth and its taste buds whetted by local seafood. Some of the most renowned ales are brewed in Norfolk and Suffolk. East Anglia sees crumbling cliffs, superb mudflats and saltmarshes or enchanting medieval wool towns such as Lavenham. Areas of Outstanding Natural Beauty abound, in the Chilterns of Bedfordshire and Hertfordshire, and in Dedham Vale, life-long inspiration of Constable. Religious buildings are everywhere, from Ely Cathedral, "the Ship of the Fens", to the fine structure of Long Melford church. The ghosts of great men haunt Cambridge: Newton, Darwin, Pepys and Byron studied here, doubtless deep in thought as they tramped the wide-open spaces of Midsummer Common or Parker's Piece. Look out for Cromer crab, samphire, grilled herring, Suffolk pork casserole and the hearty Bedfordshire Clanger.

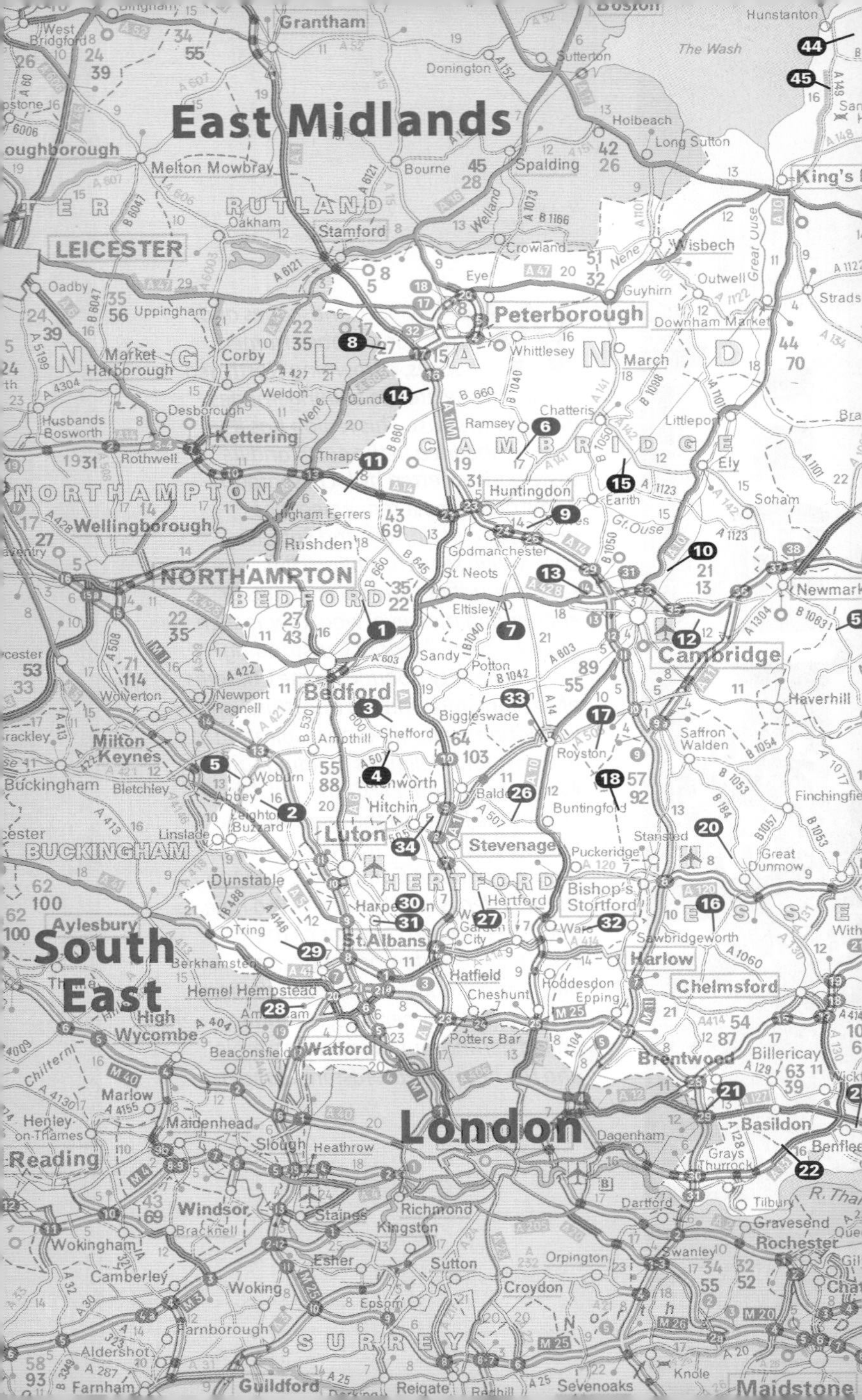
East Midlands
Grantham
Boston
Hunstanton
The Wash
West Bridgford
Donington
Sutterton
Holbeach
Long Sutton
Loughborough
Melton Mowbray
Bourne
Spalding
King's Lynn
RUTLAND
Oakham
Stamford
LEICESTER
Crowland
Wisbech
Eye
Guyhirn
Outwell
Oadby
Uppingham
Peterborough
Downham Market
Whittlesey
Market Harborough
Corby
March
Weldon
Oundle
Husbands Bosworth
Desborough
Ramsey
Chatteris
Littleport
Kettering
Rothwell
Thrapston
CAMBRIDGE
Ely
NORTHAMPTON
Huntingdon
Earith
Soham
Wellingborough
Higham Ferrers
St Ives
Rushden
Godmanchester
St. Neots
Newmarket
NORTHAMPTON
BEDFORD
Eltisley
Cambridge
Sandy
Potton
Bedford
Newport Pagnell
Wolverton
Haverhill
Biggleswade
Shefford
Ampthill
Royston
Saffron Walden
Milton Keynes
Buckingham
Bletchley
Woburn Abbey
Letchworth
Hitchin
Baldock
Buntingford
Finchingfield
Leighton Buzzard
Linslade
Luton
Stevenage
Stansted
Puckeridge
Great Dunmow
BUCKINGHAM
Dunstable
HERTFORD
Hertford
Bishop's Stortford
ESSEX
Harpenden
Welwyn Garden City
Ware
Sawbridgeworth
Aylesbury
Tring
St. Albans
South East
Berkhamsted
Hatfield
Harlow
Chelmsford
Hemel Hempstead
Hoddesdon
Epping
Cheshunt
Amersham
High Wycombe
Potters Bar
Beaconsfield
Watford
Brentwood
Billericay
Chiltern Hills
Marlow
Henley-on-Thames
Maidenhead
London
Basildon
Dagenham
Benfleet
Reading
Slough
Heathrow
Grays Thurrock
Windsor
Staines
Richmond
Dartford
Tilbury
Gravesend
Bracknell
Kingston
Wokingham
Esher
Swanley
Rochester
Orpington
Camberley
Sutton
Woking
Croydon
Epsom
North Downs
Farnborough
SURREY
Aldershot
Farnham
Guildford
Reigate
Redhill
Sevenoaks
Knole
Maidstone
R. Thames
Great Ouse
Nene
Welland
Gt. Ouse

EAST OF ENGLAND
South East
NORWICH
Great Yarmouth
Lowestoft
IPSWICH
Colchester
Southend-on-Sea
Margate
Ramsgate
Bury St. Edmunds
Felixstowe
Harwich
Sheringham
Cromer
Wells-next-the-Sea
Blakeney
Holt
Mundesley
Fakenham
North Walsham
Guist
Aylsham
Low Street
East Dereham
Swaffham
Acle
Bure
Wymondham
Watton
Gorleston-on-Sea
Yare
Mundford
Attleborough
Thetford
Bungay
Beccles
Harleston
Waveney
Halesworth
Southwold
Dennington
Yoxford
Ixworth
Saxmundham
Leiston
Aldeburgh
Lavenham
Woodbridge
Hadleigh
Stour
Halstead
The Naze
Walton-on-the-Naze
Frinton-on-Sea
Brightlingsea
W. Mersea
Clacton-on-Sea
Maldon
Bradwell-on-Sea
Burnham-on-Crouch
Foulness Point
Esbjerg
Hoek van Holland
Cuxhaven
Grain
Sheerness
Isle of Sheppey
Leysdown-on-Sea
Birchington
Whitstable
Herne Bay
North Foreland
Sittingbourne
Broadstairs
Sandwich
Deal
N O R F O L K
S U F F O L K

1 The Plough at Bolnhurst

Kimbolton Rd,
Bolnhurst MK44 2EX
Tel.: (01234)376274
e-mail: theplough@bolnhurst.com **Website:** www.bolnhurst.com

Inspectors' favourites

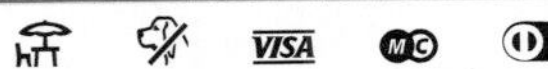

Potton Brewery Local Village Bike, Buntingford IPA

Real ale on tap, a menu teeming with tasty dishes; smooth, assured service and a vibrant yet relaxed atmosphere - The Plough is a pub with it all. The locals patently agree, for this place is often packed to the proverbial rafters, but luckily there's a garden and smart terrace to help take the summer-day strain. Originally dating back to Tudor times, the pub was fully restored to its current whitewashed splendour after a fire some decades ago. Divided into bar and dining room, the interior is no less inviting, and its thick walls, low beams and open fires create a warm, intimate feel. The menu changes according to the seasons, and there's something here for everyone, from simple snacks like devils on horseback or roast chorizo, to pub favourites like ploughman's or free range bangers with colcannon, as well as more elaborate offerings such as foie gras with shallot confit and black pudding or roast English red leg partridge.

Closing times
Closed 31 December,
2 weeks in January, Sunday dinner and Monday

Prices
Meals: £ 17 (lunch)
and à la carte £ 28/42

Typical Dishes
Plough black pudding
Cardington chicken
Lemon tart

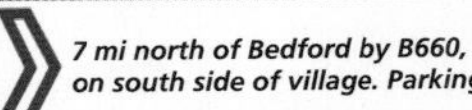

2 The Red Lion

Toddington Rd,
Milton Bryan MK17 9HS
Tel.: (01525)210044
e-mail: info@redlion-miltonbryan.co.uk **Website:** www.redlion-miltonbryan.co.uk

   MC

 **Greene King - IPA and Abbot Ale and guest beers in summer**

With its weathered slate roof, pleasant gardens and colourful hanging baskets, this smart red-brick building really is every bit a traditional country pub. Set right on the outskirts of Milton Bryan, it can be hard to find, especially since it's actually closer to the antique shops of Woburn than its postal village; but it's definitely worth tracking down. Regular groups of drinkers in the open-fired bar ensure that it retains a genuine local feel, while the spacious beamed restaurant with exposed brick walls provides a pleasant space for a relaxed meal. The same menu of classical dishes is served throughout, offering the likes of sandwiches, fishcakes and lasagne at lunch; and natural smoked haddock, rump of spring lamb or the ever-popular Aberdeen Angus steaks at dinner. Produce is sourced largely from local artisan suppliers; although in their search for quality, salmon comes from Loch Dart and fish from the day boats at Brixham.

Closing times
Closed 25-26 December, 1 January and Monday in winter

Prices
Meals: à la carte £ 22/29

Typical Dishes
Rustic pork terrine
Smoked haddock with Cheddar mash
Baked coconut cheesecake

2 mi south of Woburn by A 4012. Parking.

3 Hare & Hounds

The Village,
Old Warden SG18 9HQ
Tel.: (01767)627225 – Fax: (01767)627588
e-mail: thehareandhounds@hotmail.co.uk **Website:** www.

Inspectors' favourites

 **Youngs Bitter, Eagle IPA**

With its ornate feature bargeboards and attractive manicured shrubs, the Hare and Hounds could easily appear on the front of any chocolate box. A charming building set in an idyllic village, it boasts four cosy rooms with brightly burning fires, bucket chairs and squashy banquettes; as well as a friendly team of locals who offer a warm welcome. If you're looking to eat, there's the choice of a blackboard menu listing bar 'snacks' – although you could hardly call them so, as you might find fish and chips or pie of the day – or a monthly changing à la carte that offers robust, flavoursome dishes such as sea bass, pheasant or venison. Bread and pasta are made on the premises; meat is from local farms; fish from sustainable stocks; and they've recently planted an allotment with various herbs, salad and berries. On nicer days, head for the garden and, if you're in a big group, make a play for the large table with the huge wooden parasol.

Closing times

Closed 26 December, 1 January, Sunday dinner and Monday (except bank holidays)

Prices

Meals: à la carte £ 20/25

Typical Dishes

Goat's cheese soufflé
Braised wild boar
English cheeses

3½ mi west of Biggleswade by A6001 off B658. Parking and at Village hall.

4 The Black Horse

Ireland,
Shefford SG17 5QL
Tel.: (01462)811398 – Fax: (01462)817238
e-mail: blackhorseireland@myway.com **Website:** www.blackhorseireland.com

 **Fuller 's London Pride, Greene King IPA, Buntingford Brewery Golden Plover**

Don't be deceived by the picture perfect chocolate box exterior; if you're looking for a quaint country inn you've come to the wrong place. It may appear traditional on the outside, but inside it's as ultra modern as you can get. Contemporary light fittings are set amongst marble-style flooring and a granite-topped counter – which wouldn't look out of place in a West End cocktail bar – and there's even a walled courtyard complete with mirrors and fairy lights. The friendly staff serve up an equally eclectic mix of generously portioned dishes. Lunch could include anything from pizza or suet crust pie, through to terrines, potted crab or sea bass; whilst dinner might offer stuffed peppers or pork brawn to start, followed by confit of duck, oxtail pudding, sweet potato tagine or bean curd medallions for main course – all topped off with good, hearty puddings. Accessed via a meandering garden path, bedrooms are comfy and delightfully cosy.

Closing times
Closed 25-26 December, 1 January and Sunday dinner

Prices
Meals: à la carte £ 25/30
2 rooms: £ 55

Typical Dishes
Crab meat in pasta shell
Pan-fried loin of Cornish lamb
The Black Horse chocolate plate

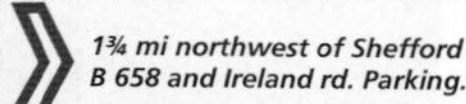
1¾ mi northwest of Shefford B 658 and Ireland rd. Parking.

England • East of England • Bedfordshire

5 The Birch

20 Newport Rd,
Woburn MK17 9HX

Tel.: (01525)290295 – Fax: (01525)290899
e-mail: etaverns@aol.com **Website:** www.birchwoburn.com

Inspectors' favourites

 **Fuller's London Pride, Adnams**

They say that appearances can be deceiving and none more so than at The Birch. An attractive creamwashed pub with shuttered windows, pleasant porch, smart topiary shrubs and hanging baskets, it couldn't be more of a contrast inside, where, akin to its sister operation The Black Horse, cavernous rooms are filled with bright colours, bold pictures and contemporary furnishings. A large conservatory and small enclosed terrace only add to its appeal, so if you don't arrive early you might find yourself battling locals and visitors for a parking space. The charming young team are well versed in the daily specials but if it's something more familiar you're after then there's always a selection of good old favourites such as pork belly, medallions of lamb or fresh fish of the day. If you prefer to watch your meal being prepared in front of you opt for fish or steak from the griddle, where dishes are cooked to order – the latter by the ounce.

Closing times

Closed 25-26 December, 1 January and Sunday dinner

Booking essential

Prices

Meals: à la carte £ 28/37

Typical Dishes

Pan-fried Halloumi cheese

Slow cooked pork

Berry meringue soufflé

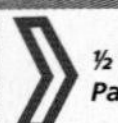

½ mi north of Woburn on A5130.
Parking.

6 The Crown

Bridge Rd,
Broughton PE28 3AY
Tel.: (01487)824428
e-mail: info@thecrowninnrestaurant.co.uk **Website:** www.thecrowninnrestaurant.co.uk

   AE

 **Greene King IPA, Digfield Ales, Elgoods, Potton Nethergate, Adnams**

Set in a pretty village of thatched cottages, just across from the village church, The Crown Inn is a much loved local: once saved from residential development by the villagers themselves, it is now owned by chef David Anderson, and its reputation as a quality eating and drinking house is as solid as ever. Inside, it is light and airy with scrubbed pine tables and cookery books on the windowsills. The pub offers a good selection of real ales and some reasonably priced wines, so it can get quite noisy with drinkers by the bar counter; if you're dining, head instead for a table on the other side of the fireplace, overlooking the pretty garden. The à la carte menu is short and varied, with a Mediterranean thread running through it; choices might include beef carpaccio, potato gnocchi or buffalo mozzarella to start and maybe fish and chips, Aberdeen Angus steak or some pasta for a main course. Service is polite and comes with a flourish.

Closing times

Closed Monday and Tuesday

Prices

Meals: £ 15 (lunch) and à la carte £ 19/27

Typical Dishes

Chicken liver pâté
Medallions of deer
Steamed syrup sponge pudding

5 mi northeast of Huntingdon by A 141 and minor road west. Parking.

7 **The Eltisley**

2 The Green,
Eltisley PE19 6TG
Tel.: (01480)880308
e-mail: theeltisley@btconnect.com **Website:** www.theeltisley.co.uk

Youngs, Wells and one regularly changing guest beer

In a mere six weeks this traditional country inn overlooking the village green morphed into a chic and stylish gastro-pub. At first glance you would imagine that it's a strictly dining affair but the contemporary bar is equally as welcoming to drinkers as to diners, who can watch their dishes being prepared from the carefully placed windows in the snug. For a more formal occasion head through to the restaurant, where grey walls meet wood and tile flooring, and bold designs are offset by swanky chandeliers. Large parties should ask for the 'Wurlitzer', a stylish high-backed semi-circular banquette, while for summer dining the smart new terrace is ideal. Cooking is simple, unfussy and relies on quality local ingredients to speak for themselves; meat is from nearby farms, vegetables from the allotment at their sister pub the 'Hare and Hounds', and everything from the bread and pasta through to the desserts and ice cream is homemade.

Closing times

Closed Sunday dinner, Monday (except bank holidays)

Prices

Meals: à la carte £ 23/33

Typical Dishes

Potato gnocchi

Seared venison loin steak

Dark chocolate mousse

12 mi west by A 1303 from Cambridge and A 428. Parking.

8 The Crown Inn

8 Duck St,
Elton PE8 6RQ
Tel.: (01832)280232
e-mail: inncrown@googlemail.com **Website:** www.thecrowninn.org

 **Golden Crown Bitter, Barnwell Bitter, Oakham JHB, Greene King IPA, Woodforde's Wherry**

If you were to dream up the perfect location for a village inn, it would probably resemble the beautiful parish of Elton, all honey stone houses and well-trimmed green – the thatched roof and inglenook fireplace of the 17C Crown Inn blending in superbly. Sit in the open main bar, the sizeable front dining room, the rear conservatory, or in brighter weather, the decked terrace, which makes a delightful spot to try some of the many, frequently changing, real ales on offer. Food is traditional in the main; you might try steak and ale pie, sausage and mash or the ever popular fish and chips – but there's a touch of the Mediterranean here too in the form of dishes such as tagliatelli or risotto, which all arrive in healthy portions. Bedrooms – three in the main house and two out the back – are smart and individually styled, with spacious bathrooms. Elton is the biggest room and boasts a sleigh bed, while Chestnut features a four poster.

Closing times

Closed 25 December, 1-7 January, Sunday dinner, Monday (except bank holiday when open for lunch)

Prices

Meals: £ 16 (weekday lunch) and à la carte £ 25/34

5 rooms: £ 60/120

Typical Dishes

Oxtail & Stilton tart

Grasmere Farm stuffed pork loin

Elton Swan profiteroles

6 mi southwest of Peterborough by A1139, A605 and minor road north. Parking and on village green opposite.

Hemingford Grey

9 The Cock

47 High St,
Hemingford Grey PE28 9BJ
Tel.: (01480)463609 – Fax: (01480)461747
e-mail: cock@cambscuisine.com **Website:** www.cambscuisine.com

Buntingford Highwayman IPA, Wolf Golden Jackal, Oldershaw Harrowby Pale, Great Oakley Gobble

Set among thatched houses in the more traditional end of the village, this 17C country pub is run by a very experienced team. Outside you'll come across two doors – one marked 'Pub', the other, 'Restaurant' – the first leading to a split-level bar, the second, to a spacious L-shaped dining room. There's a homely feel about the place, with warm fabrics and comfy seating on display in the bar, and soft, dark hues and attractively papered walls in the dining room. In winter, the best seats in the house are beside the fire, while in summer the most pleasant are near the French windows, looking out into the garden. Cooking rests firmly on the tried and tested side of things, with good value set price lunches; classic pub staples such as lamb shank and belly pork; daily changing fish specials; and a tempting sausage board. The latter, an appealing mix and match menu offering several varieties of homemade sausage, mashed potato and sauces.

Closing times

Closed 26 December

Prices

Meals: £ 15 (weekday lunch) and à la carte £ 20/31

Typical Dishes

Lobster & crayfish risotto

Roast lamb shoulder

Pear & almond tart

5 mi southeast of Huntingdon by A 1198 off A 14. Parking.

10 Crown and Punchbowl

High St, Horningsea CB25 9JG
Tel.: (01223)860643 – Fax: (01223)441814
e-mail: info@thecrownandpunchbowl.co.uk
Website: www.thecrownandpunchbowl.co.uk

 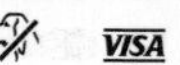 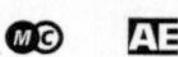 

 **Hobson's Choice**

This is more of a place for dining than drinking – as despite the fact that it's a pub, there's no real bar, just a very small counter and seating area. Service is fairly formal but there's a homely atmosphere about the place, with its wooden beams, simple furniture, assortment of framed sketches, and pleasant conservatory, terrace and gardens. To kick things off you'll be brought a board of olives and ciabatta, and to finish, homemade fudge. In between, you'll find a real mix of dishes: some British, others European; some classic – such as pie of the day or homemade burgers – some with a more ambitious edge – such as venison steak with parsnip purée or confit leg of pheasant with chestnut mash. There's a daily fish board which could include halibut with beetroot and bouillabaisse sauce, or sea bream with clam chowder and crab ravioli; as well as a tasty mix and match sausage menu. Bedrooms are simple, tidy and handy for the airport.

Closing times

Closed 26-30 December, Sunday dinner and bank holiday Monday dinner

Prices

Meals: £ 15 (lunch) and à la carte £ 24/33

5 rooms: £ 75/95

Typical Dishes

Scallops with noodles
Fillet of beef
Sticky toffee pudding

4 mi northeast of Cambridge by A1303 and B1047 on Horningsea rd. Parking.

England • East of England • Cambridgeshire

11 The Pheasant

Village Loop Road,
Keyston PE17 0RE
Tel.: (01832)710241
e-mail: info@thepheasant-keyston.co.uk **Website:** www.thepheasant-keyston.

Phipps Indian Pale Ale, Pargeter, Buntingfords Dark Mild, Grainstore Brewery Ten Fifty

Since the former managers took over, this charming thatched pub has gone from strength to strength, despite becoming less 'village local' and more 'destination dining pub'. Set in a sleepy little hamlet and framed by colourful flowers, it offers the choice of classic or contemporary dining rooms, as well as a terrace. Having spent time at London's St John restaurant, the young chef follows a 'nose to tail' eating approach, so you'll find everything from kidneys and ribs, to tongues and hearts; the trimmings going into the popular pheasant burger. Flip over the daily changing menu and you'll find an explanation of what's in season, who supplied it and a glossary of terms. Flip it back again and you'll find tasty homemade bread, followed by hors-d'œuvres, then maybe a classic coq au vin or more international Thai black bream salad. There's a good value midweek set lunch and a selection of preserves, pickles and chocolates for sale.

Closing times

Closed Sunday dinner (September-April)

Booking essential

Prices

Meals: £ 20 (lunch) and à la carte £ 36/42

Typical Dishes

Fish soup

Roast Lincolnshire rabbit

Chocolate marquise

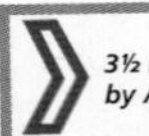

3½ mi southeast of Thrapstone by A 14 on B 663. Parking.

12 The Hole in the Wall

2 High St,
Little Wilbraham CB21 5JY
Tel.: (01223)812282
Website: www.the-holeinthewall.com

VISA 

 **Woodforde's Wherry, Nelson's Revenge, Milton Brewery Icarus**

A remotely set, 15C pub serving serious food – and not a cash machine in sight. Its name actually comes from when field workers used to leave their tankards at the pub on the way to work via a hole in the wall, allowing them to pick up their beer on the way home. With a 600 year history, you'd expect the building to have its fair share of charm, and it doesn't disappoint. Exposed beams rest overhead, and in winter, the brightly burning log fires provide the only source of warmth since there's no central heating. Between them, the team here have immense experience and the confident kitchen produces good value, flavoursome British dishes using seasonal ingredients in classical ways; so you might try 12 hour pickled brisket with oxtail, sea trout with Jersey Royals or honey-roasted poussin. Enduringly popular and mightily tasty puddings could include warm ginger cake, Eve's pudding or hot chocolate fondant.

Closing times

Closed 2 weeks in January, 2 weeks in October, 25 December, 26 December dinner, 1 January dinner, Sunday dinner and Monday

Prices

Meals: à la carte £ 23/33

Typical Dishes

Poached egg & salmon Florentine

Dingley Dell pork tenderloin

Bramley apple pie

 *5 mi east of Cambridge by A 1303 and minor road south. Parking.* 

13 The Three Horseshoes

High St,
Madingley CB23 8AB
Tel.: (01954)210221 – Fax: (01954)212043
e-mail: 3hs@btconnect.com **Website:** www.threehorseshoesmadingley.co.uk

Adnams Best and guest ales such as Potton, Cambridge, Buntingford

Set in a pretty village – famous for its stunning Hall – The Three Horseshoes, with its whitewashed walls and attractive thatched roof, fits right in. Having bought out the previous owner, the chef has taken the reigns, continuing the Italian tradition that's helped make the pub a success. To the front, scrubbed wooden furniture is set beside a welcoming fireplace and small bar; to the rear, a more formal linen-laid conservatory with Lloyd Loom chairs looks out over the garden. The bar menu offers pork scratchings, olives and a concise three course selection, while the daily changing à la carte – part written in Italian – features straightforward combinations and uncluttered, tasty dishes; maybe linguine di cozze, risotto con funghi, agnello arrosto or salmone in padella. The bustling bar has a great atmosphere, not dissimilar to an Italian trattoria, so if you're looking for a romantic table for two, make for the conservatory instead.

Closing times
Open daily
Booking advisable

Prices
Meals: à la carte £ 20/40

Typical Dishes
Bottisham smoked eel
Chargrilled veal liver
Caramelised Chinese meddlars

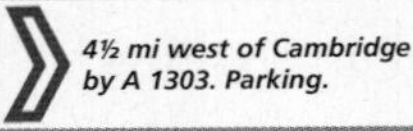

4½ mi west of Cambridge by A 1303. Parking.

14 Village Bar (at Bell Inn)

Great North Rd,
Stilton PE7 3RA
Tel.: (01733)241066 – Fax: (01733)245173
e-mail: reception@thebellstilton.co.uk **Website:** www.thebellstilton.co.uk

 **Greene King - IPA and Abott, Fuller's London Pride, Youngs, Brewers Gold, Crop Circle, Barnwell Bitter**

It's hard to believe that this sleepy market town is just minutes off the busy A1, or that this 17C inn is set on what was once the most popular coaching route from York to London. If you look a bit closer, however, you can still find evidence on the original archway from the road to the stables – now part of the entranceway – which displays the distances to the route's major cities. Famous as the birthplace of Stilton cheese, the Bell fell into disrepair before being enthusiastically restored and enlarged into what you see today. Step inside and you have the choice of a characterful bar or more modern bistro setting, with the same menu served throughout. Classically based dishes are a step above your usual pub fare, so you might find wild boar and cranberry terrine, followed by grey mullet on tomato risotto or Label Anglaise chicken with parsnip potato pancakes. Cosy bedrooms display traditional touches; three overlook the garden.

Closing times
Closed 25 December

Prices
Meals: à la carte £ 20/29
22 rooms: £ 74/131

Typical Dishes
Chicken liver parfait
Rib-eye steak
Sticky toffee pudding

4 mi south of Peterborough by A 15; in centre of village. Parking.

England • East of England • Cambridgeshire

15 The Anchor Inn

Sutton Gault CB6 2BD
Tel.: (01353)778537 – Fax: (01353)776180
e-mail: anchorinn@popmail.com
Website: www.anchor-inn-restaurant.co.uk

VISA MC AE

City of Cambridge Brewery : Hobsons Choice, Pegasus, Dionysus

It may seem like a strange name for a pub that's nowhere near the coast – but it does have some watery connections. Built in 1650, this building was originally used to house the workers who, under the direction of Oliver Cromwell, created the Hundred Foot Wash in order to alleviate flooding in this part of the fens. If you fancy a river view, head for the wood panelled rooms to the front of the bar, where you'll discover a pleasant outlook and a tempting menu. You might find scallops, smoked eel, pork loin wrapped in Parma ham or the house speciality of grilled dates wrapped in bacon with grain mustard sauce; alongside some Asian inspired offerings such as tea-infused duck with oriental salad and soy sauce. There's always some fish specials chalked on the board and occasionally dishes such as oxen or zebra from the nearby Denham Estate. Neat, pine furnished bedrooms come with local area info. There are two suites; one with river views.

Closing times
Open daily

Prices
Meals: £ 16 (lunch) and à la carte £ 20/30

4 rooms: £ 55/155

Typical Dishes
Grilled dates wrapped in bacon
Barnsley chop
Coconut & white chocolate fondant

Off B 1381; from Sutton village follow signs to Sutton Gault; pub is beside the New Bedford River. Parking.

16 **Axe & Compasses**

Dunmow Rd,
Aythorpe Roding CM6 1PP
Tel.: (01279)876648 – Fax: (01279)876254
e-mail: axeandcompasses@msn.com **Website:** www.theaxeandcompasses.co.uk

VISA MC

 **Nethergate IPA, Brentwood Best, Saffron Walden Gold**

Comforting childhood dishes like faggots and peas, corned beef hash and treacle tart, and hearty pub favourites like steak and ale pie and toad in the hole form the nucleus of this pub's varied menus. Since the owners are Essex born and bred, their tasty and attractively presented food is fruit of the fertile local landscape; from the Leigh-on-Sea cockles to the rib of beef. Order the intriguingly named Dunmow flitch pasty and pickle and you will learn about a unique local tradition dating back centuries, where couples are awarded a side of bacon if they can prove a year and a day of marital harmony. The owners wanted the Axe to be a proper British pub and the building's characterful cottage style – complete with part-thatched roof and white picket fence – certainly lends itself to the job. Inside the décor follows suit; from the exposed brick, plaster and wooden beams through to the saucy seaside postcards displayed in the gents.

Closing times
Closed 25-26 December

Prices
Meals: à la carte £ 20/25

Typical Dishes
Duo of mackerel
Tenderloin of pork
Queen of puddings

6 mi south of Great Dunmow by B 184 and minor road east. Parking.

17 **The Red Cow**

11 High St,
Chrishall SG8 8RN
Tel.: (01763)838792
e-mail: thepub@theredcow.com **Website:** www.theredcow.com

 **Adnams, Timothy Taylor Landlord and weekly-changing guest beer**

This part 14C thatched inn is everything you would expect from the most rustic of country pubs: small, cosy and hugely characterful, with heavy beams and a collection of open fires. It's divided into two; the quarry tiled part used by locals for drinking purposes and the wood floored area for dining; with picnic tables outside should the weather deem them necessary. Its young owners gave up life in the city in order to run the pub – and its bustling atmosphere suggests that the people of Chrishall are pleased they did. The simple menu of mostly British dishes reflects the seasons, with dishes like smoked mackerel and crayfish cocktail, lamb's liver or grilled lemon sole. There's a selection of classics like fish and chips, pies or burgers for lovers of pub favourites and sandwiches are also available at lunch. Old school puddings like spotted dick and bread and butter pudding are listed verbally and the charming service fits in just so.

Closing times
Closed Monday lunch

Prices
Meals: à la carte £ 17/31

Typical Dishes
Oak-smoked prawns
Grilled whole lemon sole
Eton mess

Between Royston and Duxford signed off A 505 on B 1039. Parking.

18 The Cricketers

Clavering CB11 4QT
Tel.: (01799)550442 – Fax: (01799)550882
e-mail: info@thecricketers.co.uk
Website: www.thecricketers.co.uk

  VISA MC AE

 **Adnams, Woodforde's Wherry and Nelson's Revenge**

Set in the charming village of Clavering, this attractive whitewashed pub exudes old-world charm aplenty. Rustic brick walls and ancient wooden beams are complemented by contemporary wall coverings, modern fabrics and stylish light fittings, and there's a welcoming feel about the place. You can cosy up beside the fire in the bar or head to the restaurant for a touch more formality. One menu is served throughout – priced per dish in the bar and per course in the restaurant – and cooking is precise, flavoursome and simply presented. Local produce is key; so you'll find plenty of regional meats, fresh fish and veg from their son Jamie's garden – that's Jamie Oliver by the way. A few Italian influences can also be found, including an intro of tasty homemade breads with fruity olive oil and sweet balsamic vinegar. Bedrooms are split between the courtyard and pavilion; the former simple and modern, the latter with a more traditional feel.

Closing times
Closed 25-26 December

Prices
Meals: £ 30 (dinner)
and à la carte £ 23/30

14 rooms: £ 65/110

Typical Dishes
Smoked Essex wood pigeon
Rump of Suffolk lamb
White chocolate & raspberry trifle

6 mi southwest of Saffron Walden on B 1038. Parking.

19 The Sun Inn

High St,
Dedham CO7 6DF
Tel.: (01206)323351
e-mail: office@thesuninndedham.com **Website:** www.thesuninndedham.com

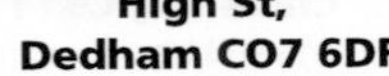

Adnams Broadside, Brewers Gold, The Naughty Vicar

Set in an idyllic village in the heart of Constable Country, this brightly painted pub offers guests a slice of sun even when the skies are cloudy and grey. The hands-on owner can usually be found front of house and he and his enthusiastic young team provide a warm welcome. Log fires contribute to the cosy feel; there's a superb burr elm bar counter, a two-tiered dining room and a pleasant garden and terrace for those long summer evenings. At lunchtime, the bar board tempts with a selection of doorstop sandwiches, terrines and tarts. The daily changing à la carte lists its simple, tasty dishes in Italian, followed by their English translation – if you don't mind sharing, try the antipasti; options like lamb stew, roast duck breast or pan-fried ox liver mean you can keep your meal all to yourself. Five contemporary bedrooms provide a restful night's slumber; Elsa, with its four-poster, is named after the resident ghost.

Closing times
Closed 25-26 December

Prices
Meals: £ 14 and à la carte £ 18/28
5 rooms: £ 68/150

Typical Dishes
Mozzarella, tomatoes & basil salad
Lemon sole
Lemon tart

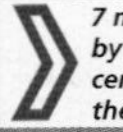

7 mi northeast of Colchester by A 137 and minor road; in the centre of the village opposite the church. Parking.

20 The Green Man

Mile End Green, Great Easton CM6 2DN
Tel.: (01371)852285 – Fax: (01371)852216
e-mail: info@thegreenmanrestaurant.com
Website: www.thegreenmanrestaurant.com

 **Fuller's London Pride**

A low slung, cottage style pub on a tiny country lane, about 20 minutes from Stansted Airport, The Green Man is as immaculate inside as it is out, with a contemporary, minimalist look. The original roof and wall beams have been retained, as has the large inglenook fireplace; there is a formal linen-clad restaurant, and a neat garden and sun-splashed terrace which look out across the fields. Food here is far removed from your typical pub grub, and although there are dishes like fish and chips or sausage and mash alongside sandwiches on the lunch menu, the kitchen has loftier ambitions in the evenings, with some interesting styles and flavours; maybe scallops with pea and mint gnocchi to start and slow roasted belly pork set on roasted fennel and chilli as a main course. Desserts are of the classic variety, with choices like plum and apple crumble or a delicious chocolate tart. Attentive, assured service completes the experience.

Closing times
Closed Sunday dinner and Monday (except bank holidays)

Prices
Meals: à la carte £ 28/44

Typical Dishes
Wood pigeon on stovies
Halibut & sautéed leeks
Chocolate fudge brownie

2½ mi north of Great Dunmow by A 184. Parking.

21 The Headley

The Common,
Great Warley CM13 3HS

Tel.: (01277)216104 – Fax: (01277)224063
e-mail: reservations@theheadley.co.uk **Website:** www.theheadley.co.uk

 **Adnams Best**

This place looks nothing like a pub from the outside and doesn't feel much like a pub inside either, but it's pub-like where it matters and that's in its food. Traditional dishes like baked salmon, steak and chips and cottage pie are well executed and tasty; simply prepared using good quality produce. There are bites and nibbles, plates to share, salads, soups and bagels, as well as hearty, old-fashioned desserts – like apple crumble or sticky toffee pudding – and all at prices to warm your cockles. A farmers' market is hosted here on the second Saturday of the month, breakfast is available every Saturday, and Sunday lunches pack them in. The upstairs tends to fill up first, with the lower floor's bar and lounge favoured by those here for a pint and a chat or a coffee and a read of the paper. Real ales and wines are listed by their characteristics – with a particularly decent selection of 'big and gutsy' reds.

Closing times
Closed Sunday dinner, Monday and Tuesday

Prices
Meals: à la carte £ 17/25

Typical Dishes
Chicken liver pâté
Sautéed sea bass
Sticky toffee pudding

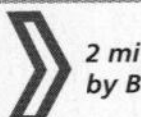

2 mi southwest of Brentwood by B 186. Parking.

22 **The Bell**

High Rd,
Horndon-on-the-Hill SS17 8LD
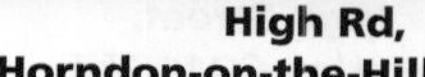
Tel.: (01375)642463 – Fax: (01375)361611
e-mail: info@bell-inn.co.uk **Website:** www.bell-inn.co.uk

 VISA 

Greene King IPA, Bass, Crouchvale Brewers Gold, Sharp's Own, Sharp's Doom Bar

If you're wondering about the hot cross buns, the story goes that past landlord Jack Turnell took over the pub on Good Friday, whereupon he nailed a bun to one of the beams in celebration. Since then, a bun has been added on every anniversary – the cement version marking a time of rationing during the war. The Bell has been run by the same family for the last 50 years, although dates back nearly 12 times that. Drinkers will find themselves at home in the wood-panelled bar, with open fire and selection of pub games, while diners can choose from a beamed area or more formal restaurant. Cooking is a step above your usual pub fare, with quality produce used to create classically based dishes with a modern touch; you might find traditional apple tart accompanied by a short glass of malted milkshake. Bedrooms in the pub are named and styled after famous Victorian mistresses, while those down the road in 17C Hill House display thoughtful extras.

Closing times

Closed 25-26 December and bank holiday Mondays

Prices

Meals: à la carte £ 22/32

15 rooms: £ 60/85

Typical Dishes

Grilled English asparagus

Roast salt marsh lamb

Rhubarb & white chocolate baked Alaska

3 mi northeast of Grays by A 1013 off A 13. Parking.

23 The Mistley Thorn

High Street,
Mistley CO11 1HE
Tel.: (01206)392821 – Fax: (01206)390122
e-mail: info@mistleythorn.com **Website:** www.mistleythorn.com

VISA

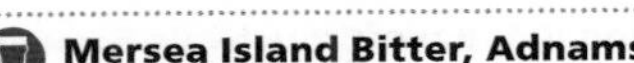

Mersea Island Bitter, Adnams

Set opposite the River Stour in the small coastal village of Mistley, this early 18C coaching inn has become something of an institution. It's just one of the proverbial pies that Californian-born owner Sherri has her fingers in, alongside her cookery school, Italian restaurant and latest book-writing venture. Simplicity is the key here; the brightly coloured walls filled with local art create a stylish yet homely feel and the cooking is of a similarly comforting yet flavoursome vein. Tasty foccacia and fruity olive oil kick things off, followed by anything from burgers, fishcakes and steaks through to soufflés, terrines and shellfish – the tempting specials often featuring fish or game. If you look closely, there's the odd reference to Sherri's American/Italian childhood and her Mom's Cheesecake with homemade ice cream has become a permanent fixture. Simple wood-furnished bedrooms boast modern bathrooms; two have river views.

Closing times
Open daily

Prices
Meals: à la carte £ 19/27
5 rooms: £ 65/130

Typical Dishes
Calamari a la plancha
Seared sea bass fillets
Elderflower jelly

9 mi northeast of Colchester by A 137 and B 1352; not far from Mistley Towers. Parking.

24 The Compasses at Pattiswick

Compasses Rd, Pattiswick CM77 8BG
Tel.: (01376)561322 – Fax: (01376)564343
e-mail: info@thecompassesatpattiswick.co.uk **Website:** www.thecompassesatpattiswick.co.uk

 **Adnams, Woodeforde's Wherry, St Austell Tribute, Everards Tiger**

Set among rolling fields in the tranquil Essex countryside, The Compasses started life as two estate workers' cottages before being transformed into the smart pub that it is today. Inside it boasts walls filled with Hugo Fircks artwork and a small counter selling meats, pâté and dips; but it's the cheery staff who really make the place. The best spot is in the barn-style restaurant, although spaces on the terrace are sought after too. Set price weekday menus represent the best value but there's also the monthly changing à la carte and daily specials to consider; you might find pork pies or Welsh rarebit at lunch and braised lamb shank or seared tuna steak in the evening. Cooking is honest, simple and well done, with a huge amount of effort put into sourcing local ingredients. Venison is from the woods behind; pheasant and partridge from the local shoots. Traditional puddings finish it all off, with knickerbocker glory a firm favourite.

Closing times
Closed Sunday dinner (October to Easter weekend)

Prices
Meals: £ 13/18
and à la carte £ 20/28

Typical Dishes
Pattiswick game terrine
Pan-fried sea bass
Liquid chocolate cake

4 mi east of Braintree by A 120 and a minor road north. Parking.

25 The Woodmans Arms

Rayleigh Rd,
Thundersley SS7 3TA
Tel.: (01268)775799 – Fax: (01268)590689
e-mail: thewoodmans@hotmail.co.uk **Website:** www.thewoodmansarms.co.uk

Adnams, Greene King IPA, Black Sheep

Sometimes when a pub starts to serve good food, its drinkers – ergo the locals – get somewhat sidelined; not so at The Woodmans Arms, where at least half the pub is dedicated to those supping pints and sipping wine, with large comfy sofas and bucket chairs to accommodate them. The smart restaurant is decorated with old black and white photos; half screens cleverly separate the drinkers from the diners without either group feeling excluded, and a cheery young team see to the needs of all. The seasonal dishes are hearty and flavourful, and whilst traditional in the main – perhaps pan-seared calves liver and bacon, roast fillet of salmon or beer battered haddock – the menu might also include a Malaysian chicken salad or Cajan spiced whitebait. Mussels are a favourite all year round, with a wider choice of seafood in the summer, while lunchtime sees lighter choices like baked potato, Welsh rarebit or honey roast ham, egg and chips.

Closing times
Open daily

Prices
Meals: à la carte £ 18/28

Typical Dishes
Griddled asparagus with pancetta
Calves liver & bacon
Steamed jam sponge

Between Basildon and Southend-on-Sea off A 127. Parking.

26 The Bull of Cottered

Cottered SG9 9QP
Tel.: (01763)281243
e-mail: cordell39@btinternet.com

 VISA MC

Greene King IPA and Abbot Ale

A popular stop-off point for travellers on their way to Stansted airport, this well-established pub is quite a picture in the summer months, when its flower baskets and tubs create a riot of colour out front. Inside, it's tradition all the way, with polished horse brasses, classic wooden furniture, crackling log fires and a tidy, homely feel. The menu follows suit, offering real pub food like calves liver, steak and kidney pie, rack of lamb or Ploughman's; with light lunches, more substantial meals, salads, burgers and Sunday roast all covered, and accompanied by a specials board and a cheese trolley. The rear dining room is a popular spot, as is the coveted alcove table in the front bar, while out the back a veritable suntrap encourages al fresco dining when the weather acquiesces. Popular music nights add spice to the winter months; so slip on your blue suede shoes, say thank you for the music and get ready to shake, rattle and roll.

Closing times
Open daily

Prices
Meals: à la carte £ 25/35

Typical Dishes
Wild mushroom risotto
Dover sole
Bread & butter pudding

6 mi southeast of Baldock by A 507; in the centre of the village. Parking at the front of the pub.

27 The Tilbury

Watton Rd,
Datchworth SG3 6TB

Tel.: (01438)815550 – Fax: (01438)718340
e-mail: info@thetilbury.co.uk **Website:** www.thetilbury.co.uk

 **Oxford Gold, Brakspear Organic, Hobgoblin**

Owned by two local boys – one of whom you might recognise as TV chef, Paul Bloxham – and run by an experienced young team, this popular red brick pub places food firmly at its centre. Cookery school events span the globe and the well executed, flavoursome dishes on the modern European menu reflect the team's commitment to sourcing first class seasonal produce from local farms. There's a real mix of dishes here; perhaps chicken liver parfait or stuffed snails 'Bourguignonne' to start; with wild boar and Chimay sausages with herb mash, honey glazed confit duck leg or stuffed lobster and scallop seabass for a main course. If your credit has been crunched, go for the excellent value three course set menu which can be enjoyed at lunch or dinner. The pub has a fresh, modern look, with an earthy colour scheme and contemporary oils for sale on the walls. There's a pleasant terrace and garden - and a petanque court should the urge grab you.

Closing times
Closed Sunday dinner

Prices
Meals: £ 17/22
and à la carte £ 25/35

Typical Dishes
Local venison pâté
Herdwick mutton pudding
Rhubarb puddings

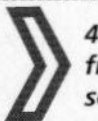 *4 mi southeast by A 602 from Stevenage and minor road south. Parking.* 

28 The Bricklayers Arms

Hogpits Bottom,
Flaunden HP3 0PH

Tel.: (01442)833322 – Fax: (01442)834841
e-mail: goodfood@bricklayersarms.com **Website:** www.bricklayersarms.com

VISA MC AE

Fuller's London Pride, Greene King IPA, Marlow Rebellion, Timothy Taylor Landlord

Country lanes: they're poorly signposted and once you're lost, they all look the same. Set on the outer reaches of a very small hamlet, The Bricklayers is tucked away by itself, so you'll need a good navigator on board when trying to locate it. Part-built in 1722, it was originally two cottages, before becoming a butcher's and blacksmith's, and later an alehouse. Inside it's rather smart, with tartan carpets, polished tables and fresh flowers everywhere – the dining areas to the side of the bar more formally laid than those in front. This is not the place to come for a quick snack – a glance at the menu will show there are none – but somewhere serving good old-fashioned, hearty, French-inspired dishes. The foie gras and steaks are particularly popular; home-smoked meats and fish have become signature dishes; and Sunday lunch is a real family affair. If you're just passing through, head to the spacious terrace for an old school pudding.

Closing times
Closed 25 December

Prices
Meals: à la carte £ 26/33

Typical Dishes
Home-smoked fish plate
Local wood pigeon
Crêpe filled with Cointreau mascarpone

4 mi north of Rickmansworth by A 404 and a minor road north. Parking.

29 The Alford Arms

Frithsden HP1 3DD

Tel.: (01442)864480 – Fax: (01442)876893

e-mail: info@alfordarmsfrithsden.co.uk

Website: www.alfordarmsfrithsden.co.uk

Marston's Pedigree, Flowers Original, Brakspears, Marlow Rebellion IPA

Set among the network of footpaths that run across the Chilterns and surrounded by Natural Trust woodland, this attractive Victorian pub is a popular destination for hikers – and when you're trying to squeeze your car into a tight space on the narrow country lane, arriving by foot may suddenly seem to have been the better option. A pleasant garden overlooks the peaceful village green – where you might spot the odd Morris dancer or two – and the warm bar welcomes four-legged friends as equally as their owners; they even get a free biscuit while you nibble on your snacks. The traditional menu has a strong British stamp and follows the seasons closely, so you're likely to find salads and fish in summer and more game and comfort dishes in winter; these might include belly pork with sticky parsnips, venison steak and kidney pudding, lamb and rabbit shepherd's pie or a tempting special from the blackboard. Good classical desserts follow.

Closing times

Closed 25-26 December

Prices

Meals: à la carte £ 20/27

Typical Dishes

Bubble & squeak

Chiltern lamb suet pudding

Lemon curd crème brûlée

4½ mi northwest of Hemel Hempstead by A 4146.
By the village green. Parking.

30 The Fox

469 Luton Rd,
Kingsbourne Green, Harpenden AL5 3QE
Tel.: (01582)713817
Website: www.thefoxharpenden.co.uk

  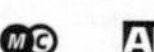 

Timothy Taylor & Adnams

This pub has a country feel, with exposed wood, thick chunky beams and similarly solid wood tables, but beware - once you've snuggled up in one of the comfy leather sofas next to the fire in the sitting room, you might not want to move. Come summer, the decked terrace is the scene of many al fresco meals and with its popular menu and relaxed, friendly atmosphere, The Fox cunningly attracts more than its fair share of customers. The menu is divided up into different sections: sharing plates, such as tapas and mezze, little dishes such as crab cake, scallops or soup; leaves, fired pizzas, pasta, stove and grill, as well as the popular rotisserie – and all supplemented with daily specials, so there's bound to be something to whet your appetite. Staff are courteous and efficient, and there's no danger you'll struggle to locate service when you need it, since they all wear T-shirts with the pub's name emblazoned across the front.

Closing times
Open daily
Prices
Meals: à la carte £ 20/32

Typical Dishes
Smoked haddock Florentine
Spit roast loin of pork
Steamed chocolate pudding

5 mi north of St Albans by A 1081.
Parking.

England • East of England • Hertfordshire

31 The White Horse

Hatching Green, Harpenden AL5 2JP
Tel.: (01582)469290
e-mail: info@thewhitehorseharpenden.com
Website: www.thewhitehorseharpenden.com

 **Adnams Bitter**

An appealing, whitewashed pub, close to the pretty village green, with two distinct parts to it. The first is its small, stylish bar, which boasts an original 17C wooden parquet floor and open log fire. Turn the corner and you reach the elaborate dining room – which actually looks and feels more like a restaurant – with its exposed beams, thick wooden tables, heavily upholstered chairs and a semi-open kitchen. Two first floor dining rooms are available for private parties, and the large terrace is very popular in the summer – but no bookings are taken here, so arrive early to bag a seat. Modern European dishes such as duo of lamb, halibut and langoustines or calves liver Dijonaise feature on the à la carte menu, and there are sharing plates, grazing boards and sandwiches alongside dishes such as seafood bouillabaisse or eggs Benedict on the bar menu. A well-versed team provide polished and professional service.

Closing times
Closed 25 December
Booking essential

Prices
Meals: £ 15 (lunch) and à la carte £ 23

Typical Dishes
Prawn, crayfish & mango salad
Duo of lamb
Chocolate fondant

5 mi north of St Albans by A 1081.
Parking.

32 Fox and Hounds

2 High St, Hunsdon SG12 8NH
Tel.: (01279)843999 – Fax: (01279)841092
e-mail: info@foxandhounds-hunsdon.co.uk
Website: www.foxandhounds-hunsdon.co.uk

 **Adnams Bitter, Adnams Broadside; and guest ale Red Squirrel Brewery Conservation Bitter**

The first thing that strikes you about the Fox and Hounds on your approach through this pretty village is its large garden and terrace; providing plenty of room for any children in your party to burn off excess energy. If you're heading inside, the spacious rear dining room is the best place to sit, the vast array of cookery books, its high ceiling and semi-panelled walls all contributing their part to its delightfully stylish feel, while the rustic bar has lots of cosy, low level seating perfect for lounging. The chef-owner has an impressive CV and a sound culinary understanding; his philosophy being to buy the best seasonal and local ingredients, and to treat them simply, cooking with style and understanding. The menu changes daily, but dishes on offer might range from Spanish charcuterie and olives to sausage and mash, via lamb's kidneys, beer battered squid with aioli or slow roast belly of organic pork.

Closing times

Closed Sunday dinner and Monday

Prices

Meals: £ 14 (weekdays) and à la carte £ 20/35

Typical Dishes

Sauté of duck hearts
Braised shoulder of lamb
Treacle tart

5 mi east of Ware by B 1004 to Widford and B 180 south. Parking.

33 The Cabinet at Reed

High St,
Royston SG8 8AH
Tel.: (01763)848366
e-mail: thecabinet@btconnect.com **Website:** www.thecabinetatreed.co.uk

 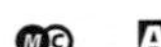 AE

 **Woodforde's Wherry, Adnams, Timothy Taylor and regularly changing guest beer**

Set foot in Reed and you'll be transported back to days of old, when houses were surrounded by moats and the pub was the hub of the village. The houses are now ringed by large grass verges but all roads do still lead to The Cabinet. Behind its white clapperboard exterior this pub hides a delightful brick-floored snug with chunky furniture; a cosy bar with an open fire and shotguns mounted on the walls; and to one side, a small, simply laid restaurant. There's an air of informality about the place which is echoed in the menus, so you'll find a list of dishes that the owners themselves would like to eat. Alongside the à la carte there are good value set lunches, with one dedicated to roasts on a Sunday. Cooking is flavoursome but dishes aren't always what they seem, as traditional recipes are given a more modern twist. In the winter, warming casseroles and pies are particularly popular, while the friendly staff are a hit all year round.

Closing times

Closed 26 December, 1 January and Monday

Prices

Meals: £ 15/25 and à la carte £ 25/45

Typical Dishes

Lobster macaroni
Seared breast of duck
Strawberry shortcake meringue

3 mi south of Royston by A 10 and side road east. Parking.

34 The Fox

Willian SG6 2AE
Tel.: (01462)480233 – Fax: (01462)676966
e-mail: info@foxatwillian.co.uk **Website:** www.foxatwillian.co.uk

 **Adnams Bitter, Woodforde's Wherry, Fuller's London Pride and one weekly changing guest beer**

Set right in the heart of the village, this bright, airy pub is extremely popular. At lunchtime, drinkers and diners vie for tables in the bar, while in the evenings local drinkers pull rank and those after a meal head for the dining room. Light wood floors and matching furniture feature throughout, and the keener eye will notice a host of subtle references to Norfolk – home of the owner's other two pubs. To whet your appetite, crisps and olives are provided while you study the menu, while tasty homemade chocolates wait at the other end of your meal. There's plenty of seafood on offer here, with the likes of haddock rarebit or oysters for starters and black bream or herb-crusted cod for main course, while fish and chips remain a best seller. There's always a good choice of game in season and for those who can't quite make up their mind, 'The Fox Slate' provides the solution. Dishes are fairly modern, with the odd Asian influence.

Closing times
Closed Sunday dinner

Prices
Meals: à la carte £ 22/33

Typical Dishes
Chicken liver parfait
Chargrilled sirloin steak
Lemon & cinnamon crème brûlée

3 mi northeast of Hitchin by A 505 and side road. Parking.

35 The White Horse

4 High St, Blakeney NR25 7AL
Tel.: (01263)740574 – Fax: (01263)741303
e-mail: info@blakeneywhitehorse.co.uk
Website: www.blakeneywhitehorse.co.uk

 **Adnams, Adnams Broadside, Woodforde's Wherry, Yetmans**

Maybe you've spent the afternoon wandering the beautiful north Norfolk coastline, spotting the various species of bird that flock along the marshes, or on a boat trip out to Blakeney Point to see the seals basking on the sandbanks. The invigorating sea air will no doubt have stoked your appetite, so afterwards head for something hearty to eat at this brick and flint former coaching inn. The same à la carte menu is served in all areas and changes according to what's freshly available and in season. Interesting combinations add a modern slant to dishes, so expect your steak to come not with chips but with potatas bravas, anchovies, sprouting broccoli, fried duck egg and chorizo – and don't be surprised to see dishes such as kibbi cakes or salad Argenteuil alongside fish and chips or omelette Arnold Bennett. Bedrooms have modern facilities and come in various shapes and sizes; some decorated in the bright blues and yellows of the seaside.

Closing times
Open daily

Prices
Meals: à la carte £ 21/33
9 rooms: £ 50/140

Typical Dishes
Oxtail terrine
Lamb rump
Almond & pistachio tart

Off A 149 following signs for the Quay, beside the church. Parking.

36 The Jolly Sailors

Brancaster Staithe PE31 8BJ
Tel.: (01485)210314
e-mail: info@jollysailorbrancaster.co.uk
Website: www.jollysailorbrancaster.co.uk

Brancaster Brewery, Woodeforde's Wherry, Adnams Broadside and various guest beers

Already the owner of two successful pubs, Clifford Nye decided to add a more casual younger sister to his collection: The Jolly Sailors. Arranged around a central courtyard, it's a refreshing break from the norm, retaining much of its original rustic character despite having been spruced up. A warming open fire provides a focal point within and the 'Children, Dogs and Well Behaved Parents' sign reminds you that all are welcome. The menu here is simple but it works well: there's a selection of baguettes, ploughman's and light bites such as smoked prawns or chicken wings, as well as freshly made pizzas – with a create your own option – and a selection of main dishes that could include scampi, curry or liver and bacon. There's also a blackboard offering a pie and fish of the day, and usually some local oysters from the beds out the front. Nursery-style puddings finish it all off, with the likes of jam roly poly and other old favourites.

Closing times
Open daily

Prices
Meals: à la carte £ 14/25

Typical Dishes
Half dozen Brancaster oysters
Fisherman's pie
Jam roly poly & custard

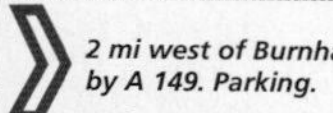

2 mi west of Burnham Market by A 149. Parking.

37 The White Horse

Brancaster Staithe PE31 8BY

Tel.: (01485)210262 – Fax: (01485)210930

e-mail: reception@whitehorsebrancaster.co.uk

Website: www.whitehorsebrancaster.co.uk

Woodforde's Wherry, Adnam's Best Bitter, Fuller's London Pride and seasonal guest beers

With glorious views over the Brancaster Marshes and Scolt Head Island, a seat on this village pub's sunny back terrace or in the spacious rear conservatory is a must. If the tables here are all taken, then the landscaped front terrace may not have the views, but it's got the parasols, the heaters and the lights to make up for it. From the outside, the pub looks like an extended house, but venture inside and you'll find a proper bar at the front, complete with bar billiards and historic photos of Brancaster. Foodwise, the oft-changing menus provide ample choice, with a seafood slant that takes in local Cromer crab, Brancaster oysters, mussels and fish from the boats at the end of the car park. The pub's popularity means that service can sometimes suffer under the strain but with the coastal views to provide a distraction you might not even notice. For those who'd like to extend their stay, bedrooms are comfy; two have their own terrace.

Closing times

Open daily

Booking essential

Prices

Meals: à la carte £ 19/30

15 rooms: £ 50/156

Typical Dishes

Mussels in white wine

Fruits of the sea

White Horse lemon tart

On A 149 Hunstanton to Wells rd. Parking.

38 The Hoste Arms

The Green,
Burnham Market PE31 8HD

Tel.: (01328)738777 – Fax: (01328)730103
e-mail: reception@hostearms.co.uk **Website:** www.hostearms.co.uk

Inspectors' favourites

Woodforde's Wherry and Nelson's Revenge, Greene King Abbot

This extended 17C inn is located in the heart of the pretty Norfolk village of Burnham Market, and it's got plenty space in which to dine, including a rustic bar with leather sofas, an informal conservatory and an enclosed rear garden and terrace. Menus are classically based but have global influences, so expect dishes like Thai fish broth, feuilleté of mixed seafood or natal lamb curry with basmati rice, alongside roasted rack of lamb, steak and kidney pudding or cod, peas and chips. Local produce is well used, so you'll find the oysters are from Loose's in nearby Brancaster, the steak comes from Arthur Howell butchers and the seafood and fish are from Lowestoft. The young staff are friendly and polite but when the place gets busy – which it does tend to – service can slow quite dramatically. Stylish, comfortable bedrooms boast a high level of facilities and include the eye-catching Zulu wing with its South African themed décor.

Closing times
Open daily
Booking essential

Prices
Meals: à la carte £ 25/35
36 rooms: £ 159/225

Typical Dishes
Salmon & dill fishcake
Rack of English lamb
Assiette of Hoste desserts

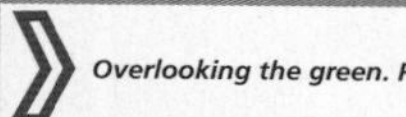

Overlooking the green. Parking.

Burnham Thorpe

39 The Lord Nelson

Walsingham Rd,
Burnham Thorpe PE31 8HL
Tel.: (01328)738241 – Fax: (01328)738241
e-mail: enquiries@nelsonslocal.co.uk **Website:** www.nelsonslocal.co.uk

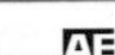 VISA MC AE

Woodforde's Wherry, Greene King Abbot Ale, Nelson's Blood Bitter and occasional guest ales

The Lord Nelson is a pub so traditional and so full of character that it's said not to have changed much since its namesake was born in this very village in 1758. Low beams and flagged floors bear witness to the whitewashed inn's own birth date of 1637; formerly known as The Plough, it was renamed in the 18C in honour of its most famous customer. Nelson memorabilia features throughout and you can even sit on a settle which once cradled the behind of the Admiral himself. Cooking is hearty and rustic, and dishes range from the traditional – like steak and chips, chunky fish broth or risotto – to the more unusual, such as crocodile, ostrich or kangaroo. There is no bar to speak of, only a hatch, so service comes to your table; the local staff are efficient, polite and used to being busy. A range of events throughout the year (think quizzes, music nights and Morris men) and the large rear garden only serve to add to the fun.

Closing times

Closed 25-26 December dinner, 1 January dinner and Monday dinner (except bank and school holidays)

Prices

Meals: à la carte £ 18/29

Typical Dishes

Baked aubergine & tomatoes

Lamb & aubergine meat balls

Florentine rice tart

2 mi south of Burnham Market by B 1355. Parking.

40 The Crown Inn

The Green, East Rudham PE31 8RD

Tel.: (01485)528530

e-mail: reception@thecrowneastrudham.co.uk

Website: www.thecrowneastrudham.co.uk

Woodforde's Wherry, Nelson's Revenge, Adnams, White Hart

The owner of this pub may be a Kiwi but he is well aware of what a rich seam there is to be mined in Norfolk in terms of food supplies, so as you tuck into generous helpings of tasty dishes like lemon sole or honey glazed pork fillet, you can rest assured that none of the ingredients had to travel too far to reach your plate; maybe from Wells-next-the-Sea, like the fresh fish and bottled ales, or neighbouring West Rudham like the asparagus. A top-to-toe makeover of this 15C pub means that original features including a 14ft fireplace sit alongside more contemporary comforts like the large leather sofas, perfect for pre-dinner drinks in the snug. Service comes from bright locals and Antipodeans who endeavour to make everybody, including children and dogs, feel welcome. For a private gathering, the upstairs Buffalo Room, with its vast collection of books, is ideal. Comfortable bedrooms with modern bathrooms complete the fresh new look.

Closing times

Closed 25 December

Prices

Meals: à la carte £ 23/30

6 rooms: £ 80

Typical Dishes

Antipasto slate for two

Sirloin steak

Mamma Coubrough spiced apple cake

Between King's Lynn and Fakenham on A 148. Parking.

41 The Saracen's Head

Wolterton, Erpingham NR11 7LX

Tel.: (01263)768909 – Fax: (01263)768993

e-mail: saracenshead@wolterton.freeserve.co.uk

Website: www.saracenshead-norfolk.co.uk

   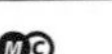

 **Adnam's Best and Woodforde's Wherry in rotation**

This idiosyncratic inn proves the point that pubs are all about people; the people who run them, the people who work in them and the people who eat and drink in them. Top of the pops here are Robert and Rachel: the father and daughter otherwise known as chef and front of house. Robert has owned the place for more than 20 years and cooks hearty, traditional dishes using local produce. The menu changes daily but might feature baked Cromer crab, pot-roast leg of lamb or roast Norfolk pheasant – not forgetting the famous, old-fashioned treacle tart. Rachel brings life to the place with her infectious friendliness and enthusiasm; unsurprisingly, the place is often busy and attracts its fair share of regulars. The rurally set, red-brick inn was built in 1806 but modelled on a Tuscan farmhouse. Its small rooms are charmingly cluttered with bric à brac, their walls filled with pictures and the spacious bedrooms offer a good level of facilities.

Closing times

Closed 25 December,
26 December dinner,
Monday, Tuesday lunch
(except after bank holidays)

Booking essential

Prices

Meals: à la carte £ 25/30

6 rooms: £ 50/90

Typical Dishes

Morston mussels

Pan-fried Gunton venison

Treacle tart

1½ mi west on Wolterton Hall rd. Parking.

42 The Hunny Bell

The Green,
Hunworth NR24 2AA
Tel.: (01263)712300 – Fax: (01263)710161
e-mail: hunnybell@animalinns.co.uk **Website:** www.thehunnybell.co.uk

Abbot Ale, Adnam's Best, Woodforde's Wherry and changing guest ales

Following a sympathetic renovation and extension, this 18C whitewashed pub looks the bee's knees: its smart country interior boasting exposed brickwork, stone flooring and restored wooden beams; offset by bold modern feature walls and a few more recent additions, including an airy conservatory dining room and a smart wood-furnished patio overlooking the green. As country cousin to the slightly eccentric Wildebeest Arms and two other eateries, the owners' collective experience really shines through, resulting in a keenly priced, seasonal menu that's modern-European meets traditional pub. For main course you might discover local pork sausages, Norfolk beer-battered cod, sage-roast chicken breast or 28-day aged sirloin steak; while at either end of the meal the chef proudly presents homemade breads and sorbets. This new addition to the Animal Inns family is as sound as a bell and 'Hunny' is sure to be the buzz word for miles around.

Closing times
Open daily

Prices
Meals: £ 20 (Sunday lunch) and à la carte £ 25/35

Typical Dishes
Crayfish & avocado tian
Poached beef tenderloin
Blood orange mousse

2½ m south by B 1149 from Holt. Parking.

43 The Walpole Arms

The Common,
Itteringham NR11 7AR
Tel.: (01263)587258 – Fax: (01263)587074
e-mail: goodfood@thewalpolearms.co.uk **Website:** www.thewalpolearms.co.uk

Inspectors' favourites

Adnams Bitter and Broadside, Woodforde's Wherry and changing guest ales

This red-brick inn is set within north Norfolk's countryside, not far from either the broads or the beaches, and with all the old-fashioned charm of one who has been providing hospitality since the 18C. The Mediterranean-influenced menus are modified daily, as dictated by suppliers and seasons, and the tasty, well-prepared dishes get the thumbs up from all comers; maybe baby octopus in red wine and tomato sauce or escabeche of red mullet to start, followed by fillet of salmon with saffron mash, Morston mussels or sauté of veal with potato gratin. The formal restaurant, with its low ceilings and clothed tables, makes a becoming backdrop for a dinner date; the gardens and terrace are great come summer, while the rustic, beamed bar is definitely the most characterful seat in the house. If you're after something light to eat, the snack menu of pub classics will oblige. Service from local staff is polite, if a little lacking in enthusiasm.

Closing times
Closed 25 December and Sunday dinner

Prices
Meals: à la carte £ 21/28

Typical Dishes
Crayfish tails
Twice cooked pork belly
Norfolk honey parfait

5 mi northwest of Aylsham by B 1354; signed The Common. Parking.

44 The Gin Trap Inn

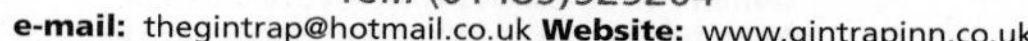

6 High St,
Ringstead PE36 5JU
Tel.: (01485)525264
e-mail: thegintrap@hotmail.co.uk **Website:** www.gintrapinn.co.uk

 **Woodforde's Wherry, Adnams Bitter and guests ales Abbot Ale, Tom Woods, Elgoods**

A vast sycamore tree stands right outside, and two old iron ploughs crown the modest doorway of this whitewashed inn, which dates back to 1667. In all those years it can rarely have looked and felt so inviting: a proper country pub, warm and comfortable, with a real fire stoked up in the stove on frosty winter evenings. There's a bar, with glossy wood-topped tables, a smartly set dining room and also a new wooden floored conservatory overlooking the garden. The blackboard menu offers favourites like fish and chips and sausage and mash while the à la carte might boast delights such as glazed clam and cockle tagliatelle with chive and caviar fish cream, braised beef bourguignon or pan-fried skate wing. Bedrooms are a very tasteful blend of subtle country patterns, and two bathrooms have luxurious roll-top baths. Think the owner looks vaguely familiar? He used to be an actor, working on shows such as The Bill and EastEnders.

Closing times
Open daily

Prices
Meals: à la carte £ 20/28
3 rooms: £ 49/140

Typical Dishes
6 Thornham oysters
Howell's pork sausages
Warm chocolate pudding

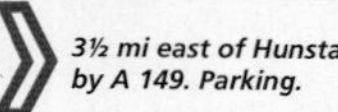
3½ mi east of Hunstanton by A 149. Parking.

45 The Rose and Crown

Old Church Rd, Snettisham PE31 7LX
Tel.: (01485)541382 – Fax: (01485)543172
e-mail: info@roseandcrownsnettisham.co.uk
Website: www.roseandcrownsnettisham.co.uk

 **Fuller's London Pride, Greene King, Adnams**

Its warren of rooms and passageways, uneven floors and low beamed ceilings place the Rose and Crown squarely into the quintessentially English bracket of inns; the larger dining rooms, the paved terrace and the children's play area in the garden add some 21C zing to the pub's 14C roots. Cooking is gutsy by nature and makes good use of local produce, with dishes such as seafood ragout, hake and cockle chowder or braised ham hock on offer alongside trusty classics like sausage and mash or steak and chips. Desserts might include steamed marmalade sponge or poached pear and cherry bakewell – and service from local staff is friendly and polite, if a little lacking in personality. They are well used to being busy and a good crowd of locals from the village can often be found enjoying a tipple or two at the bar. The modern bedrooms are quite a contrast to the pub; decorated in bright, sunny colours, they offer a good level of facilities.

Closing times
Open daily
Prices
Meals: à la carte £ 18/28
16 rooms: £ 70/110

Typical Dishes
Sweet potato ravioli
Braised oxtail
Chocolate raspberry tart

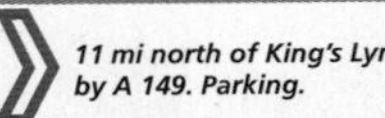
11 mi north of King's Lynn by A 149. Parking.

46 Wildebeest Arms

82-86 Norwich Rd,
Stoke Holy Cross NR14 8QJ
Tel.: (01508)492497 – Fax: (01508)494946
e-mail: wildebeest@animalinns.co.uk **Website:** www.thewildebeest.co.uk

Inspectors' favourites

  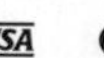  

 **Adnams Best Bitter**

With its wicker fence and chairs, tribal tree trunk tables and wild animal artefacts, this pub offers a taste of the African savannah in the unlikely setting of Norfolk. Despite the pub's exotic undertones, the food is more European in flavour, with dishes such as chicken liver parfait, pan-fried fillet of salmon or honey-roast Gressingham duck breast. The à la carte is ambitious and can verge on the over-elaborate side of admirable, but the focus is firmly on the sourcing of seasonal, local produce and the set lunch and dinner menus represent very good value for money. Service comes from friendly, well organised staff dressed in black who handle busy periods with aplomb. Should it even begin to approach balmy African temperatures, there is a pleasant terrace for outside dining. The low-ceilinged rustic interior features a part open-plan kitchen and can tend towards gloominess, but only as regards the lighting; never the atmosphere.

Closing times

Closed 25-26 December

Booking essential

Prices

Meals: £ 17/20
and à la carte £ 25/37

Typical Dishes

Glazed belly pork
Chargrilled fillet of East Anglian beef
Hot chocolate fondant

5½ mi south of Norwich by A 140.
Parking.

47 The Wiveton Bell

Blakeney Rd,
Wiveton NR25 7TL
Tel.: (01263)740101
Website: www.wivetonbell.com

Woodforde's Wherry, Yetmans, Adnams Broadside

Surrounded by the local salt marshes and nearby nature reserves, this pub is situated in a beautiful area and is ideal for walkers following the Norfolk coastal path. The neatly-kept garden provides an attractive flower display by day, whilst at night it's a fantastic setting for stargazing. Following a dramatic renovation, the inside of this pub is comfortable and up-to-date, with a pleasant bar giving way to a light and airy conservatory; host to a convivial atmosphere and bright, efficient service. You can choose from salads and light meals or the traditional à la carte menu, where a few international influences appear alongside the mainly British selection; you might find Thai fish cakes or chicken Dansak next to Briston pork belly or fisherman's pie. On either side of the property, the charming rooms come complete with a continental tuckbox, so if you're feeling lazy you can keep your PJs on and have breakfast in bed.

Closing times

Closed 25 December and Sunday dinner in winter

Booking advisable

Prices

Meals: à la carte £ 18/30

2 rooms: £ 90/120

Typical Dishes

Local mussels
Slow roast Briston belly pork
Chocolate torte

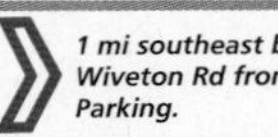

1 mi southeast by A 149 on Wiveton Rd from Blakeney. Parking.

48 The Bildeston Crown

104 High Street,
Bildeston IP7 7EB

Tel.: (01449)740510 – Fax: (01449)741843

e-mail: info@thebildestoncrown.co.uk **Website:** www.thebildestoncrown.co.uk

Adnams, Old Cannon Indian Pale Ale, Mauldons

This yellow-painted 15C pub is as eye-catching inside as it is on the out; its spacious interior featuring bold colour schemes which give it a warm, characterful feel. Sit by the inglenook fireplace in the locals bar or sink into a soft sofa in one of the lounges. If the sun is out, there's a terrace in the central courtyard, or for a more formal meal, choose the wood-floored dining room. There are two main menus: Crown Classics offers traditional British pub dishes like shepherd's pie or the ubiquitous fish and chips, while Crown Select features more elaborate dishes like venison with braised oxtail and parsnip or pork 'head to toe'. The more ambitious dishes can occasionally be a little overwrought but there is no doubt that they are tasty and that the locally sourced produce is of the highest order. Bedrooms are comfortable, spacious and stylish, with up-to-date facilities which include a built in music system.

Closing times
Closed dinner
25-26 December
and 1 January

Prices
Meals: £ 18 (weekdays)
and à la carte £ 26/40

12 rooms: £ 90/250

Typical Dishes
Cumin roasted scallop
Veal osso bucco
Tarte Tatin

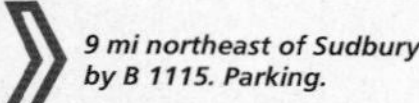

9 mi northeast of Sudbury by B 1115. Parking.

49 Queen's Head

The Street,
Bramfield IP19 9HT
Tel.: (01986)784214
e-mail: qhbfield@aol.com **Website:** www.queensheadbramfield.co.uk

 VISA MC AE

 **Adnams Bitter, Adnams Broadside**

Run by a dedicated husband and wife team (chef and front of house, respectively), this characterful cream-washed pub has been in the family for more than 11 years. Set in the heart of a small country village – beside an attractive thatched church with rare 15C round tower – it boasts three rooms; the largest, with its high beamed ceiling and scrubbed tables, opening out into a bright flower-filled garden with blue picnic benches. The central bar has lots to catch the eye, with shelves crammed full of books and a selection of tempting homemade preserves, chutneys and cakes for sale. Diners will find a blackboard snack menu displaying sandwiches and maybe a ploughman's; as well as a classically based main menu formed around the daily availability of local, seasonal and where possible, organic produce. Some Fridays you'll find local bands playing, while others are 'Paupers' evenings – where a good value set menu replaces the à la carte.

Closing times
Closed 26 December

Prices
Meals: à la carte £ 19/27

Typical Dishes
Dates wrapped in bacon
Pork steak, garlic sauce
Pavlova with fruit & cream

3 mi south of Halesworth on A 144. Parking.

50 The Castle Inn

35 Earsham Street,
Bungay NR35 1AF
Tel.: (01986)892283
e-mail: markandtanya@thecastleinn.net **Website:** www.thecastleinn.net

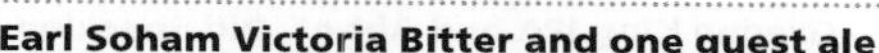

Earl Soham Victoria Bitter and one guest ale

As the name still emblazoned upon its stonework suggests, this sky-blue coloured pub used to be called The White Lion; these days it is known as The Castle Inn after the ruins behind it. Its cosy interior takes in two main dining rooms and an intimate rear bar – a perfect spot for a postprandial coffee, with its leather sofas and foodie magazines. Cooking is country based; fresh, simple and seasonal, and while lunchtime might see sausage and mash or fisherman's pie on offer alongside sandwiches, the evening menu might include pan-seared pigeon breast or duck leg confit. The Innkeeper's platter is a perennial favourite and showcases local produce, including a great pickle made by the Rocking Grannies – keep an eye out for the cake stands too, with their homemade cakes and cookies. Themed evenings include pie and wine night and film and food night, complete with popcorn. Bedrooms are homely and comfortable with a real feeling of warmth.

Closing times
Closed Sunday dinner

Prices
Meals: à la carte £ 20/30
4 rooms: £ 50/90

Typical Dishes
Aldburgh pigeon, Puy lentils
Venison & pease pudding
Plum frangipane

5½ mi west of Beccles by B 1062. Parking.

51 The Buxhall Crown

Mill Road,
Buxhall IP14 3DW
Tel.: (01449)736521
e-mail: thebuxhallcrown@hotmail.co.uk **Website:** www.thebuxhallcrown.co.uk

 VISA MC

 **Greene King IPA and Abbot, Old Speckled Hen, Olde Trip, Tom Woods Bomber County**

It's not just what you know but who you know. With more than 15 years experience each, the new owners of the Crown definitely had the 'what': they were just lacking the 'who' – that is, until they met each other whilst working at a local pub. For their first venture into the world of ownership, they chose this part 16C pub, formerly a butcher and piggery, set just outside the village centre; with its characterful beamed bar, contemporary dining room and charming paved terrace. They've really hit the right note here, especially with the food, displaying a passion for simplicity, freshness and seasonality. The appealing blackboard menu often changes twice a day, displaying dishes such as omelette Provençale, local ox liver or super-mature sirloin steak with triple cooked chips and crème fraîche – finished off with the likes of lemon posset or crème brûlée; as well as some retro favourites featuring space dust and flying saucers.

Closing times
Closed 25-26 December and Sunday dinner
Booking advisable

Prices
Meals: £ 19 (lunch) and à la carte £ 18/30

Typical Dishes
Pancetta & black pudding salad
Duck breast
Chocolate praline terrine

3½ mi west of Stowmarket by B 1115; follow the road to Buxhall across Rattlesden Junction. Parking.

52 The Beehive

The Street,
Horringer IP29 5SN
Tel.: (01284)735260 – Fax: (01284)735532
Website: www.beehivehorringer.co.uk

Greene King - IPA, Abbot Ale and Old Speckled Hen

Situated in the same village as National Trust property Ickworth House, and a perfect place for a spot of lunch after a stroll around some of its 1800 acres, this pretty flintstone pub has numerous little rooms and alcoves in which to get cosy. Owned and run by the same couple for a quarter of a century, it attracts a cheery blend of locals, visitors, couples and families – although its popularity means that it can get very busy, so it is best to book ahead. The oft-changing blackboard menu places seasonality and local produce at its centre, and offers plenty of choice, including its fair share of lighter meals. Dishes err on the traditional side of pub fodder – perhaps fish pie or sausage and mash, followed by bread and butter pudding or lemon meringue pie – although the odd European influence sneaks in too with things like veal schnitzel or Greek yoghurt. What the service lacks in personality, it makes up for in efficiency.

Closing times
Closed 25-26 December and Sunday dinner

Prices
Meals: à la carte £ 18/25

Typical Dishes
Warm mushroom & tarragon tart
Slow roast shoulder of lamb
Chocolate & truffle torte

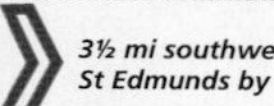
3½ mi southwest of Bury St Edmunds by A 143. Parking.

53 The Angel

Market Pl,
Lavenham CO10 9QZ

Tel.: (01787)247388 – Fax: (01787)248344

e-mail: angel@maypolehotels.com **Website:** www.maypolehotels.com

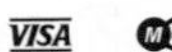 

 **Woodforde's Wherry, Adnams, Greene King IPA, Nethergate Bitter**

Lavenham is one of best preserved medieval villages in England, and its market square, with its pretty half-timbered buildings, was once at the centre of its thriving wool trade. These days, it's tourists who flock here and The Angel's front terrace is a great place from which to watch them go about their leisure. If you want to escape from the crowds awhile, try a table in the back garden instead; the same menu is served in all areas, so if the weather turns nasty, head inside to the characterful bar, the dining room or the snug. On offer are an extensive range of traditional dishes, which change with the seasons; perhaps slow roasted belly pork, grilled sea bass or a tasty steak. Bedrooms are fairly small but have a pleasing combination of ancient timbers and modern facilities; some overlook the square; others the garden. Make sure to visit the residents' lounge on the first floor to see its impressive pargeted ceiling.

Closing times
Open daily

Prices
Meals: à la carte £ 20/29
8 rooms: £ 85/100

Typical Dishes
Chicken, apricot & pistachio terrine
Steak & ale pie
Syrup sponge pudding

6 mi north of Sudbury by B 1115 and B 1071; in town centre. Parking.

54 The Ship Inn

Church Lane,
Levington IP10 0LQ
Tel.: (01473)659573 – Fax: (01473)659151

 **Adnams Best and Broadside, Norfolk Wherry**

Atmosphere is crucial when it comes to the humble pub, and on that score, The Ship Inn gets top marks. Already crammed with maritime curios, pictures and ornaments which celebrate its seafaring connections and smuggling past, its small, characterful rooms soon fill up with customers, including plenty of regulars as well as those less used to minding their heads on the whisky water jugs which hang from the ancient beams. They don't take bookings, so arrive early; if you have to go on the waiting list, make the most of it and enjoy a pint of Adnams ale from the barrel at the bar. The blackboard menus are in a constant state of flux; seafood-orientated, they also feature global influences, and some dishes are available as either a starter or a main course. Service relies partly on the DIY approach, so you'll have to order at the bar, but it seems to work well and the staff, when you can catch them, are friendly and polite.

Closing times
Closed 25-26 December

Prices
Meals: à la carte £ 13/25

Typical Dishes
Seared pigeon
Scallop risotto
Chocolate pecan pie

6 mi southeast of Ipswich by A 14.
Parking.

55 The Star Inn

The Street,
Lidgate CB8 9PP
Tel.: (01638)500275

 **Greene King - IPA & Abbot, Ruddles**

The 16C Star, set on the main road through this pretty village, is the cosy epitome of an old English inn – but with a splash of pink paint and a surprise Spanish menu. All the quintessentially inn-like attributes are here: the ancient beams stoop low, while logs smoulder in the inglenook fireplaces and the odd local or three pops in for their pint of real ale. The Spanish influence comes courtesy of hands-on owner Maria Theresa Axon, who hails originally from Catalonia. Rustic, hearty cooking uses a combination of local produce and authentic Iberian ingredients and the blackboard menus offer mostly Spanish dishes, with a decent selection of fish featuring alongside choices like locally sourced wild boar and venison. The set two course lunch menu is nicely priced, with well-paced service delivered by friendly young staff. Should the weather follow the food's example and turn Mediterranean, the lawned gardens beckon.

Closing times

Closed 25-26 December, 1 January and Monday lunch

Prices

Meals: £ 14/18
and à la carte £ 25/30

Typical Dishes

Seafood pâté
Venison fillet
Treacle tart

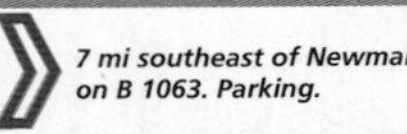
7 mi southeast of Newmarket on B 1063. Parking.

56 **The Swan**

The Street,
Monks Eleigh IP7 7AU
Tel.: (01449)741391
e-mail: swan@monkseleigh.com **Website:** www.monkseleigh.com

 **Adnams Best, Adnams Broadside**

Boasting honey yellow walls and a charming thatched roof, this attractive building is more 'destination dining pub' than local village boozer – although that doesn't mean that drinkers aren't welcome. Set on the main road of pretty Monks Eleigh, it displays a seamless mix of old and new: your first step inside reveals a fresh, modern feel but if you take a closer look many original features can still be found. For special occasions there's a characterful private dining room and when weather permits, you can eat on the small side terrace. The friendly and very experienced chef-owner has a background in Italian cuisine and a strong passion for local produce. Menus change daily and comprise of a good selection of classic and more refined pub dishes, as well as some more Italian influences; you might find duck breast, fillet steak or braised lamb alongside cannelloni or lasagne. Everything is homemade, from the bread to the ice cream.

Closing times

Closed 25-26 December, Sunday dinner and Monday

Prices

Meals: £ 18 and à la carte £ 19/29

Typical Dishes
Grilled scallops
Braised lamb
Panna cotta

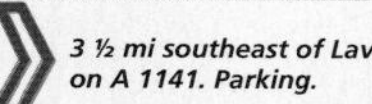

3 ½ mi southeast of Lavenham on A 1141. Parking.

England • East of England • Suffolk

57 The Crown Inn

Bridge Rd,
Snape IP17 1SL
Tel.: (01728)688324
e-mail: snapecrown@tiscali.co.uk

Adnams : Bitter, Broadside, seasonal

With its low ceilings, open fires and mismatched wooden chairs, this characterful 400 year old building on the outskirts of the village really is a true country pub. It's not just local ingredients that you'll find on the menu here, but produce that's recently been picked from the owner's garden or plucked off his trees. The eggs, milk and meats are equally as fresh, as they keep pigs, calves, goats, turkey and quail out the back – not forgetting some rescued battery hens – with the shortfall made up by carefully selected local suppliers, who are name-checked on the menu. As you would expect, cooking is seasonal and simply done, with sandwiches, ploughman's and light bites on offer at lunch and more substantial dishes such as confit duck or rib-eye steak at dinner. The blackboard specials always include a market fish of the day and to finish, there's a selection of nursery-style puddings – sticky toffee being the firm favourite.

Closing times
Closed Monday in winter

Prices
Meals: à la carte £ 15/25

Typical Dishes
Terrine of skate
Shoulder of lamb
Cappucino coffee mousse

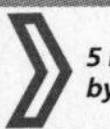
5 mi west of Aldeburgh by A 1094. Parking.

58 **The Crown**

90 High St,
Southwold IP18 6DP

Tel.: (01502)722275 – Fax: (01502)727263
e-mail: crown.hotel@adnams.co.uk **Website:** www.adnams.co.uk

 **Adnams - Bitter, Broadside, Explorer**

This smart, Georgian-fronted inn sits on the high street of this charming town, near to the brewery and only a hop, skip and a jump away from the sea. Its traditionally styled bar and dining room are often buzzing with diners and the small, oak-panelled, nautically themed locals bar towards the rear is a great place for a leisurely pint or two of Adnams of an afternoon. Should the Suffolk summer start to sizzle, it's time to head for the front terrace for a spot of sun-worship-cum-people-watching. The same modern seasonal menu is served throughout: choose from dishes such as roasted sea bass, Cromer crab cakes or steak and chips, with perhaps a berry tart or some local ice cream for dessert. Arrive early to avoid disappointment, however, as they don't take bookings. Staying awhile to explore the beautiful Suffolk coastline? Individually styled bedrooms have a contemporary feel; those towards the rear are the quietest.

Closing times
Open daily

Prices
Meals: à la carte £ 26/34
14 rooms: £ 138/218

Typical Dishes
Grilled sardine timbale
Dingley Dell pork belly
Rhubarb & Champagne jelly

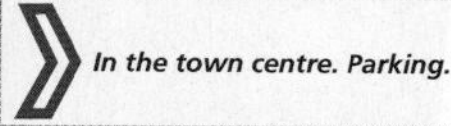
In the town centre. Parking.

59 The Randolph

41 Wangford Rd,
Reydon, Southwold IP18 6PZ

Tel.: (01502)723603 – Fax: (01502)722194
e-mail: reception@therandolph.co.uk **Website:** www.therandolph.co.uk

Adnams - Bitter and Broadside and one seasonal ale

Set in a quiet village not far from Southwold and the Suffolk Heritage coastline, this sizeable red-brick and part-timbered pub is named after Sir Winston Churchill's father. Its grand Victorian façade is suitably imposing and if you want to play the game and arrive in style, there's even room to land your helicopter in the grounds, before you take a seat on the pleasant wood-furnished terrace for an al fresco experience. If you're after a liquid lunch, make for a squashy sofa beside the cheery group of locals in the bright, contemporary bar, or for something a little more substantial, head for the large linen-laid dining room with its display of local artwork. Service if friendly but on occasion, can be a little slow. Good-sized menus feature classical pub dishes with a refined edge and plenty of local, seasonal produce; you might find peppered pigeon breast or smoked trout and avocado stack. Bedrooms are spacious and well-kept.

Closing times
Open daily

Prices
Meals: £ 19 (Sunday lunch) and à la carte £ 19/27

10 rooms: £ 65/105

Typical Dishes
Soup of the day
Cod in Adnams beer batter
Iced Indian kulfi

2 mi northwest of Southwold by A 1095 and B 1126. Parking.

60 The Crown

Stoke-by-Nayland CO6 4SE
Tel.: (01206)262001 – Fax: (01206)264026
e-mail: info@crowninn.net
Website: www.crowninn.net

   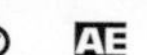 

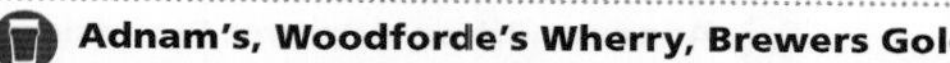

Set overlooking the Box and Stour river valleys, in a hillside village in the Dedham Vale, this spacious 16C pub is a lovely place to visit in summer, with its large lawned gardens and a smart wood-furnished patio. If you're looking for choice, then step inside and you'll find soft leather sofas and heavy wood tables spread between various little rooms and semi open-plan snugs, where wood or flag flooring gives way to boldly coloured walls. If you're into wine, the bar list provides over 30 by the glass; while in one corner, a large glass-fronted room displays a selection of top quality bottles to drink in or take away. Menus change every three weeks and feature the latest seasonal produce sourced from nearby farms and estates, supplemented by a Daily Catch and seafood specials. To the rear, spacious bedrooms take on either contemporary or country cottage styles. All overlook the countryside and some have French windows and a terrace.

Closing times
Closed 25-26 December

Prices
Meals: à la carte £ 20/33
11 rooms: £ 80/200

Typical Dishes
Crispy salt & pepper squid
Local wild rabbit pie
Date pudding

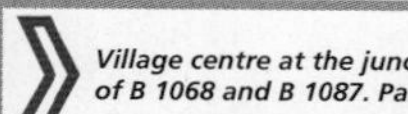
Village centre at the junction of B 1068 and B 1087. Parking.

England • East of England • Suffolk

61 The Anchor

Main St,
Walberswick IP18 6UA
Tel.: (01502)722112 – Fax: (01502)724464
e-mail: info@anchoratwalberswick.com **Website:** www.anchoratwalberswick.com

 **Adnam's Bitter, Adnam's Broadside**

Drop anchor in this unspoilt area of Suffolk coastline and head for the main street of Walberswick, the less celebrated neighbour of trendy Southwold. Here you will find a large pub garden and terrace, looking out over allotments to a sandy bank and the sea beyond. The World Crabbing Championships are an ideal time to visit as the town really comes alive but you will receive a warm welcome here whatever the time of year. Cooking is hearty, unfussy and full of flavour, with local or homemade produce being used wherever possible. Seafood features highly and you can usually find West Mersea oysters, Brancaster mussels and fish from the Aldeburgh day boats, alongside non-fishy dishes such as pheasant tagliatelle or braised Blythburgh pork belly. Desserts are comforting classics and for drinkers there's an impressive selection of wine and beer. Bedrooms aren't currently recommendable, but there are plans to refurbish them in the near future.

Closing times
Closed 25 December

Prices
Meals: à la carte £ 20/30

Typical Dishes
Fish platter
Steak, kidney and oyster pudding
Hot chocolate pudding

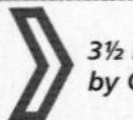

3½ mi east of A 12 on B 1387 by Corporation Marshes. Parking.

Twenty-first century London may truly be called the definitive world city. Time zones radiate from Greenwich, and global finances zap round the Square Mile, while a vast smorgasbord of restaurants is the equal of anywhere on the planet. A stunning diversity of population now calls the capital its home, mixing and matching its time between the urban sprawl and enviable acres of green open space. From Roman settlement to banking centre to capital of a 19C empire, London's pulse has rarely missed a beat. Along the way, expansion has gobbled up surrounding villages, a piecemeal cocktail with its ingredients stirred to create the likes of Kensington and Chelsea, Highgate and Hampstead, Twickenham and Richmond. Apart from the great range of restaurants, London boasts over three and a half thousand pubs, many of which now see accomplished, creative cooking as an integral part of their existence and appeal. And you can find them sprinkled right the way across from zones one to five…

East of England
South East
SURREY
Bourne End
Chiswell Green
London Colney
Welham Green
Brookmans Park
Northaw
South Mimms
Potters Bar
Bovingdon
Kings Langley
Abbots Langley
Radlett
Shenley
Aldenham
Borehamwood
Hadley Wood
Chenies
Little Chalfont
Watford
Chorleywood
Croxley Green
Bushey
Elstree
LONDON GATEWAY
BARNET
Rickmansworth
Chalfont St Giles
South Oxhey
Stanmore
Harefield
Pinner
Wealdstone
HARROW
Wembley
BRENT
Denham
Iver Heath
Iver
HILLINGDON
EALING
CAMDEN
Langley
HESTON
Heston
HAMMERSMITH
FULHAM
HEATHROW AIRPORT
Isleworth
HOUNSLOW
Staines
Stanwell
Feltham
Twickenham
RICHMOND UPON THAMES
Putney
WANDSWORTH
Wimbledon
Egham
Ashford
Hampton Court
Laleham
Sunbury
Walton-on-Thames
KINGSTON UPON THAMES
MERTON
Mitcham
Chertsey
Shepperton
Addlestone
Cheam
Carshalton
SUTTON
Wallington
Esher
Chessington
Weybridge
Claygate
Ewell
Chobham
Oxshott
Epsom
Banstead
Byfleet
Horsell
Woking
Ashtead
Chipstead
Wisley
Leatherhead
Tadworth
Ripley
Ockham
Kingswood
Fetcham
Great Bookham
East Horsley
Burpham
Clandon Park
Polesden Lacey
Box Hill
Redhill
M 25
M 40
M 4
A 40
A 4

East of England
LONDON
South East
Cheshunt
Epping
High Ongar
N. Weald Bassett
Chipping Ongar
Blackmore
Fryerning
Ingatestone
Theydon Bois
Waltham Abbey
Epping Forest
Loughton
Abridge
Pilgrims Hatch
Brentwood
Stapleford Abbotts
Chigwell
Ingrave
WALTHAM FOREST
REDBRIDGE
HAVERING
HACKNEY
Hornchurch
Upminster
Ilford
BARKING AND DAGENHAM
Bulphan
TOWER HAMLETS
NEWHAM
South Ockendon
Beckton
Aveley
THURROCK
Blackwall Tunnel
Woolwich
GREENWICH
Dartford Crossing
Grays Thurrock
Erith
BEXLEY
Northfleet
Dartford
Swanscombe
LEWISHAM
Sydenham
Sidcup
Wilmington
Darenth
Istead Rise
Swanley
Longfield
Hartley
BROMLEY
Farningham
Meopham
West Wickham
CROYDON
Orpington
Eynsford
Ash
New Addington
West Kingsdown
Biggin Hill
Warlingham
Otford
Wrotham
Woldingham
Ightham
W. Malling
Borough Green
Sevenoaks
Sundridge
Knole
Mereworth
Westerham
Ightham Mote
Shipbourne
Limpsfield
Chartwell
Oxted
Crockham Hill
Hildenborough
Hadlow

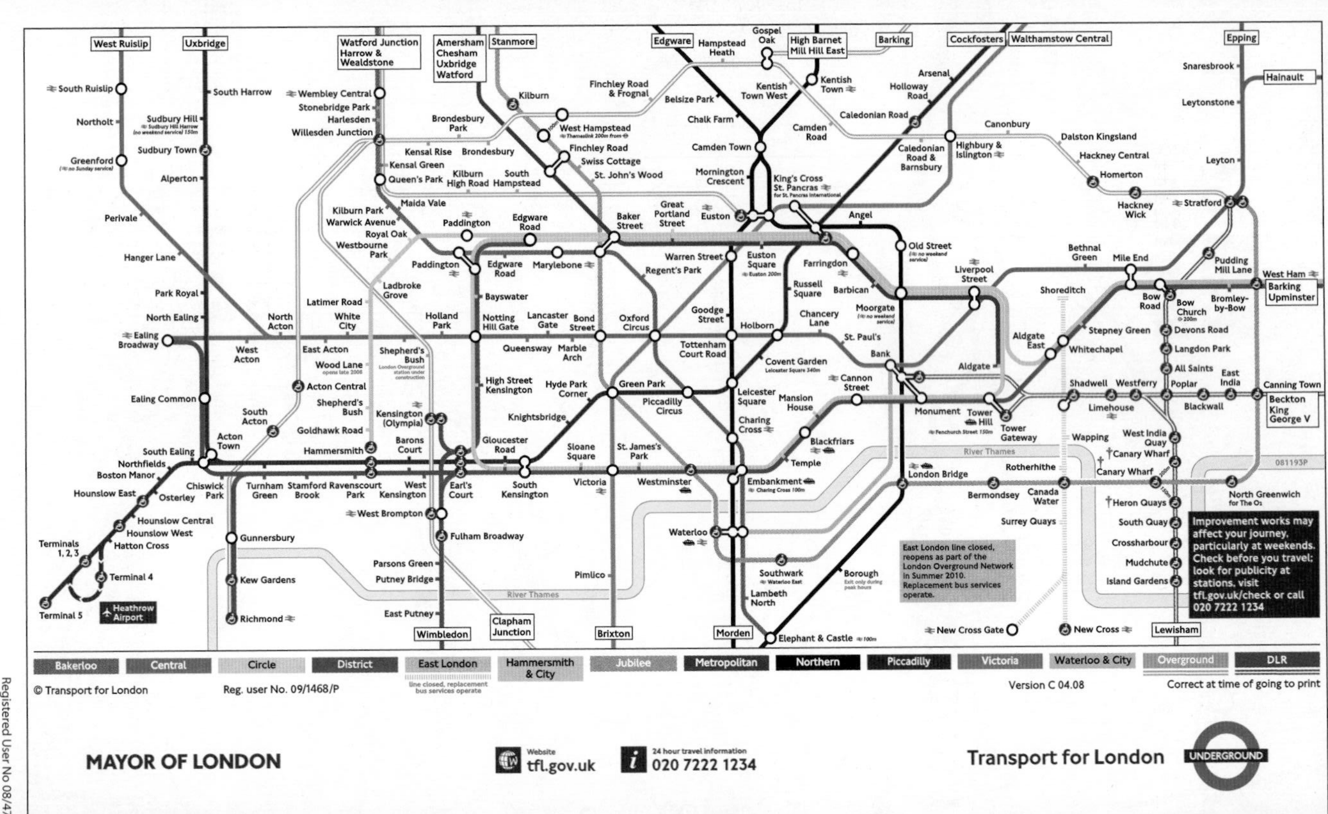

Registered User No 08/477

1 Paradise by way of Kensal Green

19 Kilburn Lane,
Kensal Green N1 8LN
Tel.: (020)89690098
e-mail: shelley@thecolumbogroup.com **Website:** www.theparadise.co.uk

VISA 

Shepherd Neame Spitfire

"For there is good news yet to hear and fine things to be seen / before we go to Paradise by way of Kensal Green", so ended a poem by G.K Chesterton, writer, philosopher, theologian and vegetarian-loather; the pub is doing its bit by reminding us that there's more to the local area than the cemetery. It's certainly eye-catching as it has been kitted out in an appealingly bohemian style with mismatched furniture, Murano chandeliers, old portraits and even the odd birdcage. Burlesque shows, comedy and music nights all happen upstairs. The bar menu is available during the day and covers most bases, from Welsh rarebit to plates of charcuterie but it's in the evening in the restaurant when the kitchen puts on its show. Mostly British ingredients come with enduring partners, like asparagus with butter, York ham with Cumberland sauce and lemon sole with Jersey Royals. Portions are man-sized and service is good-natured and natural.

Closing times
Closed August bank holiday

Prices
Meals: £ 15/30
and à la carte £ 24/31

Typical Dishes
Organic Poole harbour oysters
Rump of new season lamb
Knickerbocker Glory

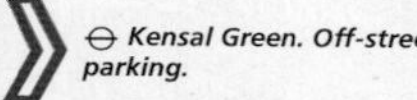

⊖ Kensal Green. Off-street parking.

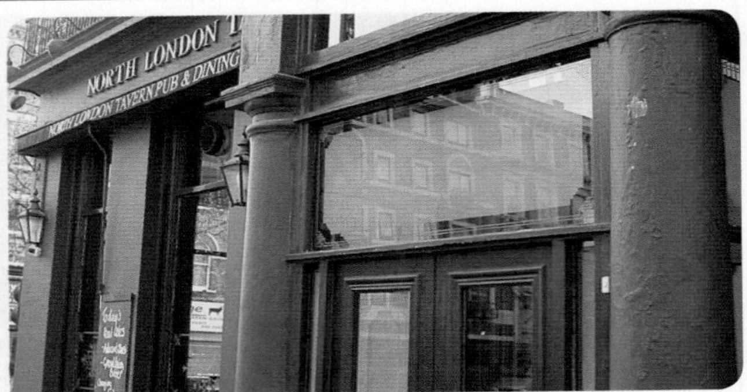

2 North London Tavern

375 Kilburn High Rd,
Kilburn NW6 7QB
Tel.: (020)76256634
e-mail: northlondontavern@realpubs.co.uk **Website:** www.realpubs.co.uk

Timothy Taylor Landlord, Brakspear Bitter, Sharp's Doom Bar, Otter Ale, Flowers, Harveys, Brains SA

It may look as though it's bursting at the seams but those groups huddled together outside are usually just the smokers out for a quick gasper. That being said, the bar is a popular local spot. The dining room is separated from the bar by a red curtain and glass panelling and it too can quickly fill up. Old church seats, mismatched tables, high ceilings and chandeliers add a little gothic character and there are photos of old Kilburn on the walls. Lunch is a simpler affair in the bar but at dinner the printed menu, which is rather needlessly repeated verbatim on a large blackboard, offers a comprehensive selection of gastropub greatest hits, from belly pork to rib-eye, tuna niçoise to apple crumble, plus a couple of veggie options. The crusty bread is terrific and each dish arrives fully garnished and appetisingly presented on a big white plate. There's a whole roast beast at weekends and the wine list keeps things mostly under £20.

Closing times
Closed 25 December, lunch 26 December and 1 January and Monday

Prices
Meals: à la carte £ 19/29

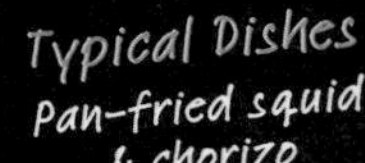

Typical Dishes
Pan-fried squid & chorizo
Sea bream, vanilla & saffron sauce
White chocolate & vanilla cheesecake

⊖ Kilburn. Parking in Cavendish Rd after 3pm.

3 The Salusbury

50-52 Salusbury Road,
Queen's Park NW6 6NN
Tel.: (020)73283286
e-mail: thesalusburypub@btconnect.com

 **Adnam's Broadside, Adnam's Bitter**

The Salusbury is a pleasingly down-to-earth pub, more shabby than chic. It's divided into two, with the left hand side the local pub part and the other side hosting a laid back dining room with mirrors and solid furniture. The Italian menu is a model of understatement, with little in the way of descriptive elaboration, and it's not until the food arrives that one realises how seriously this pub takes its cooking. There's plenty of choice from a menu which includes about five pasta dishes that can be taken as starters or main courses. Dishes are as generous in size as they are in flavour. The crisp Sardinian guttiau bread comes with aubergine and pecorino and is a great way of starting proceedings; the pappardelle with the tender duck ragu is an eminently satisfying dish; the fritto misto is made from an impressive array of fish and the tiramisu would shame many a smart Italian restaurant. The wine list offers plenty under £20.

Closing times
Closed 25-26 December, 1 January and Monday lunch

Prices
Meals: £ 22/25

Typical Dishes
Papardelle with swordfish
Monkfish & seafood cartoccio
Orange crème brûlée

 ⊖ Queens Park.

4 The Queensbury

110 Walm Lane,
Willesden Green NW2 4RS

Tel.: (020)84520171

e-mail: info@thequeensbury.net **Website:** www.thequeensbury.net

  MC

 **No real ales offered**

The Conservative Club of Willesden Green have displayed a questionable lack of fiscal foresight because it's hard to sell off your building to a property developer when you've already offloaded the half that housed your snooker room and seen it turned into a pub. That pub was The Green which eventually ran out of steam but has returned, renewed and refreshed under the new owner, as The Queensbury. The inside hasn't changed much: you enter into the bar where there's occasional live music and find the brighter dining room at the back with its antique mirrors and striking wallpaper. The blackboard menu blends pub numbers like pies and jerk chicken burgers alongside the more adventurous pork belly with chorizo; Parma ham with celeriac remoulade comes on a wooden board and desserts appear to be a particular strength of the kitchen. There's brunch at weekends and further snacky choices available in the bar.

Closing times

Open daily

Prices

Meals: à la carte £ 19/25

Typical Dishes

Parma ham, celeriac remoulade

Beef & Stilton pie

Tarte Tatin

⊖ *Willesden Green.*

5 Crown

46 Plaistow Lane, Sundridge Park BR1 3PA
Tel.: (020)84661313
e-mail: dine@thecrownsundridgepark.co.uk
Website: www.thecrownsundridgepark.co.uk

   VISA 

 **Adnams Broadside, Meantime Brewery**

The owners have been moving steadily southwards: having started in Battersea, they then bought the Rosendale in West Dulwich and now it's Bromley's turn. The Crown at Sundridge Park is a stout and fetching Victorian fellow who has been transformed into a slick, contemporary dining pub. Midweek the menu is fairly unremarkable, in an understandable bid to avoid being labelled as a 'special occasion' destination – the death knell of many an establishment. Expect everything from rump steak and lamb shank to grilled skewers of chorizo or prawns. At busier weekends the kitchen is allowed to express itself a little more and this is when you'll see rillettes and risottos, brûlées and parfaits. Whatever you're eating, you'll certainly find something to go with it as the owner is passionate about wine and already has over 300 bins. The only shame is that you have to enter through the side – the main corner entrance is just for show.

Closing times

Closed Sunday dinner and Monday (except bank holidays)

Prices

Meals: £ 19 (Sunday lunch) and à la carte £ 23/33

Typical Dishes

Paprika-cured duck breast

Halibut fillet & crushed potatoes

Summer berries crème brûlée

⊖ *Sundridge Park (rail).*

6 Prince Albert

163 Royal College St,
Camden Town NW1 0SG
Tel.: (020)74850270 – Fax: (020)77135994
e-mail: info@princealbertcamden.com **Website:** www.princealbertcamden.com

 VISA MC AE

Black Sheep Bitter, Adnams Broadside and rotating guest ales from Crouch Vale Brewery

Albert had only been Prince Consort for three years when this pub opened in 1843. In 1863, work began down the road on St Pancras and it was highly appropriate that the re-opening of this Gothic Victorian masterpiece coincided with the rebirth of the pub. The Prince Albert has kept much of its character but now comes with an appealing neighbourhood feel coupled with a welcoming atmosphere. Decent olives and homemade soda bread are on hand while choosing from the selection of satisfyingly filling dishes, where freshness and traceability are given every respect. Starters such as grilled black tiger prawns with garlic butter or a plate of mixed charcuterie are offered on the à la carte alongside main courses like chicken and mushroom pie with mash or sirloin steak, while the set price two or three course menu offers good value for money. The wine list offers over a dozen labels by the glass and plenty of choice for under £20.

Closing times
Open daily
Booking essential

Prices
Meals: £ 11/12
and à la carte £ 19/32

Typical Dishes
Confit duck
Pan-fried black bream
Rhubarb & apple crumble

⊖ Camden Town. Pay & display parking adjacent to pub.

7 Bull and Last

168 Highgate Road,
Dartmouth Park NW5 1QS
Tel.: (020)72673641
e-mail: info@thebullandlast.co.uk

VISA MC

 **Spitfire, Hooky, Old Speckled Hen, Black Sheep and one guest beer**

You'll be thankful that Parliament Hill is so close because you'll need the exercise – portions at the reinvigorated Bull and Last are man-size and that man was clearly hungry. The place was taken over in 2008 by the clued-up team behind the Prince of Wales in Putney and they hit the ground running. So named because it was once the last 'Bull' pub on the way out of London, they've kept plenty of character and, with a display of pewter tankards and door locks, added some of their own. It's bright and breezy and hugely popular so book first. Suppliers are name-checked on boards behind the bar which tells you they take their food seriously. Animals are taken whole and butchered accordingly so expect lots of terrines and homemade charcuterie, along with everything from oysters to smoked eel; the menu can change twice a day depending on available produce. There's an upstairs room used at weekends that's like a taxidermist's showroom.

Closing times
Closed 25 December
Booking essential

Prices
Meals: à la carte £ 26/32

Typical Dishes
Oxtail gnocchi
Hare pappardelle
Blueberry cheesecake ice cream

⊖ Tufnell Park. Free parking in the neighbourhood.

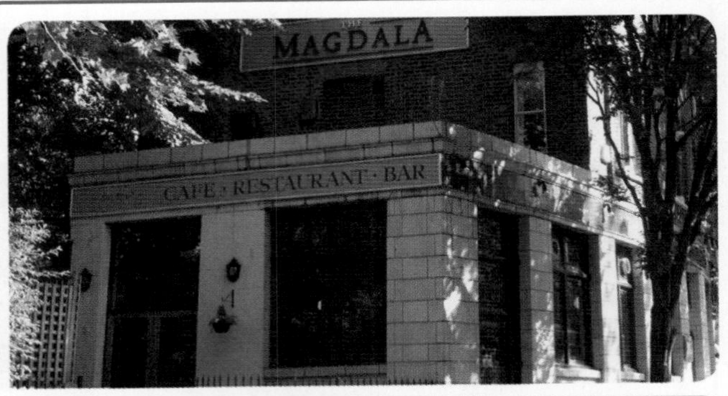

8 The Magdala

2A South Hill Park,
Hampstead NW3 2SB
Tel.: (020)74352503 – Fax: (020)74356167
e-mail: themagdala@hotmail.co.uk **Website:** www.the-magdala.com

Greene King IPA, Fuller's London Pride and changing guest ales

The Magdala has its place in history as it was outside this pub where Ruth Ellis shot her paramour in 1955. She was the last woman to be hanged in Britain and her case contributed to the eventual abolition of the death penalty. To its credit, the pub doesn't let this episode define it but instead concentrates on its community feel, general air of friendliness and decent food. The owner worked here for several years before buying it in 2007 and she certainly keeps her eye on the ball. As you walk in, it's a right turn for drinking and left for eating. The latter comes from a concise but balanced menu, with its heart and influences mostly within the British Isles. There are also interesting snacks and sharing plates, like assorted antipasti, on the supplementary blackboard. Wisely, no great risks are taken in preparation; this is about decent pub food. The menu lengthens at weekends when the upstairs room comes into play.

Closing times
Open daily
Prices
Meals: à la carte £ 19/28

Typical Dishes
Chilli & herb beef carpaccio
Lemon sole roulade
Chocolate pot

⊖ Belsize Park. Pay & display parking outside the pub; heath car park 5min walk.

9 The Wells

30 Well Walk,
Hampstead NW3 1BX
Tel.: (020)77943785 – Fax: (020)77946817
e-mail: info@thewellshampstead.co.uk **Website:** www.thewellshampstead.co.uk

 **Adnams Broadside, Black Sheep**

London pubs can be loud, hysterical affairs but The Wells is a more sober beast, as one would expect from a pub in the middle of Hampstead village. Being so near the Heath makes it feel like a country pub but, then again, it's equally close to the High Street which adds a dose of urban poise. Downstairs is usually pretty busy but head upstairs and you'll find yourself in a haven of civility. Here the dining room is divided into three, with the brightest, the pale blue room, looking down over the spring blossom. Little wonder that Sundays are full of young couples taking out their parents or vice versa. The cooking is a reflection of the pub: it is robust and hearty but with a sophisticated finish. You'll find duck confit or rump of lamb, scallops and wood pigeon but also veggie shepherd's pie and Sunday roasts. Puddings are done with particular aplomb and are generous in their proportions – look out for the apple and rhubarb crumble.

Closing times
Open daily

Prices
Meals: à la carte £ 20/33

Typical Dishes
Chicken liver, bacon & spinach toast
Rump of lamb
Blood orange & lemon posset

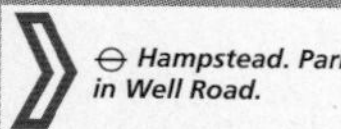
⊖ Hampstead. Parking in Well Road.

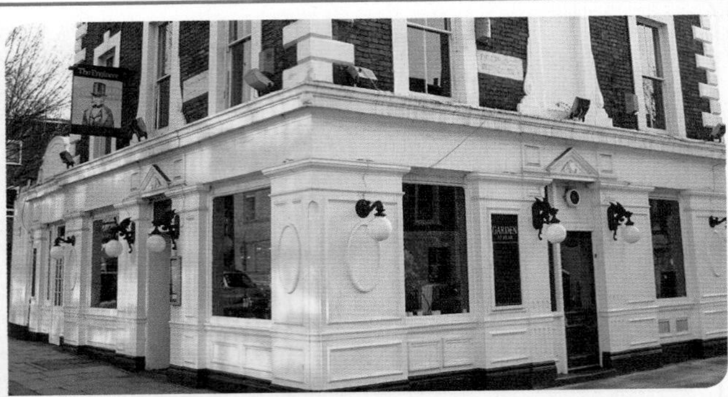

10 The Engineer

65 Gloucester Ave, Primrose Hill NW1 8JH

Tel.: (020)77220950 – Fax: (020)74830592

e-mail: info@the-engineer.com **Website:** www.the-engineer.com

  **Bombardier, St Peter's Organic Ale**

The Engineer was at the vanguard of London's gastropub movement and remains a classic example of the genre. The Grade II listed pub, with its stuccoed Italianate façade, dates from around 1850; the exact identity of the engineer in question remains open to question. The restaurant is wrapped around the front bar and the whole place appears to be in a permanent state of noisy excitement. There's a great summer terrace at the back but the pub is equally appealing on a winter's night and is also child-friendly. The staff are young and enthusiastic although they can occasionally get stretched but fortunately customers never appear to be in any hurry either. The kitchen shows a healthy respect for the provenance of its meats and balances more modern influences with pub favourites; it's always worth ordering a bowl of those fabulous Baker fries on the side. Dishes come in fairly strapping proportions and flavours have plenty of oomph.

Closing times
Open daily

Prices
Meals: à la carte £ 20/35

Typical Dishes
Smoked mackerel
Lamb neck fillet
Chocolate & ginger pot de crème

 ⊖ *Chalk Farm. On street parking meters.* 

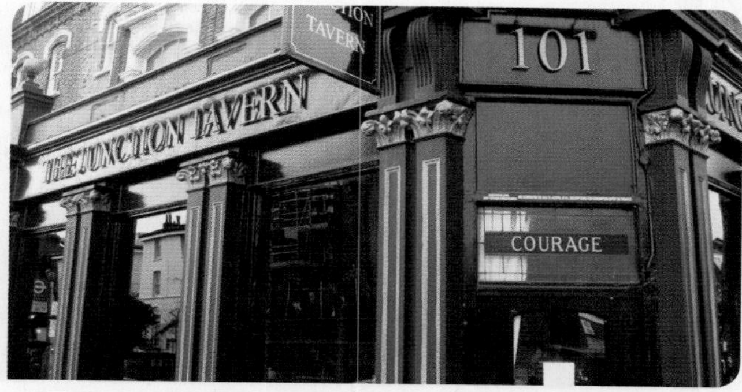

11 Junction Tavern

101 Fortess Rd,
Tufnell Park NW5 1AG
Tel.: (020)74859400 – Fax: (020)74859401
Website: www.junctiontavern.co.uk

Deuchar's IPA and 10-15 guest beers per week from independent brewers

Tufnell Park has always appealed to young professionals because, along with its Victorian terraces, it has a belligerent edge to add a little credibility. Looking like the quintessential London pub, from its matt back exterior to the huddled smokers outside, The Junction Tavern fits in well. It's a sizeable place, split by the central bar; you can eat anywhere but most prefer to be in the restaurant. The menu changes daily and portion size has been slightly reduced to give more balance to the menu as a whole. Cooking remains unfussy and relies on good flavours; there's plenty of choice, from light summer dishes such as grilled sardines and seared tuna to the more robust rib-eye and pork belly. Staff are a chatty lot and they know their beers – they offer weekly changing guest beers and hold a popular beer festival; the 'pie and a pint' choice remains a favourite. Commendably, they offer tap water without being prompted.

Closing times
Closed 24-26 December and 1 January

Prices
Meals: à la carte £ 21/27

Typical Dishes
Grilled sardines
Lemon sole
Poached pear

⊖ Tufnell Park. Pay & display parking in nearby streets.

12 The Bollo

13-15 Bollo Lane,
Acton Green W4 5LR
Tel.: (020)89946037
e-mail: thebollo@btconnect.com **Website:** www.thebollohouse.co.uk

VISA MC AE

Greene King - IPA, Alepril Fool

The Bollo is a large Victorian pub that is very much the sum of its parts and, as such, gets the stamp of approval. The original glass cupola and oak panelling give it some substance in this age of the generic pub makeover and, despite being hidden away down a suburban road, it still manages to offer a welcoming atmosphere. Tables and sofas are scattered around and there are no separate areas – this is a sit-where-you-want pub. The menu changes as ingredients come and go; the kitchen appeals to its core voters by always including sufficient numbers of pub classics be they the Bollo Burger, the haddock or the fishcakes.
But there is also a discernible southern Mediterranean influence to the menu, with regular appearances from the likes of chorizo, tzatziki, bruschetta and hummus. This is a pub where there's always either a promotion or an activity, whether that's the '50% off a main course' Monday or the Wednesday quiz nights.

Closing times
Open daily

Prices
Meals: à la carte £ 22/27

Typical Dishes
Ham hock & rabbit terrine
Suffolk pork chop
Belgian chocolate & brandy tart

⊖ Chiswick Park. Parking meters.

13 Duke of Sussex

75 South Parade,
Acton Green W4 5LF
Tel.: (020)87428801
e-mail: thedukeofsussex@realpubs.co.uk

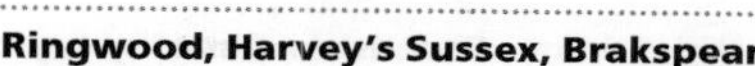

Ringwood, Harvey's Sussex, Brakspear

This grand old Victorian Duke has been given a new lease of life by an enthusiastic pair of experienced gastropub specialists. They've taken a long lease on the place, done it all up and, most importantly, introduced some very appealing menus. A hospitable atmosphere reigns throughout, but the best place to eat is in the back room, which was once a variety theatre and comes complete with proscenium arch, chandeliers and ornate plasterwork. The menu's printed daily and the Spanish influence highlights where the chef's passions lie. Rustic and satisfying stews, whether fish or fabada, suit the environment perfectly, as does a plate of Spanish cured meats or a tortilla; there are often dishes designed for sharing and on some evenings the kitchen might roast a whole suckling pig, which they start dishing out at around 7.30 – but when it's gone, it's gone. The wine list is short but affordable, with plenty available by the glass or carafe.

Closing times
Closed Monday lunch

Prices
Meals: à la carte £ 20/27

Typical Dishes
Razor clams, chorizo & chilli
Old spot pork belly
Santiago tart

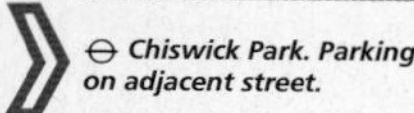

⊖ *Chiswick Park. Parking on adjacent street.*

14 Cat & Mutton

76 Broadway Market,
Hackney E8 4QJ
Tel.: (020)72545599 – Fax: (020)79861444
e-mail: catandmutton@yahoo.co.uk **Website:** www.catandmutton.co.uk

VISA MC AE

 **Adnams Broadside, Timothy Taylor Landlord**

The Cat and Mutton is your typical early Victorian corner pub with a bona fide London feel; it's a drinking pub that does decent food, rather than an eating one that reluctantly serves drinks. The ground floor can take a hammering with the after-work crowd and it has a rough and ready vibe, with exposed brick walls and a resolute lack of decorative embellishment save for a solitary picture of a cat and, unsurprisingly, a leg of mutton. Such uncompromising surroundings make it an unlikely spot in which to find decent food but that's exactly what the Cat and Mutton delivers, although this still may not be the best choice for that romantic dinner à deux. The blackboard menu offers around five choices per course, which could include anything from chilli squid to a decent steak. The open plan kitchen uses some ingredients garnered from the local market and the cooking is full-bodied and satisfying. The room upstairs is used at weekends.

Closing times

Closed 25-26 December, 1 January and Monday lunch

Prices

Meals: à la carte £ 22/60

Typical Dishes

Dorset crab on toast
Wild venison
British cheeses

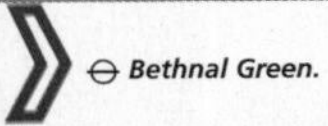
⊖ *Bethnal Green.*

15 The Empress of India

130 Lauriston Road,
Victoria Park, Hackney E9 7LH
Tel.: (020)85335123 – Fax: (020)74042250
Website: www.theempressofindia.com

  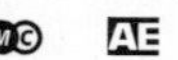

 **Timothy Taylor Landlord, Fuller's London Pride**

The building dates from the 1880s and pays homage to said title-bearer, Queen Victoria and her era, but has enjoyed various past incarnations as a nightclub, a print works and a floristry training school. These days it's a smart, open-plan pub with the emphasis firmly on dining. It's brightly lit with high ceilings, mosaic flooring, red leather banquettes and eye-catching murals picturing Indian scenes; young and enthusiastic serving staff complete the look. It offers everything from breakfast to afternoon tea; even a kid's menu is available, which is still relatively rare in the big city. The seasonally evolving menu is classically based with some Mediterranean influences, and blends the robust with the more refined, whether that's the slow-braised shoulder of mutton or poached trout. The owners use rare breeds for their meats and poultry, and these can be seen nightly and at weekends being cooked on the rotisserie.

Closing times
Closed 25 December

Prices
Meals: à la carte £ 19/29

Typical Dishes
Home-pickled Cornish herrings
Herdwick mutton & glazed turnips
Rhubarb crumble

⊖ Mile End. On-street parking meters.

England • London • Hackney

16 Prince Arthur

95 Forest Road, Hackney E8 3BH
Tel.: (020)72499996 – Fax: (020)72497074
e-mail: info@theprincearthurlondonfields.com
Website: www.theprincearthurlondonfields.com

 **Fuller's London Pride, Deuchar's IPA**

The Prince Arthur is less gastropub, more your favourite intimate little local serving proper pub grub. Much of the old character remains but the owners, brothers Tom & Ed Martin, have added some ironic touches, from stuffed animals to a collection of saucy seaside postcards. It is also still a pub for local people, with the occasional Martin Amis enthusiast thrown in for good measure. The menu matches the surroundings in its lack of pretension. Soup comes with crusty bread, prawns come by the pint and pub classics, like cottage pie and apple crumble, are always to be found. There are also hearty lamb shanks and saddles of rabbit for the more adventurous. Desserts should really be written as 'puddings' as they are of the weigh-you-down-but-make-you-feel-good variety. That being said, the deep-fried jam sandwich with carnation milk ice cream appears to be more of an attention-grabber than a culinary breakthrough.

Closing times
Closed 25-26 December, Monday-Tuesday lunch

Prices
Meals: à la carte £ 20/27

Typical Dishes
Guinea fowl terrine
Darne of sea trout
Deep-fried jam sandwich

⊖ *Bethnal Green.*

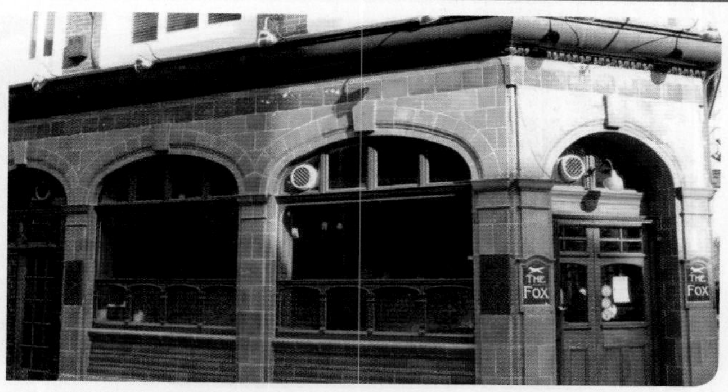

17 The Fox

28 Paul St, Shoreditch EC2A 4LB

Tel.: (020)77295708

e-mail: thefoxpublichouse@thefoxpublichouse.co.uk
Website: www.thefoxpublichouse.co.uk

VISA  AE

 **Hook Norton Hooky, Harvey's Sussex Best Bitter**

The Fox changed hands towards the end of 2006 but the new owners have wisely not interfered too much with the winning formula. For one thing, it still has that relaxed and lived-in feel despite the fresh coat of paint and the upstairs dining room continues to boast a sense of Victorian decorum in contrast to the animated bar downstairs. Now, though, the menu is slightly longer and is available throughout both floors, although the upstairs is still the best place to eat in – even the terrace is spoiled somewhat by the presence of an extractor fan. The kitchen knows its way around an animal and much of the cooking is red blooded – quite literally so if you order the onglet or ox heart. Many of the dishes come with a satisfyingly rustic edge and this no-nonsense approach married with seasonal pertinence keeps the flavours honest and to the fore. The service comes nicely paced and reassuringly knowledgeable.

Closing times

Closed Christmas to New Year, bank holidays, Saturday lunch and Sunday dinner

Booking essential

Prices

Meals: à la carte £ 24/34

Typical Dishes

Razor clams & bacon
Pork belly
Panna cotta with mango

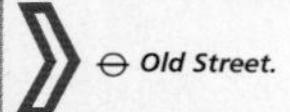 ⊖ *Old Street.*

18 The Princess of Shoreditch

76-78 Paul St, Shoreditch EC2A 4NE
Tel.: (020)77299270
e-mail: info@theprincessofshoreditch.com
Website: www.theprincessofshoreditch.com

VISA MC AE

Timothy Taylor Landlord, Black Sheep, Adnam's Broadside, Tanglefoot

The old girl may change hands now and then but she remains as popular and easy-going as ever. The ground floor is your proper pub, down to the battered floorboards through which you may even catch a glimpse of the kitchen below. Drinkers are the mainstay here but they do get an appealingly appropriate menu where platters of sausage, charcuterie and cheese are the highlights, along with pies of the cottage or pork variety. If you want to escape to more tranquil surroundings then follow the fairy lights to the spiral staircase and head up to a warm, candlelit room. Here the relatively short but balanced menu displays greater ambition. The cooking is more European in its influence and, despite the occasional affected presentation, it's clear the kitchen has confidence and ability. Flavours are good, techniques are sound and parfaits are a real highlight. The pub prides itself on the friendliness of its staff and upstairs is no different.

Closing times
Closed 24-26 December, Saturday lunch and Sunday dinner

Prices
Meals: à la carte £ 24/35

Typical Dishes
Globe artichoke salad
Pork belly & crackling
Selection of cheeses

⊖ *Old Street. On street meters.*

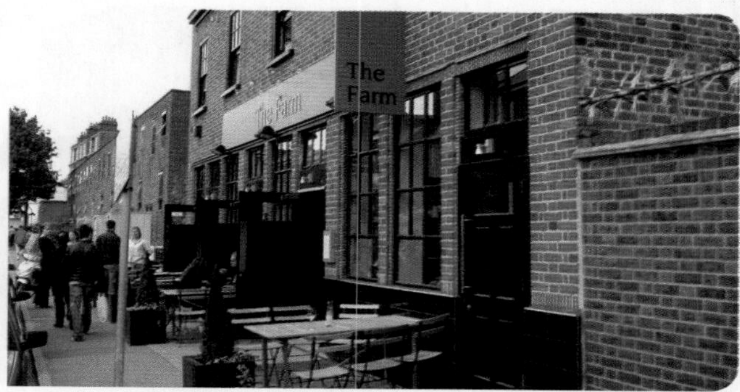

19 The Farm

18 Farm Lane,
Fulham SW6 1PP
Tel.: (020)73813331
e-mail: info@thefarmfulham.co.uk **Website:** www.thefarmfulham.co.uk

  AE

 **No real ales offered**

This inner-city farm is somewhat hidden away behind Fulham Road but this just makes you feel more like a local when you find it. The austerity suggested by the semi-industrial looking red brick façade is tempered by the warming fireplaces within. The same food is served throughout, so you can eat either in the relaxed bar area or head through to the altogether more stylish restaurant. The menu displays its ambition and international credentials through dishes such as black pudding with foie gras or duck cassoulet with Toulouse sausage but there are also more traditionally British dishes such as smoked salmon and Dover sole; if you've only time for a fleeting visit then there's always some lighter bites, which could include meze, mini Cumberland sausages or cheese and chutney. The strength of the kitchen lies in the astute sourcing and preparation of the meat dishes, particularly the very tender beef.

Closing times
Closed 25 December

Prices
Meals: £ 25 and à la carte £ 25/40

Typical Dishes
Scallop with pancetta
Clam chowder
Panna cotta with rhubarb

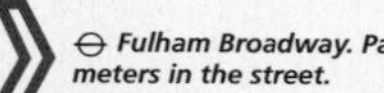

⊖ Fulham Broadway. Parking meters in the street.

20 The Harwood Arms

Walham Grove,
Fulham SW6 1QR
Tel.: (020)73861847
e-mail: admin@harwoodarms.com **Website:** www.harwoodarms.com

Inspectors' favourites

VISA MC AE

Good Old Boy, Fuller's London Pride, Black Sheep Brewery

The Harwood Arms feels less like a gastropub, more like just a local with really good food –Tuesday is quiz night and it's packed when Chelsea are playing at home. All three owners bring something to the operation: one has run pubs before and is the game specialist, one comes from a brewery and the third is Brett Graham, chef of The Ledbury. There's a bracing Britishness to the menu, along with a respect for our culinary heritage and a willingness to try something different. Potted rabbit comes with devils on horseback; trotters and crisp ears are served on toast; roe deer is stewed with sloe gin; while game tea showcases the ability of the young chef, formerly of The Ledbury. There's also a healthy respect for the seasons: even the bowl of warm doughnuts served as dessert changes from apple to rhubarb. The small section with a glass roof is laid up for eating but you can sit anywhere; service is relaxed and unflappable.

Closing times
Open daily
Prices
Meals: à la carte £ 25/35

Typical Dishes
Potted rabbit
Wood pigeon
Rhubarb doughnuts

⊖ *Fulham Broadway.*

21 Salisbury

21 Sherbrooke Rd,
Fulham SW6 2TZ
Tel.: (020)73814005
e-mail: events@thesalisbury.co.uk **Website:** www.thesalisbury.co.uk

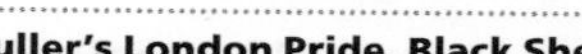
Fuller's London Pride, Black Sheep, Deuchar's IPA

The Salisbury was one of London's original foodie pubs and reopened in 2009 with a new look and the same ownership as the Spencer Arms in Putney. Unlike its more traditionally minded sister, The Salisbury is quite modern in style and is awash with colour; it's divided into two with the dining room beneath a large glass dome which slides back in summer. The cooking does follow the same theme of placing emphasis on small plates or 'English tapas' which could include anything from chipolatas to lamb cutlets. They change regularly as the kitchen can now draw on quite a repertoire but you do need to order a few and this can send the bill higher than you expect. Main courses include pasta, pies and salads; they also do a brisk trade in pie 'takeaways'. Puds display a degree of imagination while some, such as rhubarb crumble, are designed for sharing. This all adds to the general bonhomie that makes the reinvented Salisbury so pleasing.

Closing times
Closed 25-26 December and 1 January

Prices
Meals: à la carte £ 16/25

Typical Dishes
Scallops & Parma ham
Veal & mushroom pie
Chocolate truffle & honey Madeleines

⊖ Fulham Broadway.

England • London • Hammersmith and Fulham

22 Sands End

135-137 Stephendale Rd,
Fulham SW6 2PR
Tel.: (020)77317823
e-mail: markdyerbusiness@yahoo.co.uk **Website:** www.thesandsend.co.uk

Inspectors' favourites

 **Black Sheep, Hook Norton Hooky**

It's in the heart of Real Fulham – The Hurlingham may be close by but there's a laundrette even closer – and that makes the Sands End a proper local. Committed urbanites will consider the look to be junkshop chic while those who tend to head west to the countryside at weekends will insist it's more Cirencester. But what all agree on is the appeal of the food. We're all aware of the seismic improvements in the standard of pub dining but there has also been a huge knock-on benefit on that most British of nibble – the bar snack. The choice is no longer between flavours of crisps: here drinkers are offered homemade sausage rolls, Scotch eggs and Welsh rarebit soldiers. Those who prefer sitting when eating will also find much to savour from the concise menu. Snails come in garlic butter or as an accompaniment to rib-eye; steak and kidney pie sits alongside guinea fowl, and rice pudding competes for your attention with panna cotta.

Closing times
Closed 25 December
Booking advisable

Prices
Meals: à la carte £ 23/31

Typical Dishes
Warm black pudding salad
Rack of lamb
Rhubarb & stem ginger crumble

⊖ *Fulham Broadway.*

23 Anglesea Arms

35 Wingate Rd,
Hammersmith W6 0UR
Tel.: (020)87491291
Website: www.anglesea-arms.com

Ringwood 49er, Timothy Taylor Landlord, Fuller's London Pride, St Austell Tribute, Geeene King Old Speckled Hen, Sharp's Doom Bar

If, for some reason, you need another excuse to visit a pub then just remember that they can always provide a little local history. The Marquess of Anglesea was Wellington's Number Two at Waterloo – where he lost his leg – and many of the surrounding streets are named after the Duke. The pub dates back to 1909 and the builders responsible for many of the charming properties in those streets were housed in the pub. Today it continues to provide sustenance to many a local dweller or worker and does so in a friendly, laid-back manner. The blackboard menu changes in parts twice daily and the cooking is gutsy and wholesome. Oysters are a regular feature and what The Marquess would have made of seeing French classics like Beef Bourguignon on the menu doesn't bear considering. The same menu is served throughout so you can sit in the glass-roofed restaurant with the open kitchen or the characterful bar with its dark panelling and fireplaces.

Closing times
Closed 25-27 December

Prices
Meals: à la carte £ 17/46

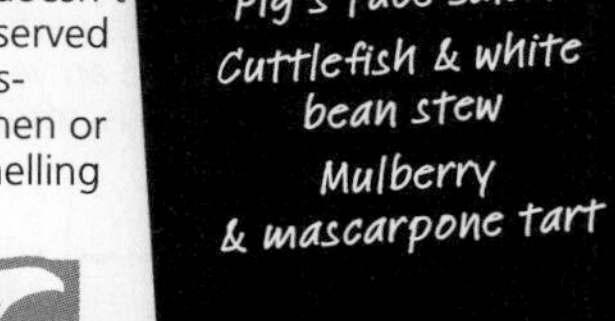

⊖ Ravenscourt Park. Paid parking Monday-Friday 9am-5pm.

Typical Dishes
Pig's face salad
Cuttlefish & white bean stew
Mulberry & mascarpone tart

24 Carpenter's Arms

91 Black Lion Lane,
Hammersmith W6 9BG

Tel.: (020)87418386 – Fax: (020)87416437

e-mail: carpsarm@googlemail.com **Website:** www.carpentersarmsw6.co.uk

VISA · MC · AE · D

Adnams Best Bitter

Pubs come in all sorts of shapes, sizes and guises; the Carpenter's Arms is from the 'doesn't actually look much like a pub' school of pub. It has changed its name a few times over the years and even spent time as a French brasserie but now, under the same ownership as Chelsea's Pig's Ear, it appears to have found its niche. Decoratively it's as understated as the exterior but there's lots of natural light and a small terrace at the back. The place attracts a younger clientele and the service is smart and sensible. The cooking continues this theme of unpretentiousness; menus are intelligently written and combinations are never too unusual. Dishes are a mix of stout British ingredients, like liver, eel, rabbit or duck, enlivened by more worldly accompaniments such as gnocchi or ricotta; the seasonal vegetables are a particular strength. Expect the food to arrive in generous dimensions – this is, after all, a pub. Really.

Closing times

Closed 1 week at Christmas

Booking essential

Prices

Meals: £ 16 (lunch)
and à la carte £ 27/33

Typical Dishes
Potted crab
Seared tuna
Passion fruit curd tart

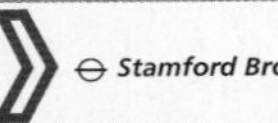

⊖ *Stamford Brook.*

25 The Dartmouth Castle

26 Glenthorne Road,
Hammersmith W6 0LS
Tel.: (020)87483614 – Fax: (020)87483619
e-mail: dartmouth.castle@btconnect.com **Website:** www.thedartmouthcastle.co.uk

VISA MC AE

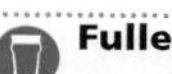 **Fuller's London Pride and guests ales such as Timothy Taylor Landlord, Deuchar's IPA, St Austell's Tribute**

Samuel Johnson once remarked "there is no private house in which people can enjoy themselves so well as at a capital tavern". He would have been taken with The Dartmouth Castle: customers are positively encouraged to dwell; there are board games available and cask ales change regularly and sometimes feature popular requests from the regulars. What would be alien to him would be the food: one of the owners has spent time in California and France and the monthly changing menu has a decidedly sunny disposition. The influences from the Mediterranean and southern Europe are evident throughout, with the likes of Tunisian lamb, assorted pastas, roast vegetables, thyme, tomatoes and fishy stews like caldeirada all featuring. Good bread with olive oil starts it all off and dishes arrive with appetisingly unfussy presentation. This is a no-nonsense, simply furnished, hospitable pub that serves distinctly pleasing food.

Closing times
Closed 25 December to 1 January, Holy Saturday and Easter Sunday

Prices
Meals: à la carte £ 20/28

Typical Dishes
Bruschetta di pomodoro
Tuscan sausages with mash
Tiramisu

 ⊖ *Hammersmith.*

26 The Havelock Tavern

57 Masbro Rd,
Brook Green, Shepherd's Bush W14 0LS
Tel.: (020)76035374
e-mail: info@thehavelocktavern.co.uk **Website:** www.thehavelocktavern.com

Inspectors' favourites

 VISA MC

Wandle, Sharp's Doom Bar, Adnam's Bitter

The great appeal of The Havelock Tavern is that it's a true and honest pub which isn't afraid of holding onto its roots. Drinkers and diners rub shoulders throughout, be it on large shared tables, the pretty courtyard terrace or the picnic benches out front, while the great value blackboard menu features modern, seasonal, gutsy dishes. There are big tubs of pistachios and succulent olives on the bar while you choose. You can then start with something muscular like pork, duck and apricot terrine or something crispy, such as deep-fried monkfish cheeks. The main courses include rare roast rump of beef and braised lamb shank with mash. Expect no respite from dessert: the chocolate brownie comes with extra chocolate sauce and, in a blatant case of stable door shutting, crème fraîche. You still have to go to the bar to order and at busy times you might have to wait, but sometimes in life there are things worth waiting for.

Closing times
Closed 25-26 December

Prices
Meals: à la carte £ 21/26

Typical Dishes
Sautéed squid
Beef casserole
Butterscotch crunch

⊖ Kensington Olympia. On-street pay & display parking.

27 Princess Victoria

217 Uxbridge Rd,
Shepherd's Bush W12 9DH

Tel.: (020)87495886 – Fax: (020)87494886

e-mail: info@princessvictoria.co.uk **Website:** www.princessvictoria.co.uk

   MC

 **Fuller's London Pride, Timothy Taylor Landlord, Hook Norton Hooky**

From tramstop to live music venue, this magnificent Victorian gin palace has seen it all. Now a chef and a sommelier have taken it over, given it a top-to-toe revamp and the old girl has a whole new lease of life. The original plasterwork and friezes remain but now the pub has a clubby, slightly masculine feel. The small front terrace forms part of the Saturday Farmers' Market and the main bar leads into a large dining room, dominated by a grand centre table. The stunning wine list has over 350 bottles, with a focus on Rhône, Pinot Noir and Riesling. Food-wise, it's a mix of old-fashioned favourites, with the odd Asian or Mediterranean influence. The Pork Board starter, which includes pig's cheek and Bayonne ham, has become a favourite, and you'll always find the Angus rib-eye; sausages are homemade and the kitchen knows its butchery. More nostalgia comes courtesy of the pudding menu, with the appearance of coupes and sundaes.

Closing times

Closed 25-26 December

Prices

Meals: £ 15 (lunch) and à la carte £ 23/33

Typical Dishes

Pork board

Chargrilled rib-eye

Crème brûlée

⊖ *Shepherd's Bush.*

28 The Queens Pub and Dining Room

26 Broadway Parade,
Crouch End N8 9DE
Tel.: (020)83402031
e-mail: queens@foodandfuel.co.uk **Website:** www.thequeenscrouchend.co.uk

 MC AE

Wells Bombardier and regularly changing guest ales

It would be hard to find a more striking example of Victoriana than The Queens Pub and Dining Room. From the original mahogany panelling to the beautiful stained glass windows and ornate ceiling, this pub has it all. The dining room, to the right as you enter, is particularly stunning – ask for tables 105 or 106 on the raised section. The open kitchen recognises that some will only want classic pub food in this environment, either you're standing in the bar or sitting in the restaurant – so you'll find beef and mushroom pie, rib-eye, plaice goujons and various sausages – while others want something slightly more ambitious, hence the likes of risotto, plates of smoked meats, sea bass and assorted choices of a more Mediterranean persuasion. Selected dishes are highlighted to form part of the "This week we love…" menu which comes in at a very affordable price. Wednesday is quiz night and there's a different guest ale every week.

Closing times
Open daily

Prices
Meals: à la carte £ 25

Typical Dishes
Mussels marinière
Seabass with spinach
Sticky toffee pudding

⊖ Crouch Hill. On-street parking meters.

29 Clissold Arms

Fortis Green Rd, Fortis Green N2 9HR

Tel.: (020)84444224

e-mail: ianshepherd-clissoldarms@btconnect.com

Website: www.jobo-developments.com

 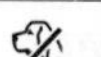 

 **Timothy Taylor Landlord, Fuller's London Pride, Harveys Sussex**

Areas of London hitherto untroubled by the rise of the gastropub can hide no longer. This time it is the leafy surroundings of Fortis Green and Muswell Hill that has seen an old favourite given a facelift. The Clissold Arms reputedly played host to The Kinks' first gig – conveniently so, as Ray Davies lived across the street. The majority of the space is now given over to those eating – drinkers are buffeted into the front section. The menu offers a daily changing list of interesting dishes; terrines are something of a house speciality, as is the whole sea bass, the ribs of beef and the 32-day aged steaks. Come for lunch and you'll encounter more typical pub grub, such as steak and ale pie, alongside the potted crab. Cooking is soundly done and portions are suitably generous. The staff just about keep their smiles when it gets busy, which it does frequently so it's prudent to book. The terrace is great for lazing on a sunny afternoon.

Closing times

Closed 1 January

Prices

Meals: à la carte £ 21/34

Typical Dishes

Mackerel & aubergine terrine

Grilled pork loin

Chocolate brownie

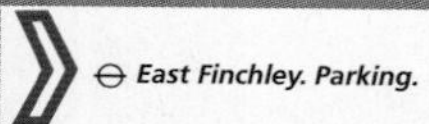

⊖ *East Finchley. Parking.*

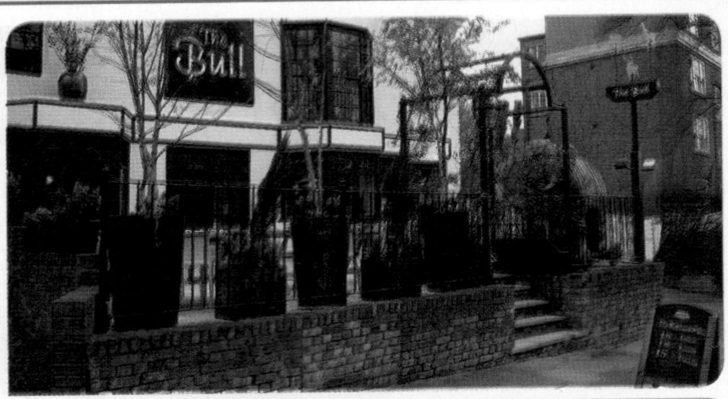

30 The Bull

13 North Hill,
Highgate N6 4AB

Tel.: (0845)4565033 – Fax: (0845)4565034
e-mail: info@inthebull.biz **Website:** www.themeredithgroup.co.uk

 VISA MC AE

 **Youngs**

If the first thing you notice is a drinks trolley then you know you're not in your, or anyone else's, local boozer. The Bull is part of the Meredith Group, along with The House and The Running Footman, and they only deal in your proper foodie pubs. The open kitchen puts the chefs on view and their food is mostly modern European, with a dominant French gene running through it; their home-baked breads are a real speciality of the house. Dishes are seasonally pertinent and the construction, ingredients and execution are aimed more at the 'serious' end of the dining pub scale, although there is a good value lunch menu to accompany the à la carte. Those who have a boat they wish to push out will find their task aided by the wine list, which does also offer sufficient numbers of affordable bottles. Weekends welcome a more family atmosphere, where brunch is offered. The room is bright, service is on the ball and Thursday night is music night.

Closing times

Closed Monday in winter

Prices

Meals: £ 15 and à la carte £ 21/30

Typical Dishes

Smoked sea trout
Shepherds Pie
Eton Mess

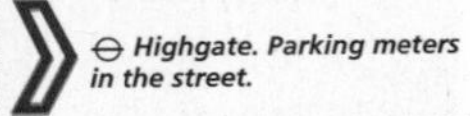

⊖ Highgate. Parking meters in the street.

31 The Old Dairy

1-3 Crouch Hill,
Stroud Green N4 4AP
Tel.: (020)72633337
e-mail: theolddairy@realpubs.co.uk **Website:** www.realpubs.co.uk

VISA

Deuchar's IPA, Adnam's Broadside, Shepherd Neame Spitfire and guest ales

Of all the pub conversions around, there can be few as characterful as The Old Dairy. Dating from 1890, the picture panels among the original red bricks and steel girders illustrate the listed building's former use when owned by Friern Manor Dairy Company. Despite the renovation and the locale's increasing gentrification, the pub has kept itself at the heart of the community by investing as much effort in the bar – which occupies quite a space – as it has in the dining room and the period photos of the area on the walls also help. The locals have certainly taken to the place and any background music is soon drowned out by the sound of contented customers. The cooking is bold and honest and how nice it is that dishes arrive exactly as described on the menu. It's modern British with a hint of Europe. The crisp sourdough gets you started and the portions are well judged and confidently flavoured. Weekend brunches are a real hit.

Closing times
Closed Monday lunch

Prices
Meals: à la carte £ 20/30

Typical Dishes
Pork & apricot terrine
Duck breast
Bread & butter pudding

⊖ Crouch Hill.

32 The Devonshire

126 Devonshire Rd,
Chiswick W4 2JJ

Tel.: (020)75927962 – Fax: (020)75921603
e-mail: thedevonshire@gordonramsay.com **Website:** www.gordonramsay.com

Inspectors' favourites

 **Fuller's London Pride, Deuchar's IPA**

The Devonshire joined Gordon Ramsay's burgeoning pub portfolio at the end of 2007 and, like The Narrow, enjoyed almost immediate success. It's in one of those roads that's a microcosm of London: pretty Victorian terraced houses at one end of the street and '60s council housing at the other, with the pub bang on the half-way line. The striking Edwardian façade is matched by the characterful oak panelling and polished wood flooring in the bar and here you can enjoy such egalitarian treats as scotch eggs or pots of pickled cockles. If, on the other hand, you want a more structured environment then head for the neatly laid out restaurant. It has a concise and good value menu, with daily-changing specials, and propounds an appealing mix of pub classics alongside other dishes that are more West End in their pedigree. There's an 'on toast' selection, which could include herring roes, as well as weekly changing soups and pies.

Closing times

Closed Monday-Tuesday and lunch Wednesday-Thursday

Prices

Meals: £ 19 (dinner) and à la carte £ 23/30

Typical Dishes

Seared Cornish mackerel
Slow roast pork belly
Steamed treacle pudding

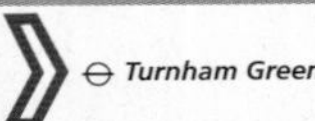

⊖ *Turnham Green.*

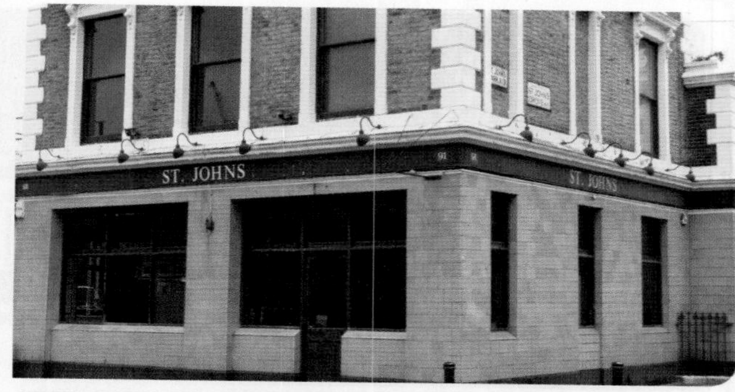

33 St John's Tavern

91 Junction Rd,
Archway N19 5QU
Tel.: (020)72721587 – Fax: (020)72721587

  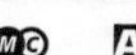

 **Timothy Taylor Landlord, Sharp's Cornish Coaster, Brakspear Oxford Gold**

Too many diners were left wondering where their guests had gone, only to receive a call saying they were sitting and waiting at St John in Clerkenwell – hence the recent addition of 'tavern' to the name. You can eat in the front bar but you're better off in the big dining room; the dark colours and fireplace may make it look more like somewhere for a winter's night but staff keep things light and perky throughout the year. The menu changes daily, with a few staples, such as the rib-eye. The open kitchen puts some time and thought into the vegetarian choices, be they the courgette and cheddar tart or the squash and halloumi parcels; but they also know how to fire up the heat when cooking a succulent pork chop. The wine list is sensibly priced, with enough carafes to make up for the 125ml glasses, although Black Sheep bitter is a popular alternative. The exterior is currently being returned to its original Victorian splendour.

Closing times
Closed 25-26 December and lunch Monday-Thursday

Prices
Meals: à la carte £ 18/29

Typical Dishes
Jellied pig's head
Lamb cutlets
Berry Pavlova

⊖ *Archway. Pay & display parking bays; free after 6.30pm.*

34 **The House**

63-69 Canonbury Rd,
Canonbury N1 2DG

Tel.: (020)77047410 – Fax: (020)77049388
e-mail: info@inthehouse.biz **Website:** www.themeredithgroup.co.uk

Inspectors' favourites

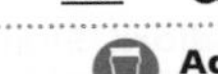

Adnams

The House is one of the smarter pubs around; indeed, with its attractive terrace it can look more like a restaurant from the outside but step inside and you'll find sufficient numbers of regulars at the bar nursing a pint and exuding a general sense of localness. Even the eating area towards the rear has that reassuringly hotchpotch feel and, while the service is clearly on the button, it is also friendly and chatty. The menu covers all corners, from the classics like shepherd's pie and apple crumble to other choices that could be considered more familiar to restaurant rather than pub goers. These might include sea bass with artichoke purée and peppered venison with spiced red cabbage. All the cooking is clean and crisp and the kitchen displays a confident yet conscientious touch; there's an emphasis on good quality, organic ingredients. The Bull in Highgate and The Only Running Footman in Mayfair share the same owner.

Closing times
Closed Monday lunch

Prices
Meals: £ 15 (lunch)
and à la carte £ 26/35

Typical Dishes
Tomato Tartare
Shepherd's pie
Rhubarb & apple crumble

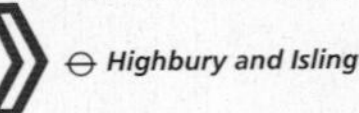

⊖ *Highbury and Islington.*

35 The Coach & Horses

26-28 Ray St,
Clerkenwell EC1R 3DJ
Tel.: (020)78371336 – Fax: (020)72781478
e-mail: info@thecoachandhorses.com **Website:** www.thecoachandhorses.com

 **Adnams Bitter, Fuller's London Pride, Timothy Taylor Landlord**

The Coach and Horses may be one of those pubs that has a palpable sense of its own Victorian heritage, with its original etched windows and panelling, but that doesn't mean it's not moving with the times. A recent refreshment of the dining room, with its tent-like ceiling and plush red walls filled with sketches and lithographs, has turned it into a very pleasant environment. Here, the near-daily changing menu is a reflection of the self-taught chef's enthusiasm for all things European, especially its sunnier Mediterranean parts. There are Spanish and Italian influences aplenty, with everything from osso bucco to polenta, chorizo to chilled soups. But our own British contribution to cuisine is not forgotten, especially in the bar where the appealing list of snacks includes Scotch eggs with mustard – surely a near perfect accompaniment to a pint. Any summer warmth provokes a stampede for the enclosed decked yard.

Closing times
Closed Christmas to New Year, Easter, Saturday lunch, Sunday dinner and bank holidays

Prices
Meals: à la carte £ 22/28

Typical Dishes
Asparagus & poached duck egg
Mullet & fennel
Buttermilk pudding

⊖ Farringdon. Parking meters across the road.

36 The Peasant

240 St John St,
Finsbury EC1V 4PH

Tel.: (020)73367726 – Fax: (020)74901089
e-mail: eat@thepeasant.co.uk **Website:** www.thepeasant.co.uk

  AE

Crouch Vale Brewers Gold, Wells Bombardier, Skinners brewery

Originally called the George & Dragon, it changed to The Peasant to celebrate Wat Tyler's revolting ones of 1381 who gathered near this spot. However, what really made the name of this classic Victorian pub was its being in the vanguard of the original gastro-pub movement. To its lasting credit, the place retains a traditional pub feel, thanks largely to the busy ground floor bar, with its tiles, arched windows, high ceiling and mosaics. This is a great place for some heartening fare, from sausage and mash to plates of charcuterie or meze, to go with your beer. Upstairs, it's more your proper restaurant experience; it's quite formally laid out, with decoration courtesy of a fairground/circus theme. The huge windows still let in plenty of light but the noise levels are just a little more subdued. Here, you'll find a degree of originality in the cooking, but the kitchen is at its best when it keeps things relatively simple.

Closing times

Closed 25 December to 1 January and bank holidays except Good Friday

Booking essential

Prices

Meals: £ 35 (dinner) and à la carte £ 23/30

Typical Dishes

Pan-fried scallops
Roast sirloin
Bread & butter pudding

⊖ Farringdon. On-street parking meters nearby; also free parking at weekends after 1.30pm.

37 The Well

180 St John St,
Finsbury EC1V 4JY
Tel.: (020)72519363 – Fax: (020)72539683
e-mail: drink@downthewell.co.uk **Website:** www.downthewell.com

 **No real ales offered**

It's thus named because of its Clerkenwell location, and the upside of The Well not being at the trendy end of St John St is that it attracts more of the locals. If you don't fall into that category, look out for the bright blue canopies which provide plenty of cover for the popular pavement benches. It's quite small inside but, thanks to some huge sliding glass windows, has a surprisingly light and airy feel, and the wooden floorboards and exposed brick walls add to the atmosphere of a committed metropolitan pub. Monthly changing menus offer modern dishes ranging from potted shrimps to foie gras and chicken liver parfait or sea trout and samphire, as well as classic English puddings like Eton Mess and some particularly good cheeses. The downstairs bar with its seductive lighting and fish tank is only available for private hire; check out the picture of a parched desert and a well which follows the curve of the wall on your way down.

Closing times
Closed 25 December

Prices
Meals: à la carte £ 20/40

Typical Dishes
Steamed cockles & clams
British rib-eye steak
English cheeses

⊖ Farringdon. On-street parking meters.

England • London • Islington

38 The Barnsbury

209-211 Liverpool Rd,
Islington N1 1LX

Tel.: (020)76075519 – Fax: (020)76073256
e-mail: info@thebarnsbury.co.uk **Website:** www.thebarnsbury.co.uk

  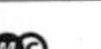

Gravesend Shrimpers, Whitstable Kentish Reserve and weekly changing guest beer

The Barnsbury may not look much like a typical pub from the outside but it ticks all the boxes within: the wooden floorboards, the big central bar and a generous scattering of locals nursing a pint. Add in a little originality such as chandeliers fashioned from wine glasses and a cabinet of Mamod steam-powered boys' toys and you have another worthy Islington pub, complete with a little garden at the back. There are a few permanently laid tables at the rear but otherwise it's sit where you want. The menu's printed on grease-proof paper (complete with some grease spots) and offers something for everyone; starters could be foie gras with quince or moules marinière, main courses pumpkin risotto or rump of lamb. There are useful 500ml carafes available and those wishing to come out early for dinner during the week benefit from a good value, pre-7pm menu. You'll find a cactus on each table, a reflection of the somewhat prickly service.

Closing times
Closed 24-26 December and 1 January

Prices
Meals: à la carte £ 26/29

Typical Dishes
Grilled sardines
Rump of English lamb
Apple tart

⊖ Highbury and Islington.
On-street parking meters.

39 The Drapers Arms

44 Barnsbury St,
Islington N1 1ER
Tel.: (020)76190348
e-mail: info@thedrapersarms.com **Website:** www.thedrapersarms.com

   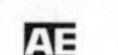

 **Shepherd Neame Spitfire, Harvey's, Black Sheep**

This handsome Georgian pub was rescued, revived and reopened in 2009 by new owners, one of whom is the son of restaurant critic Fay Maschler. Repainted and reinvigorated, it adds even more charm to this part of Islington. The chef is an alumnus of St John (and New York's Spotted Pig - the UK's best export since Beatlemania); but while his experience clearly informs his cooking, that doesn't mean it's a facsimile of St John. It does place the same emphasis on seasonality, on unfussy 'proper' British cooking and on the healthy use of less familiar cuts but there's also an acknowledgement that this is a local pub first and foremost, which is why reservations are only taken for the somewhat starkly decorated upstairs dining room. You'll find the same menu in the bar, where it's more fun and relaxed, with shelves of Penguin classics and board games as well as further bar menu featuring oysters, devils on horseback and whelks.

Closing times
Open daily

Prices
Meals: à la carte £ 18/30

Typical Dishes
Ox cheek, chicory & mustard
Pan-fried lemon sole, Jersey Royals
Lardy cake

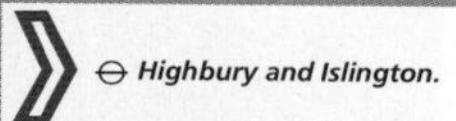
⊖ *Highbury and Islington.*

England • London • Islington

40 The Northgate

113 Southgate Rd,
Islington N1 3JS
Tel.: (020)73597392 – Fax: (020)73597393
e-mail: thenorthgate@hotmail.co.uk

The Northgate is a big, unremarkable looking Islington pub, refreshingly free from the vicissitudes of fashion. It's decked out in the usual gastropub aesthetic of mismatched furniture and local artists' work for sale on the walls. At the back you'll find the tables laid up for dining, an open kitchen, and the same sense of space, thanks largely to the wall of mirrors and the skylight. You'll also find an extraction fan that's so strong you can almost feel its tug. Staff are a pretty laid-back bunch, at times almost to the point of somnolence; go with a similarly relaxed frame of mind to avoid irritation. Where the pub scores is in the food: there's a strong Mediterranean influence on the vast blackboard. You'll find merguez and chorizo sausages, assorted pastas, a bit of Greek, some French and all in generously sized proportions with the emphasis on big flavours. Finish with something a little closer to home like treacle tart.

Closing times
Closed Monday-Friday lunch

Prices
Meals: à la carte £ 20/27

Typical Dishes
Chicken satay
Steak & chips
Cheese board

⊖ *Dalston Kingsland (rail). Free on-street parking after 6.30pm.*

41 The Admiral Codrington

17 Mossop St,
Chelsea SW3 2LY
Tel.: (020)75810005 – Fax: (020)75892452
e-mail: theadmiral-codrington@333holdingsltd.com **Website:** www.

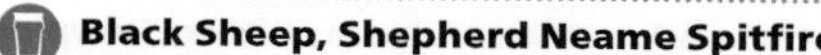

Black Sheep, Shepherd Neame Spitfire

The personnel running the place may change occasionally but the local reputation of "The Cod" remains largely unaltered. Lunch can be had in the bar or the restaurant but in the evenings the locals descend and drinkers rule, so the serving of food is restricted to the dining room. This in turn becomes something of a haven of relative peace (which presumably explains the curious appearance of a cover charge). The retractable roof remains an appealing feature as does the booth seating for larger parties. The perennial favourites are never removed from the menu, like the crispy squid and fishcakes, and it's generally a pleasing mix of British and European classics, from fish pie to veal Holstein via assorted pasta dishes and a fish of the day. The kitchen appears well-drilled and organised. The private dining room upstairs is dedicated to Mac, the cartoonist, whose work adorns the walls and they've tidied up the small terrace at the side.

Closing times
Closed 25-26 December

Prices
Meals: à la carte £ 24/34

Typical Dishes
Caesar's salad
The Admiral's cod
Mint & chocolate chip ice cream

⊖ South Kensington. Parking in the adjacent streets.

42 Builders Arms

13 Britten St,
Chelsea SW3 3TY
Tel.: (020)73499040
e-mail: buildersarms@geronimo-inns.co.uk **Website:** www.geronimo-inns.co.uk

  AE

 **Fuller's London Pride, Adnams Bitter, Sharp's Cornish Coaster**

The Builders Arms is very much like a village local – the only difference being that, in this instance, the village is Chelsea and there are quite a lot of locals to accommodate. From the outside it looks rather small but the room is long and narrow, with one side for drinkers and the other side packed with tables. They adopt a simply but effective approach to cooking – there's an easy to read menu supplemented by a daily specials blackboard that always includes a soup and fresh fish. Dishes range from devilled kidney on toast to herb-crusted lamb; others, such as the corn-fed peri-peri chicken, are designed for sharing. Presentation has an appealingly rustic edge; portions are appropriately pub-sized and prices are kept realistic. There's a weekly Bordeaux selection as well as regular wine promotions. Bookings are only taken for larger parties but simply tell the staff you're here to eat and they'll sort you out quite promptly.

Closing times
Open daily
Prices
Meals: à la carte £ 25/30

Typical Dishes
Devilled kidneys on toast
Chargrilled rib-eye steak
Bread & butter pudding

 ⊖ *South Kensington.* 

43 **Chelsea Ram**

32 Burnaby St,
Chelsea SW10 0PL
Tel.: (020)73514008
e-mail: bookings@chelsearam.co.uk

 **Youngs Bitter, Wells Bombardier, Directors**

This stalwart of the London dining scene remains as popular as ever; book or arrive early for lunch as they only have 17 tables and they get snapped up quickly, particularly the two by the fire. There's full table service and whilst it all chills out a little at dinner, timings from the kitchen are generally spot-on. 'Comforting classics' and 'honest home-cooking' is how the chef describes his food; home-made soup comes with crusty bread, lamb chops with bubble and squeak, sausages with mash and rib-eye with dauphinoise potatoes; there are also pies and casseroles and even some mean snacks to accompany a pint. To finish, you can get a proper pudding, not a dessert, and these could include sticky banana or a crumble. The wine list is on the back of the menu and offers over 20 wines by the glass. If that isn't enough for a pub, they hold a quiz night on the first Monday of each month. All in all, they appear to have cracked the formula.

Closing times
Open daily
Prices
Meals: £ 18 (dinner) and à la carte £ 19/24

Typical Dishes
Potted shrimps & smoked mackerel
Roast chicken
Rhubarb & Bramley apple crumble

⊖ Fulham Broadway. On-street parking meters and single yellow lines.

44 The Cross Keys

1 Lawrence St,
Chelsea SW3 5NB
Tel.: (020)73499111 – Fax: (020)73499333
e-mail: reservations@thexkeys.co.uk **Website:** www.thexkeys.co.uk

VISA MC AE

Courage Directors, Theakston XB, Deuchar's IPA, Old Peculiar

The Cross Keys changed hands in 2009 and gone are some of the more eclectic decorative touches. However, there are still enough quirky statues, fixtures and fittings at this 200 year old pub to satisfy those who like a bit of camp with their calamari. There's usually ample space in the front bar, where a menu of pub favourites is on offer. But go through to the restaurant at the rear if you want a more substantial and structured experience. Here you'll find a bright room with a glass roof – there are plans to replace it with a sliding one – a bucolic trompe-l'œil and an open kitchen. The menu keeps things quite short and simple; seasonal asparagus with a herb hollandaise, pork belly with pommes purée and plenty of roast meats. Desserts are of the classic chocolate profiterole variety. There are plans to add a rotisserie and give the kitchen a face-lift, which should have a knock-on effect on the overall standard of cooking.

Closing times
Open daily

Prices
Meals: £ 20 (lunch Sunday) and à la carte £ 17/25

Typical Dishes
Calamari & saffron aioli
Grilled baby chicken
Profiteroles & chocolate sauce

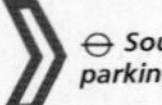

⊖ South Kensington. On-street parking meters.

45 Lots Road Pub & Dining Room

114 Lots Rd,
Chelsea SW10 0RJ
Tel.: (020)73526645
e-mail: lotsroad@foodandfuel.co.uk **Website:** www.lotsroadpub.com

VISA MC AE

Sharp's Doom Bar and Coaster, Adnam's Bitter, Wells Bombardier

Lots Road and its customers are clearly happy with one another as the pub has introduced a customer loyalty scheme, whereby anyone making their fifth visit is rewarded with a discount. These customers come from all parts of the local area, whether that's Chelsea Harbour, the antique shops and auction houses or the nearby art college. At lunch everything is geared more towards office-based bods in for a quick bite; at dinner the menu is altogether more enticing. The winning formula sees a choice that includes oysters, mussels and a savoury tart of the day; the Perthshire côte de boeuf is the house speciality. There are also pies and casseroles, in appropriate pub-like sizes and even some salads. Service remains bright and cheery, even on those frantic Thursday nights when the pub offers 'Thursday Treats' with wine tasting and nibbles. The only disappointment is the somewhat ordinary bread for which they make a not insubstantial charge.

Closing times
Open daily

Prices
Meals: £ 10 and à la carte £ 20/31

Typical Dishes
Chicken liver pâté
Beef & ale pie
Sticky toffee pudding

⊖ *Fulham Broadway.*

46 The Phoenix

23 Smith St,
Chelsea SW3 4EE
Tel.: (020)77309182
e-mail: thephoenix@geronimo-inns.co.uk **Website:** www.geronimo-inns.co.uk

 VISA MC AE

Adnams, Sharp's Doom Bar

The Phoenix may be part of an ever-expanding group of pubs but you'd never know it. It's a rather chic little number, close enough to the King's Road to be a useful pit-stop but also something of a local destination. The largest part of the pub is taken over by those very civilised locals, relaxing in the squashy sofas, enjoying a Welsh rarebit with their drinks. But work your way through to the back and you'll find the dining room, refurbished in 2008, where the murmur from the bar reminds you that you're still in a pub. Their aim is to provide pub food that's fairly priced, seasonal and, most importantly, tasty, whether that's eggs Benedict, Portland crab on toast or steak and hand-cut chips which arrive in sweet enamel pie dishes. The specials on the blackboard are precisely that and get quickly snapped up. St.George's day is proudly celebrated, there's the occasional oyster festival and regular wine and cider promotions.

Closing times
Closed 25-26 December
Booking advisable

Prices
Meals: à la carte £ 23/30

Typical Dishes
Eggs Benedict
Rack of lamb
Chocolate cheesecake

⊖ Sloane Square. On-street parking meters.

47 **The Pig's Ear**

35 Old Church St,
Chelsea SW3 5BS
Tel.: (020)73522908 – Fax: (020)73529321
e-mail: thepigsear@hotmail.co.uk **Website:** www.thepigsear.com

  AE

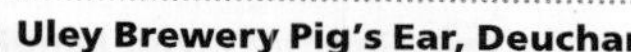

There's a timeless feel to this relaxed, foodie pub off the King's Road and the selection of board games and newspapers make it the perfect location to while away a weekend hour or three. The owners' love of cinema and music is evident in the plethora of posters and photos, a jug of Bloody Mary takes pride of place on the bar and bottles of Bréton cider are proudly served alongside the beers and wines. It can feel as if the whole of Chelsea has come out to play downstairs, so book ahead to eat in the romantic panelled dining room, or alternatively, ask if you can commandeer the Blue Room – a cosy, curtained off area with a real fire. The menu is modern British meets the Mediterranean, with dishes like beef marrow, lamb stew and dumplings, or Cornish crab Thermidor. Charcuterie is a firm staple, there's the odd steak tartare for good measure and the splendid bread comes from The Flour Station in Battersea.

Closing times
Closed Sunday dinner

Prices
Meals: à la carte £ 25/40

Typical Dishes
Fresh langoustines
Venison fillet, braised chicory
Green apple granita

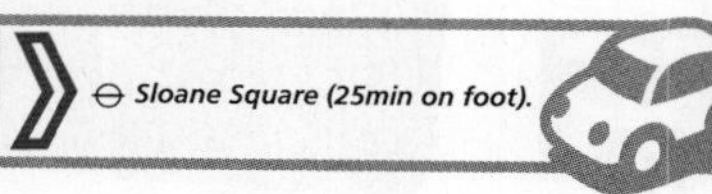

48 The Fat Badger

310 Portobello Road,
North Kensington W10 5TA
Tel.: (020)89694500 – Fax: (020)89696714
e-mail: fat_badger@me.com **Website:** www.thefatbadger.com

   AE

 **Timothy Taylor Landlord**

The last change of ownership made little difference to the Fat Badger: it still treads the line between being worn in and worn out. Stuffing sprouts from sofas and chips and scuffs abound but the locals seem to approve of the general raggedness. There's a more formally laid restaurant upstairs but its availability is largely dependent on enough punters requesting it but the same menu is served in the bar. The one decorative element that really stands out is the patterned wallpaper which only reveals its true nature on close inspection. Service can be somewhat hit and miss as not all members of staff share the same attitude towards customer service. Where the pub scores well is in the food: the kitchen doesn't try to reinvent anything but also displays a light touch, whether in the crisp cuttlefish and chorizo, the roast chicken breast or the panna cotta. Tuesday is 'wine and dine' night when bottles are half price; Monday is quiz night.

Closing times
Open daily

Prices
Meals: à la carte £ 20/29

Typical Dishes
Confit of rabbit
Shoulder of lamb
Sticky toffee pudding

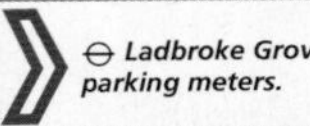

⊖ *Ladbroke Grove. On-street parking meters.*

49 **The Rosendale**

65 Rosendale Rd,
West Dulwich SE21 8EZ
Tel.: (020)86700812
e-mail: dine@therosendale.co.uk **Website:** www.therosendale.co.uk

VISA MC

Adnams and guest beers - Courage Best, Shepherd Neame Spitfire

Included among the many things that stand out about The Rosendale are that they make their own butter, as well as their own bread, and have a wine list that is remarkable in its breadth, depth and affordability. This vast former coaching inn dates from the 1820s and has a soaring ceiling and plenty of original features. There are two menus – stay in the front bar for a grill menu with your more typical pub food or go through to the dining room at the back to find dishes of a more ambitious nature. Here this can mean that what appears on the plate is quite complicated but there is no denying the quality of the ingredients and sourcing is clearly taken seriously. Fish is delivered daily from Cornwall; farms are given name checks; they hang their own meat and smoke their own fish. This is a well run pub with a great atmosphere – there may not be many things worth enduring the South Circular for, but The Rosendale is one of them.

Closing times
Closed 1 January

Prices
Meals: £ 24 (Thursday-Sunday) and à la carte £ 14/29

Typical Dishes
Home-smoked salmon
Roast loin & belly pork
Dark chocolate brownie

⊖ West Dulwich (rail). Parking in neighbouring streets.

50 The Dartmouth Arms

7 Dartmouth Road,
Forest Hill SE23 3HN

Tel.: (020)84883117 – Fax: (020)86999946
e-mail: info@thedartmoutharms.com **Website:** www.thedartmoutharms.com

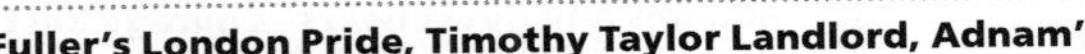

Fuller's London Pride, Timothy Taylor Landlord, Adnam's

The Dartmouth Arms' position opposite Forest Hill train station meant that this was once the sort of pub whose main selling point was as somewhere to dive into for a swift one on the way home. Since its makeover in 2004 it is now the sort of place in which to spend the evening. The original double doors now open into a friendly environment with art for sale on the walls, the usual hotchpotch of furniture and an open plan kitchen. The couple running the show know what their customers want and the menu offers an appealing mix of dishes from the single sheet of A4. Many have more of a restaurant pedigree than your average pub grub but there's commendable Britishness in evidence here, as well as a healthy regard for seasonality. So expect to see Barnsley chops, asparagus, samphire and Jersey Royals at certain times. There's also some invention so you'll find the black pudding in a risotto and crab in beignets with chilli jam.

Closing times
Closed 25-26 December and 1 January

Prices
Meals: £ 17 (dinner Monday-Thursday) and à la carte £ 19/29

Typical Dishes
Scallops with pea purée
Belly of pork
Chocolate Mocha tart

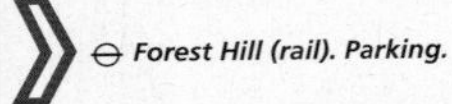

⊖ *Forest Hill (rail). Parking.*

51 The Brown Dog

28 Cross Street,
Barnes SW13 0AP
Tel.: (020)83922200
e-mail: mrbojangles@thebrowndog.co.uk **Website:** www.thebrowndog.co.uk

  MC AE

 **Westerham Brewery Grasshopper, Twickenham Original, Wandle Sam Brown Brewery**

Tucked away down a veritable labyrinth of residential streets, you almost feel you might need a ball of string to help you find your way back from The Brown Dog, and are unlikely to stumble across it in passing. Locals should count themselves lucky. Décor is charmingly stylish with cast iron fireplaces and antique furniture, eclectic artwork, and bulbous space age lamps. Set around a horseshoe bar, seating is split into snug lounge and separate dining area, and a relaxed atmosphere reigns. The daily-changing, seasonal menu takes a modern slant on traditional dishes and, although concise, is well-balanced. Good value food is popular in these parts, so make sure you book in advance; and if you're driving, factor in some time to park. Why the Brown Dog? Well, when a Geordie claims, "I'm taking the dog for a walk," what he really means is, "I'm off down the pub for a bottle of Newcastle Brown Ale." And not a lot of people know that.

Closing times
Closed 25-26 December

Prices
Meals: à la carte £ 22/29

Typical Dishes
Wild rabbit pâté
Seared scallops
White chocolate cheesecake

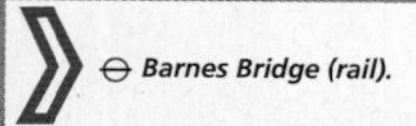
⊖ *Barnes Bridge (rail).*

52 The Victoria

East Sheen SW14 7RT

Tel.: (020)88764238 – Fax: (020)88783464

e-mail: bookings@thevictoria.net **Website:** www.thevictoria.net

 **Fuller's London Pride, Timothy Taylor Landlord**

Paul Merrett was lured away from the bright lights of TV cookery studios to take over this neighbourhood pub which is concealed to the point of secrecy in a leafy residential street. It comes divided into two: the relaxed bar, popular with locals, and the conservatory restaurant with its wood-burning stove, although the same menu is available throughout. Sourcing of quality ingredients is clearly a top priority and, while the menu descriptions can make dishes sound quite ambitious, the cooking is earthy and satisfying and flavours are well-matched. Meat lovers will appreciate the 21-day aged Devon beef that comes served on a wooden board and there's a rotisserie on the large outside terrace in the summer. The wine list is presented by style rather than region and features some interesting and lesser known names. Out-of-towners can book one of the brightly decorated bedrooms in the purpose-built extension at the rear.

Closing times

Closed 2 days between Christmas and New Year

Prices

Meals: à la carte £ 23/38

7 rooms: £ 105/115

Typical Dishes

Grilled English asparagus

Breast & leg of Guinea fowl

Fresh Alfonso mango

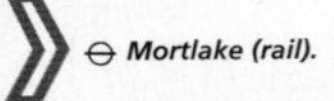

⊖ *Mortlake (rail).*

53 The Garrison

99-101 Bermondsey St,
Bermondsey SE1 3XB
Tel.: (020)70899355
e-mail: info@thegarrison.co.uk **Website:** www.thegarrison.co.uk

   AE

 **Adnams**

Close to the owners' other place, Village East, sits this part shabby-chic gastropub, part boho brasserie. Bermondsey was an area known in the 19C for its food processing as well as its tanning and the blossoming number of eateries bears witness to its bourgeoning 21C rejuvenation. The pub's full of bustle and life and the ideal venue for meeting up with friends, especially if you can snare one of the booths. If you're an even bigger party then consider hiring the downstairs room which doubles as a mini cinema. There's a refreshing wholesomeness to the cooking; there are blackboard specials, everything's homemade except for the quince paste which comes with the cheese and the menu changes every eight weeks. Dishes display this no-nonsense approach by being full in flavour and decent in size, whether that's meatloaf with purple sprouting broccoli or smoked haddock with bubble and squeak. It's all fairly priced, as is the wine list.

Closing times

Closed 25-26 December and 1 January

Booking essential at dinner

Prices

Meals: £ 14 and à la carte £ 28/45

Typical Dishes

Goats cheese salad

Orkney calves liver

Apple & cinnamon crumble

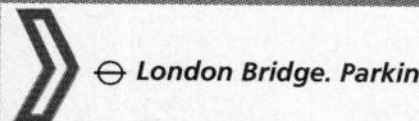

⊖ London Bridge. Parking.

54 The Hartley

64 Tower Bridge Road,
Bermondsey SE1 4TR
Tel.: (020)73947023
e-mail: enquries@thehartley.com **Website:** www.thehartley.com

  MC AE

 **IPA, Spindrift**

Local competition in this part of town may be a little thin on the ground but The Hartley still makes a valiant effort in flying the local gastropub flag. This red-bricked Victorian pub is also doing its bit to remember the diminishing local heritage by honouring, in name and decoration, the Hartley Jam Factory which once stood opposite and is now, predictably, a residential development. There are original posters, black and white photos and even jars of jam scattered around the place. The cooking also has a certain zesty appeal. Appetite-satisfying is the order of the day, with a refreshingly concise menu supplemented by daily-changing blackboard specials. Terrines, fishcakes and pies sit happily alongside more adventurous pork belly or swordfish dishes. The wine list is also kept quite short but is also kept affordable, with an adequate choice available by the glass. Service is relaxed and cool headed.

Closing times
Closed Sunday dinner

Prices
Meals: à la carte £ 22/30

Typical Dishes
Pan-fried chicken livers
Chargrilled swordfish
Lemon mousse brûlée

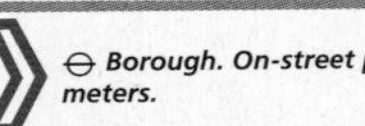
⊖ Borough. On-street parking meters.

55 The Anchor & Hope

36 The Cut,
Southwark SE1 8LP

Tel.: (020)79289898 – Fax: (020)79284595
e-mail: anchorandhope@btconnect.com

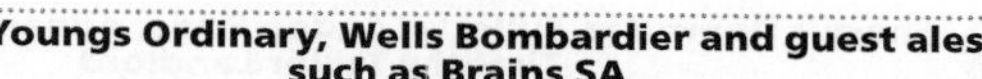

Youngs Ordinary, Wells Bombardier and guest ales such as Brains SA

The Anchor & Hope is always and understandably busy, due to some degree to its proximity to both Vic theatres but mostly because of his culinary reputation. The fact that they don't take reservations means that it's worth getting here early – in fact very early – to secure a table although if you're willing to share you'll be seated sooner. The owners are of the sleeve-rolled-up school and take charge of the cooking, the delivery of the dishes and the serving of drinks. The general buzz creates a noisy but highly convivial atmosphere. From the tiny kitchen they produce immensely satisfying dishes, in a rustic and earthy style, drawing on influences from St John restaurant in Islington, but at prices which make the queuing worth it. Menu descriptions are understated but infinitely appealing: crab on toast, grilled razor clams, rare roast venison with duck fat potato cake, beef dripping toast…

Closing times
Closed Sunday dinner and Monday lunch

Prices
Meals: à la carte £ 20/35

Typical Dishes
Grilled razor clams
Shoulder of lamb
Buttermilk pudding

⊖ Southwark. On-street parking meters.

56 The Morgan Arms

43 Morgan St,
Bow E3 5AA
Tel.: (020)89806389
e-mail: themorgan@geronimo-inns.co.uk **Website:** www.geronimo-inns.co.uk

Sharp's Doom Bar, Fuller's London Pride, Adnam's Best Bitter, Timothy Taylor Landlord

Bow and the East End are just as susceptible to 'gentrification' as the rest of London and The Morgan Arms represents another by-product of that process. Owners Geronimo Inns, who have several pubs across the capital, gave this former boozer a clever makeover which respects its heritage while simultaneously bringing it up-to-date. The bar's always busy while the dining area is more subdued. You'll find the kitchen keeps its influences mostly within Europe but also understands just what sort of food works well in a pub. The daily changing menu usually features pasta in some form and staples like whitebait – which come devilled in this instance – assorted tarts and the perennial favourite: fishcakes, accompanied by a poached egg. What's more, prices are kept at realistic levels which, together with their policy of not taking bookings, makes this pub appealing to those who live nearby and like a little spontaneity in their lives.

Closing times
Closed 25-26 December

Prices
Meals: à la carte £ 20/31

Typical Dishes
Devilled whitebait
Fish cake
Sticky toffee pudding

⊖ Bow Road. Parking meters in Tredegar Square until 6.30pm; after 6.30pm parking outside.

57 The Gun

27 Coldharbour,
Canary Wharf E14 9NS

Tel.: (020)75155222 – Fax: (020)75154407
e-mail: info@thegundocklands.com **Website:** www.thegundocklands.com

Young's Ordinary, Adnams Broadside, Greene King Abbot Ale

Anyone interested in seeing London's past juxtaposed with the present should get down to The Gun. This thoughtfully restored 18C pub in a cobbled street has a long connection to the river and was where Lord Nelson conducted his trysts with Lady Emma Hamilton. But sit on the terrace or in the back with the locals and the views are of the O2 Arena. Renewal and revitalisation are also reflected in the food side: the concise menu is a balanced combination of European influenced dishes, prepared with a light yet assured touch. Fish is a key component of the blackboard daily specials and comes from Billingsgate, no further than a hefty cast away. Those side dishes can push up the final bill and there are plenty of temptations on the wine list but this is a pub for those who know their food. There are jazz nights on Sundays; news that will attract and repel in equal measure but bite the bullet and get down to The Gun.

Closing times
Closed 25 December

Prices
Meals: à la carte £ 21/30

Typical Dishes
Pig's head terrine
Rump of Herdwick mutton
Lemon balm posset

⊖ Blackwall (DLR). Marsh Wall car park; on-street parking meters.

58 **The Narrow**

44 Narrow Street,
Limehouse E14 8DP

Tel.: (020)75927950 – Fax: (020)75921603

e-mail: thenarrow@gordonramsay.com **Website:** www.gordonramsay.com

Inspectors' favourites

 **Deuchar's IPA, Caledonian Explorer, Adnams Yuletide**

Despite receiving some negative publicity in the spring of 2009 when it was revealed that certain dishes in Gordon Ramsay's pubs are prepared in a central kitchen, The Narrow does not seem any less frenetic. This "logistical cooking", as they describe it, is used for dishes requiring a lengthy cooking process, such as the slow-roasted pork belly or beef braised in Guinness. However it gets there, the food on the plate is tasty, seasonal and commendably British, be it devilled kidneys, Morecambe Bay brown shrimps, a chicken and mushroom pie or a sherry trifle. What is also certain is that no other London pub has better views, as one would expect from a converted dock master's house; just be sure to request a table in the semi-permanent conservatory. Staff are a helpful and well organised bunch and won't let you over order. Look out for the interesting and unusual local brews from Greenwich's Meantime Brewery.

Closing times

Open daily

Booking essential

Prices

Meals: à la carte £ 21/27

Typical Dishes

Bubble & squeak with poached egg

Bangers with colcannon

Sherry trifle

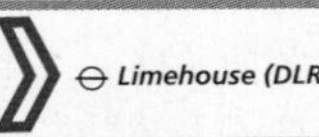

⊖ Limehouse (DLR). Parking.

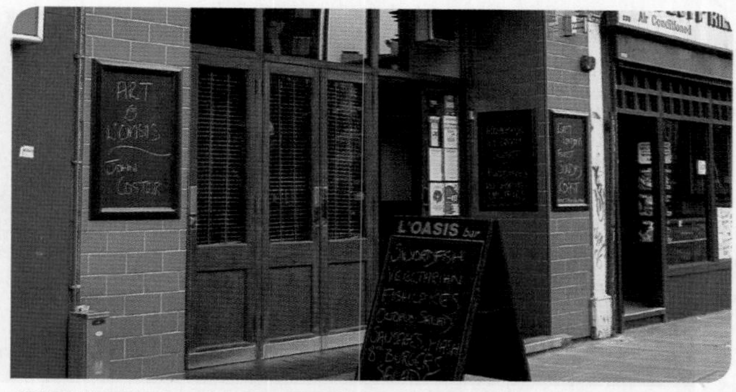

59 L'Oasis

237 Mile End Rd,
Mile End E1 4AA
Tel.: (020)7702705
e-mail: info@loasisstepney.co.uk **Website:** www.loasisstepney.co.uk

   AE

 **Adnams Bitter, Timothy Taylor Landlord, Black Sheep**

The sign at the door confidently proclaims 'proper food cooked by proper chefs'. Few would dispute that there's something very warm and sincere about L'Oasis and much of that is down to the affable owner, John Cleary, who has created a welcoming neighbourhood spot. This may be quite a narrow Victorian pub but the ornate high ceiling adds a feeling of space and local artists' work lends some colour. Regulars insist that certain dishes remain perennials: the meze trays (including a vegetarian one), the New York strip steak, the house burger and the assorted sausages and pies that come with gravy and mash are the locals' favourites. The menu certainly has a European bias but dishes also displays satisfyingly Anglo-Saxon stoutness: proper food indeed. Look out also for wine tasting evenings and the impressive selection of whisky. You may never see midnight at this oasis, but you can certainly send your camel to bed.

Closing times
Open daily
Prices
Meals: à la carte £ 20/30

Typical Dishes
Smoked trout terrine
Belly of pork
Chocolate marquise

⊖ Stepney Green. On-street parking meters.

60 The Avalon

16 Balham Hill,
Balham SW12 9EB

Tel.: (020)86758613

e-mail: info@theavalonlondon.com **Website:** www.theavalonlondon.com

VISA MC AE

 **Timothy Taylor Landlord, Sharp's Doom Bar**

This is just the sort of place the locals in and around Balham Hill have been missing all these years. A full renovation has seen what was once called The George turn into a slick and imaginatively styled pub, where Sir Edward Coley Burne-Jones prints add a suitably mythical edge to the aesthetic. The rear dining room's walls are covered in cream tiles but any resemblance to a morgue is undone by the general hustle and bustle and those eye-catching chandeliers. The menu combines British and Mediterranean influences, sometimes, as in the case of the kedgeree risotto, in the same dish. Expect roasted veal marrow bones, crab linguine, venison carpaccio, lamb cutlets, crème brûlée but also crumble, appropriately of the apple variety. The execution is no-nonsense, what-you-order-is-what-you-get. The wine list is concise but appealingly priced and there are plenty of beers. Those locals still can't quite believe that Avalon really exists.

Closing times

Closed 25-26 December

Booking advisable

Prices

Meals: à la carte £ 21/32

Typical Dishes

Wright Brothers oysters

Slow-cooked lamb shank

Sticky toffee pudding

⊖ *Clapham South.*

61 The Bolingbroke

174 Northcote Rd,
Battersea SW11 6RE

Tel.: (020)72284040 – Fax: (020)72282285
e-mail: holly@renaissancepubs.co.uk **Website:** www.thebolingbroke.com

   AE

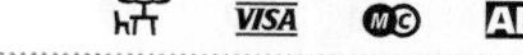

Sam Brooks Wandle Ale, Sharp's Doom Bar

The influx of professionals with young families is such that this end of Northcote Road is now known as 'Nappy Valley'. A Cath Kidston shop? Check. Artisan food markets? Check. Antique emphoria? Check. Now it's time for a decent pub and here's where The Bolingbroke comes in. Named after locally born Henry St John, 1st Viscount Bolingbroke, the place looks more like a French brasserie from outside. But step in and you'll find it decidedly pubby, albeit in a contemporary way. Its glass roof makes the fairly small dining room feel bigger, although the romantically inclined should ask for the table under the stairs. The menus change weekly, with more choice at dinner. British influences lead the way, from the asparagus and cheddar tart, to the lamb shoulder and apple crumble. Steaks and burgers are perennials but you'll also find additional Euro stars like ravioli and a niçoise salad. Unsurprisingly, there's also a children's menu.

Closing times
Closed 25-26 December

Prices
Meals: à la carte £ 21/29

Typical Dishes
King scallops, bubble & squeak
Guinea fowl, crispy polenta
Lemon curd pie

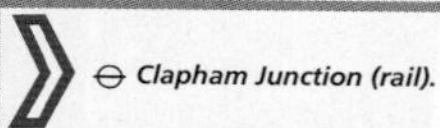

⊖ *Clapham Junction (rail).*

England • London • Wandsworth

62 Prince of Wales

138 Upper Richmond Rd,
Putney SW15 2SP

Tel.: (020)87881552

e-mail: info@princeofwalesputney.co.uk **Website:** www.princeofwalesputney.co.uk

 **Fuller's London Pride, Black Sheep and guest ale**

Those who decry the rise of the gastropub should have tried The Prince of Wales in its past: such was its reputation that it earned the nickname 'The Prince of Darkness'. Now it's a thoroughly civilised spot, thanks to its Scottish owner whose ambition was to create a 'country pub in the city'. The dining room at the back is the best place to sit as it has the feel of a billiard room in a Scottish Baronial hall complete with stuffed animals and deer antlers. This gives some clues as to the cooking: it is robust and British, with game featuring strongly. The kitchen tends to buy the whole beast so expect prime cuts, offal, then stews, pies, terrines and parfaits. There are often dishes for two such as cassoulet, a roast leg of venison or a beef and beer pie but those without the appetite of Desperate Dan will also find much that's appealing. As with all good pubs, it's part of the local community and Sunday night is quiz night.

Closing times

Closed 25 December and 1 January

Prices

Meals: à la carte £ 25/40

Typical Dishes

Parmesan gnocchi
Blanquette of veal
Prune & apple crumble

⊖ East Putney. Free parking opposite.

63 The Spencer Arms

237 Lower Richmond Road,
Putney SW15 1HJ
Tel.: (020)87880640 – Fax: (020)87882216
e-mail: info@thespencerarms.co.uk **Website:** www.thespencerarms.co.uk

VISA  

Sharp's Doom Bar, Black Sheep, Fuller's London Pride

The Spencer Arms is one of those classic Victorian pubs that have an appealingly unassuming manner. This means you can sit anywhere you like and do want you want, whether that's drinking with friends, reading the paper, eating or doing all three. The etched windows proclaim the offer of "Gutsy Grub" which is no word of a lie: food here is of the what-you-see-is-what-you-get variety which means it's satisfying and gutsy. They have introduced small plates of what could be referred to as – for lack of an alternative – 'English tapas'. These can act as starters, bar nibbles or just as shared plates and could include Scotch egg, smoked mackerel or salmon and black pudding sausage rolls; but order too many and your bill will quickly climb. Traditionalists can still order their three-courser and there are more Mediterranean flavours on the menu too, in the form of chorizo, ratatouille and panna cotta. They sell their own chutneys and pickles.

Closing times
Closed 25 December and 1 January

Prices
Meals: à la carte £ 18/25

Typical Dishes
Chicken terrine
Aged rib-eye steak
Toffee cheesecake

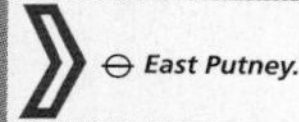
⊖ *East Putney.*

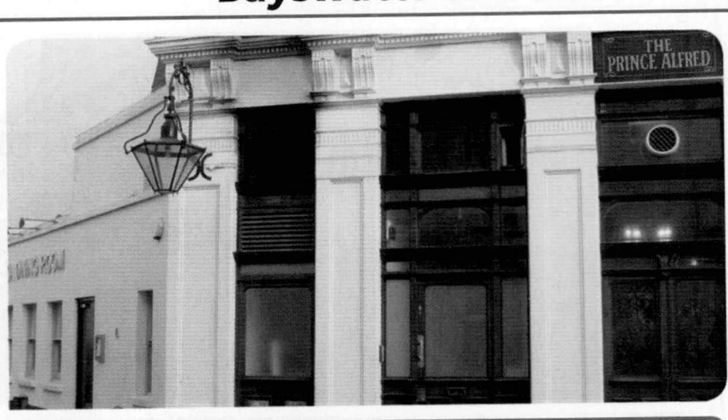

64 Prince Alfred & Formosa Dining Room

5A Formosa St,
Bayswater and Maida Vale W9 1EE
Tel.: (020)72863287
e-mail: princealfred@youngs.co.uk **Website:** www.theprincealfred.com

VISA 

Youngs Bitter, Courage Directors

Original plate glass and wooden panels dividing the assorted snugs make The Prince Alfred, built in 1863 and named after one of Queen Victoria's children, a wonderful example of a classic Victorian pub. Unfortunately, the eating is done in the Formosa Dining Room, a more recent addition on the side of the pub but, on the positive front, it's a lively room with capable cooking and makes an equally worthy stop for those out exploring Little Venice. There's a rustic theme running through the menu with a strong British accent, so traditionalists will enjoy the fish pie, potted trout, steak and ale pie and calves liver but there are also risottos, parfaits and terrines for those of a more European bent. The open kitchen is also not averse to sprucing up some classics, for example your burger arrives adorned with foie gras and truffles. Prices are realistic, even with a charge made for bread. The friendly team cope well under pressure.

Closing times
Open daily

Prices
Meals: à la carte £ 21/35

Typical Dishes
Home-cured salmon
Crispy pork belly
Sticky toffee pudding

⊖ Warwick Avenue. Parking by Warwick Avenue station (2min on foot).

65 The Warrington

93 Warrington Crescent,
Bayswater W9 1EH
Tel.: (020)75927960 – Fax: (020)75921603
e-mail: thewarrington@gordonramsay.com **Website:** www.gordonramsay.com

 **Fuller's London Pride, Greene King IPA, Adnams Broadside**

Nothing upsets a community more than when their favourite pub gets a makeover and thereafter attracts interlopers from outlying postcodes. The cleverness of The Warrington, which dates from 1857, is that the Gordon Ramsay group have spent a few million on the place but the ground floor, with its art nouveau friezes, dark wood and pillars, retains its traditional flavour and remains the haunt of locals just in for a drink, a snack or a lunchtime pie. The main eating event is upstairs in the smarter but decidedly less characterful restaurant; you'd hardly know it was there as there are no signs. It is a bright room, with friendly staff who provide service that's smooth without being too ceremonial. The cooking also keeps things relatively simple and is a mix of British and French, with cullen skink or chicken and mushroom pie jostling for your attention with steak tartare or confit of duck. The wine prices are commendably competitive.

Closing times
Closed Monday-Thursday lunch

Prices
Meals: à la carte £ 20/27

Typical Dishes
Potted duck
Chicken & wild mushroom pie
Steamed treacle pudding

⊖ Maida Vale. Parking meters in Sutherland Avenue; on-street parking in Warrington Crescent.

England • London • Westminster

66 The Waterway

54 Formosa St,
Bayswater and Maida Vale W9 2JU
Tel.: (020)72663557 – Fax: (020)72663547
e-mail: info@thewaterway.co.uk **Website:** www.thewaterway.co.uk

   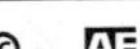

 **HSB, Fuller's London Pride**

Strictly speaking, The Waterway is not really a pub but it does always have lots of people standing outside with drinks in their hands. Approach on foot from Maida Vale and you really won't get the full effect – to see The Waterway at its best you just have to arrive by narrowboat as the terrific canalside terrace is one of its great selling points. It still doesn't resemble much of a pub on the inside but it does have that bustle and informality. The dining area is separate from the bar and here you'll find quite an appealing menu. For starters expect squid, scallops or risotto. Main courses could include beef Bourguignon or duck breast with okra; dishes are executed with a certain amount of vim. There are more accessible choices available too, especially on the terrace, like the house burger, Caesar salad and rib-eye steak. The young team of servers can sometimes place too much emphasis on functionality at the expense of personality.

Closing times
Open daily
Prices
Meals: à la carte £ 30/40

Typical Dishes
Chargrilled squid
Rump of lamb
Sticky date pudding

⊖ *Warwick Avenue.*

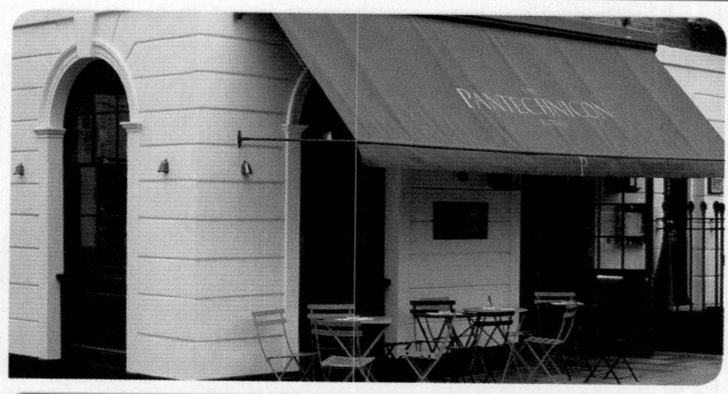

67 The Pantechnicon Rooms

10 Motcomb St,
Belgravia SW1X 8LA

Tel.: (020)77306074 – Fax: (020)77306055

e-mail: reservations@thepantechnicon.com **Website:** www.thepantechnicon.com

VISA MC AE

 **Adnams Bitter**

It took the owners over a year to transform the distinctly unprepossessing Turks Head into this smart new pub to go with their other place nearby, The Thomas Cubitt. It's named after the art and antique repository that once graced Motcomb Street until it was destroyed by fire in 1874; a painting of that fire adorns the upstairs restaurant. This being Belgravia means the menu is a sophisticated number, with oysters, caviar and shellfish having their own sections and cocktails and champagne muscling in on the wine list. Downstairs, the menu gets tweaked slightly so that starters become 'small plates' but otherwise there's little difference; influences are kept within Europe, the seafood is a strength and dishes come daintily presented. It's all very pleasant on a bright day, with light streaming in through the arched windows. The Pantechnicon Rooms and Motcomb Street look like the perfect match.

Closing times

Closed 25 December to 1 January

Prices

Meals: à la carte £ 28/40

Typical Dishes

Smoked quail

Tournedos of beef

Chocolate espresso trio

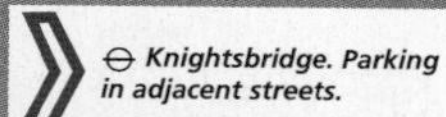

⊖ Knightsbridge. Parking in adjacent streets.

68 The Only Running Footman

5 Charles St,
Mayfair W1J 5DF

Tel.: (020)74992988 – Fax: (020)76298061
e-mail: info@therunningfootman.biz **Website:** www.therunningfootman.biz

  AE

Fuller's London Pride, Wells Bombardier, Youngs

Anyone who despairs about pubs serving Thai curry should head to this charming, historic pub which re-opened in 2007 under the ownership of the group who gave us The Bull in Highgate and The House in Islington. The Union flag flying outside tells you everything about their attitude, for here our very own culinary heritage is celebrated. The ground floor is small, atmospheric and always packed – it's first-come-first-served. Here the menu really hits the bullseye: who can resist a richly satisfying Omelette Arnold Bennett for breakfast, potted shrimps for lunch or some beer-battered haddock for dinner? You can even order a sausage sarnie to take away. Upstairs you can book and it's all rather plush in comparison; the menu is more ambitious and the prices also a little loftier. You do get to order the rib of beef for two; otherwise you may just wish you were downstairs with a pork pie and piccalilli.

Closing times
Open daily

Prices
Meals: £ 15 and à la carte £ 26/35

Typical Dishes
Smoked eel & asparagus paté
Shepherd's pie
Sticky toffee pudding

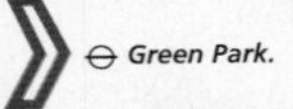
⊖ Green Park.

69 The Ebury

11 Pimlico Rd,
Victoria SW1W 8NA
Tel.: (020)77306784 – Fax: (020)77306149
e-mail: info@theebury.co.uk **Website:** www.theebury.co.uk

 **Fuller's London Pride**

Grab a passing waiter to get yourself seated, otherwise they'll assume you've just come for a drink at the bar and will ignore you. Once you have your feet under one of the low-slung tables, however, you'll find everything moves up a gear. The Ebury has always been one of London's smarter pubs and provides an object lesson in how to satisfy the punters by giving them what they want. That means a varied menu, from burger to black bream, assorted salads that show some thought and come in a choice of size, three vegetarian dishes and main courses that display a degree of originality. Add to that a kitchen that goes about its business with care, a wine list that offers plenty by the glass and carafe, a children's menu and weekend brunch that goes on until 4pm and it's little wonder the place is always so busy and lively. The waiters come dressed in black, with French accents and self-confidence. Private parties are held upstairs.

Closing times
Closed 25-26 December

Prices
Meals: £ 17 (lunch)
and à la carte £ 30/45

Typical Dishes
Goose liver parfait
Rib-eye steak
Chocolate fondant

 ⊖ ***Sloane Square. Pay & display in the street.***

England • London • Westminster

70 The Thomas Cubitt

44 Elizabeth Street,
Victoria SW1W 9PA

Tel.: (020)77306060 – Fax: (020)77306055

e-mail: reservations@thethomascubitt.co.uk **Website:** www.thethomascubitt.

Inspectors' favourites

VISA MC AE

 **Deuchar's IPA, Adnams**

The Thomas Cubitt is a pub of two halves: on the ground floor it's a veritable bun-fight, although this being Belgravia means that those buns are couched in Armani and no one actually fights. You can't reserve, it's first-come-first-served, so if you haven't arrived by around 7pm then you're probably already too late to get a table. However, you can reserve upstairs, in a dining room that's a model of civility and tranquillity. Here, service comes courtesy of a young team: the girls are chatty and the men unafraid of corduroy. Downstairs you get fish and chips; here you get pan-fried fillet of brill with oyster beignet and truffled chips. The cooking is certainly skilled, quite elaborate in its construction and prettily presented; a number of wines are available in 500ml carafes. So, take your pick: upstairs can get a little pricey but is ideal for entertaining the in-laws; if out with friends then crowd in downstairs.

Closing times

Closed 24 December to 1 January

Booking essential

Prices

Meals: £ 25 (lunch) and à la carte £ 28/40

Typical Dishes

Scotch quail's egg

Roast Gressingham duck

Ginger steamed pudding

⊖ Sloane Square. Parking meters in Elizabeth Street.

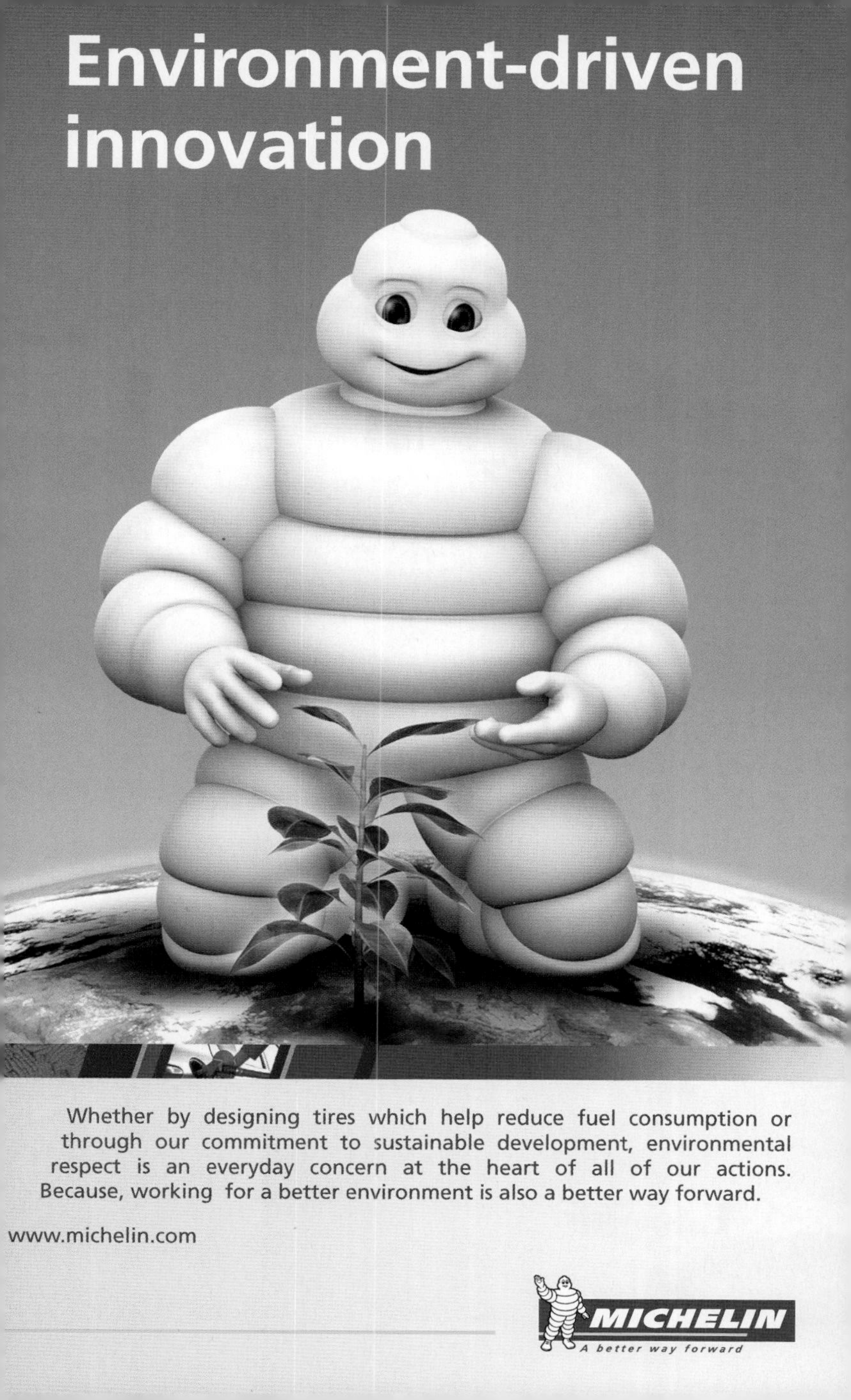
Environment-driven innovation
Whether by designing tires which help reduce fuel consumption or through our commitment to sustainable development, environmental respect is an everyday concern at the heart of all of our actions. Because, working for a better environment is also a better way forward.
www.michelin.com
MICHELIN
A better way forward

This region cradles some of England's wildest and most dramatic scenery typified by Northumberland National Park, a landscape of rolling purple moorlands and roaring rivers bursting with salmon and trout. Kielder Forest's mighty wilderness has been called "the country's most tranquil spot" while Bill Bryson has waxed lyrical upon the glories of Durham Cathedral. Those who love the wind in their hair are equally effusive about the eleven-mile footpath that accompanies the pounding waves of Durham's Heritage Coast; further north are the long, dune-backed beaches of Northumberland. Rambling across the region is Hadrian's Wall, 73 miles of iconic Roman history, while a modern slant on architectural celebrity is proffered by the Millennium Bridge, BALTIC Centre and Angel of the North. The famously bracing air whets hearty appetites for local Cheviot lamb, Coquetdale cheese or Holy Island oysters. And what could be more redolent of the North East than a breakfast of Craster kippers?

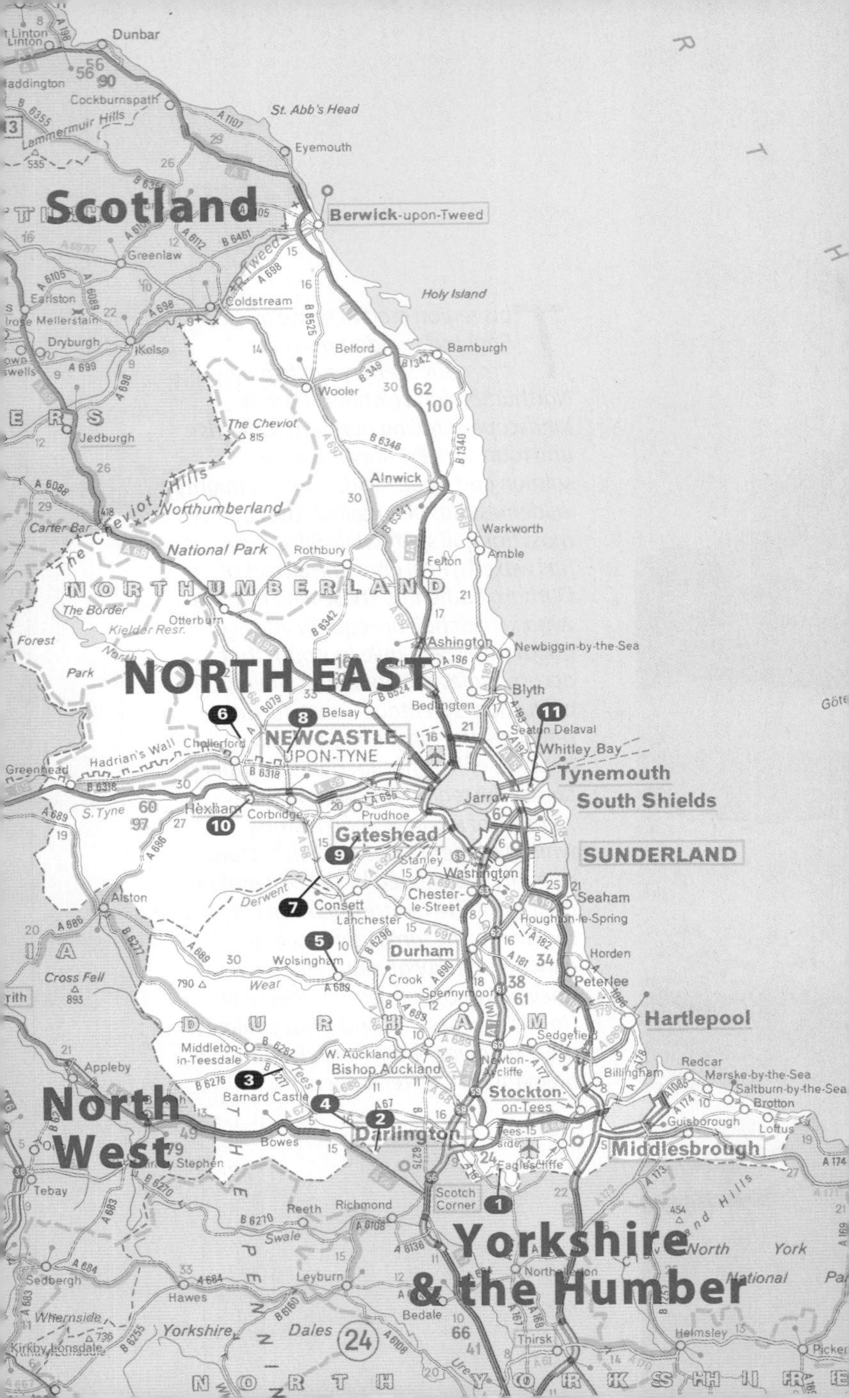

Scotland
NORTH EAST
North West
Yorkshire & the Humber
Dunbar
Cockburnspath
Lammermuir Hills
St. Abb's Head
Eyemouth
Berwick-upon-Tweed
Greenlaw
Earlston
Mellerstain
Dryburgh
Kelso
Coldstream
Holy Island
Belford
Bamburgh
Wooler
Jedburgh
The Cheviot
815
Cheviot Hills
Northumberland
National Park
Alnwick
Carter Bar
Warkworth
Amble
Rothbury
Felton
NORTHUMBERLAND
The Border
Otterburn
Kielder Resr.
Forest
Park
Ashington
Newbiggin-by-the-Sea
Blyth
Bedlington
Seaton Delaval
Whitley Bay
Belsay
NEWCASTLE-UPON-TYNE
Chollerford
Hadrian's Wall
Greenhead
Tynemouth
South Shields
Jarrow
Hexham
Corbridge
Prudhoe
Gateshead
SUNDERLAND
Stanley
Washington
Chester-le-Street
Seaham
Houghton-le-Spring
Alston
Derwent
Consett
Lanchester
Durham
Horden
Peterlee
Wolsingham
Crook
Spennymoor
Hartlepool
Cross Fell
893
790
Wear
DURHAM
Sedgefield
Middleton-in-Teesdale
W. Auckland
Bishop Auckland
Newton Aycliffe
Billingham
Redcar
Marske-by-the-Sea
Saltburn-by-the-Sea
Brotton
Appleby
Barnard Castle
Tees
Stockton-on-Tees
Guisborough
Loftus
Bowes
Darlington
Teesside
Middlesbrough
Kirkby Stephen
Eaglescliffe
Tebay
Scotch Corner
Reeth
Richmond
Swale
North York
National
Sedbergh
Hawes
Leyburn
Northallerton
Bedale
Whernside
Yorkshire
Dales
Thirsk
Helmsley
Kirkby Lonsdale
NORTH YORKSHIRE
1
2
3
4
5
6
7
8
9
10
11
24

1 The Bay Horse

45 The Green,
Hurworth on Tees DL2 2AA
Tel.: (01325)720663 – Fax: (01325)729840
e-mail: mail@thebayhorsehurworth.com **Website:** www.thebayhorsehurworth.

 **Harviestoun Bitter & Twisted, Stafford's Stallion, Jennings Sneck Lifter**

Set on a long grassy street in an attractive village, this early 18C creamwashed pub is framed by colourful planters and hanging baskets. To the rear it boasts a pleasant terrace and beer garden, whilst inside smart wood floors lead up to an attractive bar and a welcoming open fire. Drinkers and diners mingle amongst antique chairs, low stools and leather banquettes in the bar area and the relaxed, informal atmosphere continues on into the dining room; for special occasions the charming first floor private room adds some style, with its 20 foot Victorian table and adjoining lounge. Menus offer something for everyone, featuring classics such as moules marinierè, daube of beef or omelette Arnold Bennett, as well as some more familiar pub favourites such as steak and kidney pie or a ploughman's lunch. Dishes range in their presentation from simple, rustic and hearty to more modern and intricate. Lunch represents particularly good value.

Closing times
Closed Sunday dinner

Prices
Meals: £ 15 (lunch)
and à la carte £ 22/38

Typical Dishes
Potted Whitby crab
Pressed belly pork
Sticky toffee pudding

5½ mi south of Darlington; signed off A 167; in the middle of the village. Parking.

2 The Oak Tree Inn

Hutton Magna DL11 7HH
Tel.: (01833)627371

Black Sheep Best, Wells Bombardier, Timothy Taylor Landlord

They say that good things come in small packages and that's definitely the case with this charming whitewashed pub. Found on the main street of a small hamlet, opposite the church lychgate, The Oak Tree consists of a single room with white stone walls, wood panelling, a proper old-fashioned counter and six wood tables flanked by green upholstered settles. As you study the menu on the sofas beside the fire, the locals brush past you on the way to their usual bench table. Claire – who both serves the drinks and delivers the food – provides a warm welcome at the bar, while behind the scenes in the kitchen Alastair single-handedly holds the fort. The menu takes on a fairly formal format, offering generous portions of hearty, flavoursome cooking with a rustic French feel: you might find confit belly pork, onion and thyme tart or best end of lamb. More wide-ranging flavours such as cumin and chilli often appear somewhere on the list too.

Closing times

Closed 24-27 and 31 December, 1-2 January and Monday

Dinner only

Booking essential

Prices

Meals: à la carte £ 26/33

Typical Dishes

Smoked haddock & Shetland mussels

Slow roast pork belly

Rhubarb & gingerbread trifle

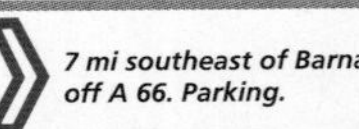

7 mi southeast of Barnard Castle off A 66. Parking.

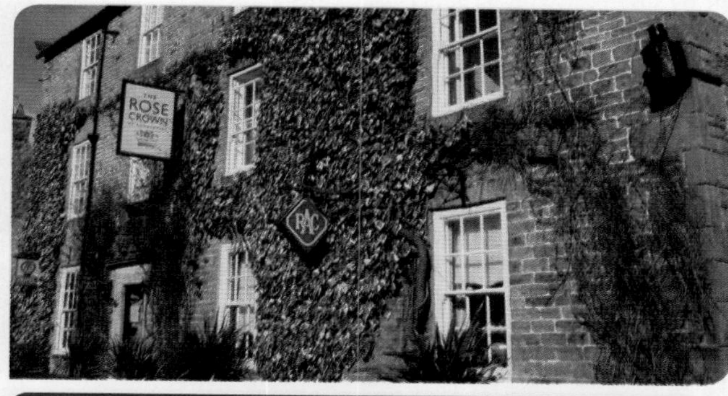

3 Rose and Crown

Romaldkirk DL12 9EB
Tel.: (01833)650213 – Fax: (01833)650828
e-mail: hotel@rose-and-crown.co.uk
Website: www.rose-and-crown.co.uk

 **Theakston Best Bitter, Black Sheep Bitter**

Set next to a Saxon church in the middle of three village greens – looking out over a water pump and some stocks – is this quintessential 18C English village inn. Wood panelling features throughout and there's a wonderfully atmospheric front bar boasting plenty of brass and a welcoming fire. There's a brasserie and dining room decorated in warm reds, while tucked away to the rear there's a cosy lounge with an impressive grandfather clock. Between the bar and brasserie menus there's a good range of dishes: a core of classics, with sandwiches at lunch and some more substantial offerings at dinner. In the evening residents tend to favour the classical dining room, with its wooden dresser, china-filled plate rail, linen-clad tables and seasonally changing four course British menu. Individually designed bedrooms are split between the inn and the courtyard: a cosy, classic style pervades but all boast modern flat screen TVs and Bose radios.

Closing times

Closed 24-26 December

Prices

Meals: £ 19/30

12 rooms: £ 89/175

Typical Dishes

Cotherstone cheese soufflé

Pan-fried pink wood pigeon

Sticky walnut tart

3½ mi southeast of Middleton-in-Teesdale on B 6277; on the village green, next to the church. Parking.

Whorlton

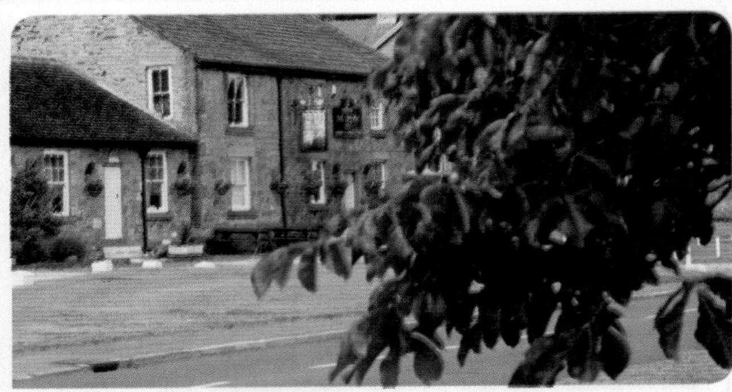

4 The Bridge Inn

Whorlton DL12 8XD
Tel.: (01833)627341 – Fax: (01833)627995
e-mail: info@thebridgeinnrestaurant.co.uk
Website: www.thebridgeinnrestaurant.co.uk

 **Timothy Taylor Landlord, Theakston Black Bull & Old Peculiar**

The flat screen television delivering live broadcasts of all the kitchen action to its dining room speaks volumes about how seriously the chefs at The Bridge Inn take their work. The resulting dishes are accomplished and full of flavour, and the kitchen knows what goes with what, be it smoked eel fillet with roast beetroot and horseradish, pigeon with black pudding and crispy bacon, or winter fruits with cinnamon ice cream. For an inexpensive option, opt for the 'dine with wine' lunch or early evening menu, consisting of a three course meal with an accompanying glass of wine. Its two rooms contrast in style: the bar is traditional, with beams, horse brasses and an open fire, while the spacious white dining room, with its contemporary edge, feels faintly stark in comparison. The beautiful Teeside village of Whorlton is a grand spot for a post-prandial stroll; keep an eye out for the suspension bridge after which the pub is named.

Closing times

Closed 25-26 December, Monday and Tuesday

Prices

Meals: £ 14/17
and à la carte £ 23/30

Typical Dishes

Pigeon breast
Chargrilled bavette of beef
Iced tangerine parfait

5 mi east of Barnard Castle by A 67 and minor road south. Parking.

5 The Mill Race

Wolsingham DL13 3AP
Tel.: (01388)526551
e-mail: info@themillracehotel.co.uk **Website:** www.themillracehotel.co.uk

  AE

 **Black Sheep Best Bitter, Timothy Taylor Landlord**

Situated in the centre of this picturesque town – known as the gateway to Weardale – The Mill Race is at least one hundred years old, although run by a team considerably younger. It has been modernised inside, with laminate floors all round, leather sofas and locals' stools in the bar and a chocolate and cream restaurant, dimly lit in the evenings, with vivid modern art for sale on the walls. The menu features well-presented, flavourful dishes more in keeping with a restaurant than a pub: perhaps leek and Gruyere cheese soufflé, crab and avocado with sweet chilli caramel, Weardale lamb done three ways or pan-roasted halibut with beetroot. It's bring your own wine night on Tuesdays and there's a good value set price menu available midweek and early Saturday nights, offering more pubby dishes such as liver and bacon, sausage and mash or steak and chips. Unfortunately, the bedrooms don't match up to the standard of the pub and its cooking.

Closing times

Closed 26 December, 1 January, Monday, Sunday dinner, and lunch Tuesday-Thursday and Saturday

Prices

Meals: £ 16 (dinner) and à la carte £ 20/35

Typical Dishes

Homemade black pudding
Weardale lamb done 3 ways
Iced peanut parfait

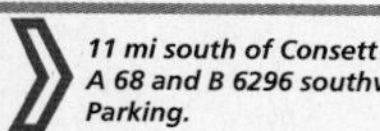

11 mi south of Consett by A 692, A 68 and B 6296 southwest. Parking.

6 Barrasford Arms

Barrasford NE48 4AA
Tel.: (01434)681237
e-mail: barrasfordarmshotel@yahoo.co.uk
Website: www.barrasfordarms.co.uk

   VISA

Gold Tankard, Nel's Best, Gladiator, Jack Snipe, Auld Hemp, Ferocious Fred

Set right in the heart of the Northumbrian countryside, close to Kielder Water and Hadrian's Wall, this personally run 19C stone inn provides an ideal base for exploring the North Tyne Valley. Retaining its traditional character, this pub provides the perfect home from home: photos of local football teams adorn the bar and the owner's certificates and copper pans hang on the walls of the dining rooms. The cosy fire is a huge draw, as are the regular vegetable, darts and quoits competitions, but the star attraction here really is the food. Menus differ between lunch and dinner; the former being a touch less formal. Pub classics such as steak pie or gammon and fat cut chips give way to more substantial offerings such as cheese soufflé or grilled rabbit, followed by local shoulder of lamb or chicken with truffle risotto. If you really can't decide, spend the night in one of the modern, comfortable bedrooms, and try something else tomorrow.

Closing times
Closed 25-26 December, bank holidays, Sunday dinner and Monday lunch

Prices
Meals: £ 14/18
and à la carte £ 19/27
7 rooms: £ 65/85

Typical Dishes
Cheddar cheese soufflé
Braised rump of beef
Sticky pistachio meringue

7 mi north of Hexham signed off A 6079. Parking.

7 Manor House Inn

Carterway Heads DH8 9LX

Tel.: (01207)255268

e-mail: info@themanorhouseinn.com

Website: www.themanorhouseinn.com

Weston's Old Rosie, High House Farm Nel's Best, Hexhamshire Devil's Elbow and regularly changing guest ales

High up on the hills between the Tyne Valley and Consett sits this stone-built pub, with Derwent Reservoir just visible in the valley below. It's a pub of two halves: turn right for a rustic, wood-floored locals bar complete with dartboard and muzak; turn left for a traditional lounge bar with banquettes and countryside views. Prefer to eat in a dining room? In that case, your choice is between the large or the smaller; the latter being rather more cosy, with an open fire. Food-wise, it's a toss up between the main menu and the specials. The former offers classic dishes like braised lamb shank, steak and ale pie or slow braised oxtail, while the hanging slate boards offer more variety and can change several times a day, depending on what is fresh in at any given time. Four comfortable bedrooms boast pleasant views – before you check out make sure you have a look around the shop for local jams, chutneys and the like to take back home.

Closing times

Open daily

Prices

Meals: à la carte £ 17/31

4 rooms: £ 43/75

Typical Dishes

Homemade chicken liver paté

Slow roasted belly pork

Choux pastry swan

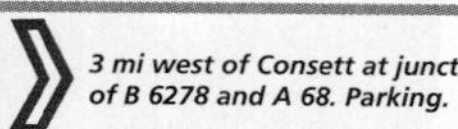

3 mi west of Consett at junction of B 6278 and A 68. Parking.

8 Queens Head Inn

Great Whittington NE19 2HP
Tel.: (01434)672267
Website: www.the-queens-head-inn.co.uk

 **Nels Best, Timothy Taylor Landlord, Wylam Gold Tankard, Tyneside Blonde, Allendale Golden Clover**

A wonderful mural above the fire in the bar depicts the Queens Head Inn as it once was; this cosy room was at one time all that existed of what is considered by some to be, at nearly 400 years of age, the oldest inn in Northumberland. Its thick brick walls have now been breached and the rear extension houses a dining room filled with bookshelves, old farming implements and general bric-à-brac; if this is a tad too formal for your requirements, grab one of the tables in front of the roaring fire next to the bar. The menus are quite formally presented, but don't let that put you off; the lunchtime menu offers anything from filled stotties to duck spring rolls, while the evening menu might mean homemade game terrine, twice baked soufflé, lambs liver and bacon or honey roast Barbary duck; with lamb and Galloway beef supplied by the farm next door. Service is as friendly as it comes, and a couple of courses shouldn't break the bank.

Closing times
Closed Sunday dinner

Prices
Meals: à la carte £ 17/28

Typical Dishes
Smoked haddock & leek fishcakes
Great Whittington rump steak
Traditional banoffee pie

 *6 mi north of Corbridge by A 68 off B 6318. Parking.* 

9 The Feathers Inn

Hedley on the Hill NE43 7SW
Tel.: (01661)843607
e-mail: info@thefeathers.net **Website:** www.thefeathers.net

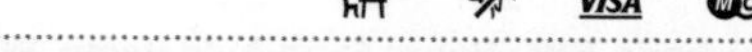

Mordue Workie Ticket, Wylam Northern Kite, Consett Red Dust

Scale the steep hill that leads up to this attractive stone pub and you'll not only work up your appetite but will be rewarded with great views over Newcastle and Gateshead. Far removed from a modern gastro-pub, this traditional inn, owned by an enthusiastic young couple, is welcoming and friendly and, in true community style, there's always something going on. Quizzes, festivals and theme nights take place throughout the year and they even stage an annual beer barrel race; perhaps their strangest claim to fame, however, is as host to the county's longest standing 'Leek Club'. As you might hope, the cooking is straightforward and British: tasty combinations of hearty, wholesome fare and good clear flavours. Ingredients are carefully sourced and suppliers are listed on the menu alongside a map. Lunch is lighter than dinner – you'll find battered North Sea fish, a generous Ploughman's featuring regional cheeses or local sausage and mash.

Closing times
Closed first 2 weeks in January, Sunday dinner and Monday

Prices
Meals: à la carte £ 15/28

Typical Dishes
Black pudding
Pot roast Hedley lamb
Burnt Northumbrian cream

6 mi north of Consett by A 694, B 6309 and minor road. Parking.

10 The Rat Inn

Anick,
Hexham NE46 4LN
Tel.: (01434)602814
e-mail: info@theratinn.com **Website:** www.theratinn.com

   MC AE

Bass Draught, Deuchar's, High House Farm Auld Hemp, Wylam Gold Tankard, Allendale Best Bitter, Secret Kingdom, Consett Steel Town

A, B or C, all vote now: A) Rat catchers used to use this as a meeting place, B) This was once home to a large rat, C) A local snitch lived here during the Jacobite rebellion. Unfortunately nobody knows the answer as to how the pub got its name, so just be grateful for the pleasant garden views across the Tyne valley and the tasty, wholesome cooking instead. Situated in a small hamlet on a hillside, this 18C former drovers inn is the perfect place to escape from the rat race of the city. A multi-levelled garden boasts arbours and picnic sets, whilst the traditional interior displays wooden beams and an open range. The daily blackboard menu is concise but covers a good range of dishes, from pastas and risottos, to pub classics such as cottage pie, and more ambitious dishes such as rib of beef or rack of lamb for two. Produce is always fresh, good quality and locally sourced; and there's no need to worry, rodent isn't on the menu.

Closing times
Closed Sunday dinner and Monday

Prices
Meals: à la carte £ 15/30

Typical Dishes
Terrine of local game
Northumbrian rib of beef
Sticky toffee pudding

1¾ mi north of Hexham off A 69. Parking.

11 Magnesia Bank

Camden St,
North Shields NE30 1NH
Tel.: (0191)2574831 – Fax: (0191)2605422
e-mail: info@blackdoorgroup.co.uk **Website:** www.magnesiabank.com

 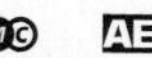 

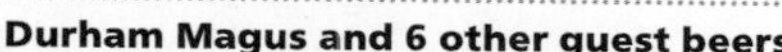

Durham Magus and 6 other guest beers

Set on the embankment above the River Tyne and North Shields fish quay, this converted Georgian building is named after the local network of alleyways and its former use as a bank. Some 139 years after first opening as a financial institution, it was renovated and reopened as a pub, and it's been a hit ever since. Inside it's spacious, almost cavernous, with wooden floors, traditional styling, a bold red ceiling and photos of the quay in its heyday. At lunchtime the bar menu offers good quality classics such steak and ale pie, while the more formal dining room displays a good selection of more substantial dishes on its set menu price menu; you might find duck confit, fish pie, potted salmon or salt and pepper squid. Served by friendly staff, food is fresh and tasty, with fish arriving direct from the quay a mere 100m away. If you're into music, you've probably already heard of The Mag, which is renowned for its regular live music scene.

Closing times
Closed Sunday dinner
Prices
Meals: à la carte £ 18/30

Typical Dishes
Fish tempura
Fish pie & minted greens
Pannetone & butter pudding

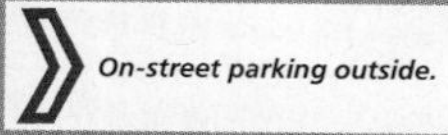
On-street parking outside.

Energised by Liverpool's swagger as 2008's European City of Culture, the north west feels like a region reborn. Dovetailed by the confident sophistication of a reinvigorated Manchester, the country's oldest industrial heartland boasts an impressive cultural profile. And yet arty urban centres are a million miles away from the rural grandeur of the region: trails and paths crisscross the area all the way from Solway Firth to Cheshire. Cumbria is a walker's paradise: from Hadrian's Wall to the glories of the Lake District, and along the vast shoreline of Morecambe Bay with its rich gathering of waders and wildfowl, there's a vivid contrast in scenery. The architectural landscape of the region covers the ages, too. Lancaster Castle reverberates to the footsteps of ancient soldiers, while Chester's walled city of medieval buildings is a true gem. Blackpool is now Europe's biggest seaside resort while the flavour of the north west is hot pot, black pudding and Morecambe Bay shrimps.

Scotland
North East
NORTH
Yorkshire & the Humber
CUMBRIA
Lake District
Cumbrian Mountains
ISLE OF MAN
Dumfries
Carlisle
Workington
Whitehaven
Barrow-in-Furness
Morecambe
Penrith
Keswick
Kendal
Windermere
Ambleside
Grasmere
Coniston
Bowness
Ulverston
Grange-over-Sands
Carnforth
Cockermouth
Maryport
Egremont
Gosforth
Broughton-in-Furness
Millom
Dalton
Greenodd
Appleby
Brough
Kirkby Stephen
Tebay
Orton
Sedbergh
Alston
Brampton
Longtown
Gretna
Annan
Wigton
Aspatria
Thursby
Silloth
Abbey Town
Bowness-on-Solway
Hexham
Corbridge
Chollerford
Hadrian's Wall
Greenhead
NEWCASTLE UPON TYNE
Belsay
Wolsingham
Middleton-in-Teesdale
Barnard Castle
Bowes
Reeth
Leyburn
Hawes
Threshfield
Yorkshire Dales
Whernside
Newton Stewart
Castle Douglas
Gatehouse of Fleet
Kirkcudbright
Dalbeattie
New Abbey
Auchencairn
Ringford
Wigtown
Whithorn
Isle of Whithorn
Port William
Glenluce
Stranraer
Cairnryan
Drummore
New Galloway
Forest Park
Luce Bay
Wigtown Bay
Solway Firth
Burrow Head
Mull of Galloway
St. Bees Head
Point of Ayre
Skiddaw
Scafell Pikes
Cross Fell
Snaefell
Derwent water
Ullswater
Buttermere
Frizington
Patterdale
Douglas
Ramsey
Peel
Ballaugh
Port Erin
Port St. Mary
Castletown
Ronaldsway
Belfast

East Midlands
West Midlands
Wales
WEST
LANCASHIRE
CHESHIRE
ANGLESEY
GWYNEDD
IRISH SEA
BLACKPOOL
LIVERPOOL
MANCHESTER
STOKE-ON-TRENT
BRADFORD
Fleetwood
Cleveleys
Lytham St. Anne's
Southport
Ainsdale
Formby
Bootle
Wallasey
Hoylake
Birkenhead
Bebington
Ellesmere Port
Liverpool Bay
Belfast
Dublin
Mostyn
Preston
Kirkham
Blackburn
Clitheroe
Gisburn
Ribble
Padiham
Colne
Nelson
Burnley
Keighley
Bingley
Skipton
Ilkley
Halifax
Todmorden
Brighouse
Accrington
Rawtenstall
Rochdale
Bury
Darwen
Leyland
Bolton
Ormskirk
Skelmersdale
Wigan
Leigh
Oldham
Huddersfield
Ashton-under-Lyne
Hyde
Stockport
Peak
St. Helens
Warrington
Widnes
Runcorn
Altrincham
Knutsford
Wilmslow
Whaley Bridge
Buxton
Bakewell
Macclesfield
Congleton
Northwich
Winsford
Middlewich
Sandbach
Frodsham
Tarporley
Crewe
Nantwich
Little Moreton Hall
Kidsgrove
Leek
Newcastle-under-Lyme
Audlem
Whitchurch
Wem
Hodnet
Uttoxeter
Chester
Wrexham
Wrecsam
Ruabon
Ellesmere
Oswestry
Llangollen
Corwen
Dee
Berwyn
Bala
Flint/Fflint
Queensferry
Mold/Yr Wyddgrug
Holywell
Prestatyn
Rhyl
St. Asaph
Denbigh/Dinbych
Abergele
Colwyn Bay/Bae Colwyn
Llandudno
Great Ormes Head
Conwy
Penmaenmawr
Llanfairfechan
Llanrwst
Betws-y-Coed
Cerrigydrudion
Bethesda
Carnedd Llewelyn
Capel Curig
Snowdonia
Snowdon
Llanberis
Beddgelert
Blaenau Ffestiniog
Ffestiniog
Penrhyndeudraeth
Porthmadog
Harlech
Criccieth
Pwllheli
Abersoch
Aberdaron
Nefyn
Lleyn Peninsula
Caernarfon
Caernarfon Bay
Bangor
Beaumaris
Menai Bridge
Newborough
Llangefni
Llanerchymedd
Amlwch
Rhosneigr
Holyhead/Caergybi
Holy Island
Isle of Anglesey
National Park

1 **The Wizard**

Macclesfield Rd,
Alderley Edge SK10 4UB
Tel.: (01625)584000 – Fax: (01625)585105
e-mail: wizardrestaurant@googlemail.com **Website:** www.wizardrestaurant.

Inspectors' favourites

VISA MC AE

Thwaites Original, Storm Ale Force

Set above the village of Alderley, in a picturesque beauty spot comprising of mature woodland, you'll find Roman mines, an ancient beacon and a natural sandstone escarpment named the 'Edge'. The area is steeped in history and even this pub is named after a local legend – which tells the story of a farmer, a white mare, a wizard and an army of sleeping warriors; thought to refer to Merlin and King Arthur's knights. Dating back over 200 years, The Wizard boasts immense charm and character, displaying wood and flag flooring, original beams, open fires, scrubbed wooden tables and antiques aplenty. In the kitchen, the chef conjures up generously proportioned dishes of seasonal produce, so you might find black pudding with sweet potato mash, or cod, ling and pollock strudel with bacon and leek fondue. Produce is locally sourced, so you're likely to find meats from Upholland, fish from Fleetwood, game from Goosnargh and veg from Cheshire.

Closing times
Open daily
Prices
Meals: £ 10 and à la carte £ 15/40

Typical Dishes
Seared scallops
Rack of lamb
Eton mess

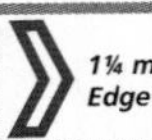

1¼ mi southeast of Alderley Edge on B 5087.

2 The Grosvenor Arms

Chester Rd, Aldford CH3 6HJ
Tel.: (01244)620228 – Fax: (01224)620247
e-mail: grosvenor-arms@brunningandprice.co.uk
Website: www.grosvenorarms-aldford.co.uk

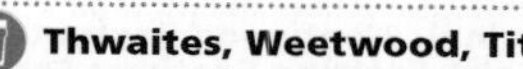

Thwaites, Weetwood, Titanic

Designed by local Victorian architect John Douglas, this 19C red brick property started life as the Talbot Inn and later became the Grosvenor Arms Hotel, before finding itself closed and in a state of disrepair. By a good turn of fortune, it fell into the right hands and now, once again, is a grand looking building. A hit with the locals, it has a convivial atmosphere and the friendly staff are welcoming to one and all. There's no shortage of choices when it comes to places to sit: the smart terrace, neatly-kept garden, plant-filled conservatory or one of several characterful rooms – which might feature attractive wood or tile flooring, half-panelled walls or unusually leaded windows. The daily changing menu also provides plenty of choice, with tasty, generous dishes ranging from pub favourites to more sophisticated options; this may include anything from chicken pie or shoulder of lamb through to crab pannacotta or aubergine moussaka.

Closing times
Closed 25 December

Prices
Meals: à la carte £ 17/30

Typical Dishes
Chicken liver parfait
Rump of lamb
Sticky toffee pudding

3½ mi south of Chester by B 5130; on the main village road. Parking.

3 **Dysart Arms**

Bowes Gate Rd, Bunbury CW6 9PH
Tel.: (01829)260183 – Fax: (01829)261050
e-mail: dysart.arms@brunningandprice.co.uk
Website: www.dysartarms-bunbury.co.uk

Thwaites Original, Weetwood Eastgate, Crouch Vale Brewers Gold, Spitting Feathers Farmhouse Ale

Sitting comfortably next to the parish church, this red brick pub is named after the local landowners of yesteryear – the Earls of Dysart – and their coat of arms hangs above the door. Originally a farm belonging to the Estate, this building took on a new role in the late 1800s, operating simultaneously as the local pub, farm and abattoir; later, the outbuildings were converted into kitchens, and a conservatory was added alongside the existing cosy oak-filled rooms. Today, open fires, heaving bookcases and mismatching furniture create a relaxed, informal feel, while French windows provide plenty of light – as well as access to the terrace and garden. Menus change daily and feature fresh, tasty British and Mediterranean dishes. These include light bites such as sandwiches and salads, as well as more substantial dishes such as lamp rump, swordfish or belly pork. Orders are sent to the kitchen via an old department store style tube.

Closing times
Open daily
Prices
Meals: à la carte £ 15/25

Typical Dishes
Grilled Bury black pudding
Braised shoulder of lamb
Vanilla & gingerbread cheesecake

3¼ mi south by A 49 then take Bunbury Mill Road. Parking.

4 The Combermere Arms

Burleydam SY13 4AT
Tel.: (01948)871223 – Fax: (01948)661371
e-mail: combermere.arms@brunningandprice.co.uk
Website: www.combermerearms-burleydam.co.uk

  MC AE

Weetwood Cheshire Cat, Thwaites Original, Wincle Sir Philip, Caledonian Over the Bar, Salopian Oracle, Wem Brewing Co Rainbow Chaser

Originally dating from the 16C, this country inn retains a sense of history with its flagged floors, snug corners and old wood beams. Its interior has now been opened up, with skylights creating a light, airy feel, and the typically 'Brunning and Price' furnishings bring a contemporary rusticity to the space, with open fires, rugs, pictures, bookshelves and candles, as well as some extra long tables; perfect for when you're in a large group. The informal menu provides plenty of choice, including an interesting selection of sandwiches at lunchtime. Dishes might include tempura squid with sweet chilli and lime dressing, braised lamb shoulder, fish pie or sausage and mash; with classic puddings like rhubarb crumble and chocolate fudge cake, and a wine list and cheese selection which also merit serious investigation. You can eat anywhere, including the beer garden, and the service is friendly and efficient.

Closing times
Open daily

Prices
Meals: à la carte £ 20/28

Typical Dishes
Cheese & spinach soufflé
Pan-fried venison rump
Sticky toffee pudding

4¼ mi east of Whitchurch on A 525. Parking.

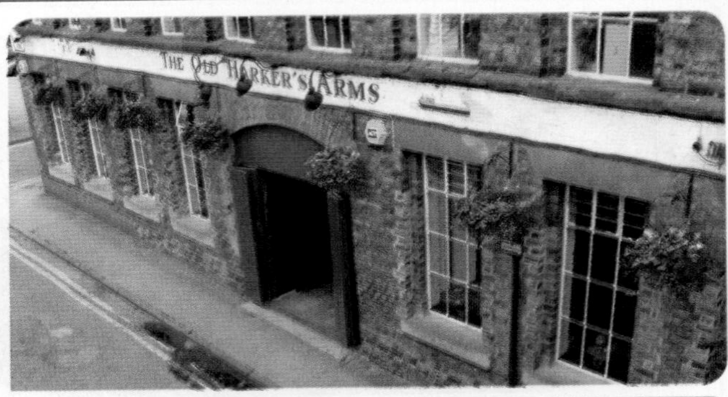

5 The Old Harkers Arms

1 Russell St,
Chester CH3 5AL
Tel.: (01244)344525 – Fax: (01244)344812
e-mail: harkers.arms@bandp.co.uk **Website:** www.bandp.co.uk/harkers

VISA MC AE

Weetwood Cheshire Cat, Thwaites Original, Flowers Original, Spitting Feathers, Crouch Vale, Hawkshead and changing guest ales

If you like water with your whisky this is definitely the pub for you. A few minutes walk from the station, this converted Victorian warehouse is situated in an idyllic canalside location and comes complete with a well stocked bar – housing no less than 100 different whiskies. Previously Mr. Harker's canal boat chandlery, the spacious interior boasts wooden floors, exposed brickwork, a ceiling lined with wine box ends and a large bar that spans two sides of the room, while an eclectic mix of pictures adorns the walls. This is a characterful, good old-fashioned drinking pub, but one that serves good food too. Cooking is rustic, unfussy and generous, and the daily-changing menu displays plenty of tasty pub favourites – which might include fish and chips, sausage and mash, rump steak or lamb chops. For snackers there's an interesting selection of light bites and for all, there's a good selection of wines and local ales.

Closing times
Open daily
Prices
Meals: à la carte £ 20/29

Typical Dishes
Stilton & walnut pâté
Haddock in beer better
Selection of 4 local cheeses

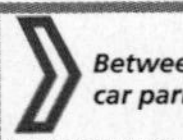

Between A 51 and the canal. NCP car park in Steam Mill St.

6 The Pheasant Inn

Higher Burwardsley CH3 9PF
Tel.: (01829)770434 – Fax: (01829)771097
e-mail: info@thepheasantinn.co.uk
Website: www.thepheasantinn.co.uk

  VISA MC AE

 **Weetwood - Best, Eastgate, Cheshire Cat and constantly changing guest ales**

Located right at the top of a large sandstone outcrop – an unusual sight in the middle of the flat Cheshire Plains – this pub, neighbour to Peckforton Castle, enjoys great views over the surrounding countryside. A lovely garden and terrace attracts walkers of the Sandstone trail, keen to be at one with nature, while inside, diners vie for seats next to the over-sized windows. The open plan interior features stone columns and reclaimed timber beams throughout, while squashy sofas in the bar provide a more relaxed feel than the formal dining room. The daily changing menu features local and, wherever possible, free range produce. You can choose between afternoon tea; cheese, fish or charcuterie deli boards; and some good old pub favourites, including maybe sausage and mash or fish pie – followed by crumble or bread and butter pudding. In the adjacent stone barn, bedrooms are compact, stylish and comfortable, and most afford good views.

Closing times
Open daily
Prices
Meals: à la carte £ 22/35
12 rooms: £ 65/140

2½ mi southeast of Tattenhall.
Parking.

Typical Dishes
King prawns pil-pil style
Rack of lamb
Meringue, red berries & cream

7 Duke of Portland

Penny's Lane,
Lach Dennis CW9 8SY
Tel.: (01606)46264
e-mail: info@dukeofportland.com **Website:** www.dukeofportland.com

VISA MC AE

Banks and changing guest ales

This spacious open-plan pub may look fairly ordinary with its high-ceilinged main room, long wooden bar and leather sofas; but anything that it lacks in character, it certainly makes up for in the kitchen. This is a place that sources its produce with conviction, gathering good quality, organic ingredients from the most local of farmers and artisan suppliers. Cooking relies on simplicity and natural flavours; and the result is a host of tasty, satisfying dishes. At lunch, plates are large and hearty, offering the likes of club stacks and fishcakes, while dinner raises the bar with a bi-weekly à la carte that might feature wild boar sausages or fillet of sea bream. They are rightly proud of their suppliers and acknowledge them on the menu; so you might find Allison Nichollson's pork ribs, Andy Holt's black pudding or Mike Heler's Cheshire cheese. For something a little lighter, there's the 'create your own' mix and match anti pasti.

Closing times
Open daily
Prices
Meals: £ 10 and à la carte £ 22/35

Typical Dishes
Black pudding & lentils
Pot roasted wild boar
Raspberry cheesecake

3½ mi west of Northwich by B 5082. Parking.

8 Chetwode Arms

Street Lane,
Lower Whitley WA4 4EN

Tel.: (01925)730203 – Fax: (01925)730203
e-mail: claudia.d@btinternet.com **Website:** www.chetwodearms.com

 **Adnams Broadside, Jennings Cumberland and one rotating guest ale**

Starting life over 400 years ago as a farmhouse, this building was converted into a roadside inn before taking up its position in the last century as a good old-fashioned pub. It's had its fair share of history, with rumours of a resident ghost and talk of a tunnel leading to the church but it's now better known for its large bowling green, pleasant terrace and great food. Having previously been run by the same family for 300 years, it's currently under the control of a local and his Austrian wife, who, along with the cosy rooms and narrow wood-panelled corridors, create a warm, welcoming feel. The wide-ranging à la carte features British and Austrian dishes, as well as a selection of medleys that are cooked on super heated rocks – these include many South African meats, such as ostrich, kudu, crocodile, springbok and even zebra. At lunch and before 7.30pm a good value set menu offers three courses for £10.

Closing times

Closed 26 December

Prices

Meals: £ 12 (Sunday lunch) and à la carte £ 25/65

Typical Dishes

Bury black pudding
Fresh fish of the day
Homemade fig & plum tart

 *6½ mi northwest of Northwich by A 533 off A 49. Parking.* 

9 The Church Green

Higher Lane,
Lymm WA13 0AP
Tel.: (01925)752068
e-mail: aidenbyrne@thechurchgreen.co.uk **Website:** www.thechurchgreen.co.uk

Deuchar's IPA, Old Speckled Hen

This gable-fronted Victorian pub was once a rowdy drinking haunt with gargantuan TVs and games machines; now keenly run by the previous head chef of The Grill Room in London's Dorchester hotel, it couldn't be more of a contrast, and appeals to the diner as much as the drinker. Its open-plan bar and restaurant are smart in browns and creams, with leather sofas and modern artwork; for a more formal feel, head towards the conservatory. The well-crafted, flavourful dishes on the main à la carte menu are more complex than one might expect in a pub: perhaps a foie gras terrine, or veal with lobster. Desserts are more traditional, if no less impressive, with choices like chocolate mousse, crumble and trifle, and some of the lunch dishes, like fish and chips or shepherd's pie, also have more of a pub flavour. The interesting wine list has some unusual recommendations by the glass and well-structured service comes from pleasant, uniformed staff.

Closing times
Closed 25 December and Sunday dinner
Booking essential

Prices
Meals: à la carte £ 25/39

Typical Dishes
Foie gras & black cherry terrine
Roast Goosnargh duck
Lime cheesecake

7 mi west of Altrincham by A 56. Parking.

10 Sutton Hall

Bullocks Lane, Macclesfield SK11 0HE

Tel.: (01260)253211 – Fax: (01260)252538

e-mail: sutton.hall@brunningand price.co.uk **Website:** www.suttonhall.co.uk

 **Wadworth 6X, Weetwood Cheshire Cat, Red Mist**

This huge out-of-towner was once part of the family estate of the Earls of Lucan; other previous incarnations include nunnery and hotel. Dating from 1530, the original black and white hall is the most characterful part of the building. The bar sits in the middle, and the warren of rooms which surround it contain space for 200 diners; the larger rooms can become noisy, so if you are here as a couple, head for one of the snugs instead. Wood floors, rugs and framed pictures covering every inch of wall space give the place an old school feel; keep an eye out for the upside down one. Daily changing menus offer classic pub meals like pies and ploughman's, alongside more interesting dishes such as potted salt fish and lemon sole. This is simple, traditional cooking, which uses plenty of local produce. Service is polite and well organised and the surrounding gardens and terraces make this a great pub to visit on a sunny day.

Closing times

Closed 25 December

Prices

Meals: à la carte £ 17/28

Typical Dishes

Potted salt fish

Rabbit pie

Sticky ginger pudding

2 mi southeast of Macclesfield by A 523 and Sutton Road. Parking.

11 The Frozen Mop

Faulkeners Lane,
Mobberley WA16 7AL
Tel.: (01565)873234
Website: www.thefrozenmop.co.uk

VISA MC AE D

Timothy Taylor Landlord, Marston Pedigree

You don't have to be a 'WAG' or 'lady who lunches' to feel right at home amongst the smart clientele of this intriguingly named pub; nobody knows quite where the name came from but it makes an interesting talking point. Set on a fairly busy country lane, this cream brick-built pub dates back to the late 19C, although you wouldn't guess it from the inside; in the usual stylish gastropub vein it's spacious and open-plan, with contemporary furnishings, low beamed ceilings, chunky pillars and wooden floors aplenty. One side of the long bar houses leather sofas and comfy tub seats, while at the other end high-backed chairs are arranged around chunky oak tables; despite this set-up you can eat anywhere, including the pleasant rear terrace in the warmer months. The narrow A3 menu is modern and wide-ranging, so it's easy to find something for everyone; there are sharing platters, salads, pastas, pizzas, grills and a variety of other dishes.

Closing times
Open daily

Prices
Meals: £ 9 (lunch)
and à la carte £ 18/23

Typical Dishes
Smoked mackerel pâté
Roast duck with cherries
Sticky toffee pudding

2 mi east by B 5085. Parking.

12 Drunken Duck Inn

Barngates,
Ambleside LA22 0NG
Tel.: (01539)436347 – Fax: (01539)436781
e-mail: info@drunkenduckinn.co.uk **Website:** www.drunkenduckinn.co.uk

Inspectors' favourites

VISA MC

Barngates Brewery : Westmorland Gold, 1077, K9, Chesters Strong & Ugly, Taglag, Cracker, Pride of Westmorland, Red Bull Terrier

Set in the heart of the Lake District, the Drunken Duck boasts stunning views out over the local tarn and surrounding fells. Owned by the same family since 1977, it's continued to grow and grow – and if it didn't have its own micro-brewery out the back, you could be mistaken for thinking that it's not a pub at all. With breathtaking scenery in every direction, there's no doubt that outside's the place to sit; but settling into the cosy bar with its beams and hop bines is just as attractive on a cold winter's day. Lunch features some comforting classics, while dinner in the restaurant steps things up a gear with formal linen-clad tables, and food and prices to match. In the afternoon head to the sitting room for a tasty cream tea, or try one of the in-house brews, named after various extinct animals. Split between the inn and courtyard, the smart, individually styled bedrooms have great outlooks; one boasts French windows and a balcony.

Closing times

Open daily

Booking essential

Prices

Meals: à la carte £ 25/45

17 rooms: £ 95/275

Typical Dishes

Ale-braised pork belly

Venison fillet

Iced honey parfait

3 mi southwest of Ambleside by A 593 and B 5286 on Tarn Hows road. By the crossroads at the top of Duck Hill. Parking.

13 The Wheatsheaf

Brigsteer LA8 8AN
Tel.: (015395)68254
e-mail: wheatsheaf@brigsteer.gb.com
Website: www.brigsteer.gb.com

  AE

Hawkshead Cumbrian Legendary Ales, Tirril, Dent

No longer hidden deep underneath Artex and thick carpets, The Wheatsheaf's inner beauty has once again been allowed to shine through. Total refurbishment means that the 18C pub is now light and airy, with tiled and wooden floors, and contemporary furnishings in each of its three rooms. The menu is proudly seasonal, Cumbrian and traceable, so you know that your smoked salmon came from Cartmel Valley and the shrimps were netted in Morecombe Bay, while wild garlic, flat mushrooms and damsons are sourced from even closer to home; the bank just outside the inn. Dishes on the à la carte might include carved loin of organic roe deer, roast crown of wild mallard, rabbit and leek stew or grilled whole local trout – all fairly priced and prepared with the greatest of care by a young, ambitious and disciplined team. Word is spreading fast, so it's a good idea to book. Three classically styled bedrooms come with pine furniture.

Closing times
Open daily

Prices
Meals: £ 15 (lunch)
and à la carte £ 20/24

3 rooms: £ 75/85

Typical Dishes
Pan-roast pigeon breast
Slow braised venison shank
Rhubarb & custard crème brûlée

3¾ mi southwest of Kendal by All Hallows Lane. Parking.

14 George and Dragon

Clifton CA10 2ER
Tel.: (01768)865381
e-mail: enquiries@georgeanddragonclifton.co.uk
Website: www.georgeanddragonclifton.co.uk

   AE

 **Lancaster Blonde, Hawkshead Bitter**

Not every pub can claim to source most of its produce from the Estate in which it sits; but then, not every pub has 12 Scottish rebels buried in the garden, either. Enter The George and Dragon and you'll soon realise you've come somewhere a bit special. It belongs to Countess Lowther, chief Cumbrian landowner, and the food is as fresh as it gets, with organic meats including lamb and Shorthorn beef from the Estate's farms, seasonal game specials from the surrounding woods and moors, and vegetables from the kitchen gardens. Dishes might include fish pie, chicken livers on toast or grilled local black pudding, and cooking is simple and effective. Although fully refurbished, the 18C coaching inn has lost none of its traditional character, helped along nicely by flagstones, fires, hop bines, rugs and sofas; plus photos which tell tales of the Lowther Estate from days long past. Comfortable, modern bedrooms are decorated in bold colours.

Closing times
Open daily

Prices
Meals: à la carte £ 21/35
10 rooms: £ 64/125

Typical Dishes
Cheese soufflé
Nord Vue sausage & mash
Chocolate fondant

3 mi southeast of Penrith by A 6. Parking.

15 The Punch Bowl Inn

Crosthwaite LA8 8HR

Tel.: (01539)568237 – Fax: (01539)568875

e-mail: info@the-punchbowl.co.uk

Website: www.the-punchbowl.co.uk

 **Westmorland Gold, Tag Lag, Bluebird, Hawkshead, Gala**

Surrounded by delightfully unspoilt countryside, The Punch Bowl Inn boasts a stylish, richly furnished bar and restaurant, with an appealingly informal feel. Both offer the same menu, with tasty, classically created dishes such as chicken liver parfait, Cumbrian cheddar cheese soufflé or roast loin and braised shoulder of lamb making good use of local, seasonal ingredients; and lighter dishes also offered at lunchtimes. Luxurious bedrooms are another highlight; individually styled, with designer décor and excellent attention to detail. Shown to your room, you are greeted by the melodious strains of Classic FM emitting from a Roberts radio. There are flat screen TVs, homemade biscuits on which to nibble, underfloor heated limestone bathrooms and extra large bath towels. Noble, with its twin roll top baths, covers the whole of the third floor and Danson boasts particularly glorious valley views. Breakfast is not to be missed.

Closing times

Open daily

Prices

Meals: à la carte £ 20/35

9 rooms: £ 94/310

Typical Dishes

Cheddar cheese soufflé

Confit belly pork

Apple tarte Tatin

5¼ mi west of Kendal by All Hallows Lane; next to the church. Parking.

16 Tweedies

Red Bank Rd,
Grasmere LA22 9SW
Tel.: (01539)435300 – Fax: (01539)435570
e-mail: enquiries@dalelodgehotel.co.uk **Website:** www.dalelodgehotel.co.uk

 **Deuchar's IPA, Theakston's Old Peculiar, Yates beers and 3 local guest beers**

After a day spent fell walking, you will be in need a hearty meal, and it doesn't get much heartier than this: so filling is the food, in fact, that a main course might well suffice; choose from classics such as steak and ale pie or fish and chips, or go for something more unusual like a half pound Hawkshead pheasant burger with sweet potato and parsnip chips. Tweedies is situated right in the heart of the Lakes in the historic village of Grasmere; famous for its Wordsworth connection (he lived and is buried here), and now home to the popular Grasmere Gingerbread Shop. Its charming bar is one for the locals; open-fired and flag-floored, with a huge array of regularly changing beers, and its name comes from the previous owner, a Mr Tweedie, who used to sell 34 different tweeds, which he would hang from the ceiling. Arrive early in summer as seats are in high demand; tables in the huge garden afford a great view of the lakes.

Closing times
Closed 25 December dinner

Prices
Meals: à la carte £ 22/34

Typical Dishes
Ham hock terrine
Crispy pork belly
Bread & butter pudding

3 mi north of Ambleside by A 591.
Parking.

Kirkby Lonsdale

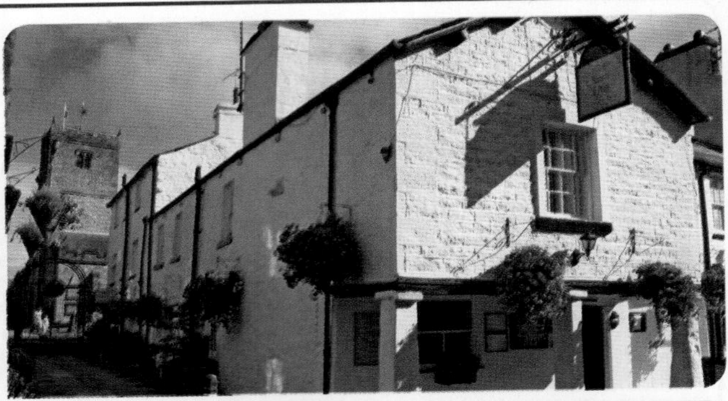

17 Sun Inn

6 Market Street,
Kirkby Lonsdale LA6 2AU
Tel.: (015242)71965 – Fax: (015242)72485
e-mail: email@sun-inn.info **Website:** www.sun-inn.info

VISA 

Timothy Taylor Landlord, Hawkshead Best Bitter

These days, every other pub in Britain claims to source its ingredients locally. The 17C Sun Inn is one such pub, but when it says locally, it really does mean locally: meat regularly comes from the butchers' down the road; cheese comes from the famous Churchmouse cheese shop next door and if lamb is on the menu, you can be pretty certain it recently frolicked in a nearby field. A tempting choice of bar nibbles keeps you busy whilst you peruse the seasonal, frequently changing menu and appealingly presented dishes come in generous portions. Everything you would look for in a pub is here; from the busy locals bar with its scrubbed wooden floors, comfy seats and open fire to the rustically refurbished restaurant; from the splendid selection of real ales and the cleverly formulated wine list to the hands-on owners and their competent staff. Immaculately kept bedrooms have a modern feel, with great lighting and good quality linen.

Closing times

Closed Monday lunch

Prices

Meals: à la carte £ 22/27

11 rooms: £ 65/160

Typical Dishes

Pan-fried chicken livers

Scallops & black pudding

Brioche & butter pudding

5½ mi southwest of Junction 36 on M 6. Long stay car park in Booth Rd.

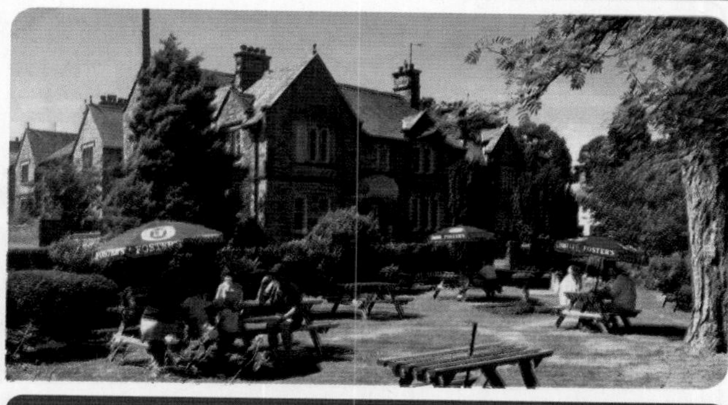

18 The Black Swan

Ravenstonedale,
Kirkby Stephen CA17 4NG
Tel.: (01539)623204 – Fax: (01539)623204
e-mail: enquiries@blackswanhotel.com **Website:** www.blackswanhotel.com

Black Sheep Bitter, Black Sheep Ale, John Smith's Cask and 2 changing guest ales

Family-owned and run, this solid Victorian Inn is so central to village life that, in 2008, they even opened the village store in it. Prince Charles did the honours and the great and the good of Ravenstonedale were there; stocked with local produce and crafts, it's now helping to keep the Black Swan where it belongs – at the heart of the community. Local produce also takes pride of place on the menu, where dishes might include black pudding, fried local trout with almonds, pie of the day or local gammon; this is hearty, traditional cooking with lots of comfort appeal. Pop in for a pint or a coffee and a slice of homemade cake; the snug bar comes complete with dartboard and an impressive selection of real ales. For a more formal meal, try the rear dining room or, on a sunny day, sit by the babbling Scandal Beck in the delightful garden. Following the style of the pub itself, bedrooms are cosy, with some antique furnishings.

Closing times

Open daily

Prices

Meals: à la carte £ 15/25

11 rooms: £ 47/110

Typical Dishes

Black pudding, pepper sauce

Smoked haddock

Lemon & ginger syllabub

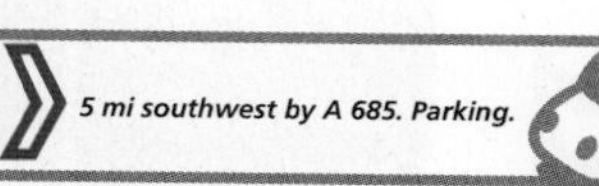

5 mi southwest by A 685. Parking.

19 The Highwayman

Nether Burrow LA6 2RJ
Tel.: (01524)2733338
e-mail: enquiries@highwaymaninn.co.uk
Website: www.highwaymaninn.co.uk

 VISA 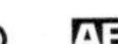 AE

Thwaites Original, Lancaster Bomber, Wainwright

(With apologies to Alfred Noyes) The meat's from the Forest of Bowland among the gusty trees, / The fish it comes from Fleetwood, tossed upon cloudy seas, / The asparagus comes from Formby, over the purple moor, / The suppliers are on the menu – menu – menu, / and the customers they come riding, up to the old inn door. Having undergone a million pound refurbishment, and with owners passionate about local, traceable food, The Highwayman is certainly delivering the goods – from all over Lancashire, Cumbria and Yorkshire – and so serious are they here about sourcing their ingredients locally, they even have framed pictures of their suppliers decorating the walls. Friendly and efficient service from the smartly attired staff oils the wheels of the dining experience, and the spacious inn with its numerous open fires, banquette seating and pleasant stone terrace makes an agreeable environment in which to enjoy the flavoursome food.

Closing times
Closed 25 December

Prices
Meals: à la carte £ 16/33

Typical Dishes
Belly pork & black pudding
Lancashire hot pot
Bread & butter pudding

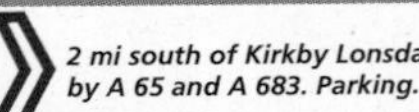

2 mi south of Kirkby Lonsdale by A 65 and A 683. Parking.

20 The Strickland Arms

Sizergh LA8 8DZ
Tel.: (01539)561010 – Fax: (01539)561068
e-mail: thestricklandarms@yahoo.co.uk
Website: www.ainscoughs.co.uk

Tirril, Coniston, Cumbria Lengendary Ales, Hawkshead, Hesket Newmarket, Thwaites Ales, Dent Ales, Derwent

Like next door Sizergh Castle, this imposing grey building is owned by the National Trust and, having been cleverly restored to its former glory, attracts locals and tourists, walkers, dogs and children in large numbers. Huge portions of hearty homecooked dishes like game casserole and lamb hotpot obviously have the hiker in mind and ensure that no one leaves this historic hostelry hungry; there's a good selection of real ales and wines by the glass and the extremely friendly Antipodean service is a bonus. Simply and stylishly decorated with period furniture, the stone and wood floors and candlelit, dark wood dining tables give it a rustic feel. There is plenty of space over two floors but if the kids still need somewhere to burn off any extra energy, there is also a large garden with pretty apple trees along one side of the pub. Popular events here include fish nights, jazz sessions, quiz nights and a real ale lovers festival.

Closing times
Open daily

Prices
Meals: à la carte £ 22/30

Typical Dishes
Bubble & squeak
Game casserole
Cumbrian rum Nicky tart

3 mi southwest of Kendal by A 391. Parking.

21 The Queen's Head

Troutbeck LA23 1PW
Tel.: (01539)432174 – Fax: (01539)431938
e-mail: feast@queensheadhotel.com
Website: www.queensheadhotel.com

 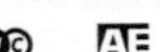 

Cumbrian Way, Hartleys XB, Old Tom, Double Hop, Dizzy Blonde and guest beers

If it's inspiring Lakeland scenery you're after, then a visit to this black and white inn, tucked away in Troutbeck Valley, is a must. Its atmospheric bar features deep flag floors and carved Elizabethan detail, while the beams crammed with coins hark back to a time when people would wedge their change in the wood, ready to pay for the drinks on a future visit. These days, it's as much about the food here as the beer; traditional, wholesome cooking, on offer all day, is served in big white bowls; the wide-ranging menu including dishes such as homemade black pudding, braised brisket of locally sourced beef or roast chump of Lakeland lamb, as well as a delicious assortment of homemade bread. Grab a seat by the window in the bar or take a pew in either of the two equally informal restaurant areas. Bedrooms are bright and modern, yet retain their coaching inn character. Rooms 10 and 11 have great fell views, and breakfast is quite a feast.

Closing times
Open daily

Prices
Meals: £ 20 and à la carte £ 25/38

15 rooms: £ 110/140

Typical Dishes
Steamed mussels
Bobotie
Baked chocolate cheesecake

4 mi north of Windermere by A 592. Parking.

22 The Bay Horse

Canal Foot, Ulverston LA12 9EL

Tel.: (01229)583972 – Fax: (01229)580502

e-mail: reservations@thebayhorsehotel.co.uk

Website: www.thebayhorsehotel.co.uk

VISA  

Lakeland Stunner, Jennings Cocker Hoop

If you've forgotten your sat nav, don't worry, just look for the GlaxoSmithKline factory and follow the perimeter fence until you're greeted by beautiful views of the sands of Morecambe Bay that stretch out to the hills of Arnside. Formerly a staging post for 18C coaches crossing the sands, this pub may not look much from the outside; inside however, it boasts a traditional beamed bar with cosy red walls and a conservatory restaurant with lovely views across the bay. There's a whole host of menus on offer – which can get confusing – but it does ensure there's plenty of choice. Cooking is a pleasant mix of classical favourites and more restaurant-style dishes; which makes sense when you learn that this pub's part-owned by John Tovey, formerly of Miller Howe; you might find fishcakes alongside South African babotie or hazelnut and mushroom pancakes. Traditional bedrooms boast extra touches and those at the front offer balcony views.

Closing times

Closed Monday lunch

Booking essential

Prices

Meals: £ 29 (dinner) and à la carte £ 20/30

9 rooms: £ 80/120

Typical Dishes

Oak-smoked salmon

Braised Lakeland lamb shank

Malva pudding

2¼ mi east of Ulverston by A 5087, turning left at Morecambe Tavern B&B and beyond industrial area, on the coast. Parking.

23 Brown Horse Inn

Winster LA23 3NR
Tel.: (01539)443443
e-mail: steve@thebrownhorseinn.co.uk
Website: www.thebrownhorseinn.co.uk

Lancaster Amber, Coniston Bluebird, Black Sheep, Timothy Taylor's, Moorhouse's

Nestled in the countryside of the Winster valley, not too far from Lake Windermere, sits this traditional 1850s coaching inn. Previously an Italian restaurant, the new owners said arrivederci to pizza and welcomed back the locals with the lure of log fires and a dartboard, plus seasonal, flavoursome food made with locally sourced ingredients. Brown horse paintings and dried hops decorate the green walls, and diners sit at candlelit tables. The lunch menu offers soup, sandwiches, salads and jacket potatoes, plus favourites such as sausage and mash and fish and chips. Blackboard specials add to the choice, with local lamb always a feature. The dinner menu offers robust, tasty food, classically prepared with prime produce, with dishes such as steak and chunky chips or deep fried squid salad – but book ahead at weekends, as this place is making a name for itself. Bedrooms are light and modern, simply decorated yet comfortable.

Closing times
Open daily

Prices
Meals: à la carte £ 20/30
9 rooms: £ 35/90

Typical Dishes
Black pudding salad
Gammon steak, fried duck egg
Lemon meringue tart

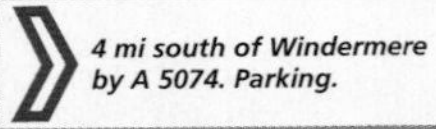

4 mi south of Windermere by A 5074. Parking.

24 The Yanwath Gate Inn

Yanwath CA10 2LF
Tel.: (01768)862386
e-mail: enquiries@yanwathgate.com
Website: www.yanwathgate.com

VISA   

Hesket Newmarket Doris' 90th Birthday Ale, Tirril Academy, Keswick Brewing Co Thirst Run

The sign above the door reads: 'This gate hangs well and hinders none, refresh and pay and travel on'; a reference to the pub's original function as a toll gate. Nowadays the Yat, as it is affectionately known, functions somewhat as a destination pub for special occasions; its carefully balanced cooking displaying finesse without being too showy. Dishes on offer might include anything from shrimps or fish and chips at lunchtime to black pudding and haggis, lemon sole or glazed pork belly in the evening. The careful sourcing of local produce is of paramount importance here and the list of suppliers on the menu is extensive. The real ale on tap is also proudly Cumbrian and everything, including bread and desserts, is made on the premises. Church candles cast their flickering light in the cosy bar – a seat by the fire is particularly atmospheric – while through the back you will find the oak panelled restaurant.

Closing times

Closed 25 December

Prices

Meals: £ 14 (weekday lunch) and à la carte £ 20/40

Typical Dishes

King scallops
Seared pork belly
Rich chocolate marquise

2 mi southwest of Penrith by A 6 on B 5320. Parking.

25 The Victoria

29 Stamford Street,
Altrincham WA14 1EX
Tel.: (0161)6131855
e-mail: the.victoria@yahoo.co.uk

 **Old Speckled Hen, Flowers IPA, Jennings Cumberland**

Despite it being located in the town centre, it's all too easy to pass by this traditional looking pub. Set on a quiet side road behind the shopping arcade, it offers a much simpler environment than the surrounding restaurants: a cream coloured bar takes centre stage and wooden tables are scattered around on a mix of carpet and tile flooring. In keeping with the atmosphere, cooking is straightforward, with dishes of fresh, locally sourced produce arriving in generous, tasty portions. The bar menu with its sandwiches and light bites is popular with the local office staff and you might find a sharing ploughman's, a fritter platter or battered butties on the list. If you're after something more substantial yet equally as interesting, the à la carte offers some original dishes; you might find asparagus scones, ploughman's tart or locally raised pink veal. There's also a good value early evening set menu. Service is friendly and efficient.

Closing times
Closed 26 December, 1 January and Sunday dinner

Prices
Meals: £ 16 (dinner) and à la carte £ 22/31

Typical Dishes
Pigeon pasty
Pot roast pheasant
Baked apple & honey roly poly

 *Pay & display parking outside; free at night.* 

26 The White Hart Inn

51 Stockport Rd,
Lydgate, Oldham OL4 4JJ
Tel.: (01457)872566 – Fax: (01457)875190
e-mail: bookings@thewhitehart.co.uk **Website:** www.thewhitehart.co.uk

Tetley's, Timothy Taylor Landlord and Best Bitter, J W Lees, Brakspear

Rurally set, overlooking Saddleworth Moor, The White Hart Inn presents you with several choices. Firstly, where to eat: will you dine near the open log fire in the cosy, beamed brasserie or more formally, in the modern, linen-clad restaurant? The library is the choice for more private dining, while the smart Oak Room is also available for functions. Once you are settled, more choice comes in the form of the seasonally changing menus. Dishes range from soups, sandwiches and smoked sardines through to roast rabbit leg or rib eyed steak. The sumptuous selection of homemade Saddleworth sausages and differently flavoured mashed potatoes are particularly popular, while a fish menu is also available on Tuesdays. Staying the night? Twelve comfortable bedrooms, named after local dignitaries, are housed in the original building, built in 1788.

Closing times
Closed 26-27 December
Dinner only
Booking essential

Prices
Meals: à la carte £ 15/32
12 rooms: £ 95/128

Typical Dishes
Confit pork terrine
Rib-eye of Lakeland beef
Sticky toffee pudding

3 mi east of Oldham by A 669 on A 6050. Parking.

27 The Red Pump Inn

Clitheroe Road,
Bashall Eaves BB7 3DA
Tel.: (01254)826227
e-mail: info@theredpumpinn.co.uk **Website:** www.theredpumpinn.co.uk

 **Moorhouse's, Grindleton, Black Sheep**

Reputedly one of the oldest inns in the Ribble Valley, this former farm is situated on a quiet country lane, with great views of the surrounding hillside. After a notorious murder in the 1930s, on which no one could – or would – shed any light, the hamlet was dubbed 'The Silent Village', and, like its name, the area remains peaceful for most of the year. In the game season, however, the local fells ring with the sound of gunshots, and pheasant, venison, mallard, grouse, partridge and rabbit can often be found on the daily specials. The traditional menu is hearty and generous, featuring regional cheeses, fish, preserves and chutneys, as well as herbs from the pub garden. This friendly pub also hosts special seasonal events such as Lamb and Game 'Fests', and homemade breads, cakes and pâtés are available for sale in the deli during summer. Bedrooms are spacious and modern with attractive handmade furniture, oversized beds and great views.

Closing times

Closed Monday (except bank holidays), some Tuesdays in winter

Prices

Meals: £ 15 and à la carte £ 18

3 rooms: £ 55/115

Typical Dishes

Venison ravioli
Belly pork
Blackcurrant sponge

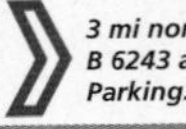

3 mi northwest of Clitheroe by B 6243 and minor road northwest. Parking.

28 Eagle & Child

Bispham Green L40 3SG
Tel.: (01257)462297 – Fax: (01257)464718
Website: www.ainscoughs.co.uk

 VISA MC

 **Slater's Top Totty, Timothy Taylor Landlord, Bowland Hen Harrier, Southport Golden Sands, Thwaites Original, Moorhouse's Black Cat Mild**

If you fancy a trip back to the good old days then this 200 year old pub is the place to come, with its wooden beams, flag floors, busy walls and seasoned group of locals propping up the bar, dogs dozing at their feet. For the best spot pass by them into the snug, where a blazing fire means it's always warm and cosy. Cooking is hearty and tasty, with the bar menu continuing the traditional theme by offering simple British classics, such as sausage and mash, cod and chips or steak and ale pie. For those who fancy something a little more adventurous, head for the daily-changing specials where you'll find maybe braised oxtail, roast suckling pig, pan-fried black bream or trio of pheasant, wigeon and partridge. It's not just the food that matters here and with as many as 12 real ales available at any one time you're spoilt for choice – even without the renowned beer festival that's held here every first May bank holiday.

Closing times
Closed 1 January dinner

Prices
Meals: à la carte £ 17/23

Typical Dishes
Deep-fried cod goujons
Steak & real ale pie
Sticky toffee pudding

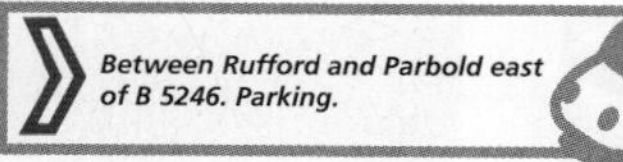
Between Rufford and Parbold east of B 5246. Parking.

29 The Clog & Billycock

Billinge End Rd,
Blackburn BB2 6QB
Tel.: (01254)201163
e-mail: enquiries@theclogandbillycock.com **Website:** www.theclogandbillycock.com

 **Thwaites Original, Wainwrights, Lancaster Bomber**

When a pub lists its suppliers on its menu, pinpoints their position on a map and has pictures of them (under the title of 'our local heroes') decorating the walls, you know that it takes its sourcing very seriously, and considering the wealth of farmland and the number of artisan producers in the region, it's only right that the Clog and Billycock should seek to mine this rich seam. Shrimps come from Morecambe Bay, there's Ribble Valley beef, Port of Lancaster smoked salmon and plenty of luscious Lancashire cheeses. The menu provides a cornucopia of tasty dishes from which to choose, the portions are generous and the prices realistic; the resulting clamour for tables and the fact that you can't book ahead means you should aim to arrive early. The pub is spacious and open-plan, with flag floors and a modern style. Its unusual name apparently comes from the attire of a former landlord; or more specifically his shoes and his hat.

Closing times
Closed 25 December

Prices
Meals: à la carte £ 24

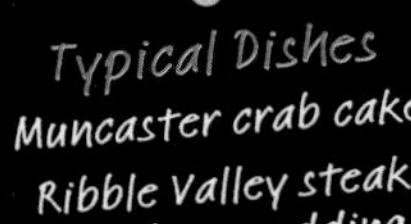

Typical Dishes
Muncaster crab cake
Ribble Valley steak & kidney pudding
Jam roly poly & custard

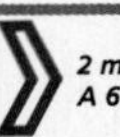
2 mi west of Blackburn, signed off A 677. Parking.

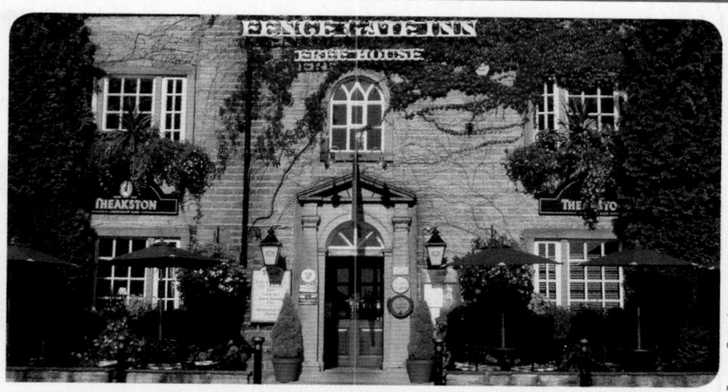

Fence Gate Inn

30 Fence Gate Inn

Wheatley Lane Rd,
Fence BB12 9EE

Tel.: (01282)618101 – Fax: (01282)615432
e-mail: info@fencegate.co.uk **Website:** www.fencegate.co.uk

Theakstons, Deuchars, Courage Directors, Bowland, Moorhouse's, Copper Dragon, Grindleton Brewhouse, Black Sheep

Set just off a busy main road, this spacious 17C pub was formerly a squire's house, a cotton merchants and a small restaurant, before finally finding its calling as an inn. As you enter you have to make a decision: right into the stylish Topiary Brasserie with its linen laid tables, plush black leather booths and modern art, or left into the pleasant oak panelled lounge bar, with its high tables, open log fire and pubby atmosphere. Using only the best regional produce, seasonally changing menus display local, national and international influences. The Brasserie offers restaurant-style dishes such as braised Bowland lamb shank or Thai cod and crab fishcakes, while the bar menu presents more pub-like fare, including open sandwiches, gourmet pies and some particularly tasty varieties of homemade sausage; maybe tomato and chilli or apple, honey and thyme. A daily specials list and a tempting selection of homemade desserts run alongside.

Closing times
Open daily

Prices
Meals: à la carte £ 21/35

Typical Dishes
Pan-seared king scallops
Fish & chips
Chocolate fondant pudding

2 mi southwest of Junction 13 on M 65 by A 6068. Parking.

31 The Bay Horse Inn

Bay Horse Lane,
Forton LA2 0HR
Tel.: (01524)791204
e-mail: yvonne@bayhorseinn.com **Website:** www.bayhorseinn.com

 **Black Sheep, Pendle Witch, Lancaster Bomber**

Flanked by the A6 and M6, and just a stone's throw away from the main Euston to Glasgow railway line, it's hard to believe how peaceful it is here. Burgundy walls, low beamed ceilings, a stone fireplace and characterful corner bar provide a cosy, welcoming atmosphere, while memorabilia and monochrome photos of local scenes adorn every wall. To the rear the dining room overlooks an attractive summer terrace to a pleasant wooded garden beyond. The young owner is passionate about sourcing the freshest seasonal produce and you will always find local offerings such as Andrew Ireland's black pudding, Port of Lancaster smoked salmon and Cumbrian lamb on the menu, with dishes ranging from good old pub classics right through to more modern, sophisticated fare. Nearby 'The Old Corn Store' houses three individually designed, beautifully appointed bedrooms – 'Oat', 'Barley' and 'Corn' – the latter, a suite with separate seating and kitchen areas.

Closing times

Closed 25-26 December, 1 January, Sunday dinner and Monday

Prices

Meals: £ 21 (lunch) and à la carte £ 18/28

3 rooms: £ 89

Typical Dishes

Scallops & parsnip purée

Braised rabbit & prunes

Bread & butter pudding

1¼ mi north by A 6 on Quernmore Road. Parking.

32 Duke of York Inn

Brow Top,
Grindleton BB7 4QR

Tel.: (01200)441266 – Fax: (01200)441250
e-mail: duke-ofyork@btconnect.com **Website:** www.dukeofyorkgrindleton.com

 **Thwaites Original, Black Sheep Bitter**

Set on the main road of a hamlet in the heart of the Trough of Bowland, this ivy-clad pub boasts a large decked terrace and pleasant views across to Pendle Hill. Inside, a sympathetic modernisation has created a fresh yet characterful atmosphere, with wooden boards and flag flooring leading up to an original bar. If you're eating, the best place to be is the light, airy dining room with its coir flooring, walls adorned with old framed restaurant menus and smart matching tables and chairs. Here you'll find a great value lunch/early evening menu and an à la carte offering plenty of choice – including a list of tempting daily market specials. Menus change seasonally and often feature local meats, although they aren't strictly rooted in local tradition or reliant on regional produce. Carefully prepared, tasty dishes made up of well sourced local ingredients range from fish soup to tempura prawns, steak and ale pie to steak of veal.

Closing times

Closed 25 December and Monday (except bank holidays when closed Tuesday)

Prices

Meals: £ 13 (before 7pm) and à la carte £ 20/28

Typical Dishes

Home-smoked salmon salad

Chargrilled rib-eye veal

Duke of York Eccles cake

3 mi northwest of Clitheroe signed off A 671. Parking.

33 The Borough

3 Dalton Sq,
Lancaster LA1 1PP
Tel.: (01524)64170
e-mail: info@theboroughlancaster.co.uk **Website:** www.theboroughlancaster.co.uk

VISA 

Thwaites Original, Wainwrights, Hawkshead, Bowland Hen Harrier, Lancaster Amber and 2 guest ales such as Dent, Black Sheep,Grindleton, Bank Top

This Victorian-fronted Georgian building has been jack of all trades, housing the Mayor and then a Working Men's Club, before finally finding its calling as a modern dining pub. Built in 1824, it retains many original features, including leaded windows and Victorian floor tiles. Leather armchairs and sofas occupy the bar area, whilst to the rear the spacious dining room features bench seats and booths, leading out onto a pleasant terrace. Cooking is straightforward, tasty and Northern through and through, featuring regional produce and dishes such as hotpot, black pudding or Fleetwood fish, the latter being served in the 'Borough News'. For something a bit different try an Ostrich burger, or the pay-per-item Deli Boards, where you can choose from a selection of fish, meat, cheese or salad to create either a light snack, main course or sharing platter. Portions are generous and the food is good, so make sure you book for weekends.

Closing times
Closed 25 December and 1 January

Prices
Meals: à la carte £ 17/29

Typical Dishes
Lancashire black pudding
Lancashire hot pot
Sticky toffee pudding

In Dalton Square adjacent to the Town Hall on the one-way system. Parking in Dalton Square.

34 The Cartford Inn

Cartford Lane,
Little Eccleston PR3 0YP
Tel.: (01995)670166
e-mail: info@thecartfordinn.co.uk **Website:** www.thecartfordinn.co.uk

VISA MC AE

Moorhouses Pride of Pendle and regularly changing guest ales such as Hart Brewery, Moorhouses Pendle Witches, Hawkshead Lakeland Gold, Theakston Old Peculiar

Set beside a toll bridge next to the River Wyre, this 17C coaching inn is becoming a popular place. Each July the village plays host to one of the county's most comprehensive agricultural shows; so if you're visiting at this time, be sure to get to the pub early. The best place to sit is outside, where you can take in panoramic views across the river and the Trough of Bowland; take a wander round and you'll find the small but very active Brewery that serves the pub. Inside, there's a spacious open-fired bar, four modern dining areas and a more formal restaurant featuring a fine collection of fungi paraphernalia. The extensive menu provides appealing, flavoursome and skilfully prepared dishes. You might find fish from Fleetwood, ham from Cumbria, cheese from Lancashire and bread from the next village, finished off with the likes of sticky toffee pudding and crème brûlée of the day. Contemporary bedrooms boast stylish feature walls.

Closing times

Closed 25 December and Monday lunch

Prices

Meals: à la carte £ 18/30

7 rooms: £ 65/90

Typical Dishes

Smoked haddock tartlet

Oxtail suet pudding

Chocolate fondant

7 mi west of Blackpool by A 585 and A 586. Parking.

35 The Three Fishes

Mitton Road,
Mitton BB7 9PQ
Tel.: (01254)826888 – Fax: (01254)826026
e-mail: enquiries@thethreefishes.com **Website:** www.thethreefishes.com

Inspectors' favourites

VISA MC AE

Thwaites Original, Lancaster Bomber, Wainwrights

In contrast to the 16C bridge and old ferry crossing that it sits between, this spacious 17C pub is surprisingly modern. Set beside a river in a small hamlet it's thought to be named after the last Abbott of Whalley, whose coat of arms displays three fishes – a depiction of the three local rivers. The food here is as regional as the history: and that might be an understatement. Photos of local food heroes and maps of suppliers' locations are the first clues as to the pride taken in sourcing ingredients; the next is the provenance of the produce being listed for every dish – you can often find Sharp's veal, Leagram's curd or Grasmere gingerbread. For something different, the Elm Wood Platters offer a good range of home cured meats and local seafood, while the 'Length of Lancashire' cheeseboard features cheeses from 10 different farms. For dessert try the locally made ice cream; maybe strawberry marmalade or milk and white chocolate chip.

Closing times
Closed 25 December

Prices
Meals: à la carte £ 18/31

Typical Dishes
Morecambe Bay shrimps
Toad in the hole
Burnt English custard

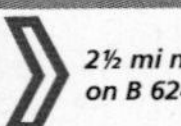

2½ mi northwest of Whalley on B 6246. Parking.

36 The Lunesdale Arms

Tunstall LA6 2QN
Tel.: (01524)274203 – Fax: (01524)274229
e-mail: info@thelunesdale.co.uk
Website: www.thelunesdale.co.uk

 **Black Sheep and weekly changing beers such as Ruskins Ale, Brysons Life Saver**

This mellow stone pub with its weather-worn sign may not look all that much from the outside, but its owner – herself a villager and a key member of the enthusiastic, friendly team here – once went to great lengths to save it from the developers' clutches. Several years on and this tenaciousness has more than paid off, with people coming from all over to enjoy the pub's relaxed atmosphere and tasty, honest cooking. The spacious interior, brightened by local art and the bar manager's photographs, boasts comfy sofas and a log burner, a separate room for private dining and a games room with pool and table football. Cooking is traditional, unpretentious and frill-free; the blackboard menu offering staples such as sausage and mash, Guinness and mushroom pie or sirloin steak, as well as a range of other choices depending on what the best local suppliers have available. Make sure to save room for one of the delicious homemade puddings.

Closing times
Closed 25-26 December and Monday (except bank holidays)

Prices
Meals: £ 14 (Tuesday-Thursday) and à la carte £ 17/26

Typical Dishes
Baked goat's cheese
Slow-roast shoulder of lamb
Blackcurrant & Cassis crème brûlée

4 mi south of Kirkby Lonsdale on A 683. Parking.

37 The Inn at Whitewell

Forest of Bowland,
Whitewell BB7 3AT
Tel.: (01200)448222 – Fax: (01200)448298
e-mail: reception@innatwhitewell.com **Website:** www.innatwhitewell.com

VISA 

Moorhouse's Blonde Witch, Skipton Brewery Copper Dragon, Bowland Brewery Sawley Tempted, Timothy Taylor Landlord

Perched high above the River Hodder, in the heart of the Trough of Bowland, this attractive creeper-clad inn started life as a 14C manor house occupied by the keepers of the Royal forest. Today, almost every room boasts a fine panoramic view up the valley; the bar with its antique tables and benches being a firm favourite and the upstairs restaurant adding a touch more formality to the scene. The menus are largely classical, so you'll find the likes of Goosnargh chicken, loin of local venison or fillet of beef for two in the restaurant, and grilled kippers or fish pie in the bar; although the odd international influence does creep in, so you might find crispy samosas or baby squid filled with chorizo on the list too. Split between the inn and coach house, the spacious bedrooms offer a choice of traditional or modern styling; some boast four-posters, fires or antique bathrooms; others are more contemporary with modern fittings.

Closing times
Open daily

Prices
Meals: à la carte £ 15/32
23 rooms: £ 77/203

Typical Dishes
Pork rillettes
Roast loin of local venison
Selection of British cheeses

6 mi northwest of Clitheroe by B 6243. Parking.

38 The Mulberry Tree

9 Wood Lane,
Wrightington Bar WN6 9SE
Tel.: (01257)451400 – Fax: (01257)451400
e-mail: info@themulberrytree.info **Website:** www.themulberrytree.info

Inspectors' favourites

Flowers IPA and other guest ales

If you enter from the far side you'll find yourself amongst the locals in the bar. If you come in via the car park you'll end up in a smart dining room with linen-clad tables. So if it's not quite what you expected, go back and try the other door. When it comes to food this pub offers a vast array of choice. The wide-ranging bar menu displays a selection of typical pub dishes with some extras chalked up on the wall, while the dining room offers a second, more substantial menu – albeit with some replication here and there – and some tapas-sized portions of the house favourites under the heading 'amuse bouche'. Combinations and presentation are fairly classical, and regionality plays a key role: you will often find Morecambe Bay shrimps, Bury black pudding, Fleetwood fish, homemade burgers and Lancashire cheeses. There are some good value mid-week deals but even at the weekends the bar menu offers generous portions at a reasonable price.

Closing times
Open daily
Prices
Meals: à la carte £ 16/45

Typical Dishes
Crispy panko Cox's apple
Breast of duck
Hot chocolate fondue

3½ mi northwest of Standish by A 5209 on B 5250. Parking.

England • North West • Lancashire

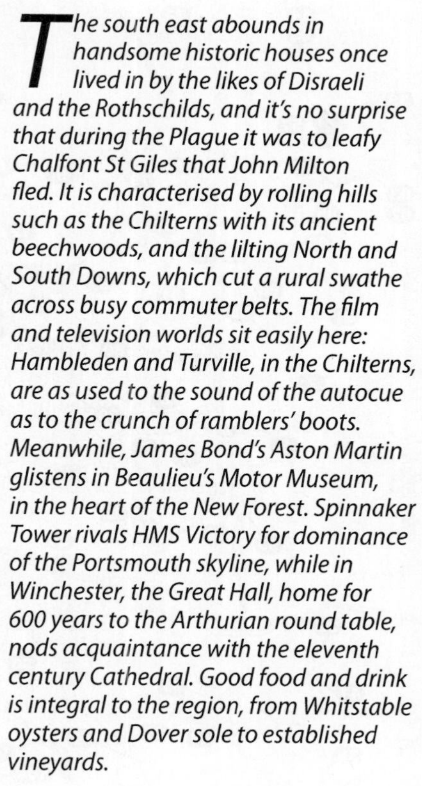

The south east abounds in handsome historic houses once lived in by the likes of Disraeli and the Rothschilds, and it's no surprise that during the Plague it was to leafy Chalfont St Giles that John Milton fled. It is characterised by rolling hills such as the Chilterns with its ancient beechwoods, and the lilting North and South Downs, which cut a rural swathe across busy commuter belts. The film and television worlds sit easily here: Hambleden and Turville, in the Chilterns, are as used to the sound of the autocue as to the crunch of ramblers' boots. Meanwhile, James Bond's Aston Martin glistens in Beaulieu's Motor Museum, in the heart of the New Forest. Spinnaker Tower rivals HMS Victory for dominance of the Portsmouth skyline, while in Winchester, the Great Hall, home for 600 years to the Arthurian round table, nods acquaintance with the eleventh century Cathedral. Good food and drink is integral to the region, from Whitstable oysters and Dover sole to established vineyards.

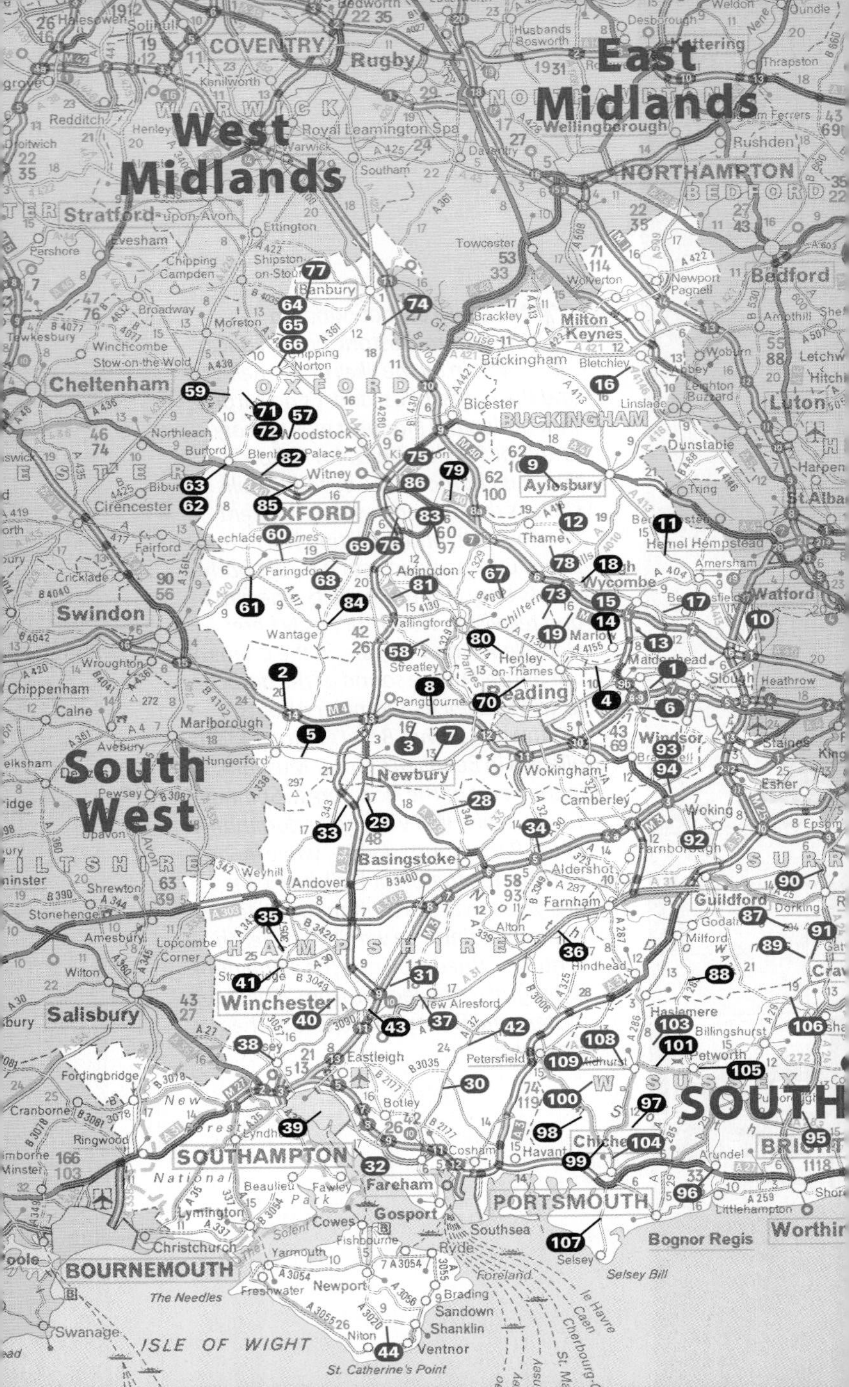

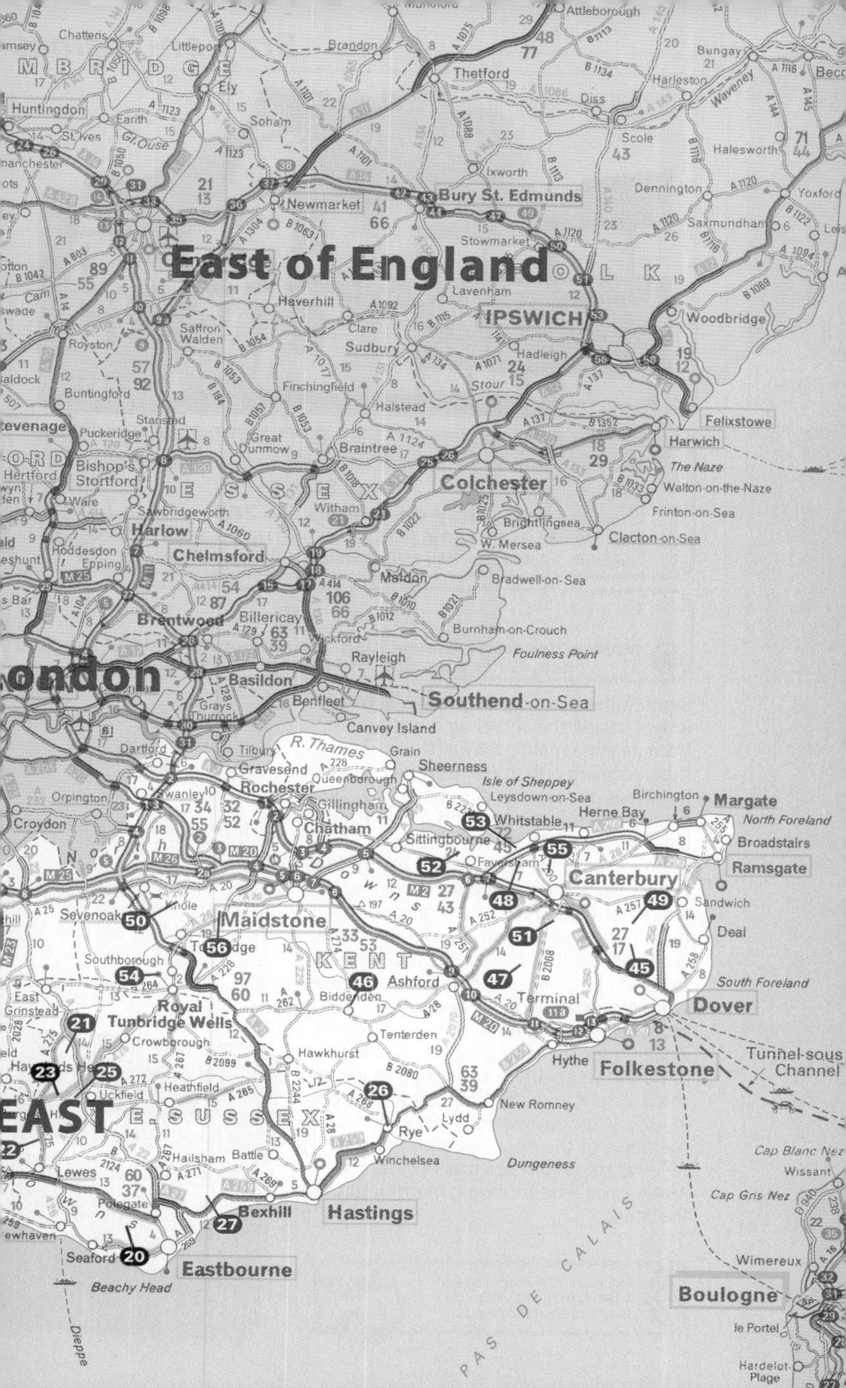
East of England
Attleborough
Chatteris
Littleport
Brandon
Thetford
Bungay
Harleston
Waveney
Ely
Diss
Huntingdon
Earith
Soham
St. Ives
Gt. Ouse
Scole
Halesworth
Ixworth
Dennington
Yoxford
Newmarket
Bury St. Edmunds
Saxmundham
Stowmarket
Lavenham
Haverhill
IPSWICH
Woodbridge
Royston
Saffron Walden
Clare
Sudbury
Hadleigh
Baldock
Buntingford
Finchingfield
Stour
Halstead
Felixstowe
Stevenage
Stansted
Puckeridge
Great Dunmow
Braintree
Harwich
Hertford
Bishop's Stortford
Colchester
The Naze
Ware
Walton-on-the-Naze
Sawbridgeworth
Witham
Frinton-on-Sea
Harlow
Brightlingsea
Clacton-on-Sea
Hoddesdon
Epping
W. Mersea
Chelmsford
Bradwell-on-Sea
Maldon
Brentwood
Billericay
Burnham-on-Crouch
Wickford
Foulness Point
Rayleigh
London
Basildon
Benfleet
Southend-on-Sea
Grays Thurrock
Canvey Island
Dartford
Tilbury
R. Thames
Grain
Sheerness
Gravesend
Queenborough
Isle of Sheppey
Orpington
Swanley
Rochester
Leysdown-on-Sea
Birchington
Margate
Gillingham
Whitstable
Herne Bay
North Foreland
Croydon
Chatham
Sittingbourne
Broadstairs
Faversham
Ramsgate
Canterbury
Sevenoaks
Knole
Maidstone
Sandwich
Deal
Tonbridge
Southborough
KENT
Ashford
South Foreland
East Grinstead
Biddenden
Terminal
Dover
Royal Tunbridge Wells
Crowborough
Tenterden
Hythe
Folkestone
Tunnel-sous Channel
Haywards Heath
Hawkhurst
Heathfield
Uckfield
New Romney
EAST
SUSSEX
Lydd
Rye
Cap Blanc Nez
Hailsham
Battle
Winchelsea
Dungeness
Wissant
Lewes
Polegate
Cap Gris Nez
Bexhill
Hastings
Newhaven
Seaford
Eastbourne
Wimereux
Beachy Head
PAS DE CALAIS
Boulogne
le Portel
Dieppe
Hardelot-Plage

1 The Hinds Head

High St,
Bray-on-Thames SL6 2AB
Tel.: (01628)626151 – Fax: (01628)623394
e-mail: info@hindsheadbray.co.uk **Website:** www.hindsheadhotel.co.uk

Inspectors' favourites

VISA MC AE

Marlow Rebellion, Greene King - IPA, Abbot Ale and Old Speckled Hen, Fuller's London Pride, Timothy Taylor Landlord

Right in the heart of the pretty village of Bray – beside the church and not too far from its alma mater, the Fat Duck – sits this charming pub, much as it has done for hundreds of years; its dark panelling, log fires and flag floors creating a characterful, almost medieval feel. With Heston Blumenthal at the helm, you'd be right to expect passionately prepared cooking, but we're not talking molecular gastronomy here: dishes are fiercely British, and some date back to Tudor times. Try a dandelion salad to start, perhaps, followed by a heart-warming oxtail and kidney pudding, and an aptly named quaking pudding for dessert. Booking for the dining rooms is essential, although reservations cannot be made in the bar, so if you arrive early, you may be in luck. With past patrons including various members of the Royal Family – Prince Philip held his stag night celebrations here in 1947 – you'll be following in distinguished footsteps.

Closing times

Closed 25-26 December

Booking essential

Prices

Meals: £ 42 and à la carte £ 28/46

Typical Dishes

Powdered goose
Beef with bone marrow
Quaking pudding

1 mi south of Maidenhead by A 308. Parking in 2 village car parks and opposite the pub.

2 Queen's Arms

East Garston RG17 7ET
Tel.: (01488)648757 – Fax: (01488)648642
e-mail: info@queensarmshotel.co.uk
Website: wwwqueensarmshotel.co.uk

Inspectors' favourites

 **Ramsbury Gold, Good Old Boy, Ringwood Best Bitter**

Situated in the heart of the Valley of the Racehorse, The Queen's Arms is a true thoroughbred among pubs. With its country pursuits theme, it celebrates all things English; catch up with the day's racing results in the hugely atmospheric, antique-furnished bar; its walls lined with fantastic photos of riders and shooters. With classics such as sausage and mash, fish pie, Eton Mess and even homemade fudge, the appealing menu continues the English theme. Food is carefully prepared and uses only the best quality seasonal ingredients, including game from local shoots. The superb bedrooms are sponsored by purveyors of country equipment and clothing; for the ultimate extravagance, book 'Miller's Club,' which comes complete with its own honesty bar and poker table – and don't forget to order your copy of The Racing Post to accompany your generous breakfast the next morning. Plans are afoot to add four more rooms in the converted stables.

Closing times
Open daily

Prices
Meals: à la carte £ 24/32
8 rooms: £ 95/130

Typical Dishes
Rare dry-aged fillet beef
Sausages & mash
Gypsy tart

3 mi southeast of Lambourn via Eastbury on Newbury Rd. Parking.

3 **The Pot Kiln**

Frilsham RG18 0XX
Tel.: (01635)201366 – Fax: (01635)201366
e-mail: info@potkiln.org **Website:** www.potkiln.org

West Berkshire Brewery - Brick Kiln, Mr Chubbs, Maggs' Mild, Full Circle and weekly changing guest ales

Set in a picturesque rural location and surrounded by fields and distant woodland, this 350 year old red brick pub is the very essence of local country pub. The owners' dogs greet you at the entrance and there's a small but pleasant wood-filled bar. To say that the food is fresh and local doesn't cover it. Bread and pasta are homemade, veg, salad and herbs come from the kitchen garden, meat is from local farms or estates and fish is delivered from the Brixham day boats. On top of that, 90% of the game and all the river fish are caught by the owner himself. The menu reads more like a newsletter with this information, as well as events and of course, the wide-ranging list of food. There's the choice of sandwiches, brunch and old pub favourites with a local/ modern twist, or some more restaurant style dishes served only in the dining area. At lunch there's a good value set menu and to wash it all down, there's beer from just down the road.

Closing times

Closed 25 December and Tuesday

Prices

Meals: £ 20 (weekday lunch) and à la carte £ 25/30

Typical Dishes

Wood pigeon salad

Pavé of venison

Marmalade bread & butter pudding

6 mi northeast of Newbury by B 4009 to Hermitage and minor road. Parking.

4 Black Boys Inn

Henley Rd,
Hurley SL6 5NQ
Tel.: (01628)824212
e-mail: info@blackboysinn.co.uk **Website:** www.blackboysinn.co.uk

   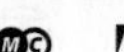 AE

 **Brakspear Ordinary**

Behind the traditional façade of this 16C brick pub, on the busy main road between Hurley and Henley, lies a stylish modernised interior. A wood burning stove separates the comfy lounge from the beamed, wood floored dining area; there's a smaller room for those after a more intimate experience, and a terrace at the rear for those occasions when only al fresco dining will do. The overall impression that Black Boys tends more towards restaurant than inn in all but name is confirmed on perusing the menu, where you'll find dishes involving rillette of duck, Salcombe crab, sautéed calf's sweetbread and foie gras with prune and Armagnac chutney. Cooking is well-crafted and flavoursome and the friendly, knowledgeable service adds its own zesty tang. Individually-styled bedrooms come with excellent fitted bathrooms; but don't be surprised if the water supply splutters somewhat, since it has had to work its way up from the inn's very own well.

Closing times

Closed 2 weeks at Christmas, last 2 weeks in August, Sunday dinner and Monday

Prices

Meals: à la carte £ 25/38

8 rooms: £ 75/110

Typical Dishes
Fresh tuna 'tartare'
Braised veal cheek
Dark chocolate mousse

4 mi east of Henley-on-Thames by A 4130. Parking.

5 The Dundas Arms

Station Rd,
Kintbury RG17 9UT
Tel.: (01488)658263 – Fax: (01488)658568
e-mail: info@dundasarms.co.uk **Website:** www.dundasarms.co.uk

Adnam's Bitter, West Berkshire Brewery - Good Old Boy, Ramsbury Brewery - Ramsbury Gold

Its fabulous location on an island between the River Kennet and the Kennet and Avon canal means that this 18C inn is the place to be come summer. Sit on the terrace and watch narrow boats glide by as you dine; if the heavens open, try the bar or the dining room instead. The pub has been family-owned for more than 40 years and its décor is as traditional as it comes with swirly paisley carpets, a coin encrusted bar and decorative blue plates lining the wall. On busier days, the more modern restaurant is opened, its window tables boasting a waterside view. The blackboard menu evolves daily depending on available produce; dishes are mainly traditional, along the lines of steak and kidney pie or roast fillet of lamb, with good use often made of more unusual cuts of meat, involving plenty of slow cooking and braising. Simply furnished bedrooms are in the former stables; all have French windows which open onto a riverside terrace.

Closing times

Closed 25-26 December, 31 December dinner and Sunday dinner

Prices

Meals: à la carte £ 19/30

5 rooms: £ 80/90

Typical Dishes

Crab au gratin

Steak & kidney pie

Raspberry brûlée

3½ mi east of Hungerford by A 4. Parking.

6 **The Royal Oak**

Paley Street,
Paley Street SL6 3JN
Tel.: (01628)620541
e-mail: royaloakmail@aol.com **Website:** www.theroyaloakpaleystreet.com

VISA MC AE D

Fuller's London Pride

A relatively unremarkable exterior does little to suggest there's a very charming pub within, but this just adds to that initial pleasure of discovery. Nick Parkinson is your host and his ability to put guests at ease is clearly one family trait he's inherited from his father, Sir Michael, whose famous encounters are captured in the photos that decorate the place. It's all very pretty inside: Boris the dog is usually found snoozing at the front bar, while the rest of the beamed room is given over to dining. The chef is Dominic Chapman, son of West Country hotelier Kit, and, like his father, he champions British food. His cooking displays confidence and a commitment to good quality, seasonal ingredients but it also suits the pub setting. Fish is handled with particular aplomb, whether it's roast halibut with spicy aubergine or smoked eel with beetroot. He's also likes his game. Service is very pleasant and gets the tone just right.

Closing times
Closed 25 December, 1 January and Sunday dinner

Prices
Meals: £ 20/25
and à la carte £ 25/35

Typical Dishes
Fried Cornish sprats
Rabbit & bacon pie
Rhubarb trifle

3½ mi southwest of Bray-on-Thames by A 308, A 330 and B 3024. Parking.

7 The Angel

Bath Rd,
Woolhampton RG7 5RT
Tel.: (0118)9713307
e-mail: mail@thea4angel.com **Website:** www.thea4angel.com

 **Otter Ale**

Conveniently situated for motorists, on the A4 between Newbury and Reading, the ivy-clad Angel sits in the heart of the village, providing passers-by and locals alike with a friendly welcome and tasty, satisfying food. Its design is distinctive; wine bottles line the ceiling, dried foliage and hops hang from the beams, and all available surfaces seem to be covered with jars and bottles filled with pastas, fruits and berries. Sit on a cushioned banquette in the bar or take a seat in the restaurant; if the weather's half decent, then you might prefer to head outside and dine al fresco. You can still pop in for a pint, but food is where the main emphasis now lies – as illustrated by the self-applied 'gastro' tag – and while the lunchtime menu offers sandwiches, the à la carte is more varied, with dishes ranging from a soup or steak and chips to mussels in white wine, slow roast belly of pork or tiger prawns with linguini.

Closing times
Closed 25-26 December and Sunday dinner

Prices
Meals: à la carte £ 21/26

Typical Dishes
King scallops & wasabi mash
Slow-roast belly of pork
Classic spotted dick

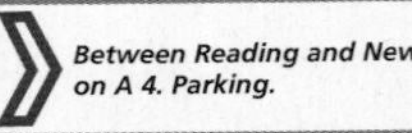
Between Reading and Newbury on A 4. Parking.

8 The Royal Oak

The Square,
Yattendon RG18 0UG
Tel.: (01635)201325
e-mail: info@royaloakyattendon.com **Website:** www.royaloakyattendon.com

Inspectors' favourites

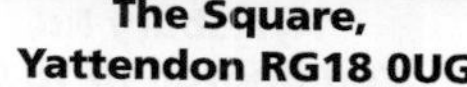

West Berkshire Brewery - Good Old Boy, Mr Chubbs

A beautiful former coaching inn bursting with country charm, The Royal Oak manages to admirably pull off the tricky feat of being both a true locals' pub and a popular destination for foodies. While the picture perfect village and its proximity to the M4 could account in part for the pub's attraction to visitors, it's the cooking which really gets them travelling here from a distance. Dishes display a fine French technique, with a menu that showcases the chef's classical repertoire: starters could include confit of pork belly or pan-fried fillet of red mullet, while main courses might feature aromatic duck breast and foie gras or local lamb cooked three ways (saddle, shoulder and sweetbreads). The beamed bar with its blazing log fires is at the pub's hub. There is also a lesser-used restaurant and, for the warmer months, a very pleasant vine-covered terrace at the rear. Classically-styled bedrooms are gradually being spruced up.

Closing times

Open daily

Booking advisable

Prices

Meals: £ 19 (lunch)
and à la carte £ 30/39

 **5 rooms:** £ 110/130

Typical Dishes
Confit of pork belly
Local lamb cooked 3 ways
Assiette of lemon

6 mi northeast of Newbury by B 009 and minor road; in the village centre. Parking opposite and in village car park.

9 The Crown

Aylesbury Rd,
Cuddington HP18 0BB
Tel.: (01844)292222
e-mail: david@thecrowncuddington.co.uk **Website:** www.thecrowncuddington.co.uk

VISA  

Fuller's London Pride, Adnams

Set in the charming village of Cuddington, this Grade II listed 16C building is the very essence of a proper English pub. Whitewashed walls and an attractive thatched roof conceal a traditionally styled interior with welcoming open fires, dancing candlelight and a multitude of artefacts from a bygone era; while a loyal band of locals keep up the drinking trade and a friendly service team help set the tone. For those looking to dine, there's a blackboard of daily specials and an à la carte that changes with the seasons: you'll find hearty comfort food in winter – maybe lamb shank or glazed duck breast – followed by rich homemade puddings; and some lighter dishes in the summer, with the likes of sandwiches and salads. If you fancy any of these in a spot in the sun, you'll have to arrive early to secure a space. For a midweek outing, try the popular 'Pie and Pud' nights, which take place every Wednesday and always go down a storm.

Closing times
Closed Sunday dinner

Prices
Meals: £ 17 and à la carte £ 18/26

Typical Dishes
Char-Sui pork
Smoked haddock Welsh rarebit
Brownie & maple ice cream

West of Aylesbury by A 418.
Parking.

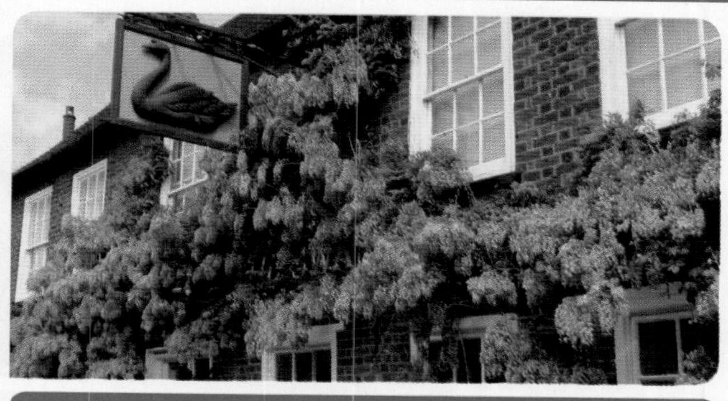

10 **The Swan Inn**

Village Rd,
Denham UB9 5BH
Tel.: (01895)832085 – Fax: (01895)835516
e-mail: info@swaninndenham.co.uk **Website:** www.swaninndenham.co.uk

 **Courage Best, Wadworth 6X, Marlow Rebellion IPA**

If you want to escape the hustle of London but without a huge commute, this pub might just be the tranquil haven you're after. Close to the A40, M40 and M25 but in a secluded little world of its own, the Swan takes up prime position in this delightful village. Number three in the owner's collection of four, this Georgian red-brick building is fronted by beautiful cascades of wisteria and framed by manicured trees, with a secluded terrace and pleasant gardens to the rear. Menus change with the seasons but you'll always find rib-eye steak and their signature bubble and squeak. This is more just than typical pub food, so you might find pan-fried salt and pepper squid for starters, followed by confit duck with nutmeg boxty potato and poached fig jus. Even the sides are interesting, including choices such as leek, pancetta and parsley crumble, while puddings are a must. And it's not often pubs open early for pre-Ascot or Wimbledon champagne.

Closing times

Closed 25-26 December

Booking essential

Prices

Meals: à la carte £ 20/27

Typical Dishes

Crispy courgette beignets

Shoulder of lamb parcel

Chocolate 'Bourbon'

6 mi northeast of Slough by A 412; in the centre of the village. Small car park.

11 The Nags Head

London Road,
Great Missenden HP16 0DG
Tel.: (01494)862200 – Fax: (01494)862945
e-mail: goodfood@nagsheadbucks.com **Website:** www.nagsheadbucks.com

AE

Fuller's London Pride, Marlow Rebellion and guest ale

This traditional 15C inn is run by the same team behind the Bricklayers Arms in Flaunden and is proving just as popular, so be sure to book ahead, especially at weekends. It has been fully made over, yet retains a wealth of original features: the two main dining areas have thick brick walls and exposed oak beams, while an extra helping of rusticity comes courtesy of the inglenook fireplace. Interesting, original menus mix Gallic charm with British classics, so you'll find things like foie gras and mushroom feuillette alongside eggs Benedict, steak and kidney pie, sausage and mash or lamb shank. Home-smoked fish travel the ten or so miles from the Bricklayers Arms, while farms that provide meats are often named on the menu. Food is flavourful and service cheerful and keen. Stylish, modern bedrooms provide a comfortable night's sleep – number one is the best – and the tasty breakfast ensures you leave satiated in the morning.

Closing times
Closed 25 December
Prices
Meals: à la carte £ 25/38
5 rooms: £ 90/110

Typical Dishes
Crab & home-smoked salmon
Fillet of pork & smoked bacon
Stuffed crêpe

Between Wendover and Amersham on A 413. Parking.

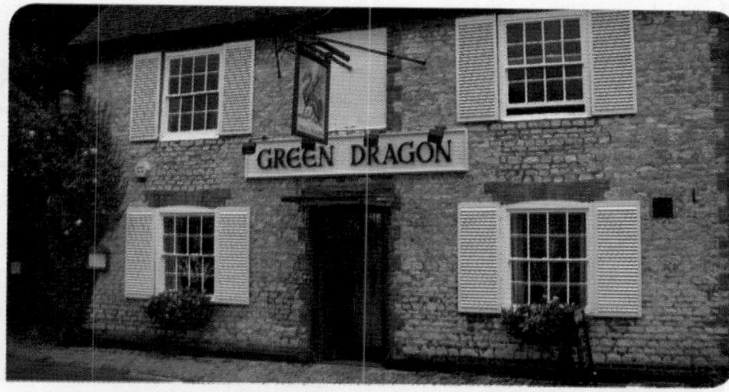

12 The Green Dragon

8 Churchway, Haddenham HP17 8AA
Tel.: (01844)291403 – Fax: (01844)299532
e-mail: enquiries@greendragonhaddenham.co.uk
Website: www.greendragonhaddenham.co.uk

 **Sharp's Doom Bar, Timothy Taylor Landlord, Brakspear's Bitter**

Having had its 15 minutes in the reality TV spotlight – when it was known as The Welsh Wok – The Green Dragon flew back down to earth with a bump. Its 350 year old stone façade remains unchanged, but with its new, improved pub signs, a fresh team at the helm and a makeover which has given it a light, modern, and much more pubby look, it is soaring to new heights. Gone is its cosy, rustic and rather dim interior; now it's all whitewashed and open plan, with slate floors, fireplaces and loud blues music. The kitchen team are enthusiastic and ambitious, and although the dishes on the regularly changing menus might sound predictable enough – perhaps warm pork and black pudding terrine, pan-roasted skate wing or shepherd's pie – what arrives on your plate is modern and adventurous, with bold flavours and top class ingredients. Lunch offers a few lighter dishes, including sandwiches and the service is attentive and efficient.

Closing times

Closed 26 December

Booking essential

Prices

Meals: £ 14 and à la carte £ 15/30

Typical Dishes

Smoked haddock 'Scotch egg'
Shepherd's pie
Dark chocolate delice

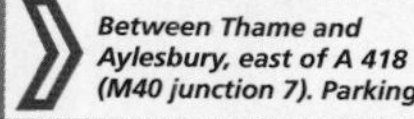
Between Thame and Aylesbury, east of A 418 (M40 junction 7). Parking.

13 The Queens Head

Pound Lane,
Little Marlow SL7 3SR
Tel.: (01628)482927
e-mail: tqhlittlemarlow@yahoo.co.uk **Website:** www.marlowslittlesecret.co.uk

Fuller's London Pride, Brakspear and monthly changing guest beer

Head in the direction of Little Marlow's 12C church and you will be on course to find The Queens Head, tucked away down a lane opposite the village's restored cattle pound. Despite its slightly dubious-sounding slogan, 'Marlow's Little Secret,' this is a popular pub, with keen young partners at its helm and staff who provide poised, friendly service. Once a spit and sawdust sort of a place, its snug bar used to be a salting room and its priest hole makes it a popular place for filming; in the past it has featured in programmes such as Midsomer Murders and Inspector Morse. The garden gets into full swing during the summer months when hungry walkers gather to refuel; the lunch menu provides a quick fix with sandwiches, ploughman's and dishes like steak or fish and chips, while the dinner menu sets the bar a little higher, with starters such as duck liver parfait or peppered squid and main courses like lamb rump and pan-fried sea bass.

Closing times
Open daily
Prices
Meals: à la carte £ 23/35

Typical Dishes
Pan-seared scallops
Chargrilled rib-eye steak
Chocolate & praline mousse

3 mi east of Marlow on A 4155 by Church Rd. Parking.

14 The Hand and Flowers

126 West St,
Marlow SL7 2BP
Tel.: (01628)482277 – Fax: (01628)401913
e-mail: theoffice@thehandandflowers.co.uk **Website:** www.thehandandflowers.

Inspectors' favourites

   AE

 **Greene King IPA, Abbot Ale**

There aren't many pubs that offer diners the opportunity of spending a whole day shadowing one of the chefs but then The Hand and Flowers is rightly proud of its food and its smart, new kitchen. Owner Tom Kerridge has developed a menu to enthuse, rather than frighten off the natives and his impressive command of assorted cooking techniques is evident, from braising to poaching, curing to roasting; dishes have depth and clarity and a lot of work goes into making them so easy on the eye. But most importantly, he never forgets that this is a pub – the beer pumps are the first thing you see, you have to duck to avoid the beams and service is never po-faced. Moreover, there are simpler dishes available at lunch and you'll even find the odd piece of culinary post-modernism: check out the salt cod Scotch egg or the whitebait served as an amuse bouche. There are four pretty bedrooms in two neighbouring cottages; 'Angus' has an outdoor Jacuzzi.

Closing times
Closed 24-26 December, 31 December lunch, 31 January dinner and Sunday dinner

Booking essential

Prices
Meals: à la carte £ 30/37

4 rooms: £ 140/190

Typical Dishes
Moules marinière
Honey roast duck tart
Warm pistachio sponge cake

From town centre follow Henley signs west on A 4155; pub on right after 350 metres. Parking.

15 The Royal Oak

Frieth Rd,
Bovingdon Green, Marlow SL7 2JF
Tel.: (01628)488611 – Fax: (01628)478680
e-mail: info@royaloakmarlow.co.uk **Website:** www.royaloakmarlow.co.uk

VISA MC AE

Brakspear, Marlow Rebellion IPA , Timothy Taylor Landlord

Set less than 15mins from the M40 and M4, the part-17C Royal Oak is the ideal getaway for those looking to escape the busy streets of London. As you approach, pleasant scents drift up from the herb garden, gentle 'chinks' emanate from the petanque pitch and the world feels at once more peaceful. You can while away the warmer days on the pleasant terrace or snuggle into pretty cushions beside the wood burning stove in winter. Rich fabrics and heritage colours provide a country-chic feel and freshly cut flowers decorate the room. Not surprisingly, it's extremely popular here and the eager team are often stretched to their limit, especially on Sundays. Cooking is mainly British-led, with the odd Asian influence, so you might find soused salmon fillet on horseradish potato salad or pigeon breast on celeriac rémoulade, followed by pan-roast pork chop with salt and pepper squid, or slow-cooked ox cheek, red onion, potato and thyme pasty.

Closing times
Closed 25-26 December

Prices
Meals: à la carte £ 20/27

Typical Dishes
Smoked pigeon breast
Slow-cooked ox cheek
Rhubarb & rosehip posset

From Marlow town centre head towards Bovingdon Green: pub is on the left as you leave the woods. Parking.

16 The Crooked Billet

2 Westbrook End,
Newton Longville MK17 0DF
Tel.: (01908)373936
e-mail: john@thebillet.co.uk **Website:** www.thebillet.co.uk

  **IPA, Bombardier, XXB, Hobgoblin - changing weekly**

This charming 17C thatched pub is the last place you expect to come across as you drive round the outskirts of Milton Keynes. Starting life as a farmhouse and later providing refreshments for passing farmers, it eventually evolved into the village pub and has stayed so ever since. The interior is smart yet informal, with the owner's artwork adorning the walls and a cheery bunch of locals propping up the bar. 2010 marks its 10th year under Emma and John, who have built up quite a reputation – so much so that you have to book to secure a table. Emma heads the dedicated kitchen team, who create modern, seasonal dishes from the daily arriving produce. Lunch offers sandwiches or a three course à la carte, while dinner adds to the latter and introduces a seven course tasting menu. Provenance is noted on the menu, as is a wine recommendation for each dish, and ex-sommelier John is always glad to guide you through the 200-strong wine list.

Closing times
Closed Sunday dinner and Monday lunch
Booking advisable

Prices
Meals: £ 19/23
and à la carte £ 25/50

Typical Dishes
Roast local quail
Steamed halibut
Banana & chocolate parfait

6 mi southwest of Milton Keynes by A 421. Parking.

The Old Queens Head

17 The Old Queens Head

Hammersley Lane,
Penn HP10 8EY

Tel.: (01494)813371 – Fax: (01494)816145

e-mail: info@oldqueensheadpenn.co.uk **Website:** www.oldqueensheadpenn.co.uk

VISA MC AE

Greene King IPA, Ruddles County

This lively pub may not be quite as old as the ancient beech woodlands that surround it – but it does have a part to play in the history of the area. Legend has it that Lord Penn inherited the pub when he won a game of cards against Charles II. Whether this is true or not, no one knows but it can be proved from the deeds of 1666 that it was purchased by Martin Lluelyn, one of the King's physicians and later Mayor of Wycombe. The dining room – formerly a barn – is the oldest part of the building, boasting old weathered beams and good views; while the surrounding rooms, although slightly newer, continue the rustic theme with their characterful open fires and cosy nooks. When it comes to the food, big, hearty dishes are the order of the day, so you might find pigeon breast on red onion tarte tatin, followed by beef bourguignon with honey-roast parsnips and oxtail dumplings. Be sure to save room though, as the homemade puddings are a must.

Closing times

Closed 25-26 December

Prices

Meals: à la carte £ 20/27

Typical Dishes

Pigeon & confit rabbit terrine

Gruyère & thyme crusted haddock

Apple brandy syllabub

4 mi north of A 40, Junction 2, via Beaconsfield by B 474. Parking.

18 The Three Horseshoes Inn

Bennett End,
Radnage HP14 4EB
Tel.: (01494)483273 – Fax: (01494)485464
e-mail: threehorseshoe@btconnect.com **Website:** www.thethreehorseshoes.net

 VISA 

Rebellion Beer

Dating back to 1745, this attractive red-brick pub is set in a fantastic hillside location deep in the Buckinghamshire countryside. With its attractive flagged floor and inglenook fireplace, the cosy bar is the place to be in the winter; although with space being limited, you might want to head through to the spacious restaurant, with its stunning beams and smart, minimalist feel. Menus reflect the chef's background, so you'll find plenty of classically prepared dishes with the odd French touch. Lunch consists mainly of soups, salads and pâtés, while dinner offers a more formal à la carte and some lighter tapas dishes; the latter served in the bar and garden. In warmer months the terrace is a lovely place to sit, boasting pleasant views over the duck pond – complete with submerged red telephone box – to the hills beyond. In contrast to the cooking, bedrooms are contemporary and lavish; the French-inspired Molières suite being the best.

Closing times

Closed Sunday dinner, Monday lunch and Tuesday after bank holiday Monday

Prices

Meals: £ 17 (lunch) and à la carte £ 24/35

6 rooms: £ 75/120

Typical Dishes

Pan-fried scallops
Duck breast
Hot chocolate fondant

5 mi west of High Wycombe by A 40 and minor road north. Parking.

19 The Bull & Butcher

Turville RG9 6QU
Tel.: (01491)638283 – Fax: (01491)638836
e-mail: info@thebullandbutcher.com
Website: www.thebullandbutcher.com

 **Brakspear's Bitter, Oxford Gold, Hooky Dark Mild, Brewers Selection**

Nestled peacefully between the Chilterns, it's hard to believe that the small village of Turville has so many claims to fame. Over the years it's provided the setting for The Vicar of Dibley, featured in several Midsomer Murder mysteries and had its 18C windmill reincarnated as Caractacus Potts' workshop in Chitty Chitty Bang Bang. Walk down the hill from the windmill and you'll find the Grade II listed Bull and Butcher, a characterful 16C two-roomed pub with a large garden and patio. Once inside, choose between high-backed chairs and pleasant countryside views in one room and an open fire, wooden beams and a unique table constructed around a well in the other. Cooking here is generous and robust, and theme nights feature everything from sushi and Thai, to South African and game; the latter offering tempting dishes such as roast pheasant with Calvados, apples and onions or saddle of fallow dear stuffed with pine nuts and rosemary.

Closing times
Open daily
Booking advisable

Prices
Meals: à la carte £ 21/28

Typical Dishes
Pan-fried pigeon breasts
Confit duck leg
Sticky toffee pudding

5 mi north of Henley-on-Thames by A 4130 off B 480. Parking.

20 The George Inn

High St,
Alfriston BN26 5SY
Tel.: (01323)870319
e-mail: info@thegeorge-alfriston.com **Website:** www.thegeorge-alfriston.com

 VISA  AE

Greene King IPA, Abbot Ale and Timothy Taylor Bath gem

A delightful South Downs village complete with bell ringers, cricket club and village green is the setting for this equally charming stone and timber building, the epitome of the traditional English inn. Some parts of it date back to the 13C and a network of smugglers' tunnels purportedly lead from its cellars. It's still very much a locals' pub, with a warm, homely feel; dried hops hang from the eaves, three rooms all boast inglenook fireplaces for cosy winter drinking and dining, while the summer swell is accommodated by the large rear gardens. They offer a good selection of dishes, and while those who prefer their culinary influences to be closer to home will be happy to see slow roast belly of pork or roasted rack of lamb on the menu; those who like food of a more international provenance will like the sound of dishes involving Thai style chicken balls, veal saltimbocca or bouillabaisse. Characterful bedrooms feature oak beams.

Closing times
Closed 25-26 December
Booking advisable

Prices
Meals: à la carte £ 15/30
6 rooms: £ 60/130

Typical Dishes
Crevettes in chilli oil
Roast rack of lamb
Bread & butter pudding

Two public car parks (1min walk) and street parking.

21 Coach & Horses

School Lane,
Danehill RH17 7JF
Tel.: (01825)740369 – Fax: (01825)740369
e-mail: coachandhorses@danehill.biz **Website:** www.coachandhorses.danehill.biz

 **Harveys Best, Dark Star Best, Hammerpot Meteor**

Some pubs tend to forget those living on their doorstep, but not this characterful stone inn. It has a formally laid area for dining, converted from the original stables, but at its hub is its charming bar, seemingly unchanged since its creation in 1847, where locals enjoy a pint and a chat; dog optional. The bar can't take all the credit for the relaxed, unpretentious atmosphere here though - the friendly, informal service also plays its part, and on sunny days the pretty garden positively encourages somnolence. Traditional menus offer a good mix of meat and fish dishes at very reasonable prices; ingredients are locally sourced wherever possible and, since beasts are bought whole and butchered in the kitchen, the blackboard specials menu often includes more unusual offerings such as venison liver or braised heart. Snacks and sandwiches are available at lunchtimes and you can purchase the ever popular Ladypots preserves at the bar.

Closing times
Closed 25 December dinner, 26 December and Sunday dinner

Prices
Meals: à la carte £ 20/30

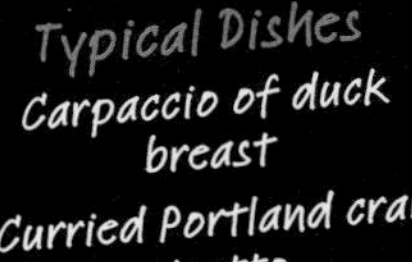

Typical Dishes
Carpaccio of duck breast
Curried Portland crab risotto
Hazelnut Muscavado tart

¾ mi northeast on Chelwood Common Rd. Parking.

22 The Jolly Sportsman

Chapel Lane,
East Chiltington BN7 3BA
Tel.: (01273)890400 – Fax: (01273)890400
e-mail: info@thejollysportsman.com **Website:** www.thejollysportsman.com

 **Dark Star Hophead and one guest beer and Old Ale in winter**

Meandering through the winding lanes of Sussex, even the journey to this pub feels like a jolly japer; staff are jolly and they serve jolly good food too. With a raised rear garden and a paved terrace, this creeper-clad pub is very popular during the summer months, but a seat by the fire in the cosy bar or in the airy dining room is just as pleasant any month of the year and the owner's hands-on approach helps it to run like the proverbial clockwork. The confident kitchen's simply presented cooking delivers the promise of the menu, letting the quality of the ingredients shine through. Fish is a particular strength and dishes might include grilled gurnard fillet, whole lemon sole or slow cooked Ditchling lamb; all display a vitality that comes from knowing which flavours go well together. Interesting bar snacks include boquerones, biltong and guindillas, and the exceptional wine list includes a lengthy selection of claret and burgundy.

Closing times
Closed 25-26 December

Prices
Meals: à la carte £ 22/32

Typical Dishes
Crab & grapefruit salad
Rump of Ditchling lamb
Strawberry & elderflower jelly

5½ mi northwest of Lewes by A 275 and B 2116 off Novington Lane. Parking.

23 The Griffin Inn

Fletching TN22 3SS
Tel.: (01825)722890 – Fax: (01825)722810
e-mail: info@thegriffin.co.uk **Website:** www.thegriffininn.co.uk

 VISA MC AE

Harvey's Best Bitter, Kings of Horsham, Hepworth Iron Horse

This red and white brick 16C coaching inn is the kind of pub everyone would like to have in their village. Well-established and owned by the same family for thirty years, it's got the cosy beamed bar packed with locals, the open fires and a linen-laid candlelit dining area. It also has its own cricket team, a terrace and a large garden - the ideal spot for summer Sunday barbeques, watching the sun set over the Downs. The buzzing atmosphere more than makes up for any slippage in service and the food here is fresh and homemade, using local produce, including Rye Bay seafood. The daily-changing menu offers modern British cooking with some Italian influences; dishes such as shellfish stew, saltimbocca of monkfish or rump of Romney Marsh lamb. A choice of individually decorated rooms is available; each comfortable, and some with four posters and roll top baths; those in the adjacent Griffin House are the best.

Closing times

Closed 25 December

Meals in bar Sunday dinner

Prices

Meals: £ 30 (Sunday lunch) and à la carte £ 22/35

13 rooms: £ 70/145

Typical Dishes

Chicken liver & foie gras parfait

Battered Rye Bay cod

Lemon polenta cake

Between Uckfield and Haywards Heath off A 272. Parking.

24 The Ginger Pig

3 Hove Street,
Hove BN3 2TR
Tel.: (01273)736123
e-mail: info@gingermanrestaurants.com **Website:** www.gingermanrestaurants.

Inspectors' favourites

 **Harvey's of Lewes**

Located just off the seafront in up and coming Hove, The Ginger Pig is the third of the Gingerman group's ventures in the Brighton area and is proving just as popular as its siblings. Entry into this striking, part-gabled building – a former smugglers' haunt - is through equally striking revolving doors. Once inside, chill out with a drink on low sofas in the contemporary bar or venture up the steps to the spacious, open plan dining area with its mix of leather banquettes and dark wood chairs and tables, beyond which lies the sun-trap of a terrace. Like the décor and the bold art hanging on the walls, the cooking here is modern and fresh, and the concise European menu offers tasty, refined dishes, all homemade using local produce, and served in filling portions. Specials are chalked up on a blackboard menu and keen, young servers form a well-drilled team – but bookings are not accepted, so those in the know arrive early.

Closing times
Closed 25 December

Prices
Meals: à la carte £ 20/35

Typical Dishes
Beetroot carpaccio
Chargrilled Scotch rib-eye
Chocolate & hazelnut parfait

Off north side of shore road, Kingsway, A 259. NCP car park (2min walk) & parking meters (2hr maximum during day).

25 The Peacock Inn

Shortbridge,
Piltdown TN22 3XA
Tel.: (01825)762463 – Fax: (01825)762463
e-mail: enquiries@peacock-inn.co.uk **Website:** www.peacock-inn.co.uk

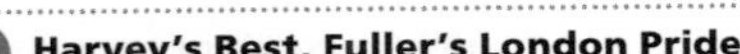

Harvey's Best, Fuller's London Pride

Early records show that this pub – previously named The Star – started life as an 18C alehouse, selling home-brewed beers to passers-by. It still sells a good selection of beers but now there is also a focus on quality pub grub, with plenty of steaks and grills on the menu and a specials board that often features fresh fish. Dishes are straightforward with no frills and might include pan-fried sea bass, roasted lamb rump or fisherman's pie. Summer is particularly appealing here, when colourful shrubs and hanging baskets welcome you and the brick BBQ in the rear garden is often doing a roaring trade. Inside is equally appealing, with the unique light oak parquet floor providing an elegant contrast with the heavy dark-wood furnishings. They are not unused to the odd celebrity appearance here; Thora Hird used to be a regular and Dame Vera Lynn sometimes drops by.

Closing times

Closed 25-26 and 31 December

Prices

Meals: à la carte £ 20/34

Typical Dishes

Haloumi & chorizo salad

Pork & apricot Stroganoff

Chocolate torte tower

8 mi east of Haywards Heath by A 272 and Shortbridge Lane. Parking.

26 Globe Inn

10 Military Rd,
Rye TN31 7NX
Tel.: (01797)227918
e-mail: theglobeinnrye@yahoo.com **Website:** www.theglobe-inn.com

 **Fuller's ESB and London Pride, Harvey's Sussex Best**

Just a short walk over the bridge from the centre of town, stands this traditional weatherboard inn – and with new owners at the helm, it's all change. Inside the contemporary décor makes it bright and airy, and beside the welcoming stove there's a mix of leather sofas, tall bar seating and smart light-wood dining tables. Menus alter regularly, following the pattern of the seasons, and there's a good range of dishes available. At lunchtime you'll find tasty deli boards and speedy tapas style offerings, alongside a main menu that covers everything from sandwiches, salads and brunch, to fish of the day, rib-eye steak and lamb's liver with bacon. In the evening, the menu is more formally laid out, offering the likes of tiger prawns in garlic, followed by cod with mozzarella, tomatoes and basil – and finished off with good old Eton Mess. The owners are keen to keep up local tradition, closely following events such as the scallop festival.

Closing times
Closed Monday
Booking essential

Prices
Meals: à la carte £ 20/30

Typical Dishes
Figs, mozzarella & Parma ham
Seared duck breast
Warm chocolate & pecan square

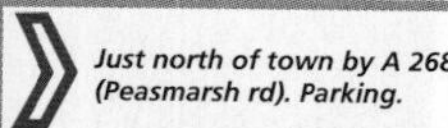
Just north of town by A 268 (Peasmarsh rd). Parking.

27 The Lamb Inn

Wartling Rd,
Wartling BN27 1RY
Tel.: (01323)832116 – Fax: (01323)832637
e-mail: alison.farncombe@virgin.net **Website:** www.lambinnwartling.co.uk

  AE

Harveys Best and a regularly changing guest ale such as Old, Bombardier

With its traditional whitewashed appearance and attractive rear courtyard, it is perhaps easy to see that this elevated roadside inn began life as a pair of cottages, and its characterful interior, with its flag floors and beamed ceilings further vouches for its early 16C origins. Quality and traceability are the bywords here when it comes to food; they bake their own bread, whilst seafood comes from Hastings and Newhaven and most of the meat hails from neighbouring Chilley Farm, who specialise in traditionally-farmed stock with no additives, and slow-reared rare breeds such as Gloucester Old Spot pork and extra mature Sussex beef. Homemade dishes might include anything from robust pies to cassoulet of duck, and mutton, enjoying something of a renaissance, also appears. Eat in the bar or in the more formal restaurant; the welcome is friendly and this place is clearly a hit with the locals, with themed evenings particularly popular.

Closing times
Closed Sunday dinner and Monday except bank holidays

Prices
Meals: £ 15 and à la carte £ 18/25

Typical Dishes
Rye Bay scallops
Local farm pork loin chop
Mincemeat bread & butter pudding

3¾ mi southeast of Herstmonceux by A 271 and Wartling Rd. Parking.

The Wellington Arms

28 The Wellington Arms

Baughurst Rd,
Baughurst RG26 5LP
Tel.: (0118)9820110
e-mail: info@thewellingtonarms.com **Website:** www.thewellingtonarms.com

  VISA MC

 **Wadworth 6X**

A country dining pub with a warm, friendly atmosphere, this former hunting lodge of the Duke of Wellington is characterful and cosy, its traditional tile floors and wooden beams blending well with more modern touches like the pretty floral blinds. They are passionate about food here: local produce is sourced with the utmost care, they grow their own vegetables and herbs and keep chickens and bees in the garden – with eggs and honey for sale at the bar alongside homemade preserves and teas, salt and soap imported from Australia. Flavoursome, modern British cooking takes centre stage on the blackboard menu, and dishes might include roast rack of English lamb, local venison potpie braised with real ale or seared turbot fillet, with good value lunch menus also featuring pub favourites such as cottage pie or fish and chips.
Service is polite and chatty – but with only eight tables set for dining, you should be sure to book ahead.

Closing times

Closed Sunday dinner, Monday and lunch Tuesday

Booking essential

Prices

Meals: £ 18 (Wednesday-Friday lunch) and à la carte £ 18/30

Typical Dishes

Hot tea-smoked trout

Home-reared rack of roast pork

Steamed sponge

8 mi north of Basingstoke by A 339 and minor road through Ramsdell and Pound Green; south of village on the Kingsclere / Newbury road. Parking.

29 Carnarvon Arms

Winchester Rd,
Whitway, Burghclere RG20 9LE
Tel.: (01635)278222 – Fax: (01635)278444
e-mail: info@carnarvonarms.com **Website:** www.carnarvonarms.com

VISA MC AE

Greene King IPA, Old Speckled Hen, Abbot Ale, LBW Ale

You might well wonder why the walls of the vaulted dining room in the barn conversion of this smart 19C inn are decorated with hieroglyphics - but it begins to make sense when you know that the pub is named after the 5th Earl of Carnarvon, who lived at nearby Highclere House and was one of the men who discovered Tutankhamen's tomb. The pub is situated on a busy country lane which runs alongside the A34, the welcome is a friendly one and you can choose to dine on leather sofas in the spacious main bar and lounge, or in one of the open plan rooms which surround it. There's plenty of choice on the modern British menu, too, from sandwiches to more substantial dishes, and all at reasonable prices. Try the pigeon pie, pot roast pork collar or honey roasted Gressingham duck breast; or perhaps the more classic sausage and mash or pan-fried liver with bacon. A myriad of small, up-to-date bedrooms are popular with businessmen during the week.

Closing times
Open daily

Prices
Meals: £ 15 (lunch)
and à la carte £ 24/35

23 rooms: £ 89/95

Typical Dishes

Jerusalem artichoke risotto
Shoulder of lamb
White chocolate crème brûlée

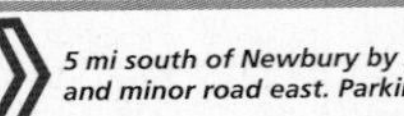
5 mi south of Newbury by A 34 and minor road east. Parking.

30 The Bakers Arms

High St,
Droxford SO32 3PA
Tel.: (01489)877533
e-mail: info@thebakersarmsdroxford.com **Website:** www.thebakersarmsdroxford.

Inspectors' favourites

 **Bowman Ales - Swift One & Wallops Wood**

Situated in a peaceful village which lies on the banks of the river Meon, this traditional whitewashed pub is run by two thoroughly keen owners and their friendly team. With a commitment to providing quality, local food in a traditional pub atmosphere, they make the most of the local produce around them. Cooking is simple and unfussy, featuring classic British combinations with the odd French or Mediterranean touch; Droxford pork or sausages and steak or chicken from Hampshire are often on the menu, with time-honoured desserts such as apple and rhubarb crumble or bread and butter pudding to follow. The pub itself is characterful, featuring a mixture of wood and parquet flooring, pine tables and chairs and leather sofas, whilst a random array of Victorian photographs, historic beer advertisements and stags heads line the walls. Beers and wines are sourced locally, and can be enjoyed over a newspaper or a game of scrabble by the fire.

Closing times
Closed Sunday dinner and Monday

Prices
Meals: à la carte £ 20/26

Typical Dishes
Hampshire pike quenelles au gratin
Crispy duck leg
Chocolate & fudge brownie

6 mi north of Fareham by A 32.
Parking.

31 The Chestnut Horse

Easton SO21 1EG

Tel.: (01962)779257

e-mail: info@thechestnuthorse.com

Website: www.thechestnuthorse.com

Badger, Sussex, Hopping Hare, Fursty Ferret, Stinger, Festival Pheasant

A colourful pub, in more ways than one, despite being not a million miles from Winchester or the M3, the Chestnut Horse is still set in a pleasantly rural village and its pretty rear terrace spills over with vibrant floral blooms. If it's an intimate atmosphere you're after of an evening, take a seat next to the log fire in the romantic red room, where you can gaze lovingly at your partner over candlelight. The green room is the natural choice for lunch, but be aware that reservations are essential at weekends if you want to eat in either room. The building dates from 1564, and the characterful timbered bar, where tankards and jugs hang from the beams, is a monument to old times. Pub favourites rub alongside more modern dishes on the extensive menu, supplemented with an interesting list of daily specials chalked up on the blackboard. Pleasant staff are on hand, and are happy to deal with any special requests.

Closing times

Closed 25 December, 26 December dinner, 1 January dinner and Sunday dinner in winter

Prices

Meals: à la carte £ 26/33

Typical Dishes

Cajun spiced monkfish

Stuffed saddle of lamb

Baked Alaska

32 The Bugle

High St,
Hamble SO31 4HA

Tel.: (023)80453000 – Fax: (023)80453051
e-mail: manager@buglehamble.co.uk **Website:** www.buglehamble.co.uk

Courage Best and 2 guest beers such as Wadworth and a Hampshire Brewery

Sister to the White Star Tavern five miles away, this attractive 12C pub is situated at the end of a narrow, cobbled high street. Adjacent to one of the slipways leading into Southampton Water – yachting's Mecca – it can get very busy in the summer with landlubbers and yachties alike. Restored to retain much of its original character, the inn boasts exposed beams and brickwork, wattle walls, stone and oak floors and a wood burning stove. The 16C ground floor dining room is intimate and cosy and has a proper bar, while above it the private dining room comes complete with its very own wine cellar. The pub is fairly small inside but there is a large terrace to spill out onto in warmer weather. The traditional menu consists of a single sheet, with dishes such as sausage and mash or homemade fishcakes. Daily specials are chalked on the board and appealing bar bites such as pork pies are also available. Booking is essential.

Closing times
Open daily
Booking essential

Prices
Meals: à la carte £ 22

Typical Dishes
Baked goats cheese
Homemade burger
Baked vanilla cheesecake

7 mi southeast of Southampton by A 3024 or A 3025 and B 3397. Parking.

33 The Yew Tree

Hollington Cross,
Andover Road, Highclere RG20 9SE
Tel.: (01635)253360 – Fax: (01635)255035
e-mail: info@theyewtree.net **Website:** www.theyewtree.net

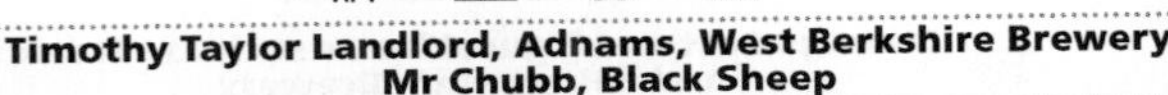

Timothy Taylor Landlord, Adnams, West Berkshire Brewery Mr Chubb, Black Sheep

Anyone expecting darts and a bit of spit and sawdust should think again: Marco Pierre White doesn't do casual and, sure enough, every table in his inn comes dressed in crisp linen; even the bar is a wondrous marble topped affair. The dining room may now be slightly larger but, through the magic of lighting, becomes more intimate in the evening. The menu reads like Marco Pierre White's CV, from Box tree apprentice to grandee of the London dining scene and only the terminally indecisive will struggle to make a choice, from a menu that blends French sophistication with British frankness. Dishes that have featured in his Big City restaurants like Parfait of foie gras or Omelette Arnold Bennett jostle for your attention with more pub-like offerings, such as pies of the steak and ale, shepherd or fish variety. There are six bedrooms available for those wishing to make a night of it; ask for the Cartoon Room.

Closing times

Closed 25-26 December dinner

Prices

Meals: £ 19 (lunch) and à la carte £ 27/50

6 rooms: £ 100

Typical Dishes

Boiled ham & piccalilli

Oxtail & kidney suet pudding

Eton mess

5 mi south of Newbury by A 343.
Parking.

34 The Hogget

London Road,
Hook RG27 9JJ
Tel.: (01256)763009
e-mail: home@hogget.co.uk **Website:** www.hogget.co.uk

 **Ringwood Best Bitter, Jennings Cocker Hoop, Marston's Pedigree**

Its unusual name refers to a boar of between one and two years of age – hence the rather cute sign – but this pub's change of moniker was only the beginning of its transformation at the hands of young new leaseholders. Were he still with us, former owner Cornelius Byford, whose picture hangs inside, would no doubt be pleased with the pub's new bay windows and heated terrace; the customers certainly seem to like the revamp, and despite its location at the junction of the A30 and A287 – with no in-built community to serve – it has become mightily popular. Its success is down to wholesome food and sensible prices; all dishes are homemade using local produce, and suppliers are name-checked on the menu. Choices range from pie and mash or rib-eye steak through to pan-fried calves liver or crab cake, with pies on a Monday, breakfast on Fridays and roasts on a Sunday. Service comes from cheery staff, including several members of the family.

Closing times
Closed 25-26 December

Prices
Meals: à la carte £ 21/28

Typical Dishes
Rib-eye steak with chips
Smoked haddock
Local cheeses

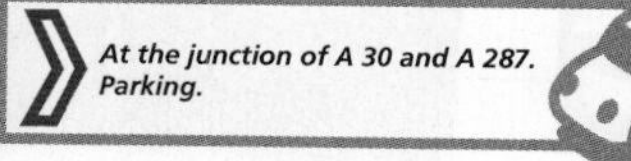
At the junction of A 30 and A 287.
Parking.

England • South East • Hampshire

35 The Peat Spade Inn

Village Street,
Longstock SO20 6DR

Tel.: (01264)810612 – Fax: (01264)811078

e-mail: info@peatspadeinn.co.uk **Website:** www.peatspadeinn.co.uk

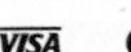  

VISA AE

Ringwood - Best and 49er and weekly changing guest beer

Well run by a keen, experienced young couple, the 19C Peat Spade Inn is the ultimate shooting and fishing pub, and therefore often teems with anglers here for the rivers and hunters here for the game. Locals certainly don't lose out though – and even have tables reserved especially for them. The country pursuits theme is reflected in the delightful décor – there are mounted fish, fishing rods and nets on the walls – and the relaxed country-life ambience is further enhanced by fine framed photos and the soft glow of candlelight. The food here is proper, proud, locally sourced pub cooking and the menu features classics such as braised faggots, fish and chips and sausage and mash; full of flavour, well presented and great value. Bedrooms are modern and stylish, with everything just so; from the plump beds to the jet showers and fluffy towels. The residents lounge has an honesty bar and is stacked with DVDs.

Closing times

Closed 25 December for food

Booking essential

Prices

Meals: à la carte £ 24/34

6 rooms: £ 130

Typical Dishes

Black pudding Scotch egg

Roast halibut

Cambridge burnt cream

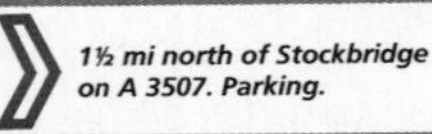

1½ mi north of Stockbridge on A 3507. Parking.

36 **The Anchor Inn**

Lower Froyle GU34 4NA
Tel.: (01420)23261
e-mail: info@anchorinnatlowerfroyle.co.uk
Website: www.anchorinnatlowerfroyle.co.uk

 **Youngs and changing guest beers from local brewery**

Sister to the Peat Spade Inn in Longstock, this pub has its focus just as firmly set on fishing and shooting. It may not look particularly ancient but step inside and its 14C origins become apparent: the traditional bar boasts low cushioned beams, open fires and horse brasses, its deep green walls filled with a captivating selection of bric-à-brac. The more formal drawing room is similarly styled, with candlelight contributing to its cosy, informal ambience. The bar menu offers simple treats like oysters or devilled lambs kidneys, while the à la carte tempts with traditional British dishes like potted rabbit or Barnsley chop; precisely crafted from well sourced English ingredients. Old school puds might include spotted dick or bread and butter pudding, but do watch those side orders as they can push the price up. Heavily beamed bedrooms named after war poets are well equipped and very comfortable, with Rupert Brooke the most luxurious.

Closing times
Closed 25 December

Prices
Meals: £ 25/32
and à la carte £ 22/55

5 rooms: £ 130/170

Typical Dishes
Ham hock & piccalilli
Sirloin & Béarnaise sauce
Strawberry parfait

5 mi northeast of Alton by A 31. Parking.

37 The Bush Inn

Ovington SO24 0RE
Tel.: (01962)732764 – Fax: (01962)735130
e-mail: thebushinn@wadworth.co.uk
Website: www.wadworth.co.uk

  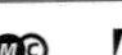 

 **Wadworths - 6X, Henry's IPA, Malt & Hop, Bishops Tipple and occasional guest ales**

Friendly, family-run 18C inn, hidden away in an idyllic spot surrounded by trees and little tributaries of the River Itchen; a picnic table in its garden the ideal setting for a lazy summer luncheon. Worry not if sunny days are but a distant memory, however, as The Bush is equally as appealing in the winter months. Four rooms surround the small central bar, their walls cluttered with pictures, china and taxidermy, and real fires give the inn a warm, cosy feel. Blackboard menus offer a wide selection of wholesome, unfussy dishes ranging from simple sandwiches and ploughman's through to steak or slow roast belly pork. Quality produce, including seafood from Loch Fyne, is carefully sourced, and since Alresford, the centre of the British watercress industry, is just down the road, expect to see the green stuff cropping up somewhere on the menu. Tables are particular sought after here at weekends, so make sure you've booked in advance.

Closing times
Open daily

Prices
Meals: à la carte £ 17/34

Typical Dishes
Sautéed lambs kidneys
Venison Wellington
Apple & Calvados pancake

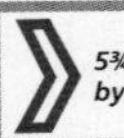

5¾ mi east of Winchester by B 3404 and A 31. Parking.

38 The Three Tuns

58 Middlebridge St,
Romsey SO51 8HL
Tel.: (01794)512639
e-mail: hannah.wilkin@btconnect.com **Website:** www.thethreetunsromsey.co.uk

Andwell's King John, Ringwood Best, Sharp's Doom Bar, Summer Lightning

Despite a mandatory modicum of modernisation in the form of a slate floor and a few black leather sofas, the thickly beamed, 300-year-old Three Tuns is still very much a proper pub, with a cosy, period feel and real ales being drunk by real locals at the bar. An ex-Navy chef, used to feeding hungry Matelots, David Palmer's culinary skills are now being put to good use feeding hungry civilians. Lunch menus offer a raft of pub favourites such as sausage and mash or homemade honey roast ham, as well as classics like eggs Benedict or smoked salmon; while things move up a notch in the evening, when you can push the boat out with dishes like sautéed calves liver, seared scallops and roast pork belly. Service is friendly and you certainly get the feeling that the staff know the ropes; eat in either the bar or in the equally rustic dining room and afterwards maybe take a post-prandial wander to the gates of Broadlands, home of the Mountbattens.

Closing times
Closed 26 December and Monday lunch

Prices
Meals: £ 8 (lunch) and à la carte £ 15/25

Typical Dishes
Scallops & chorizo
Venison & red cabbage
Chocolate Marquise

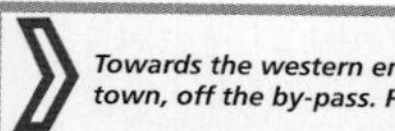

Towards the western end of the town, off the by-pass. Parking.

39 White Star Tavern, Dining and Rooms

28 Oxford Street,
Southampton SO14 3DJ
Tel.: (023)80821990 – Fax: (023)80904982
e-mail: manager@whitestartavern.co.uk **Website:** www.whitestartavern.co.uk

Inspectors' favourites

VISA MC AE

Ringwood and guest ales

Situated on the city's prime dining street, in the historic maritime district, this smart corner pub has provided nourishment and lodgings for seafarers since the late 19C; and with its eye-catching black exterior, large windows and great quality food, it still serves as a beacon to the city's visitors – be they mariners or more land-loving folk. Informal in feel and modern in style, its central bar is surrounded by airy open plan areas, with green Chesterfields and a hotchpotch of tables; while you can eat anywhere at lunchtime, the evening à la carte is only served in the dining room. Foodwise, there's everything you could want here, from sandwiches and pub classics to more sophisticated dishes with a modern European style, such as breast of pheasant or fillet of sea bass. Bedrooms are named after J class yachts and the legendary White Star liners; understated in style, they come with flat screens and modern bathrooms.

Closing times
Closed 25-26 December
Prices
Meals: à la carte £ 20/28
13 rooms: £ 89/119

Typical Dishes
Local wood pigeon
Lymington sole
Chocolate fondant

Southeast of West Quay shopping centre, off Bernard Street. Parking meters directly outside and College St car park (2min walk).

40 Plough Inn

Main Road,
Sparsholt SO21 2NW
Tel.: (01962)776353 – Fax: (01962)776400

 **Henry's IPA, Horizon, Wadworth 6X, Wadworth JCB**

Reputedly this pub began life, several hundred years ago, as coach house for Sparsholt Manor, although nobody seems quite sure of its exact vintage. Inside, it's traditionally styled and open plan with a long bar, exposed brickwork and a rustic hotchpotch of tables and chairs. The delightful lawned garden offers a profusion of picnic benches with countryside views, as well as a children's play area to keep the little ones amused for suitably long periods. Two blackboard menus cover a wide range of dishes; one offers traditional favourites with lots of comfort appeal, such as sausage and mash or steak and ale pie, while the other concerns itself with more elaborate dishes, involving maybe lamb shank, sea bass or duck breast. If pigeon is your favourite dish, you are likely to be disappointed; since the large shed in the garden is apparently the local pigeon fanciers' clubhouse, it's the one bird you're unlikely to see on the menu.

Closing times
Closed 25 December
Booking essential

Prices
Meals: à la carte £ 22/27

Typical Dishes
Salmon & crab fishcake
Slow roast belly of pork
Treacle tart

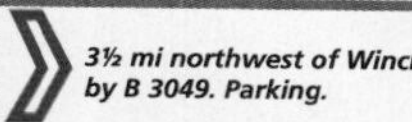
3½ mi northwest of Winchester by B 3049. Parking.

41 The Greyhound

31 High St,
Stockbridge SO20 6EY
Tel.: (01264)810833
e-mail: enquiries@thegreyhound.info **Website:** www.thegreyhound.info

VISA MC

Butcombe Bitter and summer guest beers

The Greyhound may not quite have the pedigree it once did but it can still impress. The pub comes divided into two areas: the beamed ceiling, subtle lighting and exposed brick of the rather sophisticated main dining area, with its huge – but sadly empty – inglenooks, and the more relaxing bar area, with its sofas and open fire. The kitchen has a commendably classical bent, where ingredient combinations won't scare the horses and while the emphasis may be on offering satisfying, modern pub fare, dishes still come appetisingly presented and precisely executed. Service can occasionally be a tad brusque but the job gets done efficiently enough. The cream coloured bedrooms are modern and stylish, and come with huge showers. The attractive surroundings of the market town of Stockbridge remain a great draw, as does the local stretch of the Test, one of the country's most famous fly-fishing rivers.

Closing times

Closed 24-26 and 31 December, 1 January and Sunday dinner

Prices

Meals: à la carte £ 25/40

8 rooms: £ 70/120

Typical Dishes

Greyhound fishcake

Breast of duck

White chocolate & blueberry crème brûlée

15 mi east of Salisbury by A 30.
Parking.

42 The Thomas Lord

High Street,
West Meon GU32 1LN
Tel.: (01730)829244
e-mail: enjoy@thethomaslord.co.uk **Website:** www.thethomaslord.co.uk

5 ales from Hampshire breweries such as Bowman Ales, Triple FFF, Ballards, Goddards, Oakleaf, Irvings

Anyone for cricket? Named after the founder of Lord's cricket ground, this pub is a sanctuary for all kinds of cricketing memorabilia; the highlight of which is a display case above the bar, where a collection of stuffed stoats, ferrets and squirrels play the noble game. Built in 1936, this pub fell into disrepair, but was saved by two locals who bought it and enlisted the help of the village to return it to its former glory. You can eat in the snug, with shelves crammed full of second-hand books for sale (the proceeds of which go towards new community projects), or in the larger, lighter dining room, where the constantly evolving menus change as often as twice a day. The cooking is generous and robust, mainly British, with dishes such as faggots and ham hock, and the odd hint of Mediterranean influence. Produce is passionately regional, and with over 50 suppliers, 95% of ingredients are locally sourced. How's that for a good deal?

Closing times
Open daily

Prices
Meals: à la carte £ 22/28

Typical Dishes
Potted squirrel & chutney
Braised lamb shoulder
Lemon thyme panna cotta

9 mi west of Petersfield by A 272 and A 32 south.

43 The Wykeham Arms

75 Kingsgate St,
Winchester SO23 9PE
Tel.: (01962)853834
e-mail: wykehamarms@fullers.co.uk **Website:** www.fullers.co.uk

Fuller's London Pride, Gales HSB, Chiswick, Butser

Although hidden away among the ancient, narrow streets betwixt cathedral and college, this characterful 18C inn is invariably filled with a diverse collection of tourists and locals; including maybe a judge or two and perhaps even a bishop. It's named after William of Wykeham, who founded the college, and the link is obvious everywhere you look: boys hurry past the windows, school vests line the walls of the bar, housemasters pop in for a pint of real ale on their way home from school and punters sit at school desks purloined from the classrooms. Lunch – best eaten in the surprisingly spacious bar - sees traditional dishes such as shepherd's pie and sausage and mash gracing the menu, while dinner is more elaborate, and accompanied by a very good wine list. Bedrooms are split between the inn and the St. George annex opposite; those in the annex are quieter, and come with their own terrace garden.

Closing times

Closed 25 December

Booking essential

Prices

Meals: à la carte £ 25/35

14 rooms: £ 65/115

Typical Dishes

Chicken liver parfait

Hampshire rack of lamb

Warm chocolate & hazelnut tart

Near (St Mary's) Winchester College. Access to car park via Canon Street only. Parking or street parking with permit.

44 The Taverners

High Street,
Godshill PO38 3HZ
Tel.: (01983)840707 – Fax: (01983)840517
Website: www.thetavernersgodshill.co.uk

 **Taverners Own Ale, Fuller's London Pride and weekly changing guest ale such as Butcombe, Black Sheep**

A board outside The Taverners urges locals to drop off any surplus produce they might be in possession of; perhaps some home-grown fruit or vegetables, locally caught fish, wild rabbit or pheasant. They'll receive a fair price in exchange – which is then passed onto the customer – or maybe a pint of locally brewed Taverners Beer, if they'd prefer. Inside, boards display information about seasonality and food miles, and it's this serious approach to food – and the resulting tasty dishes – which are attracting plenty of tourists to this friendly pub. Classic dishes like hand-raised pork pie with piccalilli, faggots and the quaintly named 'My Nan's lemon meringue pie' are listed on the menu, while specials are chalked up on a blackboard and change according to what's available. The spacious interior is split into three areas; the best one at the front with roaring fire. Sprawling gardens house chickens, herbs and a petanque pitch.

Closing times

Closed 2 weeks early January, Sunday dinner (except bank holiday weekends and school summer holidays)

Prices

Meals: à la carte £ 16/25

Typical Dishes

Potted duck & pickles
Moor Farm pork belly
Plum & almond tart

4 mi west of Shanklin by A 3020.
Parking.

45 The Yew Tree

Barfreston CT15 7JH
Tel.: (01304)831000
e-mail: yew.tree@live.co.uk
Website: www.yewtree.info

 **Gadd's Brewery, Ramsgate Brewery, Whitstable Brewing Co, Hop Demon Incubus**

Although you are most welcome to have a drink at the tiny bar here – which features ales from Gadds micro brewery in Ramsgate – it's the food which is the focus. Cooking is precise and unfussy, with good, clean flavours, and such is their reputation for sourcing produce locally, people now bring fresh fruit, vegetables and the occasional rabbit to their door. A good value set lunch menu features alongside the à la carte during the week; dishes might include cider-braised pork belly or pan-fried calves liver; with hearty broths for the walkers and half portions available for children. Sunday roasts entice a fair few hungry punters, there's homemade bread and butter and an impressive wine list too. Nestled next to the village's historic church, the pub has only eight tables spread over two rooms. The decked terrace adds to its capacity during the summer and the private upstairs room is popular for small parties and business meetings.

Closing times
Closed 26-27 December and Sunday dinner

Booking advisable

Prices
Meals: à la carte £ 23/31

Typical Dishes
Local asparagus
Rump of spring lamb
Chocolate mousse & roasted strawberries

9½ mi from Canterbury by A 2.
Parking.

46 The Three Chimneys

Hareplain Road,
Biddenden TN27 8LW
Tel.: (01580)291472

 **Adnams Best and Broadside, Youngs, Harvey's**

Legend has it that when French prisoners were held at nearby Sissinghurst Castle during the Seven Years' War, they were permitted to walk along the lanes but forbidden to pass the road junction where the pub lay; the pub's name being a mistranslation into English of the phrase 'les trois chemins' (the three roads). It's a hugely characterful, low-ceilinged pub, with cask ales kept on a shelf behind the bar, a restaurant and conservatory at the rear and a pleasant garden; to with plans to convert the outbuildings into a farm shop and create a small orangery. The menu is chalked up on blackboards and covers everything from liver and bacon or fillet steak to duck leg confit and pan-fried fillets of Monkfish; with asparagus grown by the farmer opposite and hearty, nursery puddings like Bakewell tart or sticky toffee pudding. Portions are large enough for a starter to constitute a light lunch, and the small wine list includes the local Biddenham wine.

1½ mi west by A 262. Parking.

Closing times
Closed 25 December
Booking essential

Prices
Meals: à la carte £ 23/35

Typical Dishes
Baked field mushrooms
Pan-roasted fillet of smoked haddock
Sticky toffee pudding

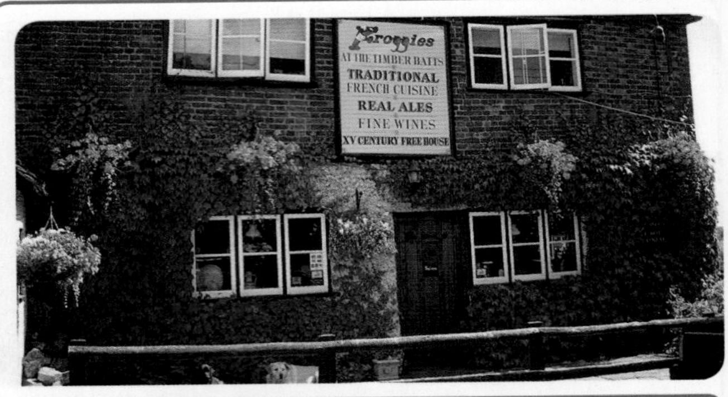

Froggies at the Timber Batts

47 Froggies at the Timber Batts

School Lane,
Bodsham Green TN25 5JQ

Tel.: (01233)750237 – Fax: (01233)750176

e-mail: post@thetimberbatts.co.uk **Website:** www.thetimberbatts.co.uk

VISA  AE

Adnams, Woodforde's Wherry, Fuller's London Pride

If you suffer from ranidaphobia, it's probably best to avoid this 15C pub, for the little green creatures are everywhere. There are knitted frogs, tin frogs, paper frogs and china frogs; there's even one that croaks at you as you walk in through the front door. The reason for all this frog frivolity is the jolly French owner, who as well as having a well-developed sense of irony, also does a mean line in mouth-watering meals. With the help of his son, the Gallic gastronome produces authentic French dishes like coq au vin, duck confit or rack of lamb; there's plenty of seafood, as well as classic desserts such as crème brûlée, tart au citron or tart Tatin – and lighter choices like sandwiches, Croque Monsieur or omelette can be enjoyed next to the inglenook in the traditional beamed bar. The French know that good food takes time; Rosbifs who appreciate this will find plenty on the wine list to divert them while they wait.

Closing times

Closed 24 December to 3 January

Prices

Meals: £ 20 (lunch) and à la carte £ 27/40

Typical Dishes

Stuffed mussels
Romney Marsh rack of lamb
Crème brûlée

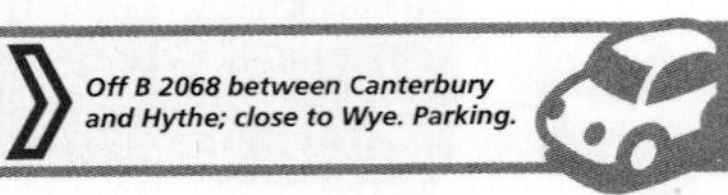
Off B 2068 between Canterbury and Hythe; close to Wye. Parking.

48 The Dove

Plum Pudding Lane,
Dargate ME13 9HB
Tel.: (01227)751360
e-mail: thedoveinn@yahoo.co.uk

 **Shepherd Neame ales - Masterbrew, Canterbury Jack and one seasonal ale**

Set in the heart of a sleepy little hamlet, in the delectable sounding Plum Pudding Lane, this attractive red-brick Victorian pub boasts well-tended gardens complete with doves and dovecotes. Inside, there's an air of rustic authenticity, as a mix of wooden chairs are set at scrubbed pine tables and roaring log fires burn in three cosy rooms. It's very much a locals pub – albeit the only pub in the area – and villagers pop in and out all day, especially at lunchtime and after work. Having begun his training here at the age of 17, Phillip returned over 10 years later as the chef-owner and has been welcomed back with open arms. His heartwarming soups and broths of the day jostle with equally appetising, seasonal dishes on the à la carte, where you might find Waterham Farm chicken with pumpkin risotto. Be sure to save room for pudding though, as the velvety crème brûlée is well worth the calories. Sunday roasts are particularly popular.

Closing times
Closed Sunday dinner and Monday

Prices
Meals: à la carte £ 25/35

Typical Dishes
Smoked ham hock terrine
Roast rack of lamb
Bitter chocolate tart

Between Faversham and Whitstable, south of A 299. Parking.

49 The Fitzwalter Arms

The Street,
Goodnestone CT3 1PJ
Tel.: (01304)840303
e-mail: thefitzwalterarms@gmail.com **Website:** www.thefitzwalterarms.co.uk

Shepherd Neame - Masterbrew, Canterbury Jack

About as far from your typical-looking boozer as it's possible to get, this striking brick building, with its castellated exterior and mullioned windows may well owe something to the fact that, before it served as a hostelry, it was reputedly the keep for Goodnestone Park, manor house of the Fitzwalter estate – famous for the beautiful country gardens where Jane Austen regularly used to take a turn. With such a history, you might think this place would have since been turned into a fancy dining pub, but thankfully, no – it has very much kept the feel of the village local, with people playing darts or bar billiards, or simply shooting the breeze by the open fire in the characterful, beamed bar. Eat in the small dining area overlooking the headstones in the churchyard, where the daily-changing blackboard menu might offer dishes such as coq au vin, faggots or John Dory. The large beer garden comes into its own in the summer months.

Closing times
Closed 25 December, 1 January, Sunday dinner and Tuesday

Prices
Meals: à la carte £ 16/28

Typical Dishes
Mulligatawny soup
Braised turbot with oysters
Custard tart

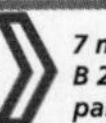

7 mi west of Sandwich by A 257, B 2046 and minor road. On-street parking in front of pub.

50 **Harrow Inn**

Common Rd,
Ightham TN15 9EB
Tel.: (01732)885912 – Fax: (01732)885912

 **Greene King - IPA and Abbot Ale**

It's located down a little lane and doesn't look much from the outside, but don't be so shallow as to let appearances mislead you; once inside this part-17C stone and brick pub, you'll find a welcoming atmosphere, with a fire flickering in the grate and candles lit on every table. This place has food at its core, with hearty, rustic dishes like game pies and coarse pâtés chalked up on a blackboard in the traditional bar, as well as a printed à la carte in the comfortable, more formal restaurant. If and when the summer sun decides to put in appearance, the small back terrace makes a convenient place to plonk your behind, but wherever you choose to sit, you'll find that the food is tasty and the service is pleasingly low-key and efficient. Handily situated for a spot of lunch or dinner on your way to or from the historic National Trust properties of Knole House, birthplace of Vita Sackville-West, or 14C medieval manor house, Ightham Mote.

Closing times

Closed 26-30 December, Sunday dinner and Monday

Prices

Meals: à la carte £ 20/32

Typical Dishes
Goat's cheese & onion tart
Scallops in pancetta
Orange & ginger tiramisu

5 mi southeast of Sevenoaks by A 25 on Common Road. Parking.

England • South East • Kent

51 The Granville

Street End,
Lower Hardres CT4 7AL
Tel.: (01227)700402 – Fax: (01227)700925
e-mail: the-granville@btconnect.com

   AE

 **Shepherd Neame Masterbrew and seasonal ale**

Just another common-or-garden pub on an unremarkable main road, you might well be thinking as you drive on by, but do so and you'll be missing a treat. Going into The Granville is like entering into another world; a world where open plan, Scandinavian-style rooms loom large; where you can watch the chefs on show in the kitchen, partake in a game of Scrabble® or sink into a leather sofa with the day's papers. The chalked up menu happily highlights local produce and keeps things brief and simple: find a table, place your order at the bar and you'll soon be tucking into juicy olives and slices of crusty homemade bread while awaiting your pork belly, duck confit or slow-roast chicken breast. Desserts are equally as mouth-watering; try the trio of lemon with sorbet sprinkled with 'sparkle dust'. With a winning combination of good food and a relaxing setting that clearly appeals to all ages, this is the kind of place you covet for your local.

Closing times
Closed 25-26 December, Sunday dinner and Monday

Prices
Meals: à la carte £ 21/35

Typical Dishes
Steamed mussels
Roast rib-eye beef
Apple & blackcurrant crumble

3 mi south of Canterbury on B 2068. Parking.

52 Three Mariners

2 Church Road,
Oare ME13 0QA
Tel.: (01795)533633
e-mail: info@thethreemarinersoare.co.uk **Website:** www.thethreemarinersoare.

 VISA MC

Shepherd Neame Masterbrew and seasonal ale

If you've been negotiating the Saxon Shore Way or Walking on the Wild Side, The Three Mariners in the sleepy hamlet of Oare is the perfect place to stop and refresh yourself. Set next to a small marina in the tidal Swale channel, this 500 year old pub offers pleasant views from its terrace over the marshes to the estuary beyond. Inside, a roaring fire and smiling waitresses await and there's a certain warmth and quirkiness about the place. A constantly evolving à la carte offers an appealing mix of carefully prepared, flavoursome dishes such as smoked pigeon salad, local skate cheeks or raisin and walnut tart, whilst the two-choice set menus offer great value for money: the Walkers' Lunch might include potted duck, chicken pie and homemade ice cream, and the Business Lunch Parma ham, sea bass and artisan cheeses. From vegetables to meats, starters to desserts, you can guarantee that there's always plenty of local produce to be found.

Closing times

Closed Monday (except bank holidays) and Tuesday dinner

Prices

Meals: £ 15 (lunch) and à la carte £ 21/28

Typical Dishes

Soft herring roes
Braised ox cheeks
Chocolate, prune & Armagnac cake

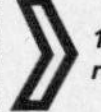

1 mi west of Faversham by minor road or A 2 and B 2045. Parking.

53 The Sportsman

Faversham Rd, Seasalter CT5 4BP
Tel.: (01227)273370
e-mail: contact@thesportsmanseasalter.co.uk
Website: www.thesportsmanseasalter.co.uk

Shepherd Neame Early Bird, Whitstable Bay, Porter

'Passionate' may well have become the most hackneyed and hyperbolic adjective of recent years, yet its use to describe Stephen Harris, self-taught chef at the Sportsman, and his approach towards his raw materials, is exceedingly apt. This is a man who grows peas, beans and the like in his garden for use in the restaurant. A man who makes his own salt, and his own butter, including a seaweed variety. A man who visits the farms from which he sources his meat in order to feed the pigs and the cows. Passion? This is a man on fire. His aim? To use the freshest food, with the least possible distance between farm and fork, and to subject it to minimal tampering. The resulting dishes may appear simple, but their execution is meticulous: this is confident cooking with clarity of flavour seldom found in a pub. Desserts are prepared in-house each day and the just-out-of-the-oven lemon tart is a classic. Book ahead; it's secluded but very popular.

Closing times
Closed 25-26 December, Sunday dinner and Monday

Prices
Meals: à la carte £ 23/34

Typical Dishes
Salmagundi
Monkshill farm lamb
Jasmine tea junket

2 mi southwest of Whitstable by B 2205 following the coast road. Parking.

54 George & Dragon

Speldhurst Hill,
Speldhurst TN3 0NN
Tel.: (01892)863125 – Fax: (01892)863216
e-mail: info@speldhurst.com **Website:** www.speldhurst.com

 **Larkins Traditional and Chiddingstone, Harveys Best and Hadlow Bitter**

This George and Dragon is a pub for all seasons: in summer, the drowsy scent of lavender drifts across the lovely outdoor terrace while on colder days, the snug interior and warm character that one expects from somewhere dating from the 13C won't disappoint. The beams, log fires and inglenooks are all there, along with a good smattering of locals which also includes the majority of the serving team; the atmosphere is never less than warm and welcoming. The same menu is served throughout so that makes the bar the more convivial choice, rather than the separate dining room. The pub also prides itself on its use of Kent's rich seasonal bounty, from its orchards and rivers to its forests and farms. The cooking is suitably rustic and forthright: warm salads, local sausages and platters of cheese and hams that arrive on wooden boards are the high points, along with the decidedly heart-warming puddings.

Closing times
Closed Sunday dinner

Prices
Meals: à la carte £ 20/28

Typical Dishes
Seared pigeon breasts
Roast belly of pork
Treacle tart

3½ mi north of Royal Tunbridge Wells by A 26. Parking.

55 The Ivy House

27 Hackington Rd,
Tyler Hill CT2 9NE
Tel.: (01227)472200

 **Sharp's Doom Bar, Shepherd & Neame Master Brew**

Despite the lick of paint given to it by its owners, this traditional pub, close to the university and just north of Canterbury, is not the most glamorous of venues, but as you tuck into your meal, the décor seems of little importance. Lunch might mean a sandwich or salad; perhaps a fillet of salmon or a simple meat dish, whilst dinner showcases confident, seasonal cooking which comes in satisfyingly substantial portions. To start, you could try smoked haddock fishcakes or a chicken liver parfait; mains might include pan-fried local skate wing, sirloin steak or roast fillet of wild sea trout. The owners know all the local suppliers and, if you find mushrooms in your risotto, chances are the chef went out and foraged for them himself. Hand pumped ales, a wine list of about 30 bins and live music once a month on a Sunday afternoon also bring in business. It may not be the finished article quite yet, but just watch that Ivy grow.

Closing times
Closed Sunday dinner and Monday

Prices
Meals: à la carte £ 18/27

Typical Dishes
Tuna cerviche
Fillet of wild sea trout
Orange & passion fruit crème brûlée

 *2 mi north of Canterbury by minor road. Parking.* 

56 The Swan on the Green

West Peckham ME18 5JW
Tel.: (01622)812271 – Fax: (0870)0560556
e-mail: info@swan-on-the-green.co.uk
Website: www.swan-on-the-green.co.uk

 **Trumpeter (own brew), Fuggles Pale (own brew), Cygnet**

A pub for serious ale-lovers who also happen to like a nice bit of grub, The Swan might have started the twenty-first century as a pub with an attached micro-brewery, but the success of the latter means that, ten years later, it's the pub which seems like the add-on. They brew their own range of cask and tank conditioned beers and, as well as providing the pub with as much of the malty stuff as it needs, sell it to other pubs and to beer festivals countrywide. Menus offer no-nonsense, hearty dishes made using local produce – perhaps calves liver and bacon or a mezze style platter for two at lunch, or baked pheasant or slow roast pork belly in the evening – this is rustic cooking, with plenty of chargrilling and some home-smoking of meats. The pub is simply furnished, with an open fire and the obligatory hanging hops, and as its name suggests, it overlooks the village green. It can get busy and both seating and parking are at a premium.

Closing times

Closed 25 December, Sunday dinner and Monday dinner

Prices

Meals: à la carte £ 21/26

Typical Dishes

Platter of fish
Pan-fried Guinea fowl
Sticky toffee pudding

7¾ mi southwest of Maidstone by A 26 and B 2016. Follow sign to church and green. Parking.

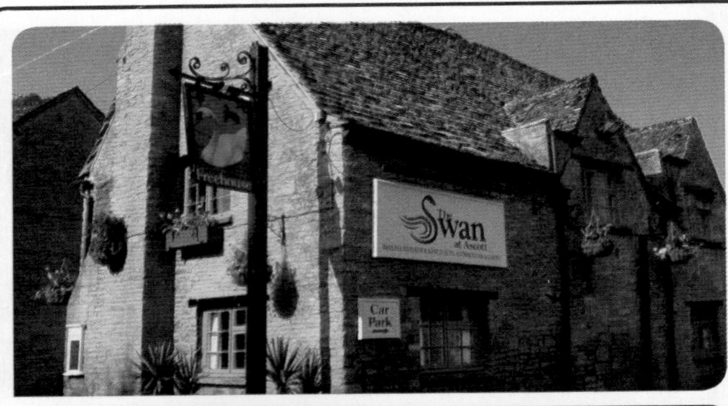

57 The Swan Inn

4 Shipton Rd,
Ascott-under-Wychwood OX7 6AY
Tel.: (01993)832332
e-mail: ricky@swanatascott.com **Website:** www.swanatascott.com

 VISA MC

Brakspear, Hook Norton, Wadworth

The fact that its owner is a former builder must have been mightily convenient when it came to the refurbishment of this 400 year old building, particularly considering the damage done by the 2007 floods. Richard's dream was to create a traditional community pub and his vision has been well and truly realised: the inn is now a mainstay of the village, with the glorious sort of atmosphere anyone would wish for in their local. The team in the kitchen share Richard's philosophy: the food is traditional, with nothing too fancy, but its quality speaks for itself – and from the stock and the bread to the ice cream and even the chips, everything is made on the premises. Dishes might include pork belly with black pudding and potato fritter, sausage and mash or omelette Arnold Bennett, with delicious desserts like dark chocolate cheesecake. Bedrooms are contemporary in style, with more planned for the future.

Closing times

Closed 25 December, Sunday dinner and Monday

Booking advisable at dinner

Prices

Meals: £ 20 (Sunday lunch only) and à la carte £ 21/29

5 rooms: £ 71/125

Typical Dishes

Goats' cheese tart

Arnold Bennett omelette

Dark chocolate cheesecake

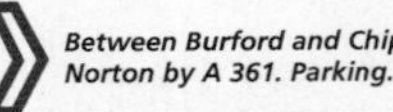

Between Burford and Chipping Norton by A 361. Parking.

58 The Sweet Olive at The Chequers Inn

Baker St,
Aston Tirrold OX11 9DD
Tel.: (01235)851272
Website: www.sweet-olive.com

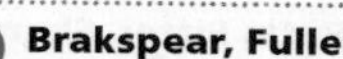 **Brakspear, Fuller's London Pride**

Down narrow winding lanes in a country village, with a loyal band of locals inside, this red-brick Victorian inn couldn't appear more British. Step inside, however, and you are greeted with a 'bonjour' from the French owner behind the bar; his compatriot behind the scenes in the kitchen. Bringing a touch of their own culture, the wine list features a selection from their homeland, Alsace, whilst panels of old French boxes deck the bar. The blackboard menus and verbally explained specials provide some interest, with French dishes such as fish soup, onglet of beef or crème brûlée, alongside others of a more international flavour, such as Moroccan lamb. In honour of the pub's name you are provided with a dish of exceptionally succulent olives to start your meal and in recognition of their new home, there is even the odd British number, such as treacle sponge with custard and ice cream. All that's left to say is 'bon appétit'.

Closing times
Closed 25 December, February, 1 week in July, Sunday dinner and Wednesday

Booking essential

Prices
Meals: à la carte £ 24/30

Typical Dishes
Tempura tiger prawns
Escalope of venison
Treacle sponge

4 mi southwest of Wallingford by minor road through South Moreton. Parking.

59 The Kings Head Inn

The Green,
Bledington OX7 6XQ

Tel.: (01608)658365 – Fax: (01608)658902
e-mail: info@kingsheadinn.net **Website:** www.kingsheadinn.net

Inspectors' favourites

Hook Norton, Butts Bitter, Sharp's Doom Bar, Donnington Brewery BB

Set on the pretty village green with a stream running alongside, this warmly welcoming 15C inn underwent a full refurbishment in 2007 due to knee deep flood damage. Thankfully, the pub lost none of its charm in the process and a seat in its low ceilinged, beamed bar, in the glow of the open fire, is as popular as ever. If the bar becomes too busy, as is its wont, the dining room is just as comfortable, if perhaps not quite as atmospheric, while the paved terrace is great for al fresco dining in the sun. The same menu is served in all areas and you'll find traditional dishes such as pan-fried lamb cutlets or homemade steak, ale and root vegetable pie, with the odd international influence thrown in. Cooking is robust and rustic in style, with local ingredients well used. Bedrooms are smart, with good facilities and some antique furniture; those in the pub itself are older and more characterful, while the others have a more stylish feel.

Closing times
Closed 25-26 December

Prices
Meals: à la carte £ 20/28
12 rooms: £ 60/125

Typical Dishes
Devilled lambs kidneys
Beef steak & ale pie
Chocolate caramel brownie

4 mi southeast of Stow-on-the-Wold by A 436 and B 4450. Parking.

60 The Lamb at Buckland

Lamb Lane, Buckland SN7 8QN
Tel.: (01367)870484
e-mail: enquiries@thelambatbuckland.co.uk
Website: www.thelambatbuckland.co.uk

 **Hooky Bitter, Sharp's Doom Bar, Brakspear**

Thankfully The Lamb is well signposted, for you'd never find it otherwise. Once inside, there's no doubting you're in the right pub though, thanks to the veritable flock of ovine-inspired items to be found here – in the form of cuddly toys, paintings, curios, life-sized models and even lamb motif carpets. This 17C stone-built building has a bar in which you can eat, a linen-laid restaurant in the heavily beamed oldest part of the building, plus a rear garden with a little sunken terrace for al fresco dining in the summer. Tasty, traditional British food is chalked on the large blackboard menu above the open fireplace, and the same food is served throughout. In quiet months, they also offer a good value fixed price menu. Family owned for a number of years, the atmosphere is one of cosy familiarity, so even if you're not a local, there's no need to feel sheepish. Altogether now; 'Four legs good, two legs baaad...'

Closing times
Closed Sunday dinner and Monday

Prices
Meals: à la carte £ 10/35

Typical Dishes
Warm scallop salad
Seared fillet of sea bass
Mango & ginger brûlée

Between Faringdon and Kingston Bagpuize off A 420. Parking.

61 The Trout at Tadpole Bridge

Buckland Marsh SN7 8RF

Tel.: (01367)870382 – Fax: (01367)870912

e-mail: info@troutinn.co.uk

Website: www.troutinn.co.uk

VISA

Youngs Bitter, Ramsbury, Fuller's London Pride, Old Hooky, Archers Golden, Moonlight, Wychwood

If you fancy trying your hand at boating, then this could be the pub for you. Set just off the Thames Path, The Trout boasts a pleasant garden running down to the river, where, upon request, you'll find an electric punt – complete with picnic hamper – and six private moorings for those arriving in their own vessels; free for the night if you're stopping to eat. It's a smart place but manages to retain a loyal band of drinkers, who congregate in the characterful flagstone bar; the diners sitting alongside them or in the airy back room. The concise main menu consists of a list of classic Gallic dishes with the odd contemporary touch, supplemented by a blackboard of daily specials that often include seafood or game – all of which is sourced from nearby farms and estates. It's a popular place, so you'll need to book but the cheery staff cope with the pressure well. Comfortable bedrooms exceed expectations; one even has its own sitting room.

Closing times

Closed 25-26 December and Sunday dinner (November-April)

Prices

Meals: à la carte £ 21/35

6 rooms: £ 75/110

Typical Dishes

Bubble & squeak

Grilled halibut

Lemon posset

4½ mi northeast of Faringdon by A 417, A 420 on Brampton road. Parking.

62 **The Highway Inn**

117 High Street,
Burford OX18 4RG
Tel.: (01993)823661
e-mail: info@thehighwayinn.co.uk **Website:** www.thehighwayinn.co.uk

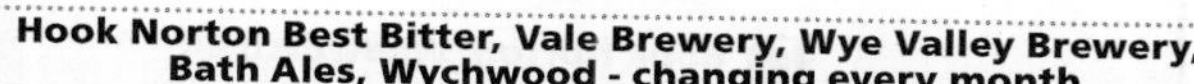

Hook Norton Best Bitter, Vale Brewery, Wye Valley Brewery, Bath Ales, Wychwood - changing every month

If you believe in fate, you might say that the Highway Inn's owners were meant to be: a local boy, he met his wife when she came over from Australia to visit her grandmother. They married in Burford, and even spent their wedding night at the 15C inn. Fast forward a few years, and it belongs to them; and having functioned as a shop and a B&B for 16 years, has now been loving restored to its original status of village inn. Twinkly lights in the bay trees draw you in; grab a table under the ticking clock, close to the roaring fire and take a look at what's on the menu. Pub dishes like fish and chips and sausage and mash are the staples here, with maybe a lamb or pork burger and specials such as risotto, fish, calves liver or lamb shank. Desserts are delicious and far from dainty, with choices like bread and butter pudding or apple and blackberry crumble. Cooking is as it should be: simple, honest and fresh. Classic, cosy bedrooms.

Closing times

Closed first 2 weeks of January

Prices

Meals: à la carte £ 25/32

9 rooms: £ 65/140

Typical Dishes

Tempura King prawns

Cotswold chicken breast

Banana tart Tatin

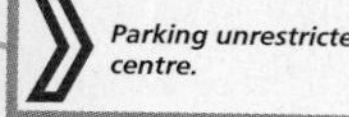

Parking unrestricted in the town centre.

63 The Lamb Inn

Sheep St,
Burford OX18 4LR
Tel.: (01993)823155 – Fax: (01993)822228
e-mail: info@lambinn-burford.co.uk **Website:** www.cotswold-inns-hotel.co.uk

Inspectors' favourites

  AE

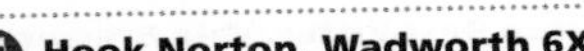

Hook Norton, Wadworth 6X

Set in picture perfect Burford – once famous for its wool and sheep fairs – it's no coincidence that this 1420s weavers' cottage is set on Sheep Street. You can't fail to be impressed by the cosiness of the place, with its characterful flag-floored bar, airy restaurant with elegant columns and courtyard terrace with traditional cottage garden. The bar offers nibbles, light bites and afternoon tea, as well as main courses and a fresh fish board, while the restaurant offers more substantial dishes from a daily market or set selection. Cooking is robust with a sound classical base and is not afraid of pushing the boundaries; so you might find dishes like trio of beef or scallops and langoustines with vanilla sauce. It's rightly popular, and at times staff struggle to keep up, but its immense charm more than makes up for that. Bedrooms are warm and cosy: Rosie has a private garden; Allium's en suite boasts a roll-top bath and plasma TV.

Closing times
Closed 25 December

Prices
Meals: à la carte £ 33/45
17 rooms: £ 112/250

Typical Dishes
Potted shrimps
Rib-eye steak & homemade chips
Banana cheesecake

Parking at Bay Tree Hotel.

64 **The Masons Arms**

Banbury Rd,
Swerford, Chipping Norton OX7 4AP
Tel.: (01608)683212 – Fax: (01608)683105
e-mail: admin@masons-arms.com **Website:** www.masons-arms.com

Hook Norton Best, Brakspear's Special

This rurally-set roadside inn – a former Masonic lodge – has retained a touch of rustic character in the form of the odd wooden beam and an inglenook fireplace, but is for the most part a modernised dining pub, with a light and airy style and a relaxed, friendly atmosphere. With westerly views over the surrounding countryside, the new extension is the best place to sit – alternatively, head for the picnic benches in the neat garden. The chef-owner has previously worked with some notable names and confidently produces precise, well-presented and flavoursome dishes which are easy on the pocket as well as on the eye. With various set menus and an à la carte, there's plenty of choice – from simple sandwiches, salads or ploughman's through to classic British dishes with a modern slant, such as mushroom and leek shepherd's pie, farmhouse lamb and mint sausages, grilled pigeon breast with hazelnut mash and even the odd chicken Korma.

Closing times

Closed 25-26 December and Sunday dinner

Prices

Meals: £ 17/25
and à la carte £ 26/33

Typical Dishes

Seared pigeon breast
Cornish monktail with mussels
Panna cotta & rhubarb

5 mi northeast of Chipping Norton by A 361. Parking.

65 The Crown Inn

Mill Lane,
Church Enstone OX7 4NN
Tel.: (01608)677262
Website: www.crowninnenstone.co.uk

Hooky Best, Wells Bombardier, Hobgoblin

This 17C inn can be found nestled amongst pretty stone houses in a picturesque village on the edge of the Cotswolds. On a sunny day you can watch the world go by from the small front terrace or head to the rear garden for a bit more seclusion; inside there's yet more choice, as you're presented with a slate floored conservatory, a beamed dining room and a rustic stone-walled bar. It's not often that you'll see the chef-owner out of his whites and he's managed to build up quite a reputation for his seafood dishes in these parts: fishcakes and king scallop and bacon salad are permanent fixtures on the menu, alongside beer battered cod and some more unusual varieties of fish such as Red Gurnard. The daily lunchtime blackboard reads like a top ten of classic pub favourites, with sausage and mash, fish and chips, and homemade steak and Hooky ale pie all featuring. Meats, fruit and veg are sourced from local farms and puddings are homemade.

Closing times

Closed 26 December, 1 January and Sunday dinner

Prices

Meals: £ 18 (lunch Sunday lunch) and à la carte £ 19/30

Typical Dishes

Scallop & bacon salad
Calves liver & horseradish mash
Warm chocolate pudding

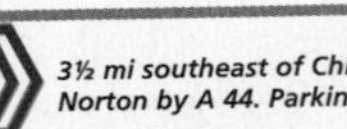

3½ mi southeast of Chipping Norton by A 44. Parking.

66 The Chequers

Church Rd,
Churchill OX7 6NJ
Tel.: (01608)659393

 VISA MC

 **Hook Norton, Greene King IPA, Flowers, Adnams Abbot Ale, Fuller's London Pride, Old Speckled Hen, Bombardier, Hobgoblin, Festival Pride**

If a brush with local life is what you're after, then a visit to this attractive Cotswold stone pub is a must. The first clue as to its position at the centre of the Churchill community is its sign, which proudly states 'The Chequers. Village Pub'. The second, is the fact that there's always a trusty band of villagers to be found at the bar – often alongside the local book club or church group. Inside it's surprisingly stylish, with flag floors, exposed stone walls and an inglenook fireplace all adding to the atmosphere. The menu, however, is more in line with the pub's traditional exterior, offering a list of classics ranging from sandwiches and pies through to more substantial dishes such as sea bass or steak. The odd inventive touch creeps into the main courses here and there but it's back to the old school with the homemade puddings. Thursday is roast duck night and regular monthly events include paella and beef Wellington evenings.

Closing times
Open daily

Prices
Meals: £ 18 and à la carte £ 20/30

Typical Dishes
Black pudding & poached egg
Crispy duck
Homemade apple lattice pie

Southwest of Chipping Norton by B 4450. Parking.

67 The Half Moon

Cuxham
0X49 5NF
Tel.: (01491)614151
e-mail: info@thehalf-moon.com **Website:** www.thehalf-moon.com

 **Brakspears Ordinary Bitter**

With original red and black floor tiling and exposed wooden beams proudly on display, you'd never guess that this 17C whitewashed pub had been all but destroyed by fire back in 2002. A sympathetic renovation salvaged what it could of the original building and characterful rustic features, while a complete interior refurbishment added a modern edge via some contemporary furnishings. The atmosphere is laid back and relaxed and there's always a warm welcome, especially from Harry the Springer Spaniel. With vegetables from the kitchen garden and meat from animals that have been taken on the hoof and properly butchered, the twice-daily blackboard menu features a good selection of local, ethical ingredients. Nothing is left to waste, so there's always plenty of offal to be found; there may be ox tongue or duck's hearts on toast, alongside less unusual offerings such as potted crab, roast hake, confit belly pork or seared beef fillet.

Closing times
Closed Sunday dinner

Prices
Meals: à la carte £ 21/28

Typical Dishes
Duck hearts on toast
Confit pork belly & lentils
Egg custard tart

In village centre on B 480. Parking.

68 The White Hart

Main Road,
Fyfield OX13 5LW
Tel.: (01865)390585
e-mail: info@whitehart-fyfield.com **Website:** www.whitehart-fyfield.com

Inspectors' favourites

   VISA

 **Constantly changing - Hook Norton Hooky Bitter, Loddon Hullabaloo, Sharp's Doom Bar, Vale Gravitas**

If you fancy a generous helping of history with your lunch, you've come to the right place. A 15C former chantry house, this intriguing building displays many original features including a two-storey, flag-floored hall with vaulted ceiling (now the dining room), a minstrels' gallery and a secret tunnel; as well as a pleasant terrace and cosy beamed bar with inglenook fireplace. Set in a picturesque village not far from Oxford, there's a wealth of produce on the doorstep: so you'll find meat from nearby farms or estates; flour – for the homemade bread – from the local mill; and fruit and veg from either the pub or locals' gardens. Catering for all, menus display honest British cooking and some internationally influenced sharing boards, followed by excellent desserts; the set lunch provides particularly good value. Service is slick and friendly and for something different, the biannual beer festival and hog roast makes a great day out.

Closing times
Closed Sunday dinner and Monday

Prices
Meals: £ 18 (lunch) and à la carte £ 25/32

Typical Dishes
Hare terrine
Belly of pork & celeriac pureé
Hot chocolate fondant

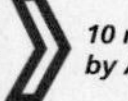
10 mi southwest of Oxford by A 420. Parking.

69 The Black Boy

91 Old High St,
Headington, Oxford OX3 9HT
Tel.: (01865)741137
e-mail: abi@theblackboy.uk.com **Website:** www.theblackboy.uk.com

 **Two guest beers such as Hareraiser, Morland Original**

It's big and it's bold; it's The Black Boy and, thanks to the new business partners on board, it's back to its beautiful best. The chef did a long stint with Raymond Blanc, so it comes as no surprise that there's a French edge to the essentially classic menu, but don't go getting the wrong idea; this is proper pub food, no messing, with unadorned mains like beer battered fish and chips, braised pork belly or sausage and mash, all for under a tenner. Bring some bling to your Black Boy burger by eating it in the small side restaurant; the low-lit bar is the less popular, but by no means less pleasant, alternative. Wines, like everything else, are sensibly priced; there are homemade breads and pizzas; while the succulent roast pork, lamb or perhaps organic Cotswold chicken goes down a storm for Sunday lunch. Tuesday night is quiz night; Thursday night's for jazz-lovers, and Sunday mornings are when the kids can get creative in the kitchen.

Closing times

Closed 24 December to 31 December, Sunday dinner and Monday

Prices

Meals: à la carte £ 18/23

Typical Dishes
Ham hock terrine
Bavette steak & frites
Crème brûlée

East of Oxford off London Rd. Some parking at the front of pub and in nearby streets.

70 The New Inn

Chalkhouse Green Rd,
Kidmore End RG4 9AU
Tel.: (0118)9723115
e-mail: thenewinn@live.co.uk **Website:** www.thenewinn.co.uk

 **Brakspear Original**

The hustle and bustle of Reading is only five miles away but you wouldn't realise it from the sleepy charms of this Oxfordshire hamlet and the comfy enticements of its focal point, The New Inn, which, though smartened up outside, still proudly bears its 16C hallmarks within. The cosy, atmospheric bar's rough floorboards, beams and open fires are all you'd expect from a proper pub of the era, and this is a fine spot to lay your hat and sup a pint. Most diners, meanwhile, head to the snazzy restaurant, where a few original beams merge tastefully with the smart wood tables and crisp white walls. Here, there's a nicely balanced menu ranging from pub favourites to more adventurous fare; you can also eat in the bar or delightful canopied terrace. A treat awaits overnighters: six bedrooms, some with balconies, which are stylish, modern, very comfy and well equipped.

Closing times
Closed Sunday dinner

Prices
Meals: £ 12 and à la carte £ 20/30
6 rooms: £ 65/85

Typical Dishes
Salmon & crayfish brûlée
Stuffed chicken in bacon
Chocolate & Cointreau mousse

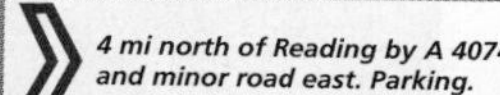
4 mi north of Reading by A 4074 and minor road east. Parking.

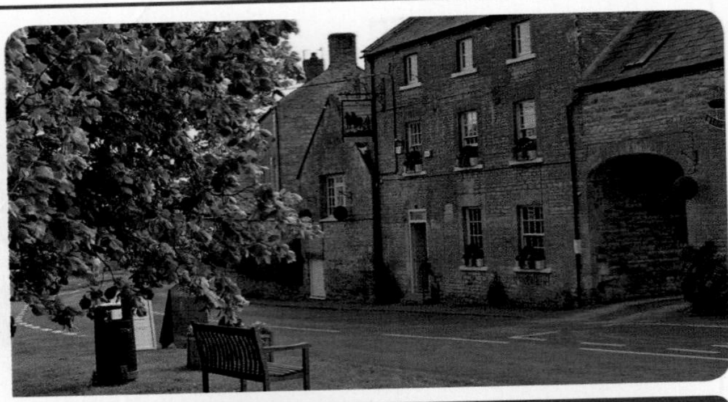

71 The Kingham Plough

The Green,
Kingham OX7 6YD
Tel.: (01608)658327 – Fax: (01608)658327
e-mail: book@thekinghamplough.co.uk **Website:** www.thekinghamplough.co.uk

Inspectors' favourites

VISA MC

Hook Norton Ales and Cotswold Brewery lagers

Chef-owner Emily Watkins was formerly sous-chef at The Fat Duck under Heston Blumenthal but that doesn't mean that she is now serving up snail porridge here in the depths of the Cotswolds. Far from it: a few touches – like the intensely flavoured steak cooked 'sous vide' or the trademark 'triple-cooked' chips may hint at her Fat Duck past, but this is a quintessentially British pub offering gutsy pub food, so expect to find hand-raised pork pies, potted duck, game pie or crisp lamb sweetbreads on the daily-changing menu, as well as a cracking collection of cheeses. The food is firmly rooted in the region and local suppliers range from former Blur bass player Alex James, to 'Roy the rabbit,' a local lady who talks to her cauliflowers and a 12 year old boy who provides the quails' eggs. There's real ale on tap, pigs' ears for your dog, and stylish, comfortable bedrooms boasting pocket sprung beds and crisp Egyptian linen.

Closing times

Closed 25 December

Prices

Meals: à la carte £ 30/45

7 rooms: £ 70/110

Typical Dishes

Pressed Cornish octopus

Lamb & barley stew

Apple jelly & cinnamon doughnut

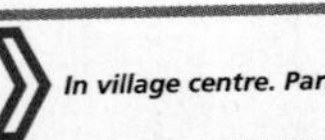

In village centre. Parking.

The Tollgate Inn

72 The Tollgate Inn

Church St,
Kingham OX7 6YA
Tel.: (01608)658389
e-mail: info@thetollgate.com **Website:** www.thetollgate.com

  MC AE

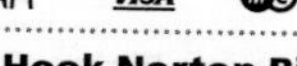 **Hook Norton Bitter, Bass**

The owners of the Tollgate Inn used to live next door to it – but loved the pub so much that they decided to buy it. They certainly couldn't ask for a better location; it sits proudly at the centre of this unspoiled Cotswolds village, its front terrace bathed in the midday sun, and attracts passing trade as well as loyal locals. The building is a Grade II listed former Georgian farmhouse which dates back to 1720 but the interior is modern and light, with comfy seating and inglenook fireplaces helping to create a relaxed feel. Food wise, the choice is more than adequate: while the easy-going lunch menu might offer a Cajun chicken salad, a burger or lasagne, the more ambitious dinner menu focuses on dishes like chargrilled tuna, roasted duck breast or pan-fried venison. If you are using the Tollgate as a base to explore the Cotswolds, you'll find that the modern bedrooms are immaculately kept and have a warm, bright feel.

Closing times
Closed Sunday dinner and Monday

Prices
Meals: à la carte £ 20/35
9 rooms: £ 65/100

Typical Dishes
Wood pigeon & quails eggs
Pan-fried duck breast
Raspberry panna cotta

3 mi southwest of Chipping Norton by B 4450 to Churchill and minor road west. Parking.

73 The Five Horseshoes

Maidensgrove RG9 6EX
Tel.: (01491)641282 – Fax: (01491)641086
e-mail: admin@thefivehorseshoes.co.uk
Website: www.thefivehorseshoes.co.uk

 **Brakspear Bitter, Oxford Gold**

Many a walker can be found in the bar of the 'Shoes, resting his weary feet and refuelling on one of the pub's famous doorstop sandwiches; others take a seat in the splendidly sun-soaked restaurant and wine room, or in the garden, with its stunning views out over the countryside. The chef has dipped into many a famous kitchen, returning with useful tips to inform his own cooking, so expect your mash to be extra luxurious, your sauce to be homemade and words like 'confit' and 'emulsion' to appear on the menu. It's all there, from comforting classics like shepherd's pie or Berkshire pork bangers, to coq au vin or haunch of fallow venison, and puddings like treacle tart or liquorice poached pear. Produce is sourced locally, with suppliers name-checked on the back of the menu; there's a hog roast once a month and popular barbecues in summer, with plans for a wood fired oven afoot. Keep an eye out for Chablis and Merlot, the resident dogs.

Closing times
Closed Sunday dinner

Prices
Meals: à la carte £ 20/30

Typical Dishes
Ham hock & foie gras terrine
Roast haunch of venison
Treacle tart

North of Henley by A 4230 and B 480, then ¾ mi west; near Stonor Park. Parking.

74 The Black Boy Inn

Milton OX15 4HH
Tel.: (01295)722111
e-mail: info@blackboyinn.com
Website: www.blackboyinn.com

 **Adnams, Greene King Abbot Ale, White Horse Brewery and guest ales**

If you're wondering about the name – so is everybody else. Its origins are unclear but suggestions include it being a reference to the swarthy Charles II; an old nickname from its days as a tobacconist's; or in recognition of a young slave found hiding in the pub's cellar. Set back from the road beside the church, this 16C sand-coloured stone building is very much a locals' pub; welcoming children, dogs and all. There's a spacious garden to the front and a traditional bar inside – while for those who prefer things a little more peaceful, there's also a conservatory dining room that opens out onto a gravel courtyard. The wide-ranging à la carte changes little from lunch to dinner, offering sandwiches, salads and pub classics all day, as well as a good selection of starters and main courses. Cooking is proudly British with just the odd international flavour: they save the best of the rest for their regular Global Gourmet evenings.

Closing times
Closed Sunday dinner

Prices
Meals: à la carte £ 27/38

Typical Dishes
Scallops with fine crab pasta
Steak
Trio of chocolate

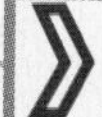 *4 mi south of Banbury by A 4260 and a minor road west via Adderbury. Parking.* 

75 The Nut Tree

Main Street,
Murcott OX5 2RE
Tel.: (01865)331253
Website: www.nuttreeinn.co.uk

MC AE

Hook Norton, Vale Spring Gold, Brakspear's Oxford Gold and others

This pub may look like your traditional thatched variety but the sight of pigs being reared in a pen is a clue to its great strength. You enter into one of those comfy bars with mind-your-head-beams and a gaggle of locals. If you're after more than just a snack head for either the dining room or the small conservatory extension; tables are smartly dressed and service is friendly yet attentive. One look at the owner-chef's appealing and nicely balanced menu and you'll start to realise that this is somewhere a little special. Its main thrust is 'proper' pub food such as fishcakes or chicken liver pâté but still executed with real care and understanding. There are also more restaurant style dishes like roasted foie gras, soufflés and others involving those pigs. By using the best ingredients it ensures that flavours are fresh, clear and eminently satisfying. The Nut Tree proves that tradition and good food can happily go together.

Closing times

Closed Sunday dinner

Prices

Meals: £ 18 (Monday-Thursday) and à la carte £ 31/43

Typical Dishes

Pavé of home-smoked salmon

Pork belly & curly kale

Sticky toffee pudding

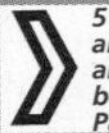

5 mi from Bicester by A 41 east and a minor road south via Lower and Upper Arncott; at T-junction beyond the motorway turn right. Parking.

76 **The Fishes**

North Hinksey Village
OX2 0NA
Tel.: (01865)249796
e-mail: fishes@peachpubs.com **Website:** www.fishesoxford.co.uk

 **Greene King IPA and 1 changing guest beer**

This pub's pretty riverside garden, with its fairytale white benches, is a large part of its charm – kick back with a champagne and Pimms on a lazy afternoon or order yourself a picnic, which comes complete with crockery, cutlery and even a blanket on which to sit. Inside, the décor moves seamlessly between the traditional – think stuffed fish in display cases – and the modern – try colourful abstract artwork and low leather seating. The atmosphere is lively, and, the garden apart, the decked terrace and the conservatory are the best places to sit. Food is fresh, free range and available all day: dishes might include sticky pork ribs, rack of lamb or sausage and mash; some choices come in small or large portions and there are a selection of deli boards for two. Wednesday night means steak night, when you can choose any wine for £16; Sunday roasts – which arrive on sharing boards – attract plenty of families.

Closing times
Closed 25 December

Prices
Meals: à la carte £ 19/40

Typical Dishes
Grilled Haloumi
Barbecued Cornish lamb
Apple & cinnamon bavarois

3 mi west of Oxford city centre by A 420 and minor road south on east side of A 34. Parking.

77 The Wykham Arms

Temple Mill Road,
Sibford Gower OX15 5RX
Tel.: (01295)788808 – Fax: (01295)788806
e-mail: info@wykhamarms.co.uk **Website:** www.wykhamarms.co.uk

 **St Austell Tinners & Tribute, Purity Mad Goose & Ubu & Gold, Wadworth 6X, Hooky Best**

If you're looking for a true village pub, The Wykham Arms may well be it. Set down narrow lanes in the middle of the countryside, this thatched pub certainly plays its role in the community. Dating back to the 17C, it boasts attractive sand-coloured stone walls adorned with pretty climbing plants, and a pleasant terrace with cast iron furniture. So as not to price out the locals, menus offer a range of dishes right through from light bites and bar snacks to the full three courses. You might find Salcombe crab and mango salad and Brixham sea bream on the lighter side, Cotswold pork belly or baby deer at the more substantial end, and minted Lighthorne lamb burger or Hereford steak sandwich at lunch. Suppliers are proudly noted on the blackboard and the chef is only too happy to answer any questions. There's a good choice of wines by the glass and what better way to celebrate an occasion than with lobster and champagne on the terrace?

Closing times
Closed 25 December and 1 January

Prices
Meals: à la carte £ 28

Typical Dishes
Seared wood pigeon
Twice cooked Cotswold pork belly
Wykham chocolate trifle

 *8 mi west of Banbury by B 4035. Parking.* 

78 Sir Charles Napier

Sprig's Alley OX39 4BX
Tel.: (01494)483011 – Fax: (01494)485311
e-mail: info@sircharlesnapier.co.uk
Website: www.sircharlesnapier.co.uk

 **Wadworth IPA and 6X**

Set in a small hamlet on the hillside, this attractive 18C flint pub might just have it all. The outside terrace and delightful gardens buzz with conversation in the warmer months, while the odd sculpture of a beast or figure peers out from behind the bushes or lies on the lawn; inside yet more creatures hide about the place – and all are for sale. It's worth heading to the cosy bar with its open fires and comfy sofas, although the beamed dining room adorned with flowers and fine art is equally as charming. Cooking is refined and has a strong French accent, offering the likes of eel and foie gras terrine followed by noisette of venison, bœuf bourguignon or steak au poivre. Dishes are skilfully prepared and capture flavours to their full; starting with a good selection of homemade bread and finishing with classics such as sticky toffee pud or apple crumble. Set menus offer good value and a well chosen wine list completes the picture.

Closing times
Closed 3 days at Christmas, Sunday dinner and Monday

Prices
Meals: à la carte £ 32/44

Typical Dishes
Seared tuna sashimi
Noisette of venison
Peanut butter parfait

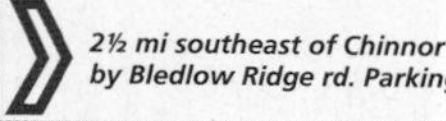

2½ mi southeast of Chinnor by Bledlow Ridge rd. Parking.

79 **The Talkhouse**

Wheatley Rd,
Stanton St John OX33 1EX
Tel.: (01865)351648
e-mail: talkhouse@fullers.co.uk **Website:** www.talkhouse.co.uk

 **Fuller's London Pride, Discovery**

Set in the picturesque village of Stanton St John, just a stone's throw from the streets of Oxford, you'll find this part-thatched 17C Cotswold stone pub. Cosy open fires welcome you into a characterful open-plan interior, where exposed stone walls, characterful flag floors and old wooden beams abound; while outside the spacious wood-furnished patio provides the perfect setting on a warm summer's day. The sizeable menu displays a good range of dishes, from pub classics right through to more elaborate offerings. So, alongside a traditional shepherd's pie or steak burger, you might find foie gras parfait with toasted sourdough, braised lamb shank with creamed polenta or roast venison with chocolate jus. The kitchen is highly skilled, especially when it comes to desserts, and the homemade ice cream provides a particularly appealing conclusion to your meal. Comfy cottage-style bedrooms are located across the courtyard in the former stables.

Closing times
Open daily

Prices
Meals: £ 12 and à la carte £ 22/35

4 rooms: £ 65/75

5 mi east of Oxford via Headington and minor road northeast from roundabout on A 40 bypass. Parking.

Typical Dishes
Home-smoked fish platter
Chicken with asparagus
Baked rhubarb brioche

80 The Cherry Tree Inn

Stoke Row RG9 5QA
Tel.: (01491)680430
e-mail: info@thecherrytreeinn.com
Website: www.thecherrytreeinn.com

 **Brakspear, Hobgoblin, Oxford Gold**

Stoke Row's first claim to fame was as a leading producer of tent pegs during WWII; its second, as home to an ornate 370ft well and cherry orchard, paid for by the Maharajah of Benares. No longer bearing fruit, the grove is now an ornamental garden but its spirit lives on in the name of the pub. Despite being 400 years old – reputedly the oldest building in the village – and having a Grade II listing, it gives off a slightly funky, just-out-of-London vibe; although a glance at the locals propping up the bar brings you back to Oxford. The chef-owner and his team create a fresh, zesty menu of worldwide flavours, with dishes ranging from traditional slow roasted belly of pork to more adventurous sea bass teriyaki stir fry. Mussels are a permanent fixture and beer also plays an important role – both in batter and as a recommended accompaniment. Named after fruit trees, bedrooms are spacious, bright and modern; Cherry aptly being the best.

Closing times
Closed 25 December and Sunday dinner

Prices
Meals: à la carte £ 25/40
4 rooms: £ 95

Typical Dishes
Crispy duck salad
Roast rack of Chiltern lamb
Treacle tart

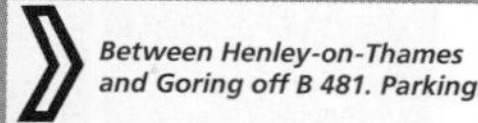
Between Henley-on-Thames and Goring off B 481. Parking.

England • South East • Oxfordshire

81 The Fish

4 Appleford Rd, Sutton Courtenay OX14 4NQ

Tel.: (01235)848242 – Fax: (01235)848014

e-mail: enquiries@thefishatsuttoncourtenay.co.uk

Website: www.thefishatsuttoncourtenay.co.uk

  AE

 **Moorland Original**

New owners have brought a taste of La France profonde to The Fish, so expect French pictures, French music and a largely French wine list as well as a profusion of French food and charming Gallic service. Feast on meaty terrines, escargots or moules marinière; such dishes mingle merrily on the menu with British pub classics such as steak and kidney pie or fish and chips, as well as dishes like Gressingham duck breast or fillet of lamb. L'entente cordiale continues on the dessert menu, with crème brûlée and tarte aux pommes clamouring for your attention alongside treacle sponge and profiteroles. This is robust country cooking in its most classic form, with pretty much everything homemade using seasonal ingredients. Head to the rear of the pub for the lovely garden and conservatory; the admirable flatness and neatness of the former is a clue to its prior use as a bowling green; the latter is the favoured spot of ladies who lunch.

Closing times

Closed January, Sunday dinner and Monday

Prices

Meals: £ 16 (Tuesday-Saturday lunch)
and à la carte £ 23/27

Typical Dishes

Dozen snails
Seared scallops
Homemade meringues

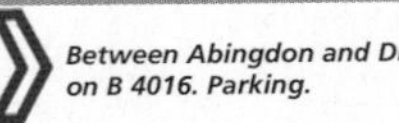

Between Abingdon and Didcot on B 4016. Parking.

82 **The Swan Inn**

Swinbrook OX18 4DY
Tel.: (01993)823339
e-mail: swanninnswinbrook@btconnect.com
Website: www.theswannswinbrook.co.uk

  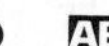

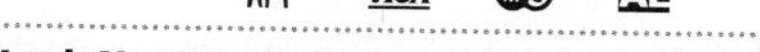

Hook Norton Best, Sharp's Doom Bar, Adnams Bitter

Situated on a country lane next to the River Windrush, with Wisteria climbing up the walls, The Swan Inn is a proper English country pub. Owned by the Dowager Duchess of Devonshire, last of the Mitford sisters, its walls are adorned with black and white photo-canvasses of her friends and family – part of her own private collection. Having been refurbished, the interior is very light and open, especially in the attractive green oak conservatory, which boasts a huge glass wall. Using local, seasonal produce as their base, menus are balanced between traditional and modern British; game and smoked meats are provided by the neighbouring Barrington Estate, while Aberdeen Angus beef comes from the leasee's uncle in the next village. Typical dishes might include braised oxtail, pan-fried sweetbreads or potted shrimps, followed by roast smoked duck breast or pan-fried sea bass. Traditional, comfortable bedrooms offer value for money.

Closing times
Closed 25 December

Prices
Meals: à la carte £ 20/30
6 rooms: £ 60/120

Typical Dishes
Upton smoked beef carpaccio
Roast cod fillet
Hot chocolate brownie

3 mi northeast of Burford by A 40 and minor road north. Parking.

83 The Mole Inn

Toot Baldon OX44 9NG
Tel.: (01865)340001 – Fax: (01865)343011
e-mail: info@themoleinn.com
Website: www.themoleinn.com

 **Hook Norton, Fuller's London Pride**

The Mole has made quite a name for itself in the local area and deservedly so. Beautiful landscaped gardens and a pleasant terrace front the building, while inside attractive beamed ceilings and exposed brick walls create a warm and welcoming atmosphere. The menu is equally appealing, catering for all tastes and appetites; you might find mushroom and roasted pepper bruschetta or sautéed squid with linguine and chorizo, followed by smoked haddock with creamed spinach and a poached egg, or twice cooked belly of pork with apple jus and gratin dauphinoise. Sourcing is a serious business and it's very much a case of 'first come, first served' if you want the full choice. The Tuesday grill and Wednesday fish night menus are decided the day before, so if there's something you've set your heart on, it's worth a quick call to reserve your dish. It's a popular place but the team are used to it, so service remains smooth and efficient throughout.

Closing times
Closed 25 December and 1 January

Prices
Meals: à la carte £ 23/30

Typical Dishes
Ham knuckle terrine
Belly of Blythburgh pork
Tarte Tatin

6 mi southeast of Oxford; between B 480 and A 4074. Parking.

84 **The Boar's Head**

Church St, Ardington, Wantage OX12 8QA

Tel.: (01235)833254

e-mail: info@boarsheadardington.co.uk

Website: www.boarsheadardington.co.uk

  VISA MC AE

Best Mates Bitter, Butts, Barbus, West Berks Wedding Ale

Built by local benefactor Lord Wantage, the picture perfect village of Ardington is in fact a Victorian model village. Set in the Vale of the White Horse, the village's centrepiece is the attractive 18C part-timbered Boar's Head, which, as Wantage was a teetotaller, paid for the village's lighting through its profits. The pub is now better known as the local provider of good food and has built itself quite a reputation over the past ten years. The central room displays cosy wooden floors and a warming fire but the bright, sunny colours and fresh flower displays help to create a fresh, informal style. Wide-ranging menus offer something for everyone: from a 'Rapide' lunch for those on the run, to a gourmet selection at dinner – there's even a seven course tasting menu to linger over. Bedrooms are modern, stylish and spacious: one boasts characterful wooden beams, another, a roll-top bath and the third, an adjoining sitting room.

Closing times

Closed 25-26 December and 1 January

Prices

Meals: £ 18 (lunch) and à la carte £ 25/38

3 rooms: £ 80/140

Typical Dishes

Local rabbit terrine

Poached fillet of roe deer

Assiette of British cheeses

2¼ mi east of Wantage by A 417. Next to the church. Parking.

85 The Fleece

11 Church Green,
Witney OX28 4AZ
Tel.: (01993)892270
e-mail: fleece@peachpubs.com **Website:** www.fleecewitney.co.uk

Greene King IPA, Old Speckled Hen

Set in a great location overlooking the green, this smart Georgian building plays a role in many areas of community life. At breakfast and lunchtime it plays host to business meetings, in the afternoon it provides a sunny spot for mums and their babies and at weekends it keeps the locals entertained with live music. They invest in some worthy values here, including sourcing ethically produced coffee, locating sustainable timber for their furniture and using local, seasonal, free range produce in their cooking. There's breakfast in the morning, sandwiches at lunchtime and a concise set menu available throughout the day. Lunch and dinner offer some interesting 'create you own' deli boards, a selection of dishes in either small or large portions, a list of classics and some daily specials written up on the mirrors; staff are well informed and infectiously enthusiastic. Bright, modern bedrooms win over business guests and visitors alike.

Closing times
Closed 25 December

Prices
Meals: £ 16 (lunch) and à la carte £ 18/30
10 rooms: £ 80/90

Typical Dishes
Homemade gravadlax
Rump steak
Sticky toffee pudding

11 mi west of Oxford by A 40.
Parking.

86 Trout Inn

195 Godstow Rd,
Wolvercote OX2 8PN
Tel.: (01865)510930
Website: www.thetroutoxford.co.uk

 **Timothy Taylor Landlord, Adnams Best, Brakspear**

One of the chief attractions of this modernised Cotswold stone inn, a few miles out of Oxford, is its idyllic riverside location and in the summer, it's not unusual to see people packed onto its fabulous terrace like sardines. Originally built in the 12C as a hospice for the nearby Godstow nunnery, the inn itself dates back to the 17C, and with nooks and crannies, roaring fires and an interesting literary history, which includes visits from the fictional character of Inspector Morse, it is also a popular destination come winter. The menu provides plenty of choice, with sections offering starters, pastas and salads, pizzas, grills, stove and sharing plates, and a specials board which allows the kitchen to show more creativity. Since there are no trout in the river, the pub's name is actually a bit of a misnomer, but the greedy chub that gather like to be handfed. A very popular place, so make sure to book ahead or be prepared to wait.

Closing times
Open daily
Booking advisable

Prices
Meals: à la carte £ 18/29

Typical Dishes
Warm chicken livers
Chargrilled lamb rump
Apple & strawberry crumble

 *3 mi northeast of Oxford off A 4114. Parking.* 

87 **Stephan Langton Inn**

Friday St,
Abinger Common, Abinger Common RH5 6JR
Tel.: (01306)730775
e-mail: eat@stephan-langton.co.uk **Website:** www.stephan-langton.co.uk

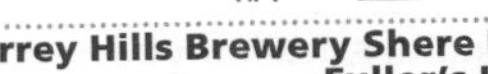

Surrey Hills Brewery Shere Drop, Dorking Brewery DBI, Fuller's London Pride

In the heart of the privately owned Wooton estate, in the tiny hamlet of Friday Street - down a long windy lane and past the pond - this pub, named after one of the signatories of the Magna Carta, can be well and truly described as off the beaten track. Modestly furnished in earthy tones, with wood floors, open fires, a bar, restaurant and popular summer terrace, it is a good illustration of how keeping things simple can often be the most successful course of action; a philosophy which is also reflected in the food. The concise seasonal menu changes daily, with the emphasis firmly on quality; game comes from the estate, bread is home baked, and you can enjoy delicious homemade fudge with your after-dinner coffee. At lunchtime, you'll find traditional homemade pies, parfaits and pickles on offer, while the evening menu involves more substantial dishes such as lamb shank, breast of Gressingham duck or pan-fried fillet of sea bass.

Closing times
Closed Sunday dinner and Monday

Prices
Meals: £ 23 (dinner) and à la carte £ 19/26

Typical Dishes
Chicken liver parfait
Confit belly of pork
Apple & rhubarb crumble

5 mi southwest of Dorking by A 25 and minor road south. Parking.

88 The Swan Inn

Petworth Rd,
Chiddingfold GU8 4TY
Tel.: (01428)682073 – Fax: (01428)683259
e-mail: enquiries@theswaninn.biz **Website:** www.theswaninn.biz

Fuller's London Pride, TEA

During the reign of Elizabeth I, Chiddingfold became famous for its glass-making, and some of the finest buildings in the country – including St Stephen's Chapel in Westminster – boasted its glass. At only 200 years old, this pub is too young to display such craftsmanship but with a 'Swan Inn' having stood on this site since the 14C, its predecessor may well have. Having been gutted by fire in 2003, it comes as no surprise that this majestic building hides a modern, stylish interior. There's a large bar, a small linen-laid dining room and a very popular terrace with an awning, so there's plenty of choice whatever the weather. Food is simple, unfussy and classical; dishes might include smoked haddock, rump of lamb or medallions of pork, while specials change twice a day in line with the latest seasonal produce. Service is courteous but can sometimes lack warmth. Bedrooms are contemporary, with good bathrooms and the latest mod cons.

Closing times

Closed Sunday dinner and Monday

Prices

Meals: à la carte £ 23/30

11 rooms: £ 105/150

Typical Dishes

Smoked salmon & crayfish tian

Smoked haddock & rarebit glaze

White chocolate parfait

On east side of A 283. Parking opposite.

Parrot Inn

89 Parrot Inn

Forest Green RH5 5RZ
Tel.: (01306)621339
e-mail: drinks@the parrot.co.uk
Website: www.theparrot.co.uk

Ringwood Best, Youngs Ordinary and guest ales such as Dorking Ruby, Hog's Back, TEA, Adnams Broadside

When this attractive 17C pub became available, the owners of a nearby cattle, pig and sheep farm took the chance to exchange their bustling London pubs for the slower pace of the country. Overlooking a vast village green, it exudes plenty of character, boasting slate floors, low beams, wood burning ranges and cosy little booths. As you might expect, there's plenty of home-reared meat on the menu and a strong emphasis on quality, local ingredients. The same generous cooking and daily specials are served throughout, with dishes including maybe pork rib eye or slow braised Aberdeen Angus beef, with the burgers in particular proving extremely popular. Sandwiched between the bar and restaurant a farm shop sells homemade bread (fresh from the oven if you arrive in the morning), cheese, chutney, jam, their own meat and a selection of pies – Nose to Tail (consisting of cheeks, tongue, loin and rump) being the speciality. Booking is advisable.

8 mi south of Dorking by A 24, A 29 and B 2126 west. Parking.

Closing times

Closed 25 December and Sunday dinner

Prices

Meals: à la carte £ 18/28

Typical Dishes

Pork & juniper terrine
Steamed mutton pudding
Warm poached pear on brioche

90 The King William IV

Byttom Hill,
Mickleham RH5 6EL
Tel.: (01372)372590
e-mail: iduke@another.com **Website:** www.king-williamiv.com

 **Alton's Pride, Shere Drop, TEA, DB Number One**

Many a rambler has sunk gratefully into a chair in the bar of the King William IV, having exhausted themselves climbing Box Hill, and even those customers who weren't planning on partaking in any exercise may have found themselves having to huff and puff their way up Byttom Hill after parking at its base. Any exertion will seem worth it when your food arrives, however, for this is robust, hearty cooking in the shape of traditional homemade pies, beef Wellington or calves liver, with heaps of simply-cooked fresh vegetables; old school desserts like homemade treacle tart, plus a daily specials board - and local handpumped ales with which to wash it all down. Every available space in the long, narrow room seems to have a table, but even so, it's worth Booking ahead since you can bet you won't be the only walker wanting to refuel. In summer, a table in the terraced garden is a treat, with views of the surrounding countryside.

Closing times
Closed Sunday dinner

Prices
Meals: à la carte £ 19/29

Typical Dishes
Avocado bake
Roast venison
Treacle tart

½ mi north of Mickleham by A 24. Difficult off-road parking nearby; public car park at the bottom of Byttom Hill.

91 Bryce's

Old School House,
Stane St, Ockley RH5 5TH
Tel.: (01306)627430 – Fax: (01306)628274
e-mail: bryces.fish@virgin.net **Website:** www.bryces.co.uk

Fuller's London Pride, Horsham Bitter

The eponymous owner opened Bryce's back in '92 and such has been its success that he's now cooking up a sea storm over at its newer sister restaurant in Worthing. This place has been left in more than capable hands, however, and the basic tenet has remained the same: to serve market-fresh seafood at market-fresh prices; simply cooked and full of flavour. The Old School House underwent a total refurbishment in 2007 and both the bar and restaurant are now contemporary in style, with an attractive copper-topped bar counter and high backed leather chairs. A lighter menu is available in the bar, with some salads, open sandwiches and steaks alongside cullen skink and fishcakes, while restaurant offerings may have more exotic origins, with dishes such as Cajun salmon or spring rolls featuring, as well as the freshest fish available, plus a tasty selection of breads. A friendly young team provide attentive service for Bryce's faithful regulars.

Closing times

Closed 25-26 December, 1 January, and Sunday dinner (November and January-February)

Prices

Meals: £ 15 and à la carte £ 31/36

Typical Dishes

Savoury soft roes on toast

Fillets of red mullet & risotto

Orange & ginger pudding

8 mi south of Dorking by A 24 and A 29. Parking.

92 The Inn @ West End

42 Guildford Road,
West End GU24 9PW
Tel.: (01276)858652
e-mail: greatfood@the-inn.co.uk **Website:** www.the-inn.co.uk

  AE

 **Fuller's London Pride, Black Sheep, Youngs Bitter**

With beautiful hanging baskets, prettily laid tables, a friendly service team, delicious desserts and the choice between a light, airy sun lounge or a lovely garden and terrace, you could easily be mistaken for thinking that you are in a tea shop. The food also belies that of a pub: it is hearty yet wholesome – quality ingredients cooked simply and well – and extremely fresh, with an on-site plucking machine for preparing game and a chiller van for collecting the latest catch. Dishes arrive in front of you exactly as described on the menu: pan-fried field mushrooms on toast is just that, thick slices of mushroom on chunky granary bread. The owner also runs a small wine business, so the choice is good, and there are frequent wine tasting sessions. For a bit of variety they hold regular, imaginative theme nights, such as 'School Dinners Night' or the '60s Retro Dinner', where the locals dress accordingly.

Closing times
Open daily

Prices
Meals: £ 25 (Sunday lunch) and £33 (Friday-Saturday dinner) and à la carte £ 28/33

Typical Dishes
Chicken liver salad
Pan-fried loin of pork
South African vinegar pudding

2½ mi southeast of Junction 3 on M 3 by A 322. Parking (40 spaces).

93 The Bee

School Rd,
Windlesham GU20 6PD
Tel.: (01276)479244
e-mail: eat@thebeepub.co.uk **Website:** www.thebeepub.co.uk

VISA

Sharp's Doom Bar, Hop Back Summer Lightning, Courage Best, Hogs Back TEA

The espresso machine on the bar is the first clue. Wood floors, eggshell-coloured walls, a mishmash of wooden furniture and a large leather Chesterfield make it abundantly clear: this is a pub which has had the gastro treatment – and judging by the number of punters making a beeline for it, it seems to have done the trick. Also doing the trick here is something few pubs can boast – a resident magician, who entertains guests every Wednesday evening. Although very much a pub for drinkers, it's the food which is causing a buzz. The daily changing menus showcase local, seasonal produce, with precisely cooked dishes such as roast rump of lamb or braised breast of veal; the two course lunch menu is particularly good value, but with starters like pigeon and wild mushroom salad and desserts like sticky toffee pudding, the trouble will be knowing which courses to go for. The garden becomes a hive of activity in summer with regular barbecues.

Closing times
Closed Sunday dinner

Prices
Meals: £ 16 (weekday lunch) and à la carte £ 20/35

Typical Dishes
Scallops with chorizo
Warm salad of duck confit
Baked egg custard tart

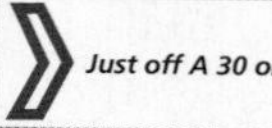

Just off A 30 on B 386. Parking.

94 The Brickmakers

Chertsey Rd, Windlesham GU20 6HT
Tel.: (01276)472267 – Fax: (01276)451014
e-mail: thebrickmakers@4cinns.co.uk
Website: www.thebrickmakerswindlesham.co.uk

 **Fuller's London Pride, Courage Best and seasonal ales**

This red-brick pub appears rather small in the shadows of the many grand houses that surround it but once inside you'll find it's a lot bigger than it first seemed. There's a bar area with tables, comfy sofas and an open fire and a linen-laid restaurant that extends out into a conservatory – probably the best place to eat. In the summer this pub really comes into its own, with the sizeable garden playing host to a good many tables, as well as a BBQ area. The bar menu features fairly straightforward dishes, such as pâté and toast or the particularly tasty Welsh Rarebit, which comes with a bottle of Lea and Perrins so you can splash away to your heart's desire. The more substantial à la carte menu displays flavoursome, well-cooked dishes that might include crayfish and crab cocktail or goat's cheese and apple salad, followed by half shoulder of lamb or stuffed chicken breast; desserts are chalked on the board alongside the specials.

Closing times
Open daily

Prices
Meals: £ 24 and à la carte £ 20/30

Typical Dishes
Mushroom fricassee in a herb pancake
Braised half shoulder of lamb
Sticky toffee pudding

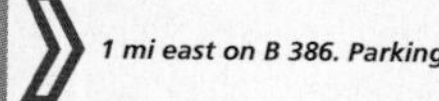
1 mi east on B 386. Parking.

95 The Fountain Inn

Ashurst BN44 3AP
Tel.: (01403)710219

 **Harveys Best, Fuller's London Pride, Courage Directors, Horsham Best**

Writer Hilaire Belloc wrote about it in his book 'The Four Men' in 1902, Laurence Olivier was a regular visitor and favoured the large seat next to the inglenook in the front bar, and it was even the setting for Paul McCartney's video for 'Wonderful Christmastime' back in 1979. It will come as no surprise, therefore that the 16C Fountain Inn is overflowing with character and charm, boasting beamed ceilings, thick brick walls, flagstone floors and open fires. There's a garden and a pond, plus a skittle alley for a spot of retro entertainment; the pub hosts a classic car get together every summer, and as in all the best pubs, the locals in the bar are more than willing to chat. Cooking is down-to-earth, fresh and full of flavour; choices might include steak, mushroom and ale pie or Sussex Smokie as well as salads and steaks, plus a large selection of daily specials – and puds like ginger treacle tart and hot chocolate fudge cake.

Closing times
Open daily

Prices
Meals: à la carte £ 20/25

Typical Dishes
Chef's terrine
Fountain burger
Homemade cheesecake

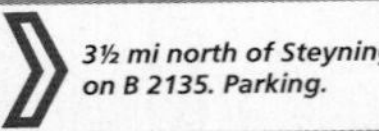
3½ mi north of Steyning on B 2135. Parking.

96 George and Dragon

Main St, Burpham BN18 9RR
Tel.: (01903)883131 – Fax: (01903)883341
e-mail: mail@burphamgeorgeanddragon.com
Website: www.burphamgeorgeanddragon.com

 **Arundel Ales, Skinners, Sussex Ales and guest bitters**

Once home to the late Mervyn Peake, artist and creator of the Gormenghast trilogy – (he is now buried in the local churchyard) – and with stunning views over the rolling English countryside, the picturesque village of Burpham seems a thoroughly fitting setting for a pub with such a typically English name. Cooking continues the English theme, with seasonal offerings from local suppliers including game from the adjacent Duke of Norfolk's Estate, and suckling pig an occasional treat for Sunday lunch – although themed evenings – think Country and Western or Burns Night – also give more far-flung flavours a look in from time to time. The menu is chalked up on blackboards and served both at scrubbed wooden tables in the bar and at more formally laid tables in the dining area. Service is attentive and the wine list short but lively. Feel a sense of timelessness as you enjoy a post-prandial riverside stroll, with views to Arundel Castle.

Closing times
Open daily

Prices
Meals: £ 5/19 and à la carte £ 18/31

Typical Dishes
Rabbit & pigeon terrine
Seafood pie with cheese crust
Rhubarb fool

3 mi northeast of Arundel by A 27. Parking.

97 The Fox Goes Free

Charlton PO18 0HU
Tel.: (01243)811461 – Fax: (01243)811712
e-mail: enquiries@thefoxgoesfree.com
Website: www.thefoxgoesfree.com

 VISA  AE

Fox Goes Free (special brew), Harveys Sussex Best, Ballards Best

Over recent years, more and more pubs have had the interior designers in and been 'gastroed'; the result being a glut of homogenous identipubs. Not so The Fox Goes Free; with its exposed stone walls, tile floors and large inglenook, this early 17C flint building retains its individual character and remains cheerfully free from over-modernisation. Interesting moments in the pub's history are recorded for posterity on the walls: a plaque contends that the first ever meeting of the Women's Institute was held here in 1915, while a more recent photograph reveals that part of a Dr. Who episode was filmed here in the days of K9 and Tom Baker. Menus are short and seasonal, with a strong reliance on local produce, including game from local shoots; you can eat in one of several dining areas, in the bar or in the rear garden overlooking the South Downs – and if you're making a weekend of it, you'll find the bedrooms comfortable and well-equipped.

Closing times
Closed 25 December

Prices
Meals: à la carte £ 20/26
5 rooms: £ 60/145

Typical Dishes
Caramelised onion tart
Roast chicken breast
Homemade cheesecake

6¾ mi north of Chichester by A 286. Parking.

98 **Fish Bar**

1 High St,
Chilgrove PO18 9HX
Tel.: (01243)519444 – Fax: (01243)519499
e-mail: info@thefishhouse.co.uk **Website:** www.thefishhouse.co.uk

 **Arundel Gold, Harvey's Best and guest ales**

Following a massive refurbishment, what was formerly The White Horse has been almost totally rebuilt, and is now a stylish inn fast gaining popularity with foodies. With limestone flooring, low beams and a 300 year old fireplace, it retains a characterful sense of history, while contemporary touches like the oyster bar and fish tanks bring it firmly into the 21C. There's a fantastic set price lunch and early evening menu alongside the à la carte; the kitchen focuses mainly on seafood dishes and these range from classics such as potted shrimps or fish and chips to those with a more international flavour such as wok-fried whole bream, with chilli, garlic, spring onions, soy and ginger. Individually styled bedrooms come with every conceivable facility, including espresso machines, and iPod docks. If you're here on a romantic getaway, you will want to make a beeline for one of the private hot tubs in the garden.

Closing times
Open daily

Prices
Meals: £ 20 (Monday-Thursday) and à la carte £ 24/34

15 rooms: £ 110/150

Typical Dishes
Carlingford oysters
Fish House pie
Glazed lemon tart

6½ mi north of Chichester by A 286 (Midhurst rd) on B 2141. Parking.

99 The Royal Oak Inn

Pook Lane,
East Lavant PO18 0AX
Tel.: (01243)527434
e-mail: info@royaloakeastlavant.co.uk **Website:** www.royaloakeastlavant.co.uk

Sharp's Doom Bar, Thatcher Gold, Goodwood Best

The contemporary combines with the more traditional in this 18C inn to provide a warm, rural atmosphere in which to wine and dine. Locals patronise the place – always a good sign – but you may have to fight them if you've got your eye on table number four; a popular corner banquette next to the fireplace. Seasonal cooking has a modern base, and you might find fish and chips and shepherd's pie on offer, alongside fillet steak, pork loin, breast of wood pigeon or calves liver. Game, supplied by the nearby Goodwood Estate, is very popular in the winter months, while weekly trips to the London markets provide the fish and vegetables. Wine is clearly the preferred tipple of Chichesterians, with bottles cleverly displayed on racks and shelves around the room, but there is also a choice of real ales on tap for those of a more beery persuasion. Bedrooms – some above the bar, others in cottages and a barn – are furnished to a high standard.

Closing times
Closed 25 December

Prices
Meals: à la carte £ 25/45
10 rooms: £ 70/300

Typical Dishes
Seared scallops & parsnip purée
Sussex pork loin steak
Chocolate marquise

Off A 286 after the hump-back bridge. Parking.

100 Three Horseshoes

Elsted GU29 0JY
Tel.: (01730)825746

 **Bowmans Wallops Wood, Flowerpot Bitter, Timothy Taylor Landlord**

The Three Horseshoes is what you would call a no frills pub - and all the better for it. Its ancient beamed interior is simple yet cosy, with flowers on each table giving the place a cheerful, homely touch. The furthest of the three rooms is the most comfy and, since it overlooks the garden, also lets in the most light. You must order at the bar and there's no special treatment for celebrities or dignitaries, as both Madonna and Prince Andrew found out when they stopped off here. As with the décor, so too with the food: a simple blackboard menu offers tasty, traditional dishes like ploughman's, casseroles and pies; this is wholesome, hearty cooking which comes served in such enormous portions that it takes a concerted effort to leave trouser space for dessert. Service is pleasantly informal, staff and locals are chatty and the large garden, with its agreeable aspect over the South Downs, makes a great spot for al fresco dining.

Closing times
Open daily

Prices
Meals: à la carte £ 22/31

Typical Dishes
Potted shrimps
Steak & kidney & Guinness pie
Raspberry & hazelnut meringue

 *5 mi southwest of Midhurst by A 272 on Elsted road. Parking.* 

101 The Halfway Bridge Inn

Halfway Bridge GU28 9BP

Tel.: (01798)861281

e-mail: enquiries@halfwaybridge.co.uk

Website: www.halfwaybridge.co.uk

Skinner's Betty Stogs Bitter, Sharp's Doom Bar, Lurgashall Halfway to Heaven

Years ago you would have approached from the front but now, due to the vagaries of modern road planning, you enter via the back. Once inside you are greeted by a series of cosy rooms featuring exposed brickwork and log fires, carefully designed to retain the 17C character while also providing a more comfortable, contemporary edge. The menu displays good, honest British cooking that comes in hearty, flavoursome portions, featuring dishes such as calves liver, sea bass or lamb shank. In addition, the daily-changing specials board lists even more pub classics and for those with a sweet tooth, plenty of old-fashioned sticky puddings. Across the 250 year old stable yard, bedrooms take on the same styling, blending rustic features with modern facilities and coming complete with everything from an umbrella to a Playstation. This pub is popular, especially in the polo season, so it pays to plan ahead, as empty tables are rarities.

Closing times

Closed 25 December

Prices

Meals: à la carte £ 22/30

6 rooms: £ 75/160

Typical Dishes

Oriental crispy duck

Game suet pudding

Upside-down treacle sponge

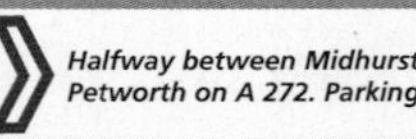

Halfway between Midhurst and Petworth on A 272. Parking.

102 The Ginger Fox

Albourne,
Henfield BN6 9EA
Tel.: (01273)857888
e-mail: info@gingermanrestaurants.com **Website:** www.gingermanrestaurants.

  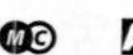  

 **Harvey's of Lewes**

It's not in Albourne village and your sat nav may well lead you somewhere else entirely, so don't take the postal address too literally. Nestling behind a large hedge, the first thing that you will see from the road is a fox chasing a pheasant along the newly thatched roof. As with their three other Gingerman establishments, the owners' main focus here rests on the food, with locality and seasonality playing an important role. The à la carte menu and blackboard specials change slightly every day and the descriptions are pleasantly straightforward, leaving the rich, deep flavours to speak for themselves; you might find braised veal cheeks, spiced lamb neck kebabs or smoked haddock, mussel and leek pie, whilst in summer a rare breed hog roast is on offer at weekends. Book in advance if you can, as only a handful of tables are set aside for walk-ins; they can be close together so opt for one by the window if it's available.

Closing times
Closed 25 December

Prices
Meals: à la carte £ 20/35

Typical Dishes
Chicken liver parfait
Fillet of sea trout
Vanilla beignets

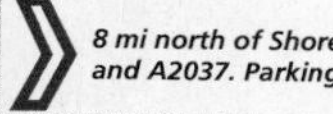

8 mi north of Shoreham by A283 and A2037. Parking.

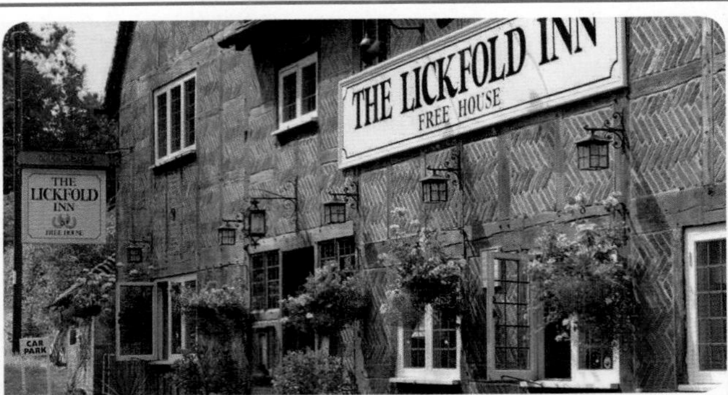

103 The Lickfold Inn

Lickfold GU28 9EY
Tel.: (01798)861285
e-mail: lickfold@evanspubs.co.uk
Website: www.evanspubs.co.uk

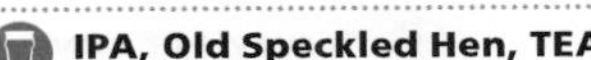 **IPA, Old Speckled Hen, TEA**

Dating back to the 1400s, this characterful red-brick pub sits at the end of a narrow, winding lane in the picturesque Sussex countryside. In contrast with its colourful DJ owner – Chris Evans – it displays a relaxed, traditional charm, boasting wooden beams, stone floors and inglenook fireplaces. More importantly, there are no signs of flashy patronage, just friendly, unassuming service as you would expect to find in any country inn. Cooking is fairly ambitious, taking a step away from traditional country pub fare and towards a more restaurant style (although a few sandwiches are available at lunch). The fish pie contains lobster and monkfish, the salad Niçoise comes with tuna cooked to your taste, and offering a dozen or so choices the cheese selection is an occasion in itself, coming complete with a descriptive menu of its very own. The dishes on offer at lunch and dinner are similar but a few more are added in the evening.

Closing times
Closed 25 December and Sunday dinner

Prices
Meals: £ 12/15
and à la carte £ 23/42

Typical Dishes
Chicken liver parfait
Sirloin or fillet steak
Apple & blackcurrant crumble

 *6 mi northwest of Petworth by A 272. Parking.* 

104 The Earl of March

Mid Lavant PO18 OBQ
Tel.: (01243)533993 – Fax: (01243)783991
e-mail: rt@theearlofmarch.com **Website:** www.theearlofmarch.com

   AE

 **Hopback Summer Lightning, Harveys Sussex Bitter, Ringood Best**

Situated on the edge of the Goodwood Estate, this pub has pleasant pastoral views across to the racecourse's main stand in the distance. The pub's owner has built up a good relationship with the Estate's latest resident, The Earl of March, who has given permission for the pub to use his family crest on its signage. A modern makeover has seen the bar and restaurant areas becoming clearly defined, the first being fitted out with comfy sofas and a blazing log fire. The à la carte menu is supplemented in the evening by daily-changing blackboard specials; in the winter, game from the local estates and in the summer fresh fish. Cooking is flavoursome and hearty, featuring simple British dishes such as stew, sea bass or steak. While eating you'll often see a Rolls Royce drive by from the nearby test centre and there's a great collection of motoring photographs from the Festival of Speed on the walls.

Closing times

Closed Sunday dinner (October to April)

Prices

Meals: £ 25 (dinner pre theatre) and à la carte £ 25/34

Typical Dishes

Seared diver scallops

Pan-fried local venison

Selection of West Sussex cheese

3 mi north of Chichester by A 286.

105 Badgers

Coultershaw Bridge,
Petworth GU28 0JF
Tel.: (01798)342651
e-mail: reception@badgers.cc **Website:** www.badgers.cc

 VISA MC

 **Youngs, TEA**

With its sash windows and River Rother location (it's just past the bridge), this smart white-painted former railway tavern is an ideal destination in pretty Petworth. Its eye-catching garden boasts weeping willows, and next door is the unique, Michelin Red Guide recommended Old Railway Station guesthouse. Badgers' interior is most pleasant: a beautiful oak-panelled bar has carvings with a 'badger and honey' theme, and lots of old photos depict its former Railway Inn-carnation. Jack Vettriano fans will find two of his sexy pictures, The Assessment and Game On, in a single-table alcove that gives a new twist to the word 'intimate'. Menus offer plenty of choice, a robust and wholesome mix of classic British dishes with global influences. There are fresh fish specials and homemade puddings too. South Downs ramblers staying on have the choice of three comfy, spacious rooms a cut above normal pub accommodation.

Closing times

Closed 25 December and Sunday dinner (October to April)

Prices

Meals: à la carte £ 22/39

3 rooms: £ 55/80

Typical Dishes

Chicken & cashew nut parcel
Spanish fish casserole
Crème brûlée

2 mi south of Petworth by A 285 at Coultershaw Bridge. Parking.

106 The Chequers Inn

Rowhook RH12 3PY
Tel.: (01403)790480
e-mail: thechequersrowhook@googlemail.com
Website: www.nealsrestaurants.biz

VISA

 **Harveys Sussex, Fuller's London Pride and guest ales**

Duck is not only the name of a bird on the menu at The Chequers Inn, but also the word your friends will shout at you as you go through the doorways. Annoying maybe, but along with its log fires, uneven floors and relaxed atmosphere, the low beamed ceilings are part of this delightful 18C inn's charm and character. Travel up a few stairs and you'll enter another rustic seating area, where farming implements hang on the walls alongside pictures of local legends. On the other side is what at first glance appears to be a corrugated metal shed but is actually Neal's restaurant, the more formally laid part of the establishment; but since the same menu is served throughout, the bar would have to be your choice for a seat every time. The menu offers aspirational cooking which showcases local produce, including game from local estates, with dishes such as belly pork, venison bresaola and pan-fried halibut, as well as fresh homemade puddings.

Closing times

Closed 25 December and Sunday dinner

Prices

Meals: à la carte £ 25/32

Typical Dishes

Scottish scallops with pancetta

Sautéed venison

Chocolate tart

3 mi west of Horsham by A 281. Parking.

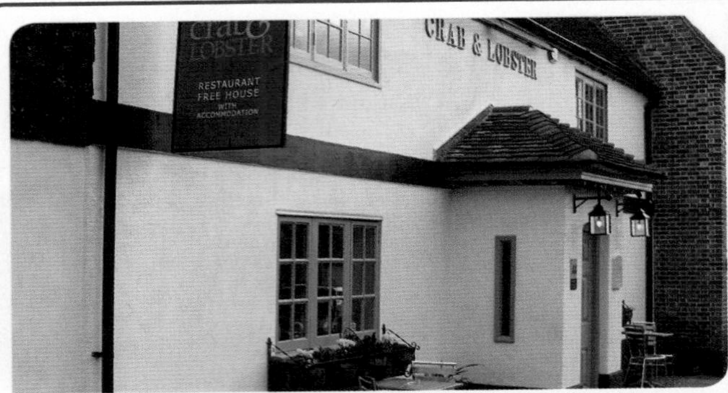

107 Crab & Lobster

Mill Lane,
Sidlesham PO20 7NB
Tel.: (01243)641233
e-mail: enquiries@crab-lobster.co.uk **Website:** www.crab-lobster.co.uk

Inspectors' favourites

    AE

 **Timothy Taylor Landlord, Harvey's Sussex Best Bitter**

350 years ago this was a busy crossing point for ships travelling to France; now it is a harbour nature reserve occupied by the diverse flora and fauna of the local marshlands. The desolate roads that skirt the bay do not prepare you for the bustling atmosphere inside this pub, where slate floors and large fireplaces sit amongst more contemporary features such as counters studded with pebbles from the nearby beach. It is comfortable, appealing and despite the bar, feels more like a place to eat than to drink. The British/Mediterranean menu displays simply constructed, cleanly presented dishes, with plenty of fish, maybe calamari, scallops or lobster to start, with pesto-crusted cod, spiced crab gratin or seafood risotto to follow; make sure you finish with a coffee, as it comes with a shot glass of smarties. Rooms are spacious and contemporary, with sea or rural views – or both in the attic room. Self-contained Crab Cottage is nearby.

Closing times

Open daily

Booking advisable

Prices

Meals: à la carte £ 24/41

4 rooms: £ 75/150

Typical Dishes

Crab parcel

Devilled local crab

Deep-fried vanilla ice cream in filo pastry

1 mi south of Chichester by B 2145, then turn right into Rookery Lane. Parking.

108 Nava Thai at The Hamilton Arms

School Lane,
Stedham GU29 0NZ
Tel.: (01730)812555 – Fax: (01730)817459
e-mail: hamiltonarms@hotmail.com **Website:** www.thehamiltonarms.co.uk

  AE

 **Fuller's London Pride, Ballard's Best, Alton's Pride**

Deep in the heart of the Sussex countryside you will find this traditional village inn. At least, so it appears from the outside. Yes, it has the picnic tables and the hanging baskets. Yes, it has the lounge with roaring fire, the bar snacks and the real ale. And yet this pub is so much more: think authentic oriental artefacts, carved wooden panels, and burning incense, in a restaurant where for nigh on two decades Thai staff in traditional uniforms have been serving up tasty Thai dishes. The monosodium glutamate-free menu is extensive, and they also provide a takeaway service, should you prefer to phone in your order. In your patronage, not only will you enjoy delicious Thai cuisine, but through the Mudita Trust, you will also be helping abused and underprivileged Thai children. May sees a Thai festival held on the green when everyone dresses in National costume and all funds raised go to the same worthy cause.

Closing times
Closed Monday
(except bank holiday)

Prices
Meals: £ 25 and à la carte
£ 20/30

Typical Dishes
Stuffed chicken wings
Tiger prawns in sweet chilli
Thai egg custard

2 mi west of Midhurst by A 272.
Parking.

109 The Keepers Arms

Trotton GU31 5ER
Tel.: (01730)813724
e-mail: info@keepersarms.co.uk
Website: www.keepersarms.co.uk

 VISA MC AE

Dark Star Hophead, Ballard's Best Bitter, Ringwood 49er

Following its refurbishment in 2007, the focus of this characterful village pub is now firmly on the food. Good value dishes offer a modern take on British classics and the short à la carte is supplemented with daily changing blackboard specials. You might start with a terrine of duck confit or a homemade fishcake, followed by roasted partridge, sausage and mash or sea bass, with rice pudding or perhaps some locally made ice cream for dessert. Cooking is flavoursome and the wine list offers some decent accompaniments. The pub is perched on a hillside and set back from the main road, and while its gastro-makeover means it's been stripped back to basics with whitewashed walls and wooden floors, the slightly raised 'Captain's table' and the four poster style 'Kazzbar' with its own blinds provide seating arrangements a little out of the ordinary, while the cosy bar offers the warmth of an open fire and the comfort of a Chesterfield sofa.

Closing times
Closed 25-26 December

Prices
Meals: à la carte £ 22/28

Typical Dishes
Carpaccio of yellow fin tuna
Slow roast pork belly
Salted peanut parfait

4 mi west of Midhurst by A 272. Parking.

Six hundred miles of relentlessly breathtaking coastline pound the majestic South West, assuring it of a dramatic backdrop whatever the season. Its prestige is bolstered by four UNESCO World Heritage sites: one of them is Dorset's spectacular Jurassic Coast, which includes the 180 billion pebbles of Chesil Beach. Further north, Dartmoor and Exmoor embody the region's untamed beauty. The built environment may be of a more recent time line, but examples are still impressive, ranging from thirteenth century Lacock, home of many a filmed costume drama, to Elizabethan Longleat with its Capabilty Brown designed parkland, and late Victorian Lanhydrock, "the great house of Cornwall". The same county boasts its very own "theatre under the stars", The Minack, where the drama of nature collides with the drama of the written word. Days out in this unforgettable region come complete with pasties and a pint of local ale, or freshly caught lobster, scallops or mussels enjoyed along the quay.

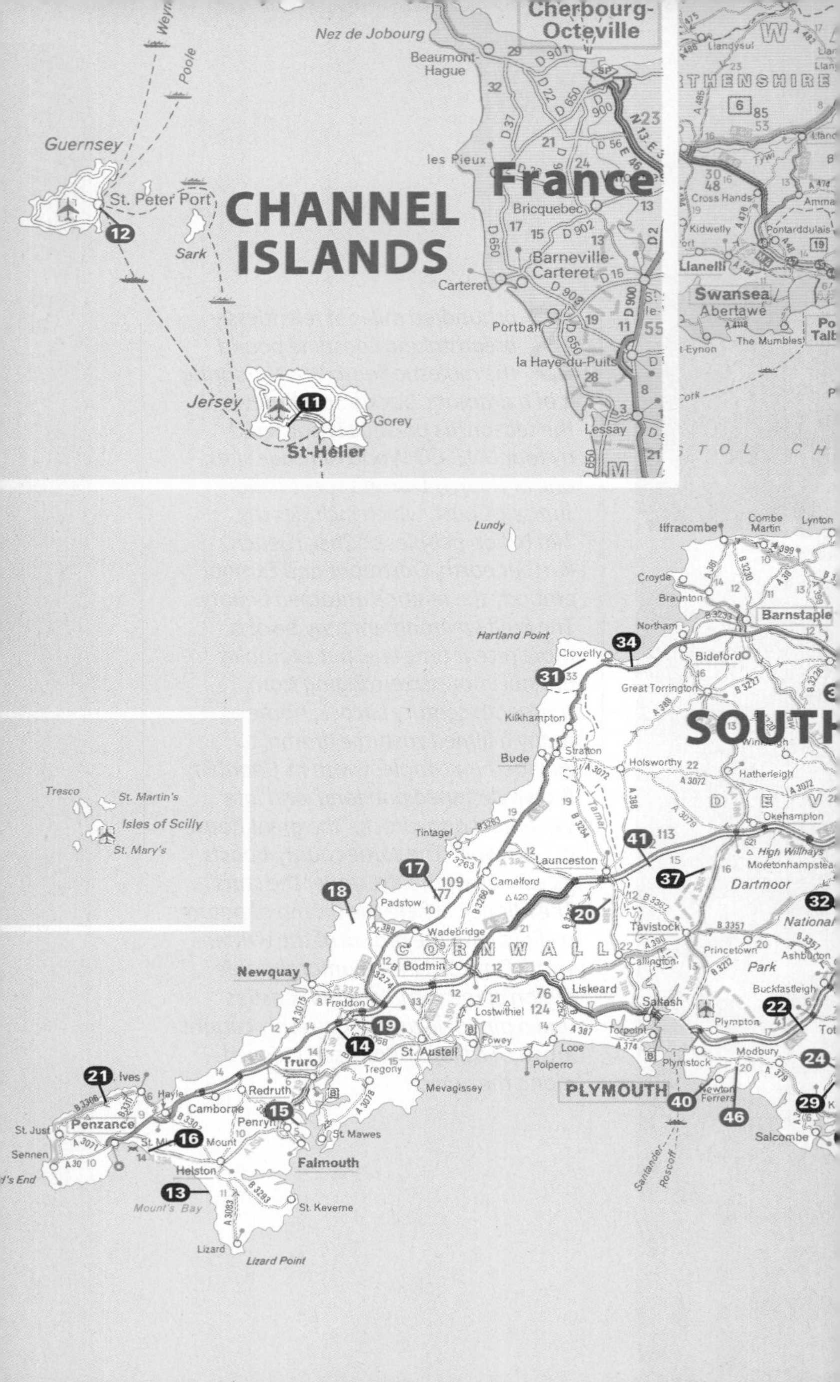

CHANNEL ISLANDS
France
Cherbourg-Octeville
Nez de Jobourg
Beaumont-Hague
les Pieux
Bricquebec
Barneville-Carteret
Carteret
Portbail
la Haye-du-Puits
Lessay
Guernsey
St. Peter Port
Sark
Jersey
St-Helier
Gorey
Weymouth
Poole
Llandysul
CARMARTHENSHIRE
Cross Hands
Kidwelly
Pontarddulais
Llanelli
Swansea / Abertawe
The Mumbles
Cork
Lundy
Ilfracombe
Combe Martin
Lynton
Croyde
Braunton
Barnstaple
Northam
Hartland Point
Clovelly
Bideford
Great Torrington
SOUTH
Kilkhampton
Stratton
Bude
Holsworthy
Hatherleigh
DEVON
Okehampton
Tintagel
Launceston
High Willhays
Moretonhampstead
Dartmoor
National Park
Camelford
Padstow
Wadebridge
CORNWALL
Tavistock
Princetown
Ashburton
Bodmin
Callington
Buckfastleigh
Newquay
Liskeard
Saltash
Fraddon
Lostwithiel
Plympton
Fowey
Torpoint
Looe
Plymstock
Modbury
Truro
St. Austell
Polperro
Tregony
PLYMOUTH
Newton Ferrers
Salcombe
St. Ives
Hayle
Redruth
Camborne
Mevagissey
Penryn
Penzance
St. Just
St. Mawes
Sennen
Mount
Falmouth
Land's End
Helston
Mount's Bay
St. Keverne
Lizard
Lizard Point
Santander
Roscoff
Tresco
St. Martin's
Isles of Scilly
St. Mary's

West Midlands
Wales
South
WEST
East
Hereford
Hay-on-Wye
Brecon / Aberhonddu
Talgarth
Merthyr Tydfil
Aberdare / Aberdar
Mountain Ash / Aberpennar
Rhondda
Pontypridd
Crickhowell
Abergavenny / Y Fenni
Ebbw Vale / Glyn Ebwy
Blaenavon
Abertillery
Pontypool
Cwmbran
Caerphilly
Bedwas
Risca
Monmouth / Trefynwy
Raglan
Usk
Chepstow / Cas-gwent
Severn Bridge
NEWPORT / CASNEWYDD
CARDIFF / CAERDYDD
Cowbridge
Penarth
Barry / Barri
Severn Estuary
Weston-Super-Mare
Clevedon
Portishead
Avonmouth
Congresbury
BRISTOL
Bath
Cheddar gorge
Wells
Glastonbury
Shepton Mallet
Frome
Street
Bruton
Wincanton
Burnham
Bridgwater
Taunton
Minehead
Dunster
Watchet
Porlock
Williton
Othery
Bampton
Wellington
Langport
Ilchester
Yeovil
Sherborne
Ilminster
Chard
Crewkerne
Beaminster
Honiton
Cullompton
Axminster
Ottery St. Mary
Sidmouth
Seaton
Lyme Regis
Bridport
Budleigh Salterton
Exmouth
Dawlish
Teignmouth
Lyme Bay
Torbay
Brixham
Kingswear
Dorchester
Abbotsbury
Weymouth
Isle of Portland
Fortuneswell
Bill of Portland
Guernsey
Jersey
St. Malo
Cherbourg-Octeville
Blandford Forum
Sturminster Newton
Gillingham
Shaftesbury
Mere
Longleat House
Warminster
Westbury
Trowbridge
Melksham
Devizes
Chippenham
Calne
Corsham
Bradford-on-Avon
Beckington
Radstock
Keynsham
Chipping Sodbury
Malmesbury
Tetbury
Nailsworth
Stroud
Dursley
Lydney
Coleford
Newnham
Gloucester
Ross-on-Wye
Newent
Great Malvern
Pershore
Evesham
Stratford-upon-Avon
Chipping Campden
Broadway
Moreton
Stow-on-the-Wold
Winchcomb
Tewkesbury
Cheltenham
Painswick
Cirencester
Bibury
Northleach
Burford
Fairford
Lechlade
Cricklade
Swindon
Wroughton
Avebury
Marlborough
Hungerford
Pewsey
Upavon
Shrewton
Stonehenge
Amesbury
Wilton
Salisbury
Fordingbridge
Cranborne
Ringwood
Wimborne Minster
Bere Regis
Wareham
Corfe Castle
Poole
BOURNEMOUTH
Swanage
St. Alban's Head
Christchurch
Lymington
Beaulieu
Lyndhurst
New Forest National Park
SOUTHAMP
Romsey
Stockbridge
Weyhill
The Needles
Freshwater
Yarmouth
ISLE OF WIGHT
WILTSHIRE
SOMERSET
DORSET
HEREFORD
GLOUCESTER
WORCESTER
R. Severn
R. Wye
Avon
Parrett
A
M

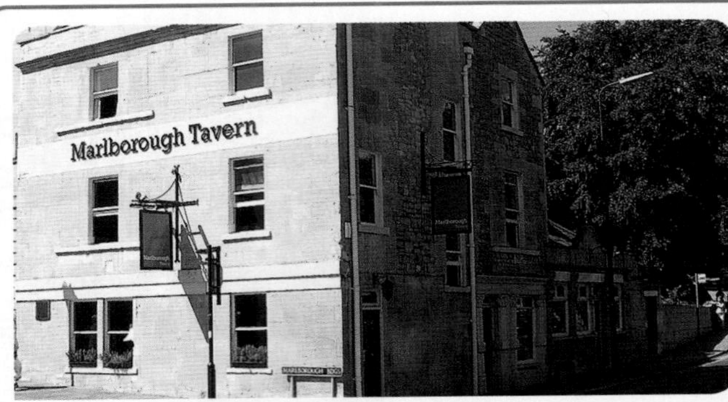

1 The Marlborough Tavern

35 Marlborough Buildings,
Bath BA1 2LY
Tel.: (01225)423731
e-mail: info@marlborough-tavern.com **Website:** www.marlborough-tavern.com

 **Butcombe Bitter, Sharp's Doom Bar**

Marlborough Buildings, a prime location right by the Royal Victoria Park and the terrace in which this pub sits, was originally built as a windbreak for the famous neighbouring Royal Crescent. Spacious and modern, with a sage green colour scheme, it features flock wallpaper, exotic lighting and a mishmash of furniture; flowers on the tables and local artists' work for sale on the walls bringing further splashes of colour. Light streams in at either end, while the section in the middle by the bar has a more intimate feel. Food is proudly local, seasonal and traceable, with unfussy, homemade dishes such as ham hock, confit leg of chicken and sausage and split pea casserole which are big on flavour and big of portion. In some pubs, service seems almost to be something of an afterthought, but not so here; staff may be casually dressed but they make a real effort with their customers, and are friendly and attentive without being overbearing.

Closing times
Closed 25 December and Sunday dinner

Booking advisable

Prices
Meals: à la carte £ 20/30

Typical Dishes
Battered Cornish squid
Roast pork & bean casserole
Jam roly poly

Northwest of city centre on east side of Royal Victoria Park. Parking bays opposite; parking also in the park (50m).

2 White Hart

Widcombe Hill,
Bath BA2 6AA
Tel.: (01225)338053
e-mail: enquiries@whitehartbath.co.uk **Website:** www.whitehartbath.co.uk

 **Butcombe, Wye Valley Dorothy Goodbody's**

This pub has a good reputation in the local community and as you pass by the small groups of drinkers sharing tapas at the bar, you understand why you had to book to secure a place. Worn wooden tables are adorned with candles and flowers, whilst outside, large umbrellas cover wooden furniture on the attractive patio area; and it's not just the welcoming atmosphere that people come for. This pub is well-known for 'getting it right' where the food is concerned, with a concise but hearty selection of dishes that capture the essence of what pub food should be. It is unfussy modern British fare, with the odd hint of Mediterranean influence and an emphasis on simplicity. Ingredients are sourced locally and come together to create dishes such as chicken breast marinated in lime and ginger or rib-eye steak with green peppercorn butter. Desserts are definitely a highlight here, ranging from mouth-watering crumble to rich chocolate truffle cake.

Closing times

Closed 25-26 December, 1 January, bank holidays and Sunday dinner

Booking essential at dinner

Prices

Meals: à la carte £ 20/35

Typical Dishes

Salt & pepper squid
Rump of lamb
Sticky fig & orange pudding

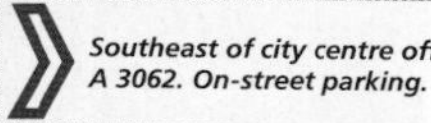

Southeast of city centre off A 3062. On-street parking.

3 The Albion Public House and Dining Rooms

Boyces Avenue,
Clifton Village, Bristol BS8 4AA
Tel.: (0117)9733522 – Fax: (0117)9739768
e-mail: info@thealbionclifton.co.uk **Website:** www.thealbionclifton.co.uk

Otter Bright, Butcombe Bitter, St Austell Tribute, Sharp's Doom Bar

Tucked away down a cobbled street in the fashionable neighbourhood quarter of Clifton, the trendy 17C Grade II listed Albion really is at the heart of the village. This pub is as a pub should be – fun, friendly and casual – with an equal split of after-work drinkers and those out for a relaxed evening meal. In warmer months the benches on the outside terrace make a pleasant spot to take in the comings and goings of the area, as well as providing the setting for the regular Sunday night BBQ. Taking London's St John restaurant as inspiration, the kitchen team welcome entire animals to their door and fans of offal are always well looked after. With a mouthwatering selection of daily changing dishes, the seasonally influenced, proudly British menu offers plenty of appeal, and the friendly service team are only too happy to deliver the tasty dishes to the table. Booking here is imperative, as drinkers tend to multiply throughout the evening.

Closing times

Closed 25-26 December, 1 January, Sunday dinner and Monday

Booking essential

Prices

Meals: £ 30 (dinner) and à la carte £ 21/39

Typical Dishes

Duck hearts & foie gras toast
Lamb's belly & polenta
Hot chocolate fondant

In Clifton Village. Parking in Victoria Square or surrounding roads.

4 The Kensington Arms

35-37 Stanley Rd,
Bristol B56 6NP
Tel.: (0117)9446444 – Fax: (0117)9248095
e-mail: info@thekensingtonarms.co.uk **Website:** www.thekensingtonarms.co.uk

  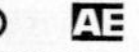 

 **Morland Original Bitter, Ruddles Best and guest ales such as Morris Mayhem**

What once languished, neglected, as a studenty 'pork-pie-and-a-pint, please' sort of a place has recently made a pain-free and highly successful metamorphosis into a trendy paragon of gastropubbism, dedicated to dining. With its high ceiling, arty design and walls filled with framed photos, mirrors and old adverts, the interior has a quirky feel. The chefs are on show at work behind you, service is eager, and the more formal upstairs dining room is used at weekends. The Kenny's kitchen takes a modern, commendably no-nonsense approach to food and dishes come served exactly as their descriptions suggest, with no unnecessary frills. Recreated pub classics like faggots and peas and sausage and mash clamour for your attention on the mainly British menu, while traditional puds such as toffee apple crumble and sticky toffee pudding provide a tempting finale.

Closing times
Closed 25 December and 1 January

Prices
Meals: à la carte £ 22/38

Typical Dishes
Stuffed squid
Venison loin steak
Upside down pear crumble

In city centre.

5 The Pump House

Merchants Rd,
Bristol BS8 4PZ
Tel.: (0117)9272229 – Fax: (0117)9279557
e-mail: info@the-pumphouse.com **Website:** www.the-pumphouse.com

 **Greene King IPA, Butcombe, Theakstons**

In the days of steam this impressive converted Victorian pumping station provided power for the bridges and machines in the docks. Its role is somewhat different today, but it still provides power of a sort – for the people of Bristol in the form of the duel fuel of food and drink. It's a vast place, but don't let that put you off – having undergone extensive refurbishment in 2007, it's now stylish and modern, with exposed stone, trendy lighting, a mezzanine restaurant and a cool outside terrace overlooking the water. Besides, it's not the décor but the cooking that's the main attraction here: modern French/British menus offer fashionable yet substantial dishes like langoustine and vanilla risotto, or roast guinea fowl with spiced red cabbage and truffle mash, and even the most traditional-sounding dish comes imaginatively served, with a splash of panache. Friendly, efficient staff will take orders either at the bar or at your table.

Closing times

Closed 25 December

Prices

Meals: £ 18 (lunch)
and à la carte £ 20/28

Typical Dishes

Salt ox tongue
Rare roast rib of beef
Bitter chocolate fondant

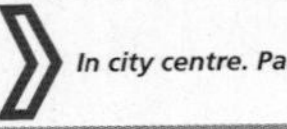

In city centre. Parking.

6 Robin Hood's Retreat

197 Gloucester Rd, Bristol BS7 8BG
Tel.: (0117)9248639
e-mail: info@robinhoodsretreat.gmail.com
Website: www.robinhoodsretreat.co.uk

Sharp's Doom Bar, Deuchar's, Butcombe and guest beers - Brakspear, Bath Ales, Cottage Brewery, Arbor Ales, Blindmans, Cheddar

A metropolitan retreat from the bustling streets maybe, but for Robin Hood it's a long way from Sherwood Forest. A red-brick Victorian pub nestling between shops, previously a bikers' haven, it has been tastefully smartened up without losing sight of the fact that it is still a pub. Drinkers are welcome, with eight constantly rotating ales on tap – but dining is now very much a focus. Considering the quality of the ingredients, all local and seasonal, and the wide choice available, the prices are very reasonable. The original and interesting menu offers a daily-changing mix of re-created British classics, using techniques that owe more than a nod to France; dishes are satisfying, comforting and flavoursome. Period décor, wonky tables and mismatched chairs add character but it's the food that is the main attraction here. The small but dedicated team have got their priorities right, focusing on fine food in traditional surroundings.

Closing times
Open daily
Booking advisable at dinner

Prices
Meals: £ 19 (lunch) and à la carte £ 27/33

Typical Dishes
Cured & roasted pigeon
Braised pork belly
Blackcurrant & white chocolate tart

In city centre. On-street parking or car park opposite.

7 Bear & Swan

13 South Parade,
Chew Magna BS40 8SL
Tel.: (01275)331100 – Fax: (01275)331204
e-mail: bearandswan@fullers.co.uk **Website:** www.bearandswan.co.uk

Fuller's London Pride, Butcombe Brewery and guest ales such as HSB, ESB, Seafarers

Thanks to a winning combination of good food, real ales, friendly staff and a warm, genuine ambience, this well-established village pub enjoys a bustling trade and a loyal local following. The bar boasts rustic stone walls and reclaimed wooden floors; take a seat by the fireside and order one of the old favourites from the 'Bear Basics' bar menu – maybe sausage and mash or a ploughman's - and if you ask nicely, they'll even pull down the big screen so you can watch the rugby while you munch. With its flickering church candles and view of the chefs hard at work, the restaurant affords a different dining experience. Although there is a smattering of international flavours, dishes are, for the most part, proudly British and ingredients locally sourced where possible, with meat from the village butcher and fish from Devon. Events like moules and frites night or seafood week create quite a buzz. Bedrooms are too modest for us to recommend.

Closing times

Closed 25 December dinner and Sunday dinner

Prices

Meals: £ 8.95 and à la carte £ 25/32

Typical Dishes

Goat's cheese on sweet potato
Chargrilled pork loin
Lemon tart

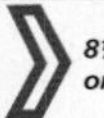

8¼ mi south of Bristol via A 37 on B 3130. Parking.

8 **Pony & Trap**

Knowle Hill,
Newtown, Chew Magna BS40 8TQ
Tel.: (01275)332627
e-mail: josh@theponyandtrap.co.uk **Website:** www.theponyandtrap.co.uk

Inspectors' favourites

 **Butcombe, Courage Best, Otter**

Having hidden his light under a bushel for some time, the young chef-owner of this traditional pub is now illuminating this corner of the South West with his cooking. Well presented, it shows a real understanding of ingredients and flavours and, with three courses for less than a pony, it's blooming good value too. A British bias means dishes like soused sardines, pork and venison terrine and lemon posset, and while it would have been easy for him to let his ambition to take over, the chef has kept plenty of pub classics like lasagne, fish pie and ham, egg and chips on the menu; albeit all made from scratch from the freshest and best ingredients available – think home cooked ham, homemade chips and eggs laid that morning by the pub's own chickens. The pub itself is cosy and friendly, with a pleasant extension and fine views east across the garden. The young serving team are quietly efficient, if a little subdued.

Closing times
Closed Sunday dinner in winter and Monday
Booking essential

Prices
Meals: à la carte £ 16/28

Typical Dishes
Pressed confit chicken
Fillet of salmon
Lemon & lime posset

1½ mi south of the village; follow signs for Bishop Stuttard. Parking.

9 The Wheatsheaf

Combe Hay BA2 7EG
Tel.: (01225)833504
e-mail: info@wheatsheafcombehay.com
Website: www.wheatsheafcombehay.com

Butcombe - Bitter, Blonde, Matthews Brewing Co

Just a stone's throw away from hectic city life, this picture perfect pub sits peacefully in a secluded wooded valley, with shrubs framing the doorway and artistically arranged flowers hanging from the walls. The hands-on owners, villagers themselves, have turned this pub around, creating a chic, stylish interior and a friendly, relaxed atmosphere – for the ultimate in comfort seek out the squashy sofas by the fire. The chef has an impressive background in country house hotels, so the food is not your usual pub fare: it may be seasonal and flavoursome, but it comes with a refined and delicate touch. The concise contemporary menu combines British and French influences, featuring dishes such as home-smoked trout with beetroot jelly, followed by Mendip beef with potato and foie gras gallette. Sharing the same designer styling as the pub, the bedrooms boast luxury showers and king size beds, while breakfast times are pleasantly flexible.

Closing times
Closed 25 December, Sunday dinner and Monday (except bank holidays when open for lunch)

Prices
Meals: £ 19 (lunch) and à la carte £ 19/55
3 rooms: £ 140/150

Typical Dishes
Asparagus, bacon & duck egg
Duck & rhubarb
Lemon meringue tart

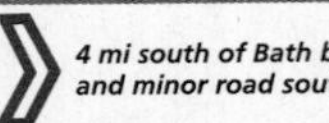

4 mi south of Bath by A 367 and minor road south. Parking.

10 Wheelwrights Arms

Church Lane, Monkton Combe BA2 7HB

Tel.: (01225)722287 – Fax: (01225)722259

e-mail: bookings@wheelwrightsarms.co.uk

Website: www.wheelwrightsarms.co.uk

  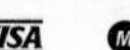

 **Butcombe Bitter, Bath Ales Gem**

The picturesque village in which this 18C pub is set seems an auspicious sign, and as you click open the latch on the front door and are encompassed by a warm, rosy glow, you know for sure that you've made an excellent choice. It's charming and intimate, with a cosy front snug perfect for a party of six and a log fire so regularly stoked it will have you peeling off layer after layer. On first glance, the menu may seem a little concise, but in fact there's plenty of choice, and the honest, hearty cooking comes in portions large enough to revive even the most exhausted of walkers. Bedrooms in the converted wheelwright's workshop are luxurious, with dark wood floors, comfy beds and fresh flowers, while bathrooms come with jet powered showers, fast-filling baths and fine French toiletries. Rugby fans are sure to want to take up the offer of two tickets to a game at Bath, and breakfast fans will be delighted with delicious bacon sandwiches.

Closing times

Open daily

Prices

Meals: £ 14 (lunch) and à la carte £ 18/26

7 rooms: £ 95/145

Typical Dishes

Smoked ham hock & mozzarella terrine

Roast monkfish

Bitter chocolate tart

2 mi southeast of Bath city centre by A 3062. Parking.

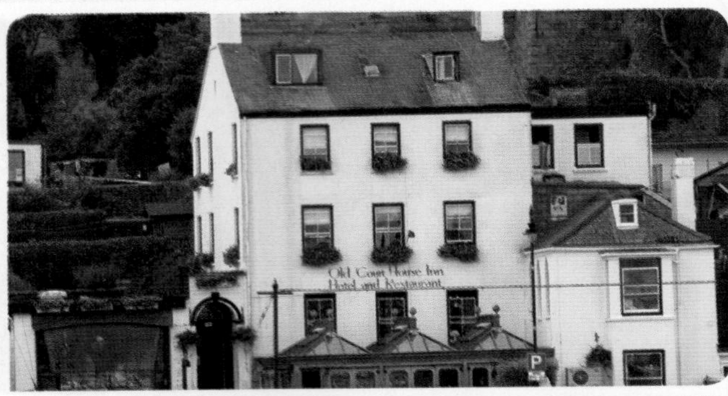

11 Old Court House Inn

St Aubin's Harbour,
Saint Aubin JE3 8AB
Tel.: (01534)746433 – Fax: (01534)745103
e-mail: info@oldcourthousejersey.com **Website:** www.oldcourthousejersey.com

   AE

Bass, Pedigree, Ginger Tosser

The owners of this whitewashed quayside inn have long been on the right tack, hence its favourable local reputation. Dating from 1450, it has been witness over the years to judicial comings and goings, as well as being a onetime storehouse for seafarers' illegal booty. There's something for everyone on the extensive menus, including daily seafood specials chosen from the wettest and freshest on offer that day. Thus, local lobster and crab sit alongside more traditional dishes like steak and lasagne, while the dessert menu includes old favourites such as sticky toffee pudding. You'll also be spoilt for choice when it comes to where to sit; the conservatory or the rustic bar are good choices for a lunchtime snack, whilst a seat on the decked terrace affords scenic views across the harbour; and if you feel like pushing the boat out, head for one of the more formal dining rooms, one of which is built in the shape of a galleon. Comfy bedrooms.

Closing times
Closed 25 December, January to February Sunday dinner and Monday

Prices
Meals: £ 10/22
and à la carte £ 15/25

9 rooms: £ 45/65

Typical Dishes
Crab & avocado tian
Fresh Dover sole meunière
Raspberry brûlée

4 mi west of St Helier. Public car park opposite and parking in street.

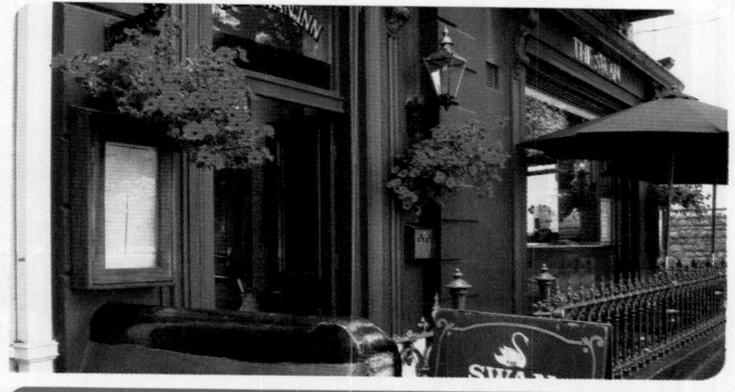

12 The Swan Inn

St Julian's Avenue,
Saint Peter Port GY1 1WA
Tel.: (01481)728969 – Fax: (01481)728969

 **Patois Guernsey Ale, Roquettes Guernsey Cider**

From façade to food, this really is a 'proper' pub. The smart bottle-green Victorian exterior makes it easy to spot and its traditional styling is warm and welcoming, especially in winter when the cosy log burners are ablaze. Having recently re-opened under the ownership of the former manager, a gregarious French fellow whose enthusiasm can be felt right at the heart of the pub, it has continued to prove a hit – particularly with the after-work crowd on a Friday night. With his wealth of on site experience, who better to keep it running like clockwork? If you're after a generous serving of something hearty and satisfying try the homemade burgers, legendary club sandwich or popular fish pie. For a more sedate dining experience climb the stairs to a room akin to those aboard the Titanic. Here you will find more ambitious dishes such as pork belly, lamb cutlets or seared fillet of sea bass – alongside some good value early week set menus.

Closing times
Closed 25 December and Sunday

Prices
Meals: £ 11 and à la carte £ 15/22

Typical Dishes
Home-cured salmon
Fish pie
Guernsey cheeses

 *In the centre of town. Parking on North Beach Pier (50yds).* 

13 The Halzephron Inn

Gunwalloe TR12 7QB
Tel.: (01326)240406 – Fax: (01326)241442
e-mail: halzephroninn@gunwalloe1.fsnet.co.uk
Website: www.halzephron-inn.co.uk

   AE

Sharp's Doom Bar, Sharp's Own, St Austell Tribute, Halzephron Gold Organic

These days, many pubs seem to change owners and chefs as often as the latter cook hot dinners, so it's always nice – and somewhat comforting – to discover somewhere like The Halzephron Inn, where things have ticked along in much the same manner for years. Why change what works? The menu offers old favourites like prawn cocktail and ploughman's, with a choice of sandwiches at midday, plus lunch and evening specials like steak and chips, fresh fish, beef stroganoff or lamb's liver and bacon. This is good old-fashioned, no-nonsense home cooking with a heart – and not a gastronaut in sight. No sexing up of the interior here either: low ceilings, old beams and cosy corners are all present and correct; with a sea view, smuggling history and yarn-spinning locals a bonus. Stay over in one of the neat bedrooms – and take a piece of the West Country home with you in the form of local clotted cream toffees, shortbread or Trelowarren teas.

Closing times
Closed 25 December

Prices
Meals: à la carte £ 20/30
2 rooms: £ 40/90

Typical Dishes
Crab, crayfish & saffron risotto
Roast duck breast
Baked white chocolate cheesecake

3½ mi south of Helston by A 3083. Parking.

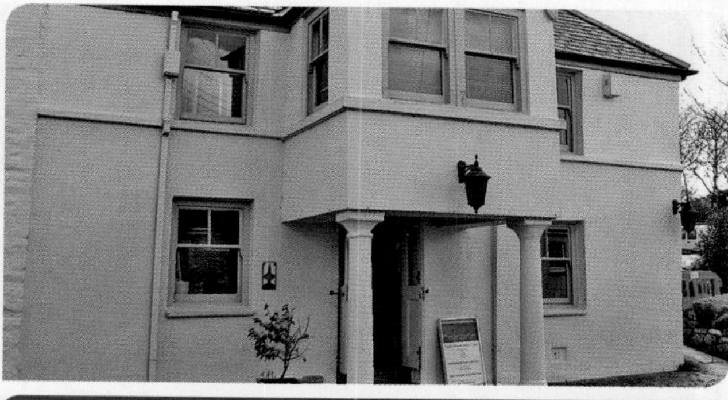

14 The Plume of Feathers

Mitchell TR8 5AX
Tel.: (01872)510387
e-mail: enquiries@theplume.info
Website: www.theplume.info

VISA 

 **Sharp's Doom Bar, Skinners Betty Stogs, Fuller's London Pride, Flowers Original**

A former coaching inn, The Plume of Feathers would have been one of the final stops for coaches on their way to the once thriving port of Falmouth, and its bedrooms – now located in the old stable block – are still its strength today. The inn was built in the 16C and its cob walls and exposed beams serve as a reminder of its ripe old age, though the smart décor and modern artwork are thoroughly 21C in their style. The concise lunch menu offers good value; the choice expands in the evenings and might include dishes like steak and chips or confit of duck leg, as well as the odd curry and plenty of seafood. World food and quiz nights on Tuesdays or steak nights on Wednesdays attract plenty of locals. For those who have travelled from further afield, bedrooms are comfortable and boast all mod cons. Room number seven, known as 'The Hen House,' is the best: furthest from the inn, it is spacious and quiet, with views across the back field.

Closing times
Open daily
Prices
Meals: à la carte £ 15/28
8 rooms: £ 54/115

Typical Dishes
Homemade fishcake
Confit Cornish duck
Chocolate cake with clotted cream

Near the junction of A 30 and A 3076. Parking.

15 Pandora Inn

Restronguet Creek,
Mylor Bridge TR11 5ST
Tel.: (01326)372678 – Fax: (01326)378958
e-mail: info@pandorainn.com **Website:** www.pandorainn.com

VISA MC AE

 **St Austell Tribute, Tinners, Hicks Special Draught (HSD), Bass**

In a scenic spot and with its own pontoon, The Pandora Inn is unsurprisingly popular during the summer months, when folks arrive by boat and moor up outside – as well as by car, by bike and on shanks' pony – so the advice is: if you want a seat, you'd be best to arrive early. With its low ceilings and tables arranged around wood burning stoves, it's also a cosy place for a meal come winter; the menu changes seasonally, so fish pie and fishcakes, tuna, patés and salads in summer – as well as bestseller cod and chips – make way for casseroles and stews in winter, with venison and game from nearby estates. Blackboard specials supplement the menu; there is beer from St Austell brewery – and no 13C harbourside pub would be complete without a seafaring legend to go with it: The Pandora Inn was apparently thus named by a naval captain who was sent to Cornwall as a punishment after his ship, The Pandora, ran aground on the Great Barrier Reef.

Closing times

Closed 25 December

Prices

Meals: à la carte £ 15/32

Typical Dishes

Scallops on pea risotto
Grilled sardines
Satin dark chocolate tart

 ***4 mi north of Falmouth by A 39, B 3292 and minor road east from Penryn. Parking.*** 

16 **Victoria Inn**

Perranuthnoe TR20 9NP
Tel.: (01736)710309
e-mail: enquiries@victoriainn-penzance.co.uk
Website: www.victoriainn-penzance.co.uk

Sharp's Doom Bar, St Austell Tribute

Two minutes walk from the beach and the beautiful views of St. Michael's Mount, the village of Perranuthnoe plays host to what is allegedly the oldest inn in Cornwall. Run by a husband and wife team, you will not be able to miss this pub, just think pink and follow the locals. Inside it is characteristically Cornish; rustic and relaxed, with photos from yesteryear hanging on exposed stone walls and a welcoming wood burning fire. The food is great whether you eat in the more formal dining room or stay in the atmospheric surroundings of the bar. The carefully thought out, classical menu is crafted from local, seasonal produce; the emphasis being on quality ingredients and cooking techniques that allow the natural flavours to stand out. The fish in particular is extremely fresh and, depending on the catch, you may find salmon, crab, prawns, haddock or scallops. Rooms are simple, with a strong nautical design theme.

Closing times
Closed 25-26 December, 1 week January, Sunday dinner, and Monday (in winter)

Prices
Meals: à la carte £ 22/33
2 rooms: £ 45/70

Typical Dishes
Pork cheek
Cornish hake
Orange panna cotta

3 mi east of Marazion, south of A 394. Parking.

17 **St Kew Inn**

Saint Kew PL30 3HB
Tel.: (01208)841259
e-mail: stkewinn@btconnect.com
Website: www.stkewinn.co.uk

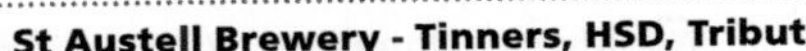
St Austell Brewery - Tinners, HSD, Tribute

St Kew Inn was built in the 15C to serve the masons who constructed the magnificent next door church and, with its flag floors, stone walls and wooden beams, it's not short on character itself. Village regulars can be found propping up the bar or warming themselves by the fire, sipping the St Austell beer that's kept in wooden casks. The pub sits in a quintessentially English location and its attractive front garden with picnic tables is as much of a draw as the pub itself, come the warmer weather. A ginormous electric umbrella means that sudden summer showers are not a problem, and there are heaters too, should it turn nippy. Cooking is fresh and tasty, with a wide range of appealing, good value dishes from which to choose; lunch means dishes like Fowey mussels, Welsh rarebit, corned beef hash and a range of sandwiches, while dinner offers similar (minus the sandwiches), plus perhaps some grilled lemon sole or pan-fried lamb's liver.

Closing times
Open daily

Prices
Meals: à la carte £ 18/32

Typical Dishes
Welsh rarebit
Neck of lamb
Rice pudding

3 mi northeast of Wadebridge by A 39 and minor road north. Parking.

18 **The Cornish Arms**

Churchtown,
Saint Merryn PL28 8ND
Tel.: (01841)520288
Website: www.rickstein.com

 **St Austell - Tinners, Tribute, Proper Job, Chalky's Bite**

When St Austell Brewery leased The Cornish Arms to Rick Stein, the locals went into panic at the thought of their beloved haunt being turned into a gastropub. They needn't have worried though, as despite the addition of a smart terrace with high wooden tables sheltered behind tall glass screens, it remains a proper pub through and through. Set in the shadow of a large church, it boasts paisley carpets, battered wooden furniture, a pool table and a slot machine, not forgetting cards, darts and pool teams – a fact that keeps the locals very happy indeed. The typical pub menu is concise, offering classics such as steak and ale pie, ploughman's and freshly made scampi in a basket; and cooking is sound and sensibly priced. If you didn't know about its famous owner, you'd never guess: the only clues are a small specials board featuring the odd fresh fish dish and the locally brewed Chalky's Bite, named after Stein's late four-legged friend.

Closing times
Open daily
Prices
Meals: à la carte £ 16/30

Typical Dishes
Mussels & chips
Steak & Tribute pie
Lemon posset

West of Padstow on B 3276.
Parking.

19 Viners

Carvynick,
Summercourt TR8 5AF
Tel.: (01872)510544 – Fax: (01872)510468
e-mail: info@vinersrestaurant.co.uk **Website:** www.vinersrestaurant.co.uk

 **Sharps Doom Bar, Eden Ale, Special Reserve, Skinners Betty Stogs and Cornish Knocker**

Keep a look out for the signs to this charming stone-built pub; it's well-concealed in the Cornish countryside, situated just past an upmarket caravan site and golf club. Rustic in parts, it tends towards the more sophisticated, restaurant-style end of pub dining, but this is of no real consequence, for the enthusiastic young staff proffer a warm welcome and the atmosphere is informal and relaxed. Chef-owner Kevin Viner is something of a culinary godfather in these parts, guiding younger talent with his more than capable hands. He holds regular cookery demonstrations and his awards and memorabilia adorn the walls. Menus are a combination of old favourites (which the locals won't allow him to remove) and more ambitious offerings; so dishes might range from sautéed mushrooms on toast or moules marinière, to chicken and foie gras terrine, lobster or slow roasted pork belly, with plenty of local meats, fish and cheese from which to choose.

At Carvynick Golf and Country Club, 1½ mi northwest of the junction of A 30 and A 3058. Parking.

Closing times

Closed Sunday dinner, Monday, and Tuesday-Saturday lunch

Prices

Meals: £ 15 (weekday dinner Tuesday-Friday dinner) and à la carte £ 32/38

Typical Dishes

Twice baked cheese soufflé
Duo of Gressingham duck
Chocolate temptation

20 Springer Spaniel

Treburley, PL15 9NS

Tel.: (01579)370424 – Fax: (01579)370424

e-mail: springerspaniel@btconnect.com

Website: www.thespringerspaniel.org.uk

  MC

 **Skinner's Betty Stogs, Sharp's Doom Bar, St Austell Tribute**

Like its namesake, this former 18C coaching inn is popular and friendly, with a reassuringly familiar warmth. The wide ranging, seasonally inspired menus have something for everyone and use only local, traceable produce: vegetables and game from local farms, seafood from Cornish waters and organic meat from the owners' cattle and sheep farm in the neighbouring village. Dinner menus include traditional dishes such as venison and game casserole or confit of duck, whilst daytime menus have lighter offerings such as ploughman's lunches. For children there is a Little Jack Russell menu and if it's not too busy you may get the chance to meet Nutmeg, who inspired it. The dogs are not the only link here to hunting: shooting magazines are scattered about and prints depicting a chase adorn the walls, with the inevitable picture of a springer spaniel amongst them. Like this friendly, family-loving dog, the pub itself is a good all-rounder.

Closing times

Open daily

Prices

Meals: à la carte £ 19/27

Typical Dishes

Crayfish tails

Braised rabbit with bacon

Vanilla panna cotta

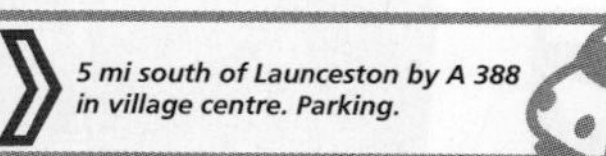

5 mi south of Launceston by A 388 in village centre. Parking.

21 The Gurnard's Head

Treen,
Zennor TR26 3DE
Tel.: (01736)796928
e-mail: enquiries@gurnardshead.co.uk **Website:** www.gurnardshead.co.uk

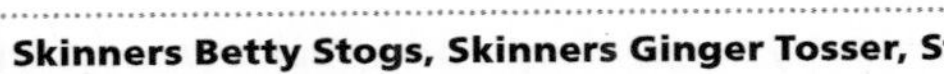

Skinners Betty Stogs, Skinners Ginger Tosser, St Austell Tribute

Surrounded by nothing but fields, livestock and scenic views, this shabby-chic pub is as it should be – warm, welcoming and down to earth. A rather handy bus service drops you nearby and the name emblazoned across the roof makes certain you don't miss it. Inside, local artwork adorns the walls, newspapers and board games are scattered about the place and even on the bleakest day, warm stone floors and blazing fires make it cosy. Relying on regionally sourced or locally foraged produce, the modern cooking displays the odd Mediterranean touch. You might find lamb steaks on couscous or red mullet with tapenade, alongside deep-fried Gurnard or salt and pepper squid. Tasty puddings round it all off and there are some interesting wines by the glass. Comfy bedrooms boast good linen and toiletries, while breakfast offers fresh juices and artisan preserves. Reminiscent of simpler times, there's no television, internet or mobile phone signal.

Closing times
Closed 4 days January

Prices
Meals: à la carte £ 20/24
7 rooms: £ 75/140

Typical Dishes
Squid & chorizo stew
Rack of Penwith hogget
Lemon posset & fennel shortbread

6 mi west of St Ives by B 3306.
Parking.

22 The Turtley Corn Mill

Avonwick TQ10 9ES
Tel.: (01364)646100 – Fax: (01364)646101
e-mail: mill@avonwick.net
Website: www.avonwick.net

 **Tamar, Jail Ale, Butcombe Blonde, Otter Ales**

A delightful – and very busy – 18C mill on the banks of the River Glaze Brook, complete with a working water wheel and a giant chess set; its own lake and an island, home to ducks and geese. It is set in six acres so there's plenty of space in which to stroll and this sense of space extends inside too, with what seems like room for a small army. The style here is natural and light, with scrubbed oak floors, pretty pot plants and those trademark Brunning pub bookshelves. Tasty dishes range from the more traditional – think prawn cocktail, smoked salmon, sausage and mash or fish pie – to the more international: perhaps a tapas plate to share, seafood cassoulet, some nachos or spaghetti Bolognese. The varying portion sizes – they serve starters, main courses and lighter bites, as well as sandwiches and paninis – ensure all appetites are catered for. Very comfortable, neutrally decorated bedrooms with plenty of space and a host of luxuries.

Closing times
Closed 25 December

Prices
Meals: à la carte £ 15/30
4 rooms: £ 89/110

Typical Dishes
Chicken liver pâté
Smoked haddock & salmon fishcakes
Sticky toffee pudding

1½ mi south of South Brent by minor road. Parking.

23 The Quarrymans Rest

Briton St,
Bampton EX16 9LN
Tel.: (01398)331480
e-mail: info@thequarrymansrest.co.uk **Website:** www.thequarrymansrest.co.uk

Inspectors' favourites

   AE

 **Sharp's Doom Bar, Dod's, Bay's, Otter, Avocet**

Despite several name changes – the most recent being inspired by the local stone and slate mine – this 17C inn has not relinquished its rustic roots and has managed to stay an honest village pub. The large bar with its traditional décor and welcoming open fire gives way to a slightly more formal dining room with high-backed leather chairs. The appealing menu has strong seasonal and regional influences and the cooking is careful and knowledgeable, as you would expect from an experienced chef. He prides himself on sourcing local produce: meat and West Country cheese from a traditional butcher, cream and beef from a nearby farm, fish from the Brixham day boats and bread from the local baker. For starters you may find potted salt beef or tempura tiger prawns; to follow, braised knuckle of Devon lamb or fillet of sea bass, and to finish, homemade cheesecake or orange and treacle tart. Like the food, the bedrooms offer good value for money.

Closing times
Closed Sunday dinner

Prices
Meals: à la carte £ 20/24
3 rooms: £ 40/80

Typical Dishes
Potted salt beef
Wild sea bass
Panna cotta & ginger parkin

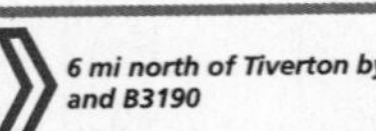
6 mi north of Tiverton by A396 and B3190

24 The Normandy Arms

Chapel St,
Blackawton TQ9 7BN
Tel.: (01803)712884 – Fax: (01803)712734
e-mail: peter.alcroft@btconnect.com **Website:** www.thenormandyarms.co.uk

 **Dartmoor Best Bitter, Tribute, HSD, Old Speckled Hen**

It's always a good sign when the owners of a pub take time to chat with their customers, and at this immaculately whitewashed inn, you'll find this hospitality extended to regulars and visitors alike. The pub was closed for a couple years before Sharon and Peter arrived and gave the place a facelift, and you get the feeling that the villagers missed it and are now making up for lost time. There's a comfy lounge area by the entrance and two rooms set for dining; with locals tending to drink in the more atmospheric bar room, where a grandfather clock keeps time. Unfussy cooking is proudly homemade using local produce and the blackboard bar menu offers pub favourites like sausage and mash, while a printed à la carte showcases more elaborate, restaurant-style dishes. This is a great place to be on the May Day bank holiday, when people descend on Blackawton from far and wide for the annual worm charming competition.

Closing times

Closed 25 December, 1 January, 1 week in spring, Sunday dinner, Monday (except in August) and lunch Tuesday-Saturday

Booking essential at dinner

Prices

Meals: à la carte £ 22/32

Typical Dishes

Chicken liver & foie gras parfait

Fillet of Blackawton beef

Chocolate fondant

4 mi west of Dartmouth by A3122 and minor road. Off street parking directly outside.

25 **Masons Arms**

Branscombe EX12 3DJ
Tel.: (01297)680300 – Fax: (01297)680500
e-mail: reception@masonsarms.co.uk
Website: www.masonsarms.co.uk

Branscombe Vale Brewery Branoc and Summa That, Otter Bitter and Masons Ale, St Austell Tribute

Set in a picturesque village, this immensely charming 14C building started life as a tiny cider-house, before becoming an inn and later the Masons Arms – renamed after regular visits from the workers building Exeter Cathedral. This pub really is a cut above the rest, boasting characterful period features and beams aplenty. Menus rely on local produce but influences are European, so next to each other you might find French-inpired toffee and banana crème brûlée, Italian-influenced hazelnut panna cotta and good old British sticky toffee pudding. The highlight of the bar menu is the local crab, landed on the beach just 10mins away, while in the restaurant one dish from every course has the main ingredient sourced from within ten miles; often, local meats can often be found cooking on the spit over the fire too. Split between the inn and cottages, bedrooms boast beams, antique furnishings and the odd jacuzzi, four-poster or scenic view.

Closing times
Open daily

Prices
Meals: £ 30 (dinner)
and à la carte £ 20/29

21 rooms: £ 56/170

Typical Dishes
Quail's eggs salad
Grilled lamb cutlets
Roast hazelnut panna cotta

Between Seaton and Sidmouth; south of A 3052; in the village centre. Parking.

26 The Drewe Arms

Broadhembury EX14 3NF
Tel.: (01404)841267
e-mail: info@thedrewe.arms.com **Website:** www.thedrewe.arms.com

 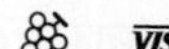 

 **Otter Bitter and two rotating guest beers**

Set close to the church, in a beautiful cob and thatch village, The Drewe Arms is a quintessential English pub. Exposed beams and dark wood furnishings set the tone, and roaring open fires and flickering candlelight create a warm welcome, especially in the winter. There's the choice of two characterful dining areas, both serving freshly prepared dishes crafted from quality, local produce – but each with its own menu. Sandwiches, light bites and pub classics such as ham hock, mussels Provençale or sirloin steak are on offer in the bar, while the restaurant steps things up a gear, featuring more modern and international influences. You might find carpaccio of venison, or potted crab, lobster and mussel terrine – followed by a complimentary sorbet – then maybe tarte tatin of sweet potato and fennel, pork belly with white and black pudding, or seared fillet of halibut with wasabi mash. Warm lemon tart with iced banana parfait could follow.

Closing times
Closed Monday
Booking essential
Prices
Meals: à la carte £ 22/35

Typical Dishes
Carpaccio of venison
Fillet of sea bass
Hazlenut meringue

5 mi northwest of Honiton by A 373. Parking; also in village square.

27 **Lamb Inn**

Crediton,
Crediton EX17 4LW
Tel.: (01363)773676
e-mail: thelambinn@gmail.com **Website:** www.lambinnsandford.co.uk

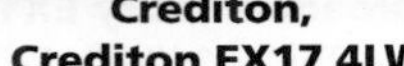

Cotleigh Tawny Bitter and 3 guest ales - Teignworthy, O'Hanlons, Roosters, Skinners, Sharps

This sleepy 16C period coaching inn is as picturesque a village pub as you can find. The delightfully attractive exterior is matched by a charming, characterful interior and pleasantly dated décor: low ceilings, chunky mismatched tables and wooden pews, a welcoming open fire, and even an original skittle alley. A variety of events take place throughout the month, including salsa lessons, jazz, casino and cocktail evenings and open mic nights. On the wall, the blackboard displays a frequently changing menu of satisfying and warming dishes that show strong influences from the chef's homeland in France. Presented in a simple, unassuming manner, they might include starters of smoked salmon crostini or butternut squash soup, followed by confit of duck or winter stews. Service is laid back but the excellent cooking makes up for it and there is always a good selection of ales on tap. The recently converted bedrooms are spacious and charming.

Closing times
Open daily

Prices
Meals: à la carte £ 16/23
3 rooms: £ 69/95

Typical Dishes
Cucumber & poached prawns
Pan-fried seabass
Tarte Tatin

2 mi north of Crediton by minor road. Parking in the square or the Village Hall car park.

28 The Floating Bridge

By Lower Ferry,
Coombe Rd, Dartmouth TQ6 9PQ
Tel.: (01803)832354
e-mail: floatingbridge@dartmarina.com **Website:** www.dartmarina.com

  AE

 **St Austell Tribute, Otter Ale and one guest ale**

It's not often that you can drop into conversation that you've come by boat, so make the most of the opportunity and take the lower ferry from Kingswear to Dartmouth, whether you're travelling on foot or by car. Unusually situated on the ferry slip road, you may not normally give this pub a second glance but if you need something to tide you over it's well worth a visit, especially in the holiday season. In the large period bar you will find the locals having a chat amongst the seafaring pictures and traditional décor, whilst next door the spacious main dining room provides a more contemporary feel, with blond wood floors, comfy seating and more modern artwork. The menu is traditional and predominantly local, displaying tasty, wholesome fare; out of season the choice is limited to four dishes per course but in summer this expands and is supplemented by a blackboard selection, often in the form of fresh fish specials.

Closing times
Closed 5-31 January;
November to March Sunday dinner and Tuesday

Prices
Meals: à la carte £ 15/25

Typical Dishes
Scotch egg
Hot pot
Treacle tart

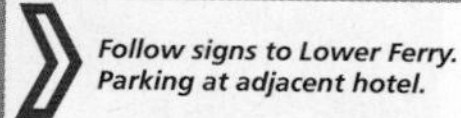
Follow signs to Lower Ferry. Parking at adjacent hotel.

29 Fortescue Arms

East Allington TQ9 7RA

Tel.: (01548)521215

e-mail: info@fortescue-arms.co.uk

Website: www.fortescue-arms.co.uk

Butcombe Bitter, Dartmoor IPA

Built about 200 years ago as part of the Fallapit estate – then owned by the Fortescue family – this well run, ivy-clad pub has two distinct sides to it: turn left and you're in a small beamed bar, with black flagged floors and an open fire; turn right and you enter a smart dining room with rustic stone walls. Although the Austrian chef-owner is apparently known for sculpting things out of lard, the cooking here is thankfully of a rather more traditional bent. On the bar menu you'll find hearty, flavoursome pub classics – think fish pie, stews and casseroles – alongside warm organic bread and a blackboard menu of daily specials. The constantly evolving dining room menu offers more refined dishes such as roast local lamb loin or local roe deer fillet, as well as the odd dish which pays homage to the chef's roots - maybe Austrian potato goulash or Apfelstrudel. First floor bedrooms are pine furnished, with shower-only bathrooms.

Closing times

Closed Monday lunch

Prices

Meals: à la carte £ 25/30

3 rooms: £ 40/60

Typical Dishes

Avocado & crayfish

Calves liver & spring onion mash

Crème brûlée & rhubarb

4 mi northeast of Kingsbridge by B 3264, A 381 and minor road. Parking.

30 The Puffing Billy

Station Rd,
Exton EX3 0PR
Tel.: (01392)877888
Website: www.eatoutdevon.com

 **Teignworthy Neap Tide, Bay's Brewery Gold, Otter Bitter**

Robert Louis Stevenson once said that 'it is better to travel hopefully than to arrive'; but then he hadn't been to the Puffing Billy. Set just around the corner from Exton station, this spacious pub is light, modern and airy; and boasts a distinct sense of style. It's a popular place, so you might want to reserve your seats but don't worry, wherever you sit you can guarantee that the welcoming service will be first class. Modern stools, tub chairs and contemporary lighting fill the bar, while the more formal dining room displays stylish banquettes and high-backed chairs set at polished tables. On your journey through the menu you'll discover something to suit every taste. If you like comforting classics that could be steak and kidney pie; if your taste buds fancy something more regional it might be local chicken with rustic Devon cheese; or if you're looking for something from afar, it may be crab cakes in chilli and coriander.

Closing times
Closed Christmas to New Year

Prices
Meals: à la carte £ 21/29

Typical Dishes
Crab cakes
Lamb & rosemary jus
Vanilla rice pudding

Brown tourist sign off A376 to Exmouth, 3 mi from junction 30 M5. Parking.

31 The Hart Inn

The Square,
Hartland EX39 6BL
Tel.: (01237)441474
e-mail: bjornmoen@hotmail.com **Website:** www.thehartinn.com

Sharp's Doom Bar, Courage Directors, Bath Gem, Otter Ale

Set on the original coaching route from Bideford to Bude, this spacious inn boasts stonework dating back to the 14 and 16C, making it one of the oldest buildings in Hartland; whilst a rustic interior, exposed stone walls, huge beams, open fires and homely furnishings create a warm and friendly atmosphere. Formerly 'The New Inn', it's thought that the name was changed when the draymen delivering the beer kept going to the wrong address; its new title is believed to make reference to the pub being the 'heart' of the village, where the local hunt used to meet. The chef is Danish so the regularly changing menu sees some Scandinavian influences, although produce remains local and seasonal; meat and vegetables are supplied by the surrounding farms and fish is delivered from nearby Appledore. Portions are generous and definitely not for the faint-hearted; dishes may include braised shoulder of Lundy lamb, roast spatchcock or baked sea bass.

Closing times
Closed Sunday dinner and Monday

Prices
Meals: à la carte £ 15/23

Typical Dishes
Teriyaki duck salad
Pressed pork belly
Vanilla panna cotta

Between Bideford and Bude off A 39. Parking.

32 The Rock Inn

Haytor Vale TQ13 9XP
Tel.: (01364)661305 – Fax: (01364)661242
e-mail: info@rock-inn.co.uk
Website: www.rock-inn.co.uk

 **Jail Ale, Otter Bright, Dartmoor Best**

Having built up an appetite walking on Dartmoor, eat to the sound of birdsong in the quintessentially English garden of this 18C coaching inn, tucked away in amongst a row of cottages in a tiny, very picturesque, rural village. From salads and sandwiches to steak and chips, the simple bar menu is a good choice for lunch; although a more elaborate restaurant menu is also available for dinner. The interior is bursting with rustic character, with several log fires, wood beams, oak furniture and flag floors. The bedrooms, quirkily named after past winners of the Grand National, are set on different levels and the sloping floors simply add to the charm. Once frequented by the quarrymen who transported granite along the railway, this pub is still popular with locals. It has been run by the same family for many years, and the green, white and black flag flying out front is a fitting symbol of the Devonshire pride to be found here.

Closing times
Closed 25-26 December

Prices
Meals: £ 15 (weekdays)/18 and à la carte £ 20/23
9 rooms: £ 70/117

Typical Dishes
River Teign mussels
Creedy carver duck breast
Chocolate tart with orange sorbet

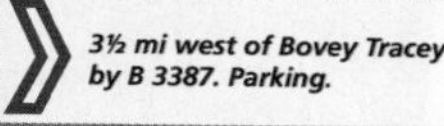
3½ mi west of Bovey Tracey by B 3387. Parking.

33 The Holt

178 High St,
Honiton EX14 1LA
Tel.: (01404)47707
e-mail: enquiries@theholt-honiton.com **Website:** www.theholt-honiton.com

VISA 

Otter Brewery - Ale, Bitter, Bright, Head, Amber

'Holt: the burrowed lair of an animal, especially an otter'. Q: So why would you name your pub after this? A: For the good reason that your parents own the nearby Otter Brewery. The McCaig family's mission statement is to provide a 'distinctive and sustainable taste of Devon', through both their food and their ales; it really is a family affair, with one brother out front and one behind the scenes, and mum and dad supplying a selection of real ales from down the road. There is a strong drive towards local produce, with a great deal of effort put into sourcing; sustainable methods are also key, so the eco-friendly menus are printed on recycled hops and paper. The interesting menu changes every 6 weeks, with tapas and light dishes on offer at lunch and a more substantial à la carte menu in the evening. Much of the food is homemade, including the tasty sausages, and the smoking of produce also takes place entirely on site.

Closing times

Closed 25-26 December and 1 January

Prices

Meals: à la carte £ 20/26

Typical Dishes

Home-smoked salmon
Pan-fried lamb chump
Passion fruit & raspberry Pavlova

At lower end of High Street. Dowell Street car park (2min walk).

34 The Hoops Inn

Horn's Cross EX39 5DL
Tel.: (01237)451222 – Fax: (01237)451247
e-mail: sales@hoopsinn.co.uk
Website: www.hoopsinn.co.uk

  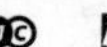 AE

 **Hoops Special Ale, Old Ale, Sharp's Doom Bar**

Ravaged by a fire in March 2009, this historic pub sustained a quarter of a million pounds worth of damage and needed to have half of its roof re-thatched. Thankfully, much is now as it was pre-blaze and the 13C pub's quaint character remains intact: a confusion of rooms and cosy snugs set around the bar; with ancient beams decorated with horse brasses and china, a tank of tropical fish and a restaurant for intimate candlelit dinners à deux. The same menu is served throughout and dishes might include fish cassoulet, cottage pie, lamb shoulder and beef Bourguignon, with old fashioned puds like jam roly poly or knickerbocker glory. Four superior bedrooms in the original inn boast four-posters and half-testers whilst those in the rear coach house offer simpler, cosier comforts. Check out the stained glass windows lining the corridor between the two, which depict the shields of the Knights of the Round Table. Occasional falconry days.

Closing times
Open daily
Prices
Meals: à la carte £ 15/30
13 rooms: £ 95/105

Typical Dishes
Turbot & mussels in cream sauce
North Devon fillet steak
Eton Mess

½ mi west on A 39 going to Clovelly. Parking.

England • South West • Devon

35 Bickley Mill

Stoneycombe,
Kingskerswell TQ12 5LN
Tel.: (01803)873201 – Fax: (01803)875129
e-mail: info@bickleymill.co.uk **Website:** www.bickleymill.co.uk

 **Otter Ale, Springtide Teignworthy**

Hidden away in the sleepy village of Stoneycombe lies this converted flour mill dating back to the 13C. A Free House since 1971, when it was adapted to allow for guest bedrooms, as much thought has been given to the outside of this establishment as the inside. The first thing that strikes you on arrival is the pleasant garden with its large decked terrace; a delightful area in which to soak up the sun. This is a pub for all seasons, however, and there are numerous cosy areas inside ideal in which to dine when dark wintry nights draw in. Although this pub has been modernised and has contemporary art hanging on the walls, it still manages to retain its rustic charm with features such as its open fire, stone walls and exposed beams. Pub staples have also been given a makeover here; the mash with your sausages might contain cheddar and chives or your salmon might be cured with beetroot. Boldly decorated bedrooms have a real sense of style.

Closing times

Closed 26-27 December and 1 January

Prices

Meals: £ 15 (lunch Monday-Saturday) and à la carte £ 19/30

9 rooms: £ 68/90

Typical Dishes

Devilled lamb's kidneys

Garlic crusted pollock fillet

Tiramisu

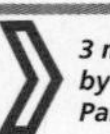

3 mi south of Newton Abbot by A380 and minor road east. Parking.

36 The Masons Arms

Knowstone,
South Molton EX36 4RY
Tel.: (01398)341231
e-mail: dodsonmasonsarms@aol.com **Website:** www.masonsarmsdevon.co.uk

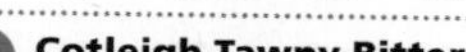

VISA MC AE

Cotleigh Tawny Bitter

Our 2010 Pub of the Year is a pretty thatched inn set in a secluded village in the foothills of Exmoor. It was built in the 13C by the masons who also constructed the village church, and exudes rural charm; its cosy beamed bar with inglenook fireplace often playing host to locals, their guns and their dogs. Before relocating to Devon with his family, chef-owner Mark Dodson spent 12 years as head chef at The Waterside Inn, and it therefore comes as no surprise to find French and British classics on the menu, created using the finest of locally sourced produce. Dishes like Devon beef fillet and monkfish loin are sophisticated but never over-wrought; deliciously fresh and attractively presented, with pronounced, assured flavours. Dine beneath a celestial ceiling mural in the bright rear dining room, with views out over the rolling hills towards Exmoor. Charming service further complements the food and booking is unsurprisingly essential.

Closing times
Closed first week in January, Sunday dinner and Monday

Booking essential

Prices
Meals: £ 34 (Sunday lunch) and à la carte £ 26/42

Typical Dishes
Seared scallops with Thai salad
Roulade of pork belly
Trio of rhubarb desserts

7 mi southeast of South Molton by A 361; opposite the village church. Parking.

37 The Dartmoor Inn

Moorside,
Lydford EX20 4AY
Tel.: (01822)820221 – Fax: (01822)820494
e-mail: info@dartmoorinn.co.uk **Website:** www.dartmoorinn.com

Inspectors' favourites

 VISA MC AE

Dartmoor Best, Otter Ale, St Austell Tribute

There's something refreshingly different about a pub which politely asks its customers to turn off the modern menace that is their mobile phone, and although not necessarily the most picturesque of buildings on the outside, this roadside dining pub on the edges of Dartmoor certainly provides an experience above the average when you venture in out of the cold. Gently rustic, with an intimate fireside bar, there are also several dining rooms with linen-laid tables and prints on the walls, and a sheltered terrace to the rear. Keenly run, the seasonal menu serves modern dishes with a Mediterranean influence, whilst a cheaper, more informal 'Easy Dining' menu is also served in both of the bars. After eating, browse in the boutique for a memento of your visit. If you are staying over, three large and stylish bedrooms with modern colour schemes and distinctive beds provide a good night's sleep.

Closing times
Closed Sunday dinner and Monday lunch

Prices
Meals: £ 20 (Tuesday-Thursday) and à la carte £ 25/40

3 rooms: £ 85/125

Typical Dishes
Cornish crab & salmon tartlet
Devon Ruby beef
Marinated prune fritters

1 mi east on A 386. Parking.

38 Church House Inn

Village Rd,
Marldon TQ3 1SL
Tel.: (01803)558279
Website: www.churchhousemarldon.com

 **Otter Ales, Bay's Gold, Dartmoor Best, Bass**

Hidden away in the sleepy village of Marldon, the Church House Inn started life at the turn of the 13C, when it was built to provide accommodation for the artisans who were constructing the nearby church. It was later turned into a meeting house for the church congregation and finally, became the local inn. Rebuilt in the 18C, the pub still displays some of its original Georgian windows – due largely to the fact that the neighbouring cricket pitch has now had 'sixes' outlawed. Inside it's immensely charming, with beamed ceilings, lots of nooks and crannies and even an old bread oven; drinkers and diners mingle together in the bar and spacious first floor dining room, where local artwork adorns the walls. Cooking is traditional and tasty, featuring quality regional produce in generous helpings. You might find asparagus or homemade pâté, followed by Exmoor sirloin steak, local sea bass or honey glazed duck. Service is smooth and assured.

Closing times
Open daily

Prices
Meals: à la carte £ 22/33

Typical Dishes
Duck & pistachio terrine
Fillet of salmon
Raspberry panna cotta

Between Torquay and Paignton off A 380. Parking.

39 The White Horse Inn

7 George Street,
Moretonhampstead TQ13 8PG
Tel.: (01647)440267
Website: www.whitehorsedevon.co.uk

VISA MC AE

Otter Ale, O'Hanlon's Yellowhammer, Teignworthy Spring Tide

Located right in the heart of a busy market village, this 17C stone pub is thought to be home to several ghosts; you might see a man in a top hat, hear the cries of the maids from the former coaching yard, or, more likely, notice nothing at all. The locals aren't put off by the stories at any rate and can be found propping up the slightly shabby front room bar in great numbers. Pass them by and head through to the converted stables and hayloft, where you'll be pleasantly surprised to find two spacious stone-floored dining rooms with rustic charm and character aplenty; and an inner courtyard with large open windows and a light, airy feel. There's a well-balanced menu which features tasty, unfussy dishes, ranging from good British classics such as steak or fish and chips through to more diverse Mediterranean offerings. Despite there being more than a hint of Italian influence, the produce remains local and seasonal wherever possible.

Closing times
Closed Monday

Prices
Meals: à la carte £ 18/30

Typical Dishes
Selection of home-cured meats
Confit pork belly
Panetone & butter pudding

In heart of village. Two car parks within 1min walk.

40 The Ship Inn

Noss Mayo PL8 1EW
Tel.: (01752)872387 – Fax: (01752)873294
e-mail: shipinn@nosmayo.com
Website: www.nossmayo.com

 **Jail Ale, Devon Dew, St Austell Tribute, Proper Job, Tamar**

Wonderful waterside views are one of the main attractions of this fine pub, set in a peaceful spot on the south side of the Yealm Estuary. It's well run, very large and very busy, with friendly staff who cope admirably under pressure. Its oldest part dates from the 18C and its characterful interior features wooden floors and open fires aplenty, while its collection of maritime memorabilia, including ships' bells and numerous old photographs, gives a tangible sense of seafaring history. The à la carte changes almost daily and offers classic dishes like roast shank of Devon lamb and seared sea bass fillet as well as more international flavours. The bar menu meanwhile keeps things simple with favourites like sausage and mash, ploughman's and sandwiches. Desserts come from the tried-and-tested stable and might include apple crumble or bread and butter pudding. Tie up your boat outside, but make sure the skipper doesn't overdo the shandies.

Closing times
Open daily

Prices
Meals: à la carte £ 21/33

Typical Dishes
Crayfish tail cocktail
Breast of duck on noodles
Glazed lemon tart

10½ mi southeast of Plymouth; signed off A 379; turn right into B 3186. Restricted parking, particularly at high tide.

41 The Harris Arms

Portgate EX20 4PZ
Tel.: (01566)783331 – Fax: (01566)783359
e-mail: info@theharrisarms.co.uk
Website: www.theharrisarms.co.uk

Bays Brewery, Sharp's Doom Bar, Exe Valley

Much more than just a stopping off point on the way down to Cornwall, The Harris Arms' reputation attracts 'locals' from Okehampton to Tavistock, Launceston to Bodmin. The owners of this traditional 16C pub offer a very friendly welcome and have helped create a warm, relaxed ambience with their hands-on style. Award-winning winemakers previously based in New Zealand and France, it stands to reason that their wine list is excellent, with bottles personally selected and fairly priced. It's not only the wine that impresses here though. The aroma of home cooking and spices fills the air and robust, hearty, confidently flavoured food shows off the chefs' artistic talent. The owners pride themselves on local and seasonal cooking and have a regularly changing specials board, whilst puddings are proudly homemade. Sit in the front bar or in the back extension overlooking the decked terrace, and keep an eye out for Reg the cat.

Closing times

Closed 25-26 December, 1 January, bank holidays, Sunday dinner and Monday

Prices

Meals: £ 17 (Sunday lunch) and à la carte £ 19/27

Typical Dishes

Baked goat's cheese
Confit of Devon pork belly
Harris Arms crêpes

3 mi east of Launceston by A 388 and side road. Parking.

42 Jack in the Green Inn

London Rd,
Rockbeare EX5 2EE
Tel.: (01404)822240 – Fax: (01404)823445
e-mail: info@jackinthegreen.uk.com **Website:** www.jackinthegreen.uk.com

  VISA

Otter Ale, Butcombe Bitter, Black Isle Yellowhammer

Food obviously matters to the owners of this efficiently-run pub near to Exeter airport; ingredients are sourced from local suppliers, menus are dictated by the seasons, every dish is well-presented and they even produce monthly recipe cards so that regulars can recreate their favourite dishes at home. Another thing that plainly matters to the owners is service; staff are friendly and efficient and offer a warm welcome. Enjoy an aperitif in the leather-furnished lounge, where colourful photos of food whet your appetite, before heading into one of the characterful, beamed dining rooms. The à la carte offers unfussy dishes like ham hock terrine, steak or grilled fillet of sea bass, with highlighted dishes made solely from Devonshire ingredients. The value-for-money bar menu (which can be eaten anywhere) provides a large choice of pub favourites, with dishes such as ploughman's, pies or sausage and mash.

Closing times
Closed 25 December to 5 January and Sunday

Prices
Meals: £ 25 and à la carte £ 25/35

Typical Dishes
Black pudding salad
Chicken and mushroom pie
Chocolate mousse

6¼ mi east of Exeter by A 30.
Parking at the back.

43 The Tower Inn

Church Rd,
Slapton TQ7 2PN
Tel.: (01548)580216
e-mail: towerinn@slapton.org **Website:** www.thetowerinn.com

 **Butcombe Bitter, Otter Bitter, Otter Ale, St Austell Tribute**

Luckily this pub is signposted because, tucked away up a narrow lane in a corner of the quaint little village, you might otherwise miss it. Built in 1347 as cottages for the men who were working on the chantry, much of the tower still overlooks its rear walled garden. The interior is everything you would expect to find in a proper English pub; several cosy adjoining rooms with stone walls, beams, flag floors and, for people of height, dangerously low ceilings. Separate dinner and lunch menus offer wholesome, hearty food including daily specials and an appealing array of traditional puddings. This pub is a great base from which to explore the local area and its history, so stay in one of the simple annex bedrooms and explore the Slapton Ley nature reserve and the misleadingly-named Slapton Sands (they're covered in pebbles), where American troops practised for the D-Day landings in 1944 in the ill-fated Exercise Tiger.

Closing times

Closed November to April
Sunday dinner and Monday

Prices

Meals: à la carte £ 17/30

3 rooms: £ 50/75

Typical Dishes

Start Bay scallops with black pudding
Steak & kidney pudding
Selection of local cheeses

6 mi southwest of Dartmouth by A 379; signed between Dartmouth and Kingsbridge. Parking with exceptionally narrow access.

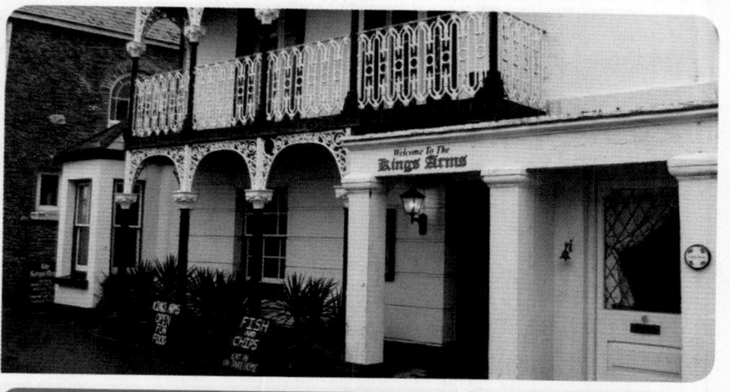

44 The Kings Arms

Dartmouth Rd, Strete TQ6 0RW
Tel.: (01803)770377
e-mail: kingsarms_devon_fish@hotmail.com
Website: www.kingsarms-dartmouth.co.uk

  MC

 **Otter Ales, Adnams**

Behind its rather dour exterior hides a pub of consequence, serving the best, the wettest and the freshest seafood from Devon's sandy shores. The wide-ranging menu changes with the seasons and offers classical, honest-to-goodness dishes like herring roes on toast, grilled lemon sole and fillet of turbot. There are oysters and mussels, lobster and crab, scallops and fish in abundance; all locally caught, simply cooked and very tasty. Non-seafood dishes might include confit of duck, rack of lamb or steak and chips, with traditional desserts such as sticky toffee pudding and lemon tart, and plenty of West Country cheeses. Like the food, the atmosphere is pleasingly down-to-earth. There is a snug – some might call it cramped – bar and a raised dining room with pictures of local seascapes on the walls; on a sunny summer's day, head instead for the delightful rear garden which boasts fantastic views out over Start Bay.

Closing times
Open daily

Prices
Meals: à la carte £ 22/35

Typical Dishes
Seared scallops, Puy lentils
Roast whole sea bream
Glazed lemon tart

4 mi southwest of Dartmouth by A 379. Parking.

45 The Steam Packet Inn

St Peter's Quay,
Totnes TQ9 5EW
Tel.: (01803)863880 – Fax: (01803)862754
e-mail: steampacket@buccaneer.co.uk **Website:** www.steampacketinn.co.uk

 VISA MC AE

Jail Ale, Otter Bright, Courage Best

Named after the postal ships that used to carry the mail, the Steam Packet Inn is situated in a fantastic location on the River Dart, just five minutes walk from the centre of Totnes. With a vast terrace that catches the sun from dawn til dusk and a large conservatory looking out over the water, this is a great spot to relax and watch the coming and goings on the river; but, plenty of other people know this too, so get here early on sunny days. The eclectic, wide-ranging menu has something for everyone, ranging from classic lemon sole and West Country steak to kofta kebabs and even Thai dishes. Fish in particular is a speciality – delivered daily from Looe – and the blackboard displays the day's latest catch. The pleasant service is provided by local, friendly staff, who are pushed to their limit on the busiest days. Should you run out of steam, there are four elegant bedrooms, each cosy and snug but with a contemporary feel.

Closing times
Open daily

Prices
Meals: à la carte £ 17/27
4 rooms: £ 60/80

Typical Dishes
River Exe mussels
Haddock fillet in Jail Ale batter
Tarte Tatin

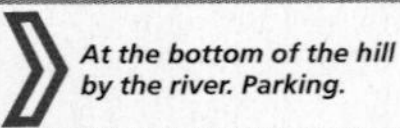
At the bottom of the hill by the river. Parking.

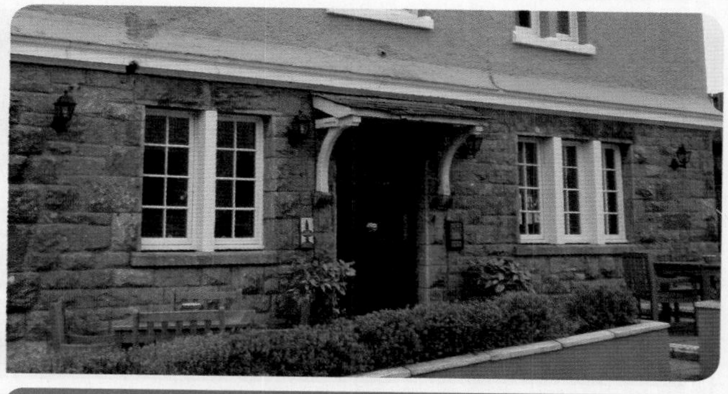

46 Rose & Crown

Market St,
Yealmpton PL8 2EB
Tel.: (01752)880223
e-mail: info@theroseandcrown.co.uk **Website:** www.theroseandcrown.co.uk

 **Otter Ale, Fuller's London Pride, Old Speckled Hen**

You can't miss this pub: it's huge, pink and right in the town centre. Sitting beside the fountain on the Mediterranean-style terrace or on a comfy sofa in front of the fire, you'll soon forget about the outside world. Wooden floorboards, rough plaster walls and a central bar provide a traditional feel; while the airy atmosphere and lightly hued décor adds a more modern edge. Cast your eyes over the quotes stencilled on the ceiling as you enter; and keep walking if you're after a touch more formality. The daily changing menu is the same at lunch and dinner, with everything from sandwiches and light bites right through to the full three courses; you might find mushrooms on toast, carpaccio of beef or cockle, clam and mussel marinière. They aim to surprise, so food arrives smartly presented on maybe tiles or slates. Despite this ambitious style, flavours remain uncompromised and it's surprisingly good value. Service is notably efficient.

Closing times
Open daily

Prices
Meals: £ 13 (lunch) and à la carte £ 20/33

Typical Dishes
Carpaccio of beef
Crediton duck breast
Pear trifle

7 mi southeast of Plymouth by A 379. Parking.

47 **The Cow**

58 Station Road,
Ashley Cross, Poole BH14 8UD
Tel.: (01202)749569 – Fax: (01202)307493
e-mail: info@thecowpub.co.uk **Website:** www.thecowpub.co.uk

Ringwood Best, Fuller's London Pride, Roosters Farmhouse Ale

Formerly a run-down hotel, this is now a bright and vibrant suburban pub, which features wood tables, stripped floorboards and a relaxed atmosphere throughout. It is divided into two distinct areas which are very different yet equally appealing: the chilled out bar is furnished with brown leather sofas, cow-themed canvases and a flat screen TV, while the more formal bistro is adorned with wine-themed prints and French posters. At lunch you can eat in either side, choosing from baguettes, pies, or more filling dishes, such as mussels or hearty British classics. The evening welcomes in a substantial à la carte – served only in the bistro – which features appealing starters, such as roast quail with truffled potato, and some equally interesting mains, maybe salmon fillet in porridge oats or ballotine of chicken breast and Parma ham. Whatever you choose you can rest assured that it will be good quality, expertly prepared and well-presented.

Closing times
Closed Sunday dinner

Prices
Meals: à la carte £ 23/30

Typical Dishes
Smoked haddock & quail Scotch egg
Roast loin of venison
Dark chocolate truffle torte

At Parkstone Station. Parking.

Dave Young 2006

48 **The Bull**

34 East St,
Bridport DT6 3LF

Tel.: (01308)422878 – Fax: (01308)426872

e-mail: info@thebullhotel.co.uk **Website:** www.thebullhotel.co.uk

 VISA  AE

 **Otter Bitter, Otter Ale**

From the moment you set foot inside this Grade II listed building and are greeted by a vast contemporary portrait behind an informal reception desk, you realise it's no ordinary place. This former regency style coaching inn has undergone a massive transformation, which has left an eclectic mix of period features and chic, contemporary décor – a touch of grandeur amongst the bustling streets of this busy market town. The ground floor is surprisingly compact, featuring a small bar room overlooking a courtyard and a simple, fairly informal dining room. The menu here sees a mix of classic English and Mediterranean brasserie dishes, each crafted from local farm meat or fresh fish from nearby Lyme Bay. Upstairs, uniquely styled bedrooms follow a modern designer theme, boasting boldly patterned feature walls, wacky pictures and stylish bathrooms; the residents bar and lounge are particularly alluring and there's even a luxurious ballroom.

Closing times
Open daily

Prices
Meals: à la carte £ 28/45
14 rooms: £ 60/180

In town centre on south side of main street. Parking.

Typical Dishes
Grilled scallops
Prune-stuffed duck breast
Chocolate fondant

49 The Stapleton Arms

Church Hill,
Buckhorn Weston SP8 5HS
Tel.: (01963)370396 – Fax: (01963)370396
e-mail: relax@thestapletonarms.com **Website:** www.thestapletonarms.com

VISA MC AE

Butcombe Bitter, Cheddar Ales Potholer, Moor Brewery Revival and local and national guest ales

If you're carrying on down the A303 towards Devon and Cornwall having admired the engineering feat that is Stonehenge, you might do well to stop off for a meal in The Stapleton Arms. It's situated in pretty Buckhorn Weston, a village with its own historical claim to fame: a mention in the Magna Carta. There's nothing ancient about the interior of this pub though – it's up-to-date, smart and stylish with an elegant dining room. This modernity hasn't scared off the locals, and you'll find your muddy boots, dogs and children are all similarly welcome. On a sunny day, sit out the front on the terrace or in the rear garden. With a wide-ranging, daily-changing menu, this pub offers traditional choices like ploughman's or grilled pork chop alongside dishes like salmon fillet and a Thai red curry of mussels and tiger prawns. Spacious, contemporary rooms are available, with underfloor heating a nice touch for cold feet on wintry mornings.

Closing times
Open daily

Prices
Meals: à la carte £ 15/25
4 rooms: £ 72/120

Typical Dishes
Confit duck salad
Roast breast of guinea fowl
Pistachio crème brûlée

7 mi west of Shaftesbury by A30 and minor road north. Parking.

50 The Chetnole Inn

Chetnole,
Sherborne DT9 6NU
Tel.: (01935)872337
e-mail: enquiries@thechetnoleinn.co.uk **Website:** www.thechetnoleinn.co.uk

Sharp's Doom Bar, Otter Bitter, Shepherd Neame Spitfire

A well run pub set on a T-junction opposite this rural village's church. To the left as you enter is a comfy, sofa-furnished locals' bar with dartboard, jukebox, slot machine and skittle alley. To the right you'll find a cosy beamed room set for dining, with flagged floors, bunches of hops and a warming wood burner. The style here is understated and uncluttered, with decorative herbs in plant pots and simple farmhouse furniture. Like the décor, the cooking's strength lies in its simplicity, and tasty, value-for-money choices might include game terrine, sausage and mash or steak and Guinness pie, with sandwiches also available at lunchtime. The dinner menu adds more spice with dishes such as Thai style salmon fishcake or pan-roasted sea bass fillets, and the specials also compete for your attention. Duck isn't on the menu, but you might well see a few waddle past if you sit in the garden. Pleasant, pine-furnished bedrooms.

Closing times
Open daily
Prices
Meals: à la carte £ 20/25
3 rooms: £ 60/85

Typical Dishes
Scallops & parsnip purée
Rump of spring lamb
Passion fruit crème brûlée

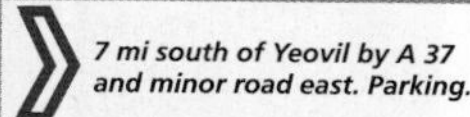
7 mi south of Yeovil by A 37 and minor road east. Parking.

51 The Acorn Inn

28 Fore St,
Evershot DT2 0JW

Tel.: (01935)83228 – Fax: (01935)83707
e-mail: stay@acorn-inn.co.uk **Website:** www.acorn-inn.co.uk

 VISA MC AE

 **Golden Arrow, Champflower, Somerset & Dorset Ale**

Situated in a quintessentially English picture postcard village, this characterful coaching inn has its own unique history to tell: it featured in Thomas Hardy's classic 'Tess of the d'Urbervilles'. Boasting stone walls, oak panelling and flag flooring, no surface is left bare, as pictures aplenty adorn the walls and a vast array of memorabilia is scattered over every worktop. As you might hope, the lunchtime menu displays a selection of British pub classics, with dinner welcoming in some more sophisticated choices. Dishes might include stuffed roasted quail or parmesan, tarragon and truffle oil soufflé, followed by saddle of rabbit or fillet of English beef with seared scallops; for dessert there may be hazelnut crème brûlée or bananas in Malibu caramel. After dinner you can complete your 'Hardy' experience by staying in one of the individually designed English country bedrooms, each named after a character or place from his book.

Closing times
Open daily

Prices
Meals: à la carte £ 23/35
10 rooms: £ 60/125

Typical Dishes
Smoked haddock chowder
Slow cooked pork neck
Chocolate brownie

9 mi south of Yeovil by A 37; in Holywell turn west. Parking.

52 The Museum Inn

Farnham DT11 8DE
Tel.: (01725)516261 – Fax: (01725)516988
e-mail: enquiries@museuminn.co.uk
Website: www.museuminn.co.uk

Ringwood and 2 guest ales

Set in the heart of a picture postcard village, this part-thatched 17C country inn was built by the founding father of modern archaeology – General August Lane Fox Pitt Rivers – with the purpose of providing refreshment and accommodation for the nearby museum. A sympathetic refurbishment has retained many of the original features, including flag stone floors and an inglenook fireplace, while the walls are adorned with a range of hunting artefacts. There are plenty of places to sit: the bar, two adjoining rooms, a conservatory, and at weekends the 'Shed', which despite its corrugated tin exterior, is a smart linen-laid dining room. The menu offers some good British classics such as kidneys or rabbit pie, alongside dishes of a more Mediterranean nature; cooking is seasonal, unfussy and focuses on the quality of the local, traceable ingredients. Spread across the site, bedrooms range from small and cottagey, to spacious with a four-poster.

Closing times
Open daily

Prices
Meals: à la carte £ 27/36
8 rooms: £ 110/165

Typical Dishes
Thai monkfish sausage
Saltimbocca of red mullet
Pistachio & cardamom panna cotta

7½ mi northeast of Blandford Forum by A 354. Parking.

England • South West • Dorset

53 **The Talbot**

Iwerne Minster DT11 8QN
Tel.: (01747)811269
e-mail: enquiries@the-talbot.com
Website: www.the-talbot.com

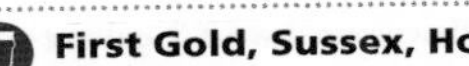
First Gold, Sussex, Hopping Hare

Until the late 19C the Bower family were Lords of the Manor here and the large Talbot hound that guards this mock-Elizabethan building is thought to have originated from their family crest. Unlike many modern gastro-pubs, this inn retains an unfussy, pub-like feel, with a lounge bar and simply-laid dining room to the front and an aptly named 'Village Bar' – where the locals will be playing pool or darts – and enclosed terrace to the back. Cooking is hearty and generous – as befits a pub of little pretension – and local produce is a must. Sausages are made by the village butcher, beef and lamb are supplied by the local Estate and even sandwiches or Ploughman's feature local cheese. Menus often change daily and might include starters of Gloucester Old Spot and pistachio terrine, followed by slow-roasted shoulder of lamb or rump steak with pepper sauce. Bedrooms, named after local hills, are comfortable, well-appointed and up-to-date.

6 mi south of Shaftesbury by A 350. Parking.

Closing times
Open daily

Prices
Meals: à la carte £ 20/30
5 rooms: £ 65/95

Typical Dishes
Smoked chicken risotto cakes
Stuffed loin of pork
Roast nectarine tarte Tatin

54 The European Inn

Piddletrenthide DT2 7QT
Tel.: (01300)348308
e-mail: info@european-inn.co.uk
Website: www.european-inn.co.uk

 **Palmers Copper, St Austell Proper Job, Hopback Summer Lightning**

Thus named to honour the European involvement in the Crimean war, in which the first landlord purportedly fought, this relaxing little inn is a gem of a place and the locals (and their dogs) seem to love it. The welcoming owners are ambassadors for the local area and the beautiful West Dorset countryside; when it comes to sourcing fresh, seasonal and sustainable local produce, they are at a distinct advantage, as his parents are the owners of nearby Wraxall Farm. Dishes on the concise menu might include salt cod fritters, pan-fried pigeon breast, fish and chips or wild mushroom risotto. If you fancy one of the traditional puddings, you may find yourself faced with a difficult decision: will it be apple crumble with custard, rice pudding, rhubarb tart or lemon posset?
Not European, but very popular nonetheless, are the regular Thai nights. Bedrooms are stylish and breakfast is as tasty and filling as the previous night's dinner.

Closing times

Closed 1 week January-February, Sunday dinner and Monday

Booking advisable at dinner

Prices

Meals: à la carte £ 20/29

2 rooms: £ 55/80

Typical Dishes

Purple sprouting broccoli

Loin & fillet of Wraxall lamb

Rhubarb tart

North of Dorchester on B 3143 between White Lackington and Piddlehinton. Parking.

55 Village Pub

Barnsley GL7 5EF

Tel.: (01285)740421 – Fax: (01285)740925

e-mail: info@thevillagepub.co.uk

Website: www.thevillagepub.co.uk

 VISA MC

Hook Norton Best Bitter, Sharp's Doom Bar, Butcombe IPA

Say 'Barnsley' and you probably think of football, but this attractive Cotswold stone village in Gloucestershire if a far cry from the energetic fans and bustling streets of the better known Yorkshire industrial town. Even before you arrive on the doorstep, the name 'Village Pub' gives you a good idea of what to expect: an inn full of character, from the charming paved terrace, to the cosy open-fired interior – where exposed stone, woodwork and a mix of flag and oak flooring pervade. Characterful bedrooms echo this rustic style, boasting wooden beams, antique furniture and either a four poster or Victorian iron bedstead. Based on the latest local produce available, menus change not only daily but between services too. Dishes vary in style between pub and restaurant, rustic and refined, featuring everything from classic British favourites such as fish and chips, through to more extravagant offerings such as turbot or foie gras parfait.

Closing times

Open daily

Prices

Meals: à la carte £ 22/31

7 rooms: £ 90/160

Typical Dishes

Homemade pastrami

Pork shoulder

Sticky toffee pudding

4 mi northeast of Cirencester on B 4425. Parking.

56 The Catherine Wheel

Bibury GL7 5ND
Tel.: (01285)740250
Website: www.barnsleyhouse.com

 VISA

 **Hooky Bitter, Sharp's Doom Bar and monthly changing guest beer**

Having generated some steady business at Barnsley House and built up a good trade at The Village Pub, the owners decided to embark upon a new adventure in the form of a less designery, more down-to-earth type of establishment: set just up the road, this is the Catherine Wheel. A weathered 15C stone building, it hasn't always been a pub but the large premises suit its use. Nothing to do with fireworks, it's supposedly named after a nearby local landmark. Drinkers can cosy up in front of the roaring log fires, where wooden furniture sits on slate floors and old village photographs hang from exposed stone walls; while diners can join them or head for the more formal restaurant, with its wooden beams and Welsh dressers filled with pottery and china. The menu displays plenty of pub classics such as ham, egg and chips or shepherd's pie, while puddings are of the comfort variety. Bedrooms are not currently recommended but a refit is planned.

Closing times
Closed Sunday dinner
Prices
Meals: à la carte £ 20/25

Typical Dishes
Fish pie
Homemade beef burger
Rice pudding

West on B 4425 over the bridge towards Barnsley. Parking.

57 Horse & Groom

Bourton-on-the-Hill GL56 9AQ
Tel.: (01386)700413 – Fax: (01386)700413
e-mail: greenstocks@horseandgroom.info
Website: www.horseandgroom.info

Goff's Jouster, Wye Valley Bitter, Battledown's Tipster, Purity's Ubu, North Cotswold's Pigbrook and others

Situated in a remote Cotswold village on the side of a hill it's not surprising that this Georgian yellow-stone pub attracts mainly diners, as, unless you live here, it's a long way to go just for a drink. The relaxed atmosphere makes it popular across the age groups and the friendly, well-paced service stands the test of even the busiest hour. Original beams, pine flooring and exposed stone feature throughout, while an attractive marble-topped counter steals the focus in the bar area. Here two blackboards compete for attention: the first, a growing list of names of those waiting for a table and the second, a much more appealing list of classic British dishes and some more ambitious fare. Local produce features strongly in the hearty, unfussy cooking and despite generous portions most diners manage to find room for all three courses. If the drive back is too much after you've had your fill, then modern, stylish bedrooms await.

Closing times

Closed 25 December and Sunday dinner

Booking essential

Prices

Meals: à la carte £ 19/32

5 rooms: £ 75/160

Typical Dishes

Ricotta & squash roulade

Fillet of black bream

Maple syrup custard tart

1 mi west of Moreton in the Marsh by A 44. Parking.

58 The Gumstool Inn

Calcot GL8 8YJ
Tel.: (01666)890391 – Fax: (01666)890394
e-mail: reception@calcotmanor.co.uk
Website: www.calcotmanor.co.uk

 **Sharps Own, Butcombe Gold and Butcombe Blonde**

Set in the grounds of the Calcot Manor Hotel, part of a 700 year old Estate, this converted farm out-building is now a highly attractive country pub. With wood-panelled walls, flag flooring, orange and brown chairs and modern artwork, it successfully combines classic country style with contemporary chic. Warm and cosy in the winter, bright and airy in the spring and with a paved terrace ideal for summer, it's welcoming whatever the weather. The wide-ranging monthly menu is seasonal, rustic and hearty, yet also accommodates lighter appetites by offering some scaled down main courses. The extensive daily specials also provide some interesting choices, such as pan-fried skate with avocado or Arbroath smokie cheese soufflé. Service is polite and friendly but make sure you give back what you get, as in the past miscreants were placed on a local gumstool and, as punishment for their offences or profanities, ducked in a pond.

Closing times
Booking essential

Prices
Meals: à la carte £ 25/35

Typical Dishes
Chicken liver parfait
Crispy confit duck
Baked toffee and banana cheesecake

3½ mi West of Tetbury on A 4135, in grounds of Calcot Manor Hotel. Parking.

59 Eight Bells Inn

Church St,
Chipping Campden GL55 6JG

Tel.: (01386)840371 – Fax: (01386)841669
e-mail: neilhargreaves@bellinn.fsnet.co.uk **Website:** www.eightbellsinn.co.uk

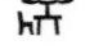  

Hook Norton Best, Goff's Jouster, Purity UBU

Situated in the old wool merchants' town of Chipping Campden, with its historic high street, this pub is a great base from which to explore the Cotswolds. Dating from the 14C, when it accommodated the stonemasons building the nearby St. James' church, it gets its name from the fact that it was used to store the bells for the church tower, and even has a 'priest hole' rumoured to lead underground to the church. The menu offers an appealing blend of traditional and more contemporary dishes, ranging from fish and chips or toad in the hole to slow-roasted shank of lamb or a Thai-style curry, with specials chalked up on a board. The bustling beamed bar, popular with locals, is the most atmospheric place to sit, but a sandwich and a pint will go down just as well in the terraced garden. If you're staying over, you'll find the bedrooms warmly decorated and well looked after; with its ancient beams, room seven is the most characterful.

Closing times
Closed 25 December

Prices
Meals: à la carte £ 22/32
7 rooms: £ 60/125

Typical Dishes
Spicy lamb koftas
Pork & leek sausages
Apple & rhubarb cobbler

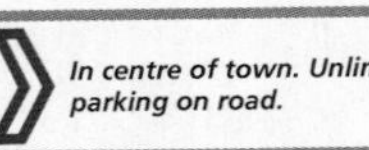

In centre of town. Unlimited parking on road.

60 The Green Dragon Inn

Cockleford GL53 9NW

Tel.: (01242)870271 – Fax: (01242)870171

e-mail: green-dragon@buccaneer.co.uk

Website: www.green-dragon-inn.co.uk

 VISA MC AE

Otter Ale, Butcombe, Courage Directors

There can't be many pubs in which you can say the mice are part of the furniture - but here they literally are. Many of the seasoned oak furnishings, including tables, the bars and even the lynch gate in the car park, are made by Robert 'Mouseman' Thompson, and his distinctive hand carved mouse hallmark scampers merrily along each one. As you watch the burning embers reflecting off beamed ceilings and bare wooden floorboards, you'll agree that the furniture is far from the only characterful thing about this 17C Cotswold stone pub, however. Fancy a game of skittles? Masquerading as a function room, the skittle alley opens out onto the peaceful patio garden, and comfortable, modern bedrooms named after famous racehorses can be found in an annexed block. Alongside British staples come other dishes with more of a colourful Mediterranean pedigree, and lighter meals also available for lunch. Book ahead to avoid disappointment.

Closing times

Closed 25-26 December dinner and 1 January dinner

Booking essential

Prices

Meals: à la carte £ 22/32

9 rooms: £ 70/95

Typical Dishes

Local asparagus

Thai red curry with prawns

White peach & chocolate bavarois

5 mi south of Cheltenham by A 435. Parking.

61 The Colesbourne Inn

Colesbourne, GL53 9NP
Tel.: (01242)870376
e-mail: info@thecolesbourneinn.co.uk
Website: www.thecolesbourneinn.co.uk

A large pub in spirit and in stature, this early 19C coaching inn sits in the heart of the Cotswolds, halfway between Cirencester and Cheltenham. Three rooms, each with large open fireplace, feature beamed ceilings and flagged floors, with walls covered in photos and dried hops and pewter tankards hanging from the ceiling. Robust, hearty homemade cooking gets the thumbs up from all comers, with produce having travelled as short a distance as possible between field and fork. Unfussy dishes like sausage and mash or steak and ale pie reside on the bar menu alongside sandwiches, soups and salads, while the à la carte features more elaborate offerings like squid, chorizo and basil risotto, poached saddle of lamb, or Chinese style pork. Situated in the former stables and named, somewhat unusually, after local farmers' fields, the bedrooms keep it relatively simple décor-wise, with antique furniture and a few four posters.

Closing times
Open daily
Prices
Meals: à la carte £ 17/34
9 rooms: £ 55/75

Typical Dishes
Oxtail ravioli
Stuffed Badminton rabbit
White chocolate & strawberry truffle pot

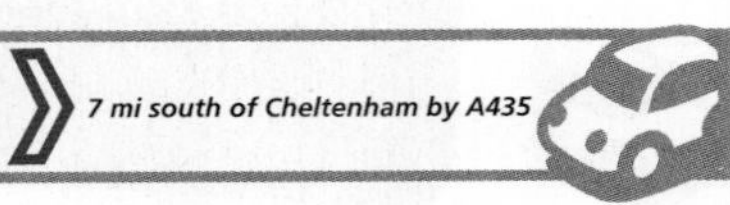

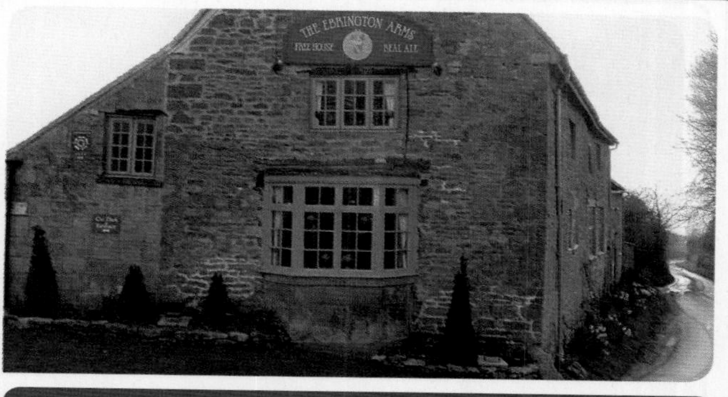

62 The Ebrington Arms

Ebrington GL55 6NH
Tel.: (01386)593223
e-mail: info@theebringtonarms.co.uk
Website: www.theebringtonarms.co.uk

Uley Bitter, Stroud Brewery - Tom Long and Budding

Cider Ken, Chicken Farmer Paul, Richard the Shepherd: they may sound like characters from a novel, but are, in fact, real people, the likes of whom can be found exchanging banter in their village local, the Ebrington Arms. The pub snuggles into this charming chocolate box village in the glorious Cotswold countryside; its beamed, flag-floored bar with blazing log fire providing the hub from which locals and visitors come and go, while owners Claire and Jim oversee proceedings with humour and grace. The stylish dining room, with its gilt-framed mirrors, provides an intimate atmosphere for a meal; there are monthly food nights – and fish and chips to take away. Robust, traditional dishes are cooked using local ingredients and up-to-date techniques; perhaps some slow roast belly pork, lamb leg steak, or beef, Guinness and horseradish pie. Bedrooms have countryside views; room three, with its four-poster bed and luxury bathroom, is the best.

Closing times
Closed first week in January, Sunday dinner and Monday (except bank holidays)

Prices
Meals: à la carte £ 20/28
3 rooms: £ 85/110

Typical Dishes
Crab cakes
Slow-roasted belly pork
Chocolate Marquise

2 mi east of Chipping Campden by B 4035. Parking.

63 The Wild Duck Inn

Drake's Island,
Ewen GL7 6BY

Tel.: (01285)770310 – Fax: (01285)770924
e-mail: wduckinn@aol.com **Website:** www.thewildduckinn.co.uk

  MC AE

Duckpond Bitter, Dorothy Goodbody, Butcombe Bitter, Theakston's Best, Old Speckled Hen, Greene King Abbot Ale

This characterful stone-built pub has stood in the pretty rural village of Ewen since 1563 and retains not only its original features but plenty of charm too. Secluded gardens and paved terraces lie to the front and back, whilst inside there are exposed stone walls, oak floors, open fires, objets d'art and dried hops aplenty. Originally a barn, the main dining area is made up of various small rooms separated by beams and original wood frames, which creates a great atmosphere. In line with the rustic feel, the cooking takes on a traditional style and menus are filled with pub classics and old British favourites: maybe roast chicken or fish and chips, alongside sirloin or rib-eye steaks. To complete the whole 'olde English' experience head for the large, characterful bedrooms in the original building, with their high ceilings, wooden beams and distinct period feel. From start to finish you'll take to this pub like a duck to water.

Closing times
Closed 25 December dinner

Prices
Meals: à la carte £ 20/30

12 rooms: £ 70/135

Typical Dishes
Thai style crab & prawn risotto
Roast lamb rump
Sticky toffee pudding

3¼ mi southwest of Cirencester by A 429. Parking.

64 The Fox Inn

Lower Oddington GL56 0UR
Tel.: (01451)870555 – Fax: (01451)870666
e-mail: info@foxinn.net
Website: www.foxinn.net

Hook Norton Bitter, Wickwar Bitter, Abbot Ale, Purity UBU

Finding yourself in Lower Oddington, you may wish to study the medieval wall painting of the seven deadly sins depicted within scenes of the Last Judgement at the local 11C church of St. Nicholas. And whilst the avaricious are spending their money in Stow-on-the-Wold's many antique shops, gluttons should head to the nearby ivy-clad Fox Inn where they can indulge to their hearts' content in classic, hearty British food. Popular with both locals and visitors, this pub can become busy, so if you're prone to anger, it's best to book ahead. Rustically romantic, with its flag floors, wooden beams and open fires, the red-painted dining room is perfect place for the lustful to enjoy a candlelit meal. Feeling slothful after you've eaten? Stay the night in one of the sumptuously furnished bedrooms. The envy of others who just can't compete, the team at The Fox must feel justifiably proud of their charming village inn.

Closing times

Closed 25 December

Booking essential

Prices

Meals: à la carte £ 20/32

3 rooms: £ 95

Typical Dishes

Eggs Benedict
Seafood tagliatelle
Ginger cheesecake

3 mi east of Stow-on-the-Wold by A 436. Parking.

65 The Ragged Cot

Cirencester Rd,
Minchinhampton GL6 8PE
Tel.: (01453)884643 – Fax: (01453)731166
e-mail: info@theraggedcot.co.uk **Website:** www.theraggedcot.co.uk

Inspectors' favourites

 **Pedigree, Ringwood, Cumberland and guest ales**

Originally a very small 18C roadside inn that was later sympathetically extended, this pub has recently seen a full refurbishment, opening under new management in April 2008. It boasts a modern bar and three rooms for eating, the largest featuring an A frame roof and floor to ceiling doors which open out onto a wood-furnished terrace, with garden booths and a foliage-draped pergola beyond. Lunch is a list of small and medium sized dishes that can be eaten alone or made into courses, while dinner is more structured, with five or six choices of starter, main course and dessert. Cooking is rustic, robust and uses mainly local ingredients; offal lovers will often find ox tongue and cheek, tripe, deep fried pig's ears, braised pig's head or even mysterious 'pork bits' on the menu. Bedrooms are pleasant, with neutral colours and simple, modern facilities: each is named after a Penguin book, with the cover displayed in a frame at the door.

Closing times
Closed Sunday dinner

Prices
Meals: à la carte £ 20/26
9 rooms: £ 90/120

Typical Dishes
Homemade terrine of the day
Beer-battered fish & chips
Selection of West Country cheeses

4 mi south of Stroud by A 419 and minor road south. Parking.

66 The Bell

Sapperton GL7 6LE
Tel.: (01285)760298 – Fax: (01285)760761
e-mail: thebell@sapperton66.freeserve.co.uk
Website: www.foodatthebell.co.uk

 **Uley Old Spot, Otter Bitter, Butcombe Bitter, Bath Ales Gem, Wickwar Cotswold Way**

On a warm summer's day head for this pretty village, where, set above the road, you can relax amongst the neatly-lawned gardens and paved terraces of this charming pub. Inside, exposed stone and wood beams feature throughout, while colourful, contemporary art adorns the walls of the bar and surrounding rooms. From the warm welcome to the smiling departure the service is friendly, efficient and well-paced, even during the daily rush. The wide-ranging monthly menu displays an array of British dishes with the odd Mediterranean touch and some seafood specials. Cooking is refined yet rustic and ranges from classic pies through to more ambitious foie gras; while a quick glance at the back of the menu assures you of the local or regional origins of the produce used. Completing the package is the interesting wine list, which features a number of unusual choices from some lesser-known provinces. All in all, this pub is as sound as a bell.

Closing times
Closed 25 December

Prices
Meals: à la carte £ 22/36

Typical Dishes
Fresh whitebait
Casserole of English veal
Pear Frangipane

 *5 mi west of Cirencester by A419. Parking.* 

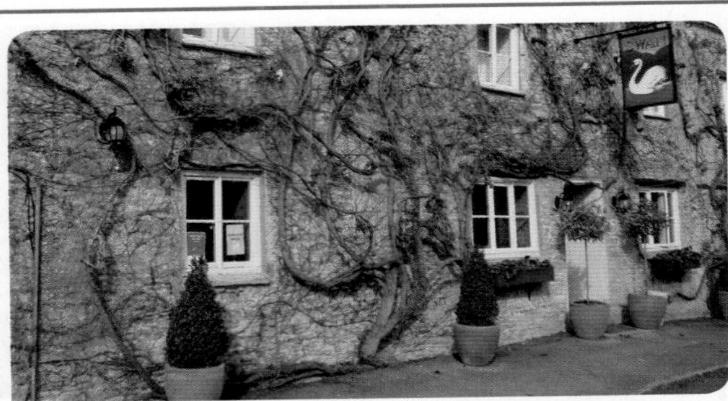

67 **The Swan**

Southrop GL7 3NU
Tel.: (01367)850205 – Fax: (01367)850517
e-mail: info@theswanatsouthrop.co.uk
Website: www.theswanatsouthrop.co.uk

Hooky, 6X and a guest beer

This swan is a very smart and well-heeled bird; a little bit of London come to the country. The couple running it previously owned west London restaurant, Snows on the Green, but decided to up sticks, bringing their family as well as their expertise to this splendid creeper-clad inn, in the picture perfect village of Southrop. There are some restaurant-style dishes on the menu, but these are combined with classic pub staples; so expect dishes such as chicken liver and foie gras parfait or roast haunch of venison to be found alongside steak, kidney and mushroom pie and Lancashire hot pot. The other main influence on Sebastian's cooking is his mother's Italian roots, hence the bruschetta, ribollita and other Mediterranean delights on the menu – and the fresh foccacia delivered to the tables by the charming Lana when you arrive. Modern art graces the walls, flowers brighten the tables and there's a happy mix of visitors and locals.

Closing times
Closed 25-26 December and Sunday dinner

Prices
Meals: £ 16 (Monday-Thursday) and à la carte £ 23/34

Typical Dishes
Foie gras & fried egg
Steak, kidney & mushroom pie
Chocolate fondant

3 mi northwest of Lechlade on Eastleach rd. Parking around the village.

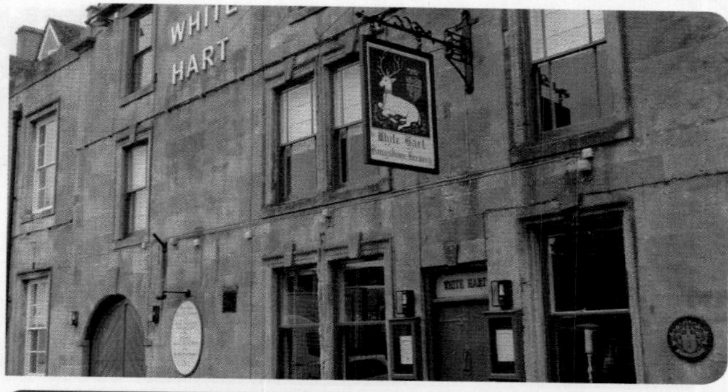

68 The White Hart Inn

The Square,
Stow-on-the-Wold GL54 1AF
Tel.: (01451)830674 – Fax: (01451)870525
Website: www.whitehartstow.com

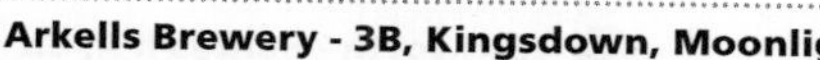

A preliminary peek through the windows of this 13C property, which sits proudly on the town square, reveals bright colours, plumped up cushions and red leather armchairs by the fire. Venture through to the back and the effect of its makeover is even more dramatic – its experienced owners have created a stylish, comfortable space, which features oil paintings of dogs, horses and stags by local artist Alexandra Churchill. Cooking, in the capable hands of Paul, is classic, understated and very tasty. Seafood is a passion of his, so dishes such as John Dory, scallops and vermouth; salmon fishcakes and the popular potted shrimps feature alongside the timeless sausage and mash or steak and chips. Desserts feature old favourites such as sticky toffee pudding or apple crumble, and the set price menu, available at both lunch and dinner, is a real bargain. Bedrooms of various shapes are cosy and modern; the best, naturally, is called 'Stag'.

Closing times
Closed 4 days in May and 4 days in October

Prices
Meals: £ 15 and à la carte £ 22/25

5 rooms: £ 100/120

Typical Dishes
Potted shrimp
Confit duck leg
Petit pot au chocolat

In the town centre. Parking at the rear of the inn and in The Square.

England • South West • Gloucestershire

69 The Trouble House

Cirencester Rd,
Tetbury GL8 8SG
Tel.: (01666)502206
e-mail: info@troublehouse.co.uk **Website:** www.thetroublehouse.co.uk

   AE

 **Wadworth - Henrys IPA, 6X**

Reputedly haunted – hence the 'trouble' in its title – this pub's murky past was surely well and truly exorcised by the arrival of former Big City chef Martin Caws and his wife for their first solo venture. Martin's cooking shows all the understanding and appreciation of good ingredients that one would expect from a chef with such a pedigree, but it's commendably unfussy on the plate, with flavours kept natural and complementary. Produce is carefully sourced, so fish comes fresh off the day boats from Devon and Cornwall, meat from Cirencester and Huntley, eggs from Tetbury and cheese from Chipping Campden. The pub itself remains decidedly unremarkable in its façade and location, with cars belting along the road outside, but that just seems to make the warm and characterful interior, with its flagstones and fireplaces, just that little more welcoming and cosy and proves that it's not just books one shouldn't judge by their covers.

Closing times
Closed one week in January, Sunday dinner and Monday

Prices
Meals: à la carte £ 19/35

Typical Dishes
Foie gras parfait
Cornish lobster risotto
Praline parfait with raspberries

2 mi northeast on A 433. Parking.

70 Horse & Groom Village Inn

Upper Oddington GL56 0XH
Tel.: (01451)830584
e-mail: info@horseandgroom.uk.com
Website: www.horseandgroom.uk.com

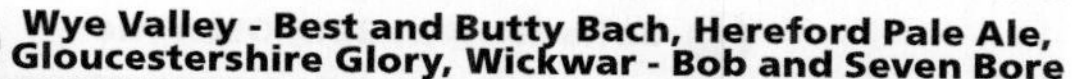

Wye Valley - Best and Butty Bach, Hereford Pale Ale, Gloucestershire Glory, Wickwar - Bob and Seven Bore

However busy it gets – and it gets very busy – the owners and their team keep on smiling; their enthusiasm was one reason the pub got so busy in the first place so they've only themselves to blame. Another reason is the warm and comfortable surroundings, with its open fireplace, the tidy and well stocked bar, beams and a separate area set for dining. Lunch is particularly popular, especially with those no longer burdened by employment, and the atmosphere is jolly and welcoming. The menu is quite substantial and it's apparent that sourcing is undertaken seriously: the Gloucester Old Spot, Cotswold lamb and Hereford beef have clues in their names; venison comes from the nearby Adlestrop Estate; fish from Brixham and most of the fruit and veg from Oddington itself. It's not just the food that's taken seriously: there are plenty of interesting cask ales and an impressive selection of wines by the glass too.

Closing times
Open daily

Prices
Meals: à la carte £ 20/30
7 rooms: £ 69/109

Typical Dishes
Goan style haddock fishcakes
Oriental seabass
Sticky toffee pudding

2 mi east of Stow-on-the-Wold by A 436. Parking (50 spaces).

71 The White Hart Inn

High St,
Winchcombe GL54 5LJ

Tel.: (01242)602359 – Fax: (01242)602703
e-mail: info@wineandsausage.com **Website:** www.wineandsausage.com

   AE

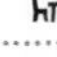 **Goffs Jouster, BOB, Otter Ale**

Refurbished and re-launched as Winchcombe Wine and Sausage, this 16C former coaching inn does what it says on the tin, plus a bit more. You want wine? A well-stocked, decently-priced wine shop contains the owner's top 100 wines from around the world – take your pick, pay £5 corkage and enjoy with dinner in the pub; the top 25 each week are also available by the glass. You want sausages? They have their own menu here – choose from flavours such as lamb, mint and apricot or Gloucester old spot. You want somewhere to eat? Try the atmospheric and aptly named Eating Room, complete with picture of comedy pig. And the bit more? Well, they don't just serve wine and sausages. And you don't have to eat in The Eating Room. Real ales, cider, whisky et al; a large selection of hearty homemade dishes, a characterful bar, a rustic dining room and chatty, friendly service; all this plus comfortable bedrooms in which to sleep off your excesses.

Closing times

Open daily

Prices

Meals: £ 15 (lunch) and à la carte £ 20/30

11 rooms: £ 60/115

Typical Dishes

Pigeon breast salad

Beef Welllington

Warm chocolate tart

8 mi northeast of Cheltenham by B 4632; in town centre. Parking.

72 The Red Lion Inn

Babcary TA11 7ED
Tel.: (01458)223230 – Fax: (01458)224510
e-mail: redlionbabcary@btinternet.com
Website: www.redlionbabcary.co.uk

   AE

 **Teignworthy Spring Tide, Otter Bright, Glastonbury Ales Mystery Tour**

Following a brief closure due to fire in early 2008, this attractive thatched pub re-opened its doors with a tasteful blend of old and new. Brightly coloured paintwork and soft sofas now welcome you in, leading over flagged floors and up to the wooden bar. Big stacks of wood are piled beside the fire – this time of a more welcoming kind – and the blackboard lunch menu presents homemade snacks in the form of pies and casseroles. Bread is baked daily and, come Sunday evening, there's often the smell of freshly made pizza wafting from the oven. Dinner consists of modern, contemporary dishes, made using local ingredients and with a little added flair; lamb rump or veal cutlets might be offered alongside dishes with a more Asian influence, which really come into their own on the regular curry nights. For pudding there may be strawberry crème brûlée or poached nectarines on the list and there's always a good selection of homemade ice creams.

Closing times
Closed Sunday dinner

Prices
Meals: à la carte £ 17/28

Typical Dishes
Pear & walnut salad
Calves liver & bacon
Rhubarb crumble

4½ mi northeast of Ilchester by A 37. Parking.

73 The Three Horseshoes Inn

Batcombe BA4 6HE
Tel.: (01749)850359 – Fax: (01749)850615
Website: www.thethreehorseshoesinn.co.uk

 **Butcombe Bitter, Wadworth Bishop's Tipple, Henry's IPA**

Set down a network of country lanes in the peaceful Vale of Batcombe, this former smithy and coaching inn boasts tasteful decoration and smartly laid tables. Styled on a French auberge, it's passionately run and has a fun upbeat atmosphere; bringing the local community together with regular 'quiz gourmand' evenings. The chef and owner share a passion for honest, classically prepared food with Larousse and Floyd playing pivotal roles in the kitchen's inspiration. Produce is organic and locally sourced, and the pub's kitchen garden and free-roaming poultry provide a good proportion of what you see on your plate. There's also plenty of homemade produce on offer – including tasty bacon and sausages. The philosophy here is one of simplicity and although straightforward, dishes exude confidence. Sunday lunch and the weekend fish boards are particularly popular. If you're looking for somewhere to stay, bedrooms are bijou, cosy and neat.

Closing times
Closed 25 December dinner, Sunday dinner and Monday

Prices
Meals: à la carte £ 20/33

3 rooms: £ 55/75

Typical Dishes
Grilled goats' cheese
Roast Somerset lamb shoulder
Homemade treacle sponge

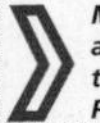
Midway between Castle Carey and Frome, signed off A 359; tucked away behind the church. Parking.

74 **The Queen's Arms**

Corton Denham DT9 4LR
Tel.: (01963)220317
e-mail: relax@thequeensarms.com
Website: www.thequeensarms.com

VISA MC AE

Moor Revival, Butcombe, Meantime IPA, Artbrew Art Nouveau and changing guest beers

Set down twisty turny one track lanes in what seems like the middle of nowhere, this 18C stone pub can be hard to locate – but the ambience here is so informal and relaxed, your blood pressure should swiftly return to normal on arrival. The comfy firelit bar with its motley collection of stools, sofas, settles and benches, is at the pub's hub, but you can't reserve a seat here, so if you want to be sure of a meal, especially at weekends, your best bet is to book ahead for the adjacent dining room. Big on sourcing seasonal, local produce, the team here not only make their own bread but also keep pigs and chickens, with pork pies for sale at the bar. Hearty, flavoursome cooking comes in big bowls and might include lunchtime cock-a-leekie broth or steak and kidney tartlet, with dishes like pan-fried red mullet or three bean and spinach stew on offer in the evening. Bedrooms are modern and stylish with flat screen TVs and smart bathrooms.

Closing times
Open daily

Prices
Meals: à la carte £ 20/25
5 rooms: £ 85/130

Typical Dishes
Roast black pudding
Marinated rack of lamb
Lemon meringue pie

3 mi north of Sherborne by B 3145 and minor road west. Parking.

75 The Manor House Inn

Ditcheat BA4 6RB
Tel.: (01749)860276
e-mail: info@manorhouseinn.co.uk
Website: www.manorhouseinn.co.uk

 VISA MC

Butcombe, Otter Ales

Originally owned by Lord of the Manor Edmund Dawe, this 17C red-brick coaching inn on the Somerset Levels boasts exposed stone walls and polished flag floors, which, combined with roaring log fires and chunky wood furniture, create a warm and welcoming atmosphere. Champion racehorse trainer Paul Nicholls comes from the village and the Bath & West showground is just down the road, so it's no surprise that racing is at the heart of this pub – you'll often find the locals in the restored skittle alley avidly watching the latest meet. There are no light bites on offer here, just some good meaty (and veggie) dishes to get your teeth into. Using locally grown or reared produce, cooking is traditional and honest with the odd international touch; Sunday lunch in particular provides good variety and value for money. Named after some of Nicholls' famous winning racehorses, the former stables house cosy bedrooms equipped with good mod cons.

4 mi south of Shepton Mallet by A 37 and minor road left. Parking.

Closing times
Closed 25 December

Prices
Meals: £ 25 and à la carte £ 18/28

3 rooms: £ 50/90

Typical Dishes
Warm mushroom tart
Rack of lamb with herb crust
Vanilla panna cotta

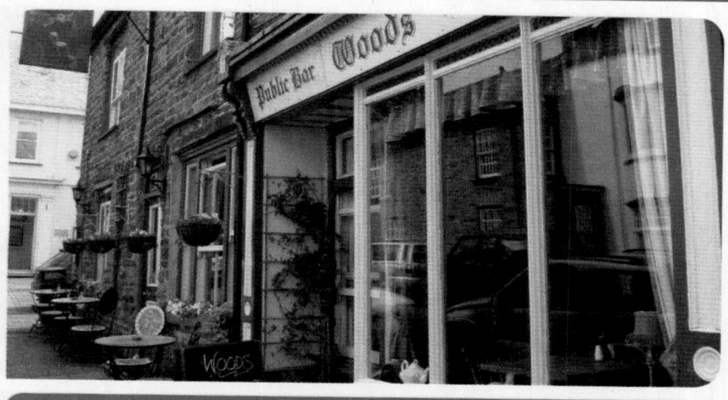

76 Woods

4 Banks Square,
Dulverton TA22 9BU
Tel.: (01398)324007 – Fax: (01398)323366

VISA MC

St Austell, Exmoor, Cottage, Otter, Bays, Exeter, O'Hanlons, Woods own ale and guest ales

Converted in 2004 by the current owner – an experienced and highly regarded local publican – this former bakery can't quite decide whether it wants to be a pub or a restaurant. It doesn't really matter though because as soon as you walk through the door you know you're in for a treat: the décor is charming, a great deal of the furniture has been made by the owner himself and the walls are lined with French and culinary-themed paintings paying homage to the chef. Local, traceable produce is important here and as such, most meat comes from the owner's farm. Cooking offers classical dishes with a French slant – light bites and a few more substantial plates at lunch, with dishes stepping it up a gear at dinner. A passionately compiled wine list provides the perfect accompaniment. Once a year, the chef turns the town into a mini Marseille, as he brings French ingredients together in a culinary celebration and tables spill onto the street.

Closing times
Open daily
Prices
Meals: à la carte £ 15/30

Typical Dishes
Exmoor roe deer pâté
Old Spot pork
Chocolate fondant

13 mi north of Tiverton by A 396 and B 3222. 3 car parks and on-street parking.

Hinton St George

Lord Poulett Arms

77 Lord Poulett Arms

High St, Hinton Saint George TA17 8SE
Tel.: (01460)73149
e-mail: steveandmichelle@lordpoulettarms.com
Website: www.lordpoulettarms.com

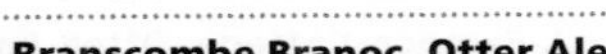

Branscombe Branoc, Otter Ale

The traditional Lord Poulett Arms offers everything you could possibly want from a pub. A picture perfect, lavender framed terrace overlooks a boules pitch to a wild, untamed secret garden, whilst inside dried hops, lovely old tables and squashy armchairs are set in a detailed country interior filled with books, glowing candles and a roaring log fire. Using local produce, the kitchen creates an interesting seasonal menu with its roots planted firmly in the Med. At lunchtime there is a selection of gourmet sandwiches and lighter dishes, while in the evening the menu expands; there is always a 'West Bay catch of the day' and extra mature local steak on offer, usually accompanied by tasty triple cooked chips. These are followed by a selection of locally made ice creams, tempting desserts and West Country cheeses. Giving a new meaning to pub accommodation, smart, stylish bedrooms boast radios, local juices and roll-top or slipper baths.

Closing times

Closed 26 December and 1 January

Prices

Meals: à la carte £ 19/30

4 rooms: £ 59/88

Typical Dishes

Rhubarb & beetroot salad
Catch of the day
Banoffee 'Eton Mess'

1 mi northwest of Crewkerne by minor road. Parking.

78 The Devonshire Arms

Long Sutton TA10 9LP
Tel.: (01458)241271 – Fax: (01458)241037
e-mail: mail@devonshirearms.com
Website: www.thedevonshirearms.com

Teignworthy Reel Ale, Moor Beer Revival, Bath Ales Spa

While it appears grand and traditional from the outside, this creeper-clad hunting lodge could not be more contemporary on the inside. Spacious rooms feature mellow lighting, high-backed leather chairs and informally laid light-wood tables, with the striking décor creating a truly modern feel. This extends through to the spacious bedrooms, where rattan furniture sits nicely alongside coir flooring and neutral shades. You can eat in the bar, the restaurant, on the front terrace overlooking the green or in the large back garden, although here it may take a little longer for the serving team to reach you. There's a good value set menu or a light bites selection at lunch, with a concise but more substantial à la carte following in the evening. French and British influences prevail, with the occasional Asian touch creeping in. Signature dishes include crab crème brûlée and fillet of West Country beef, with homemade ice cream to follow.

Closing times

Closed 25-26 December

Prices

Meals: à la carte £ 23/30

9 rooms: £ 70/120

Typical Dishes

Warm bacon salad
Quantock duck breast
Vanilla & passion fruit crème brûlée

4 mi east of Langport by A372.
Parking.

England • South West • Somerset

79 The Pilgrims at Lovington

Lovington BA7 7PT
Tel.: (01963)240597
e-mail: jools@thepilgrimsatlovington.co.uk
Website: www.thepilgrimsatlovington.co.uk

VISA MC AE

 **Cottage Brewery Champflower**

The Pilgrims in the pub's name were, according to legend, those who searched for King Arthur's Tomb; Lovington being the last stop before they entered the hazardous marshlands at Glastonbury Abbey. Modern day wayfarers would also do well to stop here: although unremarkable in outward appearance, this pub's charming interior more than makes up for it. The bar, strewn with cookbooks, gives way to a light, fresh restaurant, and the single sitting policy encourages you to linger over dinner. Their motto 'the pub that thinks it's a restaurant,' gives a hint of what to expect food wise: a British/Mediterranean menu which uses only regional produce, including meat from local farms, home-grown vegetables and West Country cheese. The old cider barn now houses comfortable, contemporary bedrooms with luxurious walk-in showers and roll-top baths. Substantial breakfasts often include homemade bread, hot specials and a full-English cooked to order.

Closing times

Closed Sunday dinner, Monday and Tuesday lunch

Prices

Meals: à la carte £ 20/37

5 rooms: £ 80/110

Typical Dishes

Scallops & black pudding
Duo of beef
Somerset cheeses

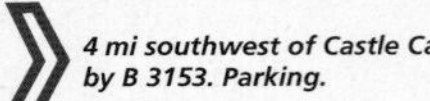

4 mi southwest of Castle Cary by B 3153. Parking.

80 The Vobster Inn

Lower Vobster BA3 5RJ
Tel.: (01373)812920 – Fax: (01373)812247
e-mail: info@vobsterinn.co.uk
Website: www.vobsterinn.co.uk

Butcombe Bitter, Butcombe Blonde, Blind Man's Buff Ale

Its owners' propensity to produce good food, coupled with their enthusiastic, hands-on approach has made the Vobster Inn a real destination pub, and though they may have put themselves on the map, they haven't forgotten the locals, so you are as welcome to snuggle up on a sofa for a drink, a bowl of chips and a chat as you are to enjoy a three course meal in the spacious restaurant. Mr and Mrs Davila hail from Galicia in North West Spain, so you might find paella or Spanish omelette alongside cottage pie or Ploughman's on the menu; Mediterranean ingredients and techniques are married with local produce - fish specials come courtesy of the catch at St Mawes - and the cooking has an honest, rustic edge to it. Want to stay longer? The Vobster Inn is well situated to explore the many famous sights of the South West and the simple bedrooms are modern and well equipped, particularly the family room which overlooks the garden.

Closing times

Closed Sunday dinner and Monday lunch

Prices

Meals: à la carte £ 22/28

3 rooms: £ 55/95

Typical Dishes

Duck's livers en croute

Pan-fried Guinea fowl

Lime & mango cheesecake

6 mi northwest of Frome by A 362 towards Radstock; Vobster is signed after approx 5 ½ mi. Parking.

81 The Royal Oak Inn of Luxborough

Exmoor National Park, Luxborough TA23 0SH
Tel.: (01984)640319 – Fax: (01984)641561
e-mail: info@theroyaloakinnluxborough.co.uk
Website: www.theroyaloakinnluxborough.co.uk

Cotleigh Tawny, Exmoor Ale, Palmers IPA, Quantock Ale

Set in a secluded wooded valley between the Brendon and Croyden Hills, the beautiful landscapes of Luxborough are a well kept secret. Passing through this peaceful countryside is the Coleridge Way, a walk that follows the routes that the romantic poet took when drawing inspiration for some of his greatest works. The Exmoor Park authorities are understandably reluctant to put up signs, so it can be tricky finding this red sandstone pub, but it's definitely worth the search; just follow the local hunt. The seasonal menu offers substantial dishes of classically prepared, boldly flavoured foods and despite an international edge to the cooking, focuses on quality, local ingredients: Exmoor meat and Cornish seafood create dishes such as grilled sardines, steamed mussels, slow roasted belly of pork or pan-fried lamb's liver with bacon. Bedrooms are compact but charming and each comes with its own teddy bear; one has its own terrace.

Closing times
Closed 25 December

Prices
Meals: à la carte £ 13/27
11 rooms: £ 55/100

Typical Dishes
Platter of smoked duck
Game casserole
Raspberry bavarois

Off A 39 east of Minehead (signed) or off B 3224 Exford to Taunton road. Parking.

82 The Talbot Inn

Selwood St,
Mells BA11 3PN
Tel.: (01373)812254 – Fax: (01373)813599
e-mail: enquiries@talbotinn.com **Website:** www.talbotinn.com

 VISA MC

 **Butcombe Ales**

As you would hope when you discover that it's owned by the Earl of Oxford and Asquith, this 15C coaching inn immediately creates an impression. Entering via a large archway you cross a cobbled courtyard and pass a secluded terrace with a vine-covered pergola, before being given the choice of two doors; whichever you choose will lead you to an atmospheric dining room, where candles flicker and low beamed ceilings are hung with hops. In line with the décor, the cooking takes on a true country style: it's reliable and robust, featuring generous portions and well-established flavours. With one menu for meat and another for fish, the chef is rightly proud of the variety offered, especially since everything from rolls to ice creams is homemade. The fact that people without bookings are often turned away, even on a Monday, is a testament to the quality of the cooking. Bedrooms are classical, some a little modest: ask for the Manor Suite.

Closing times
Open daily

Prices
Meals: £ 13/16
and à la carte £ 23/33
8 rooms: £ 95/145

Typical Dishes
Grilled scallops
Chargrilled fillet steak
Lemon meringue pie

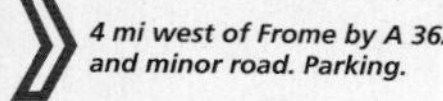
4 mi west of Frome by A 362 and minor road. Parking.

England • South West • Somerset

83 Tarr Farm Inn

Tarr Steps TA22 9PY
Tel.: (01643)851507 – Fax: (01643)851111
e-mail: enquiries@tarrfarm.co.uk
Website: www.tarrfarm.co.uk

  VISA MC

Exmoor Ale, Exmoor Gold and a guest ale

At 55m in length and with 17 spans, Tarr Steps is one of Britain's finest clapper bridges. It dates back to around 1000 BC and, according to local legend, was built by the devil in order to win a bet. Here, in the idyllic Exmoor countryside, you'll find Tarr Farm Inn, a true destination pub, run by a highly regarded team who can't do enough for you. There's seating for every occasion, so you can have afternoon tea outside, lunch by the bar and dinner in the restaurant. Lunch ranges from sandwiches to a hearty three courses, while the evening menu displays some more ambitious choices. This might include char-grilled Devon sirloin steak, rack of Exmoor lamb with sweetbreads and ratatouille or pan-fried Cornish sea bass with cockles and clams. Bedrooms are elegant and luxurious, providing every conceivable extra and a fine breakfast. Judy is happy to organise a range of outdoor activities and even takes guests walking or riding herself.

Closing times
Open daily

Prices
Meals: à la carte £ 22/30
9 rooms: £ 75/150

Typical Dishes
Squid & chorizo
Fillet of venison
Dark chocolate fondant

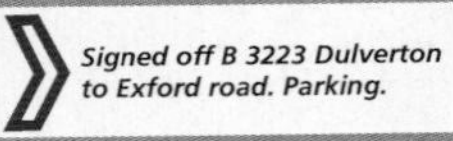

Signed off B 3223 Dulverton to Exford road. Parking.

84 The Rising Sun Inn

West Bagborough TA4 3EF
Tel.: (01823)432575
e-mail: jon@risingsun.info
Website: www.risingsun.info

VISA MC AE

 **Exmoor Ale, Butcombe**

Having previously survived a fire that raged through the surrounding hillside, the future of this inn was once again in the hands of the gods when it went into receivership. Its prospects were secured, however, when white knights appeared in the form of Jon and Christine Brinkman, an ambitious, experienced couple with no fear of hard work and dedication. In a few months they turned the place around and they continue to work towards re-establishing this pub as the hub of the village; even the self-playing piano is a part of the collective experience. If you're feeling peckish then you will be pleased to find a good balance of traditional and modern dishes on the menu, each crafted from local ingredients and presented with an obvious element of care. Around you a seamless mix of wood and slate creates a warm, intimate atmosphere and you rest assured that with this couple at the helm, the Sun will continue to rise more brightly every day.

Closing times

Closed Sunday dinner in winter

Prices

Meals: à la carte £ 14/25

2 rooms: £ 55/85

Typical Dishes

Confit of duckling

Fillet of red mullet

Warm chocolate brownie

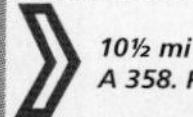

10½ mi northwest of Taunton off A 358. Parking in the road.

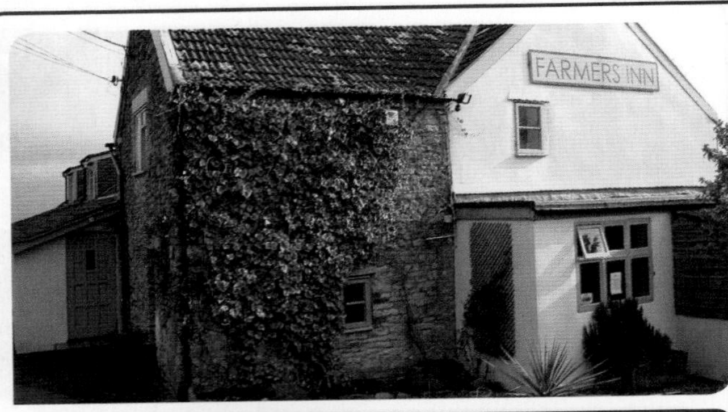

85 The Farmers Inn

Higher West Hatch, Taunton TA3 5RS
Tel.: (01823)480480 – Fax: (01823)481177
e-mail: letsgostay@farmersinnwesthatch.co.uk
Website: www.farmersinnwesthatch.co.uk

Otter Ale, Exmoor Ale, Branscombe Best, Yellowhammer

Having been owned in the 1930s by an ex-Met policeman, this soft-stone inn became one of the area's first nightclubs in the 1970s and one wonders what Mr Cridge, the 1906 landlord whose picture takes pride of place in the bar, would have made of it all. Today, you will find the welcoming owners serving local ales and ciders (one home-brewed) behind a timber-framed bar. The traditional snack menu and the monthly-changing lunch and dinner menus are created using local ingredients, including produce from the neighbouring dairy farm. Dishes are modern British and European in their roots; flavoursome but with the occasional tendency towards over-ambition. Five individually designed bedrooms harbour antique furniture, sumptuous fabrics, magnificent bathrooms and luxuries to rival any top hotel. One has its own courtyard, another has French doors into the gardens and most have sitting areas and views across the Somerset levels.

Closing times
Open daily

Prices
Meals: £ 15 (lunch) and à la carte £ 25/30

5 rooms: £ 85/130

Typical Dishes
Dorset Blue Vinny roulade
Haunch of wild boar
Chocolate & amaretti cake

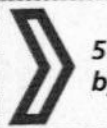

5 mi southeast of Taunton by A 358. Parking.

86 The Royal Oak Inn

Exmoor National Park, Winsford TA24 7JE
Tel.: (01643)851455 – Fax: (01643)851009
e-mail: enquiries@royaloakexmoor.co.uk
Website: www.royaloakexmoor.co.uk

 **Exmoor Ale, Exmoor Gold, Exmoor Stag**

Close to where the Winn Brook ford flows over a winding country lane in the heart of Exmoor National Park you'll find the picturesque village of Winsford and the equally delightful Royal Oak inn. A thatched 12C building full of rustic charm, it was formerly a farmhouse and dairy before later finding its calling as a country pub. In tune with its surroundings, the cooking here uses local, seasonal produce and everything from the bread to the ice cream is homemade. Dishes are predominantly British, arriving with no unnecessary fussiness and exactly as described on the menu. Open to residents during the week (upon request) and to visitors at weekends, the adjacent restaurant steps things up a gear at dinner. If you fancy staying the night, the smart, individually styled bedrooms offer four-poster, queen or king size beds and come with homemade biscuits, jet powered showers and the option of private therapy treatments in your room.

Closing times
Open daily

Prices
Meals: £ 25 (dinner) and à la carte £ 18/28

8 rooms: £ 70/150

Typical Dishes
Exe Valley smoked salmon
Devon Ruby rib-eye steak
Cambridge burnt cream

5 mi north of Dulverston by B 3223; opposite the village green. Parking.

87 The Red Lion Inn

Axford SN8 2HA
Tel.: (01672)520271
e-mail: info@redlionaxford.com **Website:** www.redlionaxford.com

 **Ramsbury Ale, Axford Ale**

Just a short drive from the famous market down of Marlborough, this 16C flint and red-brick country inn overlooks the River Kennet and the valley beyond. Mature gardens lead up to the floor, which opens into a characterful beamed area with old wood fittings; candles and vases of flowers sit on cloth-covered tables in the various interconnecting rooms, and work from a local artist adorns the walls. The vast inglenook fireplace is a focal point in winter, the terrace affords great views in summer and the snug's squashy sofas are a hit all year round. The bar menu offers the dishes such as sardines, salad of wood pigeon and homemade faggots, while the restaurant offers a huge array of more substantial, generously proportioned plates. Cooking follows a traditional, country style, with local fish and game dishes a speciality; you might come across monkfish tail, cod pavé or lobster thermidor; guinea fowl, braised rabbit or fillet of venison.

Closing times
Closed 2 weeks after Christmas, Sunday dinner and Monday

Prices
Meals: à la carte £ 17/30

Typical Dishes
Wiltshire ham hock terrine
Monkfish tail
Tiramisu

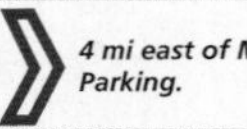

4 mi east of Marlborough.
Parking.

88 The Royal Oak

Cues Lane, Bishopstone SN6 8PP
Tel.: (01793)790481
e-mail: royaloak@helenbrowningorganics.co.uk
Website: www.royaloakbishopstone.co.uk

 **Arkell 2B, Arkells 3B, Moonlight, Donnington SBA**

Tucked away in a quiet village this pub may not appear to be anything out of the ordinary, but once inside the pleasant country atmosphere and excellent food say otherwise. Taken over in 2006 by organic crusader Helen Browning, it has definitely fallen into the right hands: 'local', 'organic' and 'fair-trade' are the buzz words and a great deal of consideration is given to their carbon footprint. With produce coming from Helen's nearby farm and other small suppliers just down the road, the constantly evolving menu relies on the latest seasonal produce to inform its content, which makes a refreshing change from the usual pub format. Cooking is classic and British but dishes still manage to remain creative, thanks to the chef taking the simplest of recipes and injecting his own techniques: the dying art of curing being one of his particular passions. One thing's for sure, this pub is a real find, a gem in the Wiltshire countryside.

Closing times
Open daily

Prices
Meals: à la carte £ 19/32

Typical Dishes
Bacon fraise
Smoked sausages
Tudor style chocolate mousse

6 m east by A 4312 off A 420. Parking.

89 The Northey

Bath Road,
Box SN13 8AE
Tel.: (01225)742333
e-mail: office@ohhcompany.co.uk **Website:** www.ohhcompany.co.uk

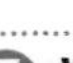 **Wadworth 6X, Wadworth IPA and guest ales such as Horizon**

The traditional exterior of this family-run, roadside pub, a few miles from Bath, is in stark contrast to the modern Mediterranean styling to be found on the inside. Large leather sofas and outsized barrel-tables provide lounge space for drinkers, but the majority of the pub is set aside for diners and the oft-changing menu seems to take its inspiration from the décor, offering a blend of Mediterranean and British cooking. Choose from dishes such as Italian platter, Greek salad with calamari or moules marinière; pan-fried calves liver, fillet steak, and haddock and chips. Bread is made on the premises daily and vegetarians will be particularly happy with the recently extended selection of dishes just for them. For those with a musical bent, there's live jazz every other week; a reminder, perhaps, of the days when it was run by Maisie Gay, a music hall artist, and frequented by Noel Coward and friends.

Closing times
Open daily

Prices
Meals: à la carte £ 20/35

Typical Dishes
Scallops & pea purée
Duck with raspberry sauce
Egg custard tart

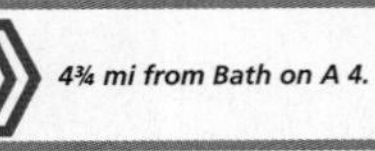
4¾ mi from Bath on A 4. Parking.

90 The Ship Inn

Burcombe Lane,
Burcombe SP2 0EJ
Tel.: (01722)743182
e-mail: theshipburcombe@mail.com **Website:** www.theshipburcombe.co.uk

 **Wadworth 6X, Courage Best, Butcombe Bitter**

Watch your footing on the way in, as the steps go straight down from the door. Once safely seated you'll find everything is shipshape, with modern furniture blending nicely with old wooden beams and the sun streaming in through the many windows. The real selling point here has to be the beautiful riverside garden but you may have to compete to get a spot in the summer. When it comes to the food they really push the boat out, with the chef leaving his own mark on every dish, be it at the recipe stage or in the creative presentation. The cooking is a mixture of British and Mediterranean, arriving artistically in large white bowls or on slate tiles, and being generous in size and flavour. At lunch, the light bites menu offers something for everyone, while the seasonal evening menu and twice-daily blackboard specials play host to more substantial dishes; maybe rosemary crusted rack of lamb or Pollock fillet with lemon and parsley.

Closing times
Open daily

Prices
Meals: à la carte £ 23/32

Typical Dishes
Seared scallops & prosciutto
Pork belly
Lemon & ginger crunch

 *5¼ mi west of Salisbury by A 36 off A 30. Parking.* 

91 The Horse and Groom

The Street,
Charlton SN16 9DL
Tel.: (01666)823904
e-mail: info@horseandgroominn.com **Website:** www.horseandgroominn.com

   AE

Old Speckled Hen, Ruddles Best, Arkells 3B

It's a lazy summer's day, the birds are singing, there's not a cloud in the sky and you are relaxing in the neatly-kept garden of this 16C Cotswold stone pub; what could be better – an outside bar maybe? Which, coincidently, this pub just happens to have. It's not just in the fine weather that this pub draws the crowds; a sympathetic renovation has provided a smart restaurant and a warm, welcoming bar, where there is always a convivial atmosphere. Featuring local, seasonal ingredients – many from within 40 miles – the menu displays everything from Ploughman's and platters to British pub classics and some more contemporary dishes. Every weekday there's a 'Let's do Lunch' set menu and the flexible kitchen staff host special events throughout the week: Tuesday is 'Ladies Night', while Fridays are set aside for the locals. Bedrooms are stylish and beautifully appointed, with sumptuous bathrooms, fine toiletries and complimentary wi-fi.

Closing times
Open daily

Prices
Meals: £ 17 (lunch) and à la carte £ 20/30

5 rooms: £ 90/100

Typical Dishes
Scallop & asparagus salad
Rack of lamb
Glazed lemon tart

2 mi north of Malmesbury by B 4040. Parking.

92 The George

High St,
Codford Saint Mary BA12 0NG
Tel.: (01985)850270
e-mail: boydjorob@aol.com **Website:** www.thegeorgecodford.co.uk

 **Yeovil Ales - Stargazer, Summerset, Ruby, Spring Forward, Sharp's - Doom Bar, Cottage Brew - Whippet Special**

After an evening of cultural delights at the Woolstone Theatre, cross over the road to this 18C black and white pub. Unspectacular in appearance, it is occupied largely by the locals who have discovered its strength – the food – and chat cheerily at the bar. The chef has a long-established history in the area and together with his protégé they pull out all the stops in the kitchen; classic pub recipes to keep the locals happy and some more ambitious dishes, which go down well with the visitors. For starters you might find caramelised goat's cheese with pineapple and chilli chutney, followed by local pheasant and ale casserole or loin of pork with roast pear and black pudding; then treacle and raspberry jam tart with Earl Grey syrup to finish. Bedrooms do not meet the same high standards as the cooking but whatever the pub may lack in décor and furnishings, it definitely makes up for with talent in the kitchen.

Closing times
Closed Sunday dinner and Tuesday

Prices
Meals: à la carte £ 21/35

Typical Dishes
Seared Cornish scallops
Roast rump of Wiltshire lamb
Bourbon vanilla crème brûlée

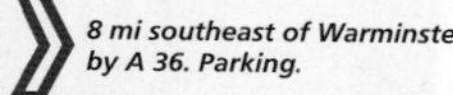
8 mi southeast of Warminster by A 36. Parking.

93 Bath Arms

Clay St,
Crockerton BA12 8AJ
Tel.: (01985)212262
e-mail: batharms@aol.com **Website:** www.batharmscrockerton.co.uk

 **Porter's Ale, Crockerton Classic, Courage Best**

A down-to-earth pub with big ambitions, the Bath Arms offers a warm welcome, open fires and plenty of country appeal, with a wealth of outdoor space. It is situated on the Longleat Estate and is run by local boy Dean Carr – originally from Warminster – who returned from his culinary experiences in the Big Smoke to put some love back into this community pub. Dishes such as roast scallop with carrot and spicy sultanas or fillet of halibut with asparagus, green beans and pancetta bring a touch of modernity to the daily changing menu. The favourites – like the popular fishcakes or the sticky beef – as well as the grills and the snacks keep it practical; ideal for sating the appetite built up by a brisk walk at nearby Shearwater Lake. The two ultra-spacious, contemporary bedrooms are proof, if ever it were needed, that you should never judge a book by its cover. More bedrooms are planned for the near future.

Closing times
Open daily

Prices
Meals: à la carte £ 21/27
2 rooms: £ 80/95

Typical Dishes
Roast scallops
Sticky beef & red cabbage
Lemon curd cheesecake

2 mi south of Warminster by A 350 on Shear Water rd. Parking.

94 The Potting Shed

The Street, Crudwell SN16 9EW
Tel.: (01666)577833
e-mail: bookings@thepottingshedpub.com
Website: www.thepottingshedpub.com

 **Timothy Taylor Landlord, Bath Gem, Butcombe Best**

Much to the delight of the villagers, the new owners have transformed this previously rough and ready local into a classic country dining pub, with soft candle lighting and a relaxed atmosphere. Situated just across the road from its sister establishment, The Rectory Hotel, its name is an allusion to the large garden beds planted with organic herbs and vegetables at its rear; inside, the gardening theme continues, with features such as trowel door knobs and wheelbarrow lights. The kitchen provides a rustic, seasonal menu which gets to the heart of proper pub cooking; there's nothing fancy here, just well-flavoured, wholesome dishes like sausage and mash or fish and chips, served in generous portions. Puddings display a more adventurous streak – if you've chosen the liquorice ice cream be prepared to leave with a black tongue. Your four-legged friends won't go hungry either, thanks to the thoughtfully provided jar of biscuits on the bar.

Closing times
Closed Sunday dinner

Prices
Meals: à la carte £ 17/27

Typical Dishes
Chicken liver parfait
Shank of spring lamb
Warm apple fritters

4 mi north of Malmesbury by A 429. Parking.

95 Forester Inn

Lower Street,
Donhead St Andrew SP7 9EE
Tel.: (01747)828038 – Fax: (01747)828038
e-mail: possums1@btinternet.com

 **Butcombe, Ringwood, Gales**

A thatched, 13C pub set in a charming Wiltshire village, with rustic charm galore in the form of exposed stone walls, wood floors and large inglenook fireplaces. Sup on a pint of real ale alongside the locals in the characterful, beamed bar; then depending on your mood and that of the weather, you can either remain here to eat, dine under the vaulted ceiling in the open plan extension, or go al fresco out on the terrace. Cooking is modern British in style, with influences from the Mediterranean and Asia; fish makes quite an appearance and you can expect to see seafood platters aplenty come summer. The menu changes daily but might include dishes such as tempura prawns and Thai style crab cake or pan-fried foie gras on toasted brioche to start, and roasted Cornish hake, veal Milanese or crisp belly of pork to follow, with locally sourced artisan cheeses a treat with which to finish.

Closing times
Closed 25-26 December, Sunday dinner

Prices
Meals: £ 16 (lunch) and à la carte £ 20/32

Typical Dishes
Soft herring roes
Bouillabaisse
Banana tarte Tatin

 *5 mi east of Shaftesbury by A 30. Parking.* 

96 The Angel Inn

High St, Heytesbury BA12 0ED
Tel.: (01985)840330
e-mail: theangelheytesbury@btconnect.com
Website: www.theangelatheytesbury.co.uk

   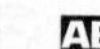

 **Old Trip, Old Speckled Hen, St Albans**

A former landlord of the Angel was apparently once heard to say that he caught the sound of Lawrence of Arabia's motorcycle speeding away as he left Heytesbury House en route to his home at Clouds Hill Cottage and his fatal accident. No-one knows the truth but as a stalwart of the village, this pub must have many such stories to tell. Organised around a central bar, the lounge and dining areas display an eclectic mix of wooden beams, exposed brickwork and bright, bold colours, leading out into an idyllic courtyard. Study the menu and you'll find sharing boards of maybe Greek mezze or a whole baby camembert – and if you're after a little more, some good pub classics such as gammon steak or eggs Benedict. For substantial appetites, there's a selection of well-hung steaks sourced from the nearby farm or Castle Brae in Scotland, set alongside some good vegetarian options, such as sweet potato lasagne or butternut squash and spinach risotto.

Closing times
Open daily

Prices
Meals à la carte £ 18/26

Typical Dishes
Warm chorizo & potato salad
Pan-fried calves liver
Sticky toffee pudding

4 mi southeast of Warminster on A36. Parking.

97 The Lamb Inn

High St,
Hindon SP3 6DP
Tel.: (01747)820573 – Fax: (01747)820605
e-mail: info@lambathindon.co.uk **Website:** www.lambathindon.co.uk

VISA AE

Young's Ordinary, Wells Bombardier, St Austell Tribute

Country cousin to two London establishments, this pub is part of the Boisdale group, paying tribute to the Outer Hebridean port of the same name. From the outside this is a classic English inn, but inside, the rich red décor, dark wood tables, log fires and tartan carpets are unmistakeably Scottish; walk through the bar you almost expect to find a row of moose heads lining the walls. As you might anticipate, haggis and smoked salmon are always on the menu, with the celebrated Boisdale beef burger, a selection of British classics and some Mediterranean blackboard specials alongside. Produce is predominantly local or, of course, from Scotland. In the centre of the room locals crowd around the bar but they are happy to make a path so that visitors can access the impressive selection of whiskies that it holds. The Scottish theme is continued in the bedrooms, where traditional country-style décor and furnishings abound.

Closing times
Open daily

Prices
Meals: à la carte £ 18/33
17 rooms: £ 70/110

Typical Dishes
Cheese soufflé
Stourhead Farm rump steak
Sticky toffee pudding

12 mi west of Wilton by A 30 on B 3089. Parking.

98 The Tollgate Inn

Ham Green,
Holt BA14 6PX
Tel.: (01225)782326 – Fax: (01225)782805
e-mail: alison@tollgateholt.co.uk **Website:** www.tollgateholt.co.uk

 **Sharp's of Cornwall, Moles of Melksham, Three Castles of Pewsey, Goffs of Gloucester and others**

With beautiful hanging baskets alive with colour, a warm, friendly ambience and cosy décor, it's easy to see why this pub is popular with locals and visitors alike. In the bar area you can settle in beside the fire with a newspaper or feed the affections of Bella the resident cat, before climbing the stairs to the dining room – once a chapel – where the building's original windows are still on display. The traditional British cooking features well-honed recipes and plenty of local produce. At lunch there is a keenly-priced set menu and a selection of tried and tested 'light bites', including dishes such as eggs Benedict or smoked kippers. In the evening this moves on to a more substantial à la carte, where there are plenty of good meaty dishes and complimentary sides of vegetables and potatoes – a pleasant rarity in modern times. Bedrooms are cosy and thoughtfully appointed, displaying fresh flowers, fridges and complimentary wi-fi.

Closing times

Closed 25 December, 1 January, Sunday dinner and Monday

Booking essential

Prices

Meals: £ 15/19 and à la carte £ 25/34

4 rooms: £ 50/100

Typical Dishes

Scallops & lentil purée
Pork tenderloin
Hot chocolate fondant

Midway between Bradford-on-Avon and Melksham on B 3107. Parking.

England • South West • Wiltshire

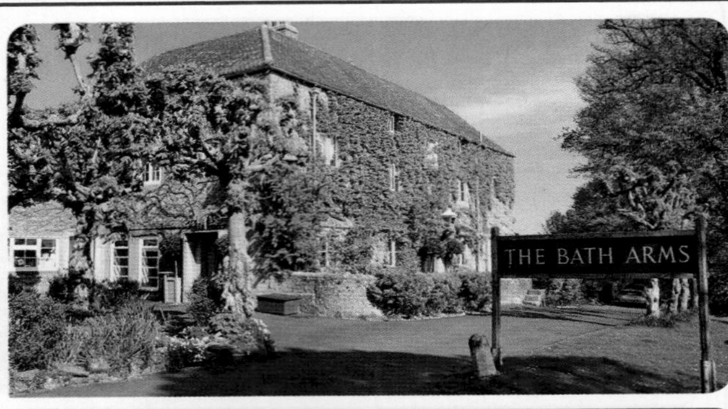

99 The Bath Arms

Longleat,
Horningsham BA12 7LY
Tel.: (01985)844308 – Fax: (01985)845187
e-mail: enquiries@batharms.co.uk **Website:** www.batharms.co.uk

Inspectors' favourites

Horningsham Pride and fortnightly changing guest ale such as Golden Apostle

After a day out in the parklands of the Longleat Estate, dine under the watchful eye of Lord Bath in this stylish pub, where specially commissioned paintings of the flamboyant aristocrat adorn the walls. The modern British menu uses seasonal ingredients and features daily-changing dishes presented in an honest, straightforward manner. The chef admirably rises to the challenge of sourcing all produce from within 50 miles: meat from Longleat, Stourhead and Cranborne, fish from Brixham and St. Mawes, and even local organic vodka. Choose from the bar menu, which might include confit of duck leg or pork belly, or the 3 course dinner menu, which may feature grilled brill or braised lamb shank; all meals are accompanied by excellent fresh bread. The uniquely designed bedrooms are colourful and eclectic; try the vibrant, eccentric Flashman room, or the sumptuous Peacock room. The latest addition, a beauty treatment room, is also worth a visit.

Closing times
Open daily

Prices
Meals: £ 14/30
and à la carte £ 30

15 rooms: £ 85/150

Typical Dishes
Locally smoked salmon
Longleat lamb
Rhubarb crème brûlée

3 mi southwest of Warminster by A 362 and minor road. Parking.

100 The Millstream

Marden SN10 3RH
Tel.: (01380)848308 – Fax: (01380)848337
e-mail: info@the-millstream.net
Website: www.the-millstream.net

 **VISA** 

 **Wadworth 6X, Henry's IPA and Wadworth seasonal ales**

A charming pub decorated in a delightfully eye-catching style, with chic country furnishings, antique tables and plenty to keep you entertained between courses; the level of detail a fine reflection of the owners' passion for the place. Lights twinkle, cards and ceramics are for sale, glossy magazines are scattered about and chairs piled high with cookery books, while Oscar Wilde quotations and fine paintings punctuate the wall space. Food here is freshly prepared, using quality local and seasonal ingredients, and the traditional pub dishes come with contemporary influences and a French edge. Champagne is available by the glass, a blackboard informs you of upcoming events - perhaps opera, a hog roast or a picnic - and there are plans in the pipeline for a cookery school and a takeaway menu. The motto at The Millstream is 'live a little, drink a little, laugh a lot,' and to this might well be added 'eat a little or a lot, but eat well.'

Closing times
Closed Monday (except bank holidays)

Prices
Meals: à la carte £ 21/33

Typical Dishes
Squid bruschetta
Shoulder of pork
Baked vanilla cheesecake

6½ mi southeast of Devizes by A 342 and minor road north. Parking.

101 The Old Spotted Cow

The Street,
Marston Meysey SN6 6LQ
Tel.: (01285)810264
e-mail: anna@theoldspottedcow.co.uk **Website:** www.theoldspottedcow.co.uk

 **Pophams Pride, Butcombe Bitter**

With its sheep and chickens, and looking for all the world like somebody's private farmhouse, this pub – the most northerly in Wiltshire – sits firmly in the country dining league. Once neglected but now lovingly restored, it is enthusiastically run by Anna Langley, and provides a proper pub for locals with plenty of real ales to accompany the honest, rustic, seasonal cooking. Dishes range from pub classics like devilled whitebait or beer-battered fish and chips to the more unusual roasted Pollock and chorizo or spicy grilled pork belly; a good combination of British sustenance and worldly spices that find their influences in Anna's grandmother's Lancastrian recipes and her own upbringing in Kenya. Popular events include Sunday roasts, summer barbecues and monthly spice nights. The contemporary bedroom is very comfortable and, as you breakfast by the fire in the morning, don't be surprised if your hostess pops out to say a quick hello.

Closing times
Closed Monday (except bank holidays)

Prices
Meals: à la carte £ 18/28
1 room: £ 50/75

Typical Dishes
Prawns & chorizo
Braised brisket
Lemon & honey posset

Between Fairford and Cricklade. Parking.

102 The Wheatsheaf at Oaksey

Wheatsheaf Lane,
Oaksey SN16 9TB
Tel.: (01666)577348
e-mail: info@thecompletechef.co.uk **Website:** www.thecompletechef.co.uk

 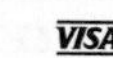   

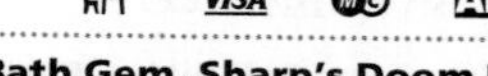 **Bath Gem, Sharp's Doom Bar, English Rose**

Dating back several hundred years, this Cotswold-stone building still shows evidence of its historic roots: above the fire is a lintel reputed to be made from a Roman coffin lid and carved crosses – allegedly to ward off witches – adorn the wooden beams and chimney. The original woodwork and features help the bar retain its traditional character, whilst the crash of skittles and falling dominoes create a homely feel. It's a hit with the locals, who like to linger by the fire with a pint or partake in the pub quiz but there is also a strong emphasis on food, in the bar and the more contemporary rear dining room. The constantly evolving blackboard menu relies on good flavours and simple techniques, offering traditional, heart-warming dishes: mains may include wholesome casseroles or cassoulets, with bread and butter pudding or crumble to follow. Water is presented in old Bombay Sapphire bottles, a unique gesture towards eco friendliness.

Closing times
Closed Sunday dinner and Monday

Prices
Meals: à la carte £ 19/27

Typical Dishes
Ham hock terrine
Steak & mushroom pudding
Chocolate fondant

5½ mi north of Malmesbury; signed from A 429. Parking.

103 The Bell

The Square,
Ramsbury SN8 2PE

Tel.: (01672)520230 – Fax: (01672)520832
e-mail: jeremy@thebellramsbury.com **Website:** www.thebellramsbury.com

Ramsbury Brewery : Bell Bitter, Ramsbury Gold

The Bell takes up a prominent position within the village and since being spruced up by its new owners in 2007, has gone from strength to strength. Head past the bar, around the odd dog or two and you'll find yourself amongst large, cosy sofas, plump enough to swallow you up; here you can look through the constantly evolving array of menus. To help make deciding that little bit easier, dishes have been divided up into sections, the newest feature being the tempting locally sourced steaks and their mouthwatering garnishes: the 'classic' and 'seasonal' selections are just as hard to resist though, and all coupled with charming, honest service. The atmospheric bar is the perfect place to dine, but if you prefer things a little quieter head for the pleasant restaurant. With dishes ranging from terrine of local pigeon breast or home-cooked Wiltshire ham, to river crayfish or whole Cornish lobster, The Bell definitely strikes the right note.

Closing times
Closed 25 December and Monday dinner

Prices
Meals: £ 15/20
and à la carte £ 22/32

Typical Dishes
Kennet crayfish
Lamb & sweetbread pudding
Bramley apple crumble

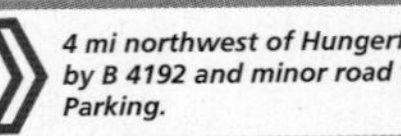

4 mi northwest of Hungerford by B 4192 and minor road west. Parking.

104 The George & Dragon

High Street,
Rowde SN10 2PN
Tel.: (01380)723053
e-mail: thegandd@tiscali.co.uk **Website:** www.thegeorgeanddragonrowde.co.uk

 **Butcombe, Brains, Timothy Taylor, Fuller's London Pride**

When the current owners took over in 2004 they had a hard act to follow, but they admirably rose to the challenge and are now comfortably settled in. Bringing with them London experience and lots of charm, their mission was to inject life and energy into the laid-back countryside, which they seem to have done: their regular village events, including quiz nights, monthly summer BBQs and wine and cheese evenings are extremely popular. Early every morning a fresh catch of fish arrives on the doorstep from St. Mawes and the excellent fish specials are created from whatever is in the box that day. Alongside this, the main menu features a selection of comforting British classics, available in two sizes, which may include devilled lamb's kidneys or rack of lamb: which, in the winter, can be taken by a huge stone-housed fire. If you're feeling weary, the uniquely styled, well-equipped, trendy-meets-old-world bedrooms are not to be missed.

Closing times

Closed Sunday dinner

Booking essential

Prices

Meals: £ 18 (lunch) and à la carte £ 25/40

3 rooms: £ 55/105

Typical Dishes

Baked fig & goat's cheese

Assiette of fish

Trio of chocolate plate

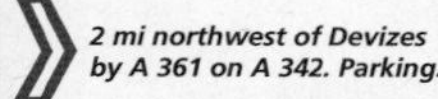

105 The Gastrobistro at the Pheasant Inn

19 Salt Lane,
Salisbury SP1 1DT
Tel.: (01722)414926
e-mail: gastrobistro@googlemail.com **Website:** www.gastrobistro.co.uk

 **No draught ales offered**

The enthusiastic owner of this curiously named inn is an anglophilic Frenchmen who has made the Cathedral City his home, so you are just as likely to find steak and chips or sponge pudding on the menu as you are chicken chasseur or ragoût of lamb - all freshly made with local produce and served with a hefty dollop of Gallic charm. The plaque on the wall dates the black and white timbered building back to 1638, but it has the air of one even older, and its rough quarry tiled floors, inglenook fireplaces and ancient beams all add to its distinctive character, as does the cobbled courtyard, the recently installed piano and the rows of empty champagne bottles which pay homage to the owner's home region. Comfy sofas and a super smart happy hour with free nibbles attract their fair share of drinkers, but most people come here to dine, with great value lunch and early evening menus, blackboard fish specials and a popular Sunday lunch.

Closing times

Closed 25 December dinner, 1 January, dinner Sunday and Monday

Prices

Meals: £ 14 and à la carte £ 20/35

Typical Dishes

French onion soup
Mussels marinière
Tarte Tatin

In city centre north of the cathedral. Salt Lane car park 1 min walk.

106 The Bridge Inn

Upper Woodford SP4 6NU
Tel.: (01722)782323
e-mail: enquiries@thebridgewoodford.co.uk
Website: www.thebridgewoodford.co.uk

 VISA MC AE

 **Hopback Summer Lightning, Wadworth 6X, Ringwood Best**

Situated in the Woodford Valley, a few miles south of Stonehenge, and a few miles north of Salisbury, the aptly named Bridge Inn stands on the banks of the Avon overlooking the river crossing; its garden, with picnic tables from which to watch the swans and ducks, an al fresco diner's delight. The pub is modern, with a light, airy feel. Its relaxed atmosphere means that locals with their dogs rub shoulders with diners and you can peek through the glass windows to see the chefs hard at work in the kitchen. Lunch sees a light bites menu of interesting sandwiches, while the à la carte offers classics such as fishcakes, crab linguini or salmon with couscous. Specials and puddings are listed on blackboards, as is the recipe of the month, and the fresh, tasty food is neatly presented, not on china, but on wood or slate. This is the sister pub to The Ship Inn at Burcombe; get your hands on a loyalty card and you can reap the benefits of both.

Closing times
Open daily
Prices
Meals: à la carte £ 23/33

Typical Dishes
Sautéed pigeon breast
Crab & leek linguini
Rhubarb trifle

North of Salisbury off A 360; follow signs for The Woodfords. Parking.

Upton Scudamore

107 The Angel Inn

Upton Scudamore BA12 0AG
Tel.: (01985)213225 – Fax: (01985)218182
e-mail: mail@theangelinn.co.uk
Website: www.theangelinn.co.uk

 **Wadworth 6X, Butcombe and one guest beer**

It's lucky for the locals that this friendly pub is on their doorstep, as there's not much more to this quiet village than a few houses. It has quite a local reputation and deservedly so; service is efficient and comes with a smile, whether you're basking in the sun on the decked terrace or getting cosy beside the fire in the country-cottage interior. Candles and flowers adorn the tables in both the restaurant and the bar, with local artists' paintings decorating the walls. Upon arrival you are greeted with delicious homemade bread, complete with olives and herb oil, whilst at the other end of the meal luscious homemade ice creams and sorbets await. The kitchen has got the balance between pub and restaurant cooking just right, with a menu of hearty main dishes and a blackboard filled with fish specials, courtesy of near-daily arrivals. Rooms are comfortable, modern and spacious; each with pristine, individually co-ordinated furnishings.

Closing times
Closed 25-26 December and 1 January

Prices
Meals: £ 15 (lunch) and à la carte £ 20/30
10 rooms: £ 80/88

Typical Dishes
Sesame crusted tuna
Breast of wood pigeon
Trio of rice puddings

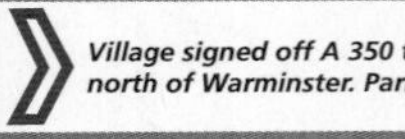

Village signed off A 350 to the north of Warminster. Parking.

Garder

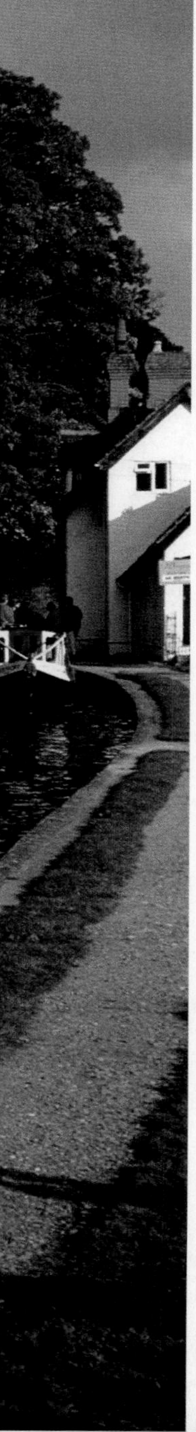

The names Gas Street Basin, Custard Factory and Mailbox may not win any awards for exoticism, but these are the cutting edge quarters fuelling the rise of modern day Birmingham, at the heart of a region evolving from its grimy factory gate image. Even the Ironbridge Gorge, the cradle of the Industrial Revolution, is better known these days as a fascinatingly picturesque tourist attraction. The old urban landscapes dot a region of delightful unspoilt countryside with extensive areas of open moorland and hills, where stands Middle Earth, in the shape of Shropshire's iconic Wrekin hill, true inspiration of Tolkien. Shakespeare Country abounds in pretty villages, such as Henley-in-Arden, Shipston-on-Stour and Alcester, where redbrick, half-timbered and Georgian buildings capture the eye. Taste buds are catered for courtesy of a host of local specialities, not least fruits from the Vale of Evesham and mouth-watering meats from the hills near the renowned gastro town of Ludlow.

North West
Wales
WEST
Chester
Wrexham / Wrecsam
Shrewsbury
Telford
Welshpool / Y Trallwng
Newtown / Drenewydd
Llandrindod Wells
Builth Wells / Llanfair-ym-Muallt
Hereford
Leominster
Worcester
Kidderminster
Brecon / Aberhonddu
Abergavenny / Y-Fenni
Monmouth / Trefynwy
Llangollen
Oswestry
Ludlow
SHROPSHIRE
POWYS
HEREFORD
WREKIN

Chesterfield
Bakewell
Chatsworth House
Park
Clay Cross
Hardwick Hall
Tuxford
Ollerton
Mansfield
Newark-on-Trent
Little Moreton Hall
Leek
Matlock
Alfreton
DERBY
Sutton-in-Ashfield
Southwell
Ashbourne
Ripley
Heanor
Hucknall
STOKE-ON-TRENT
Belper
NOTTINGHAM
Ilkeston
Stone
Uttoxeter
Derby
Bingham
West Bridgford
Sudbury
Long Eaton
Stafford
Abbots Bromley
Burton-upon-Trent
Rempstone
Rugeley
East Midlands
Swadlincote
Loughborough
Cannock
Ashby de la Zouch
Brownhills
Lichfield
Coalville
LEICESTER
Walsall
Tamworth
LEICESTER
Sutton Coldfield
Atherstone
Hinckley
Oadby
MIDLANDS
Uppingham
Nuneaton
Market Harborough
Halesowen
Solihull
Bedworth
Lutterworth
COVENTRY
Husbands Bosworth
Rugby
Rothwell
Redditch
Kenilworth
WARWICK
NORTHAM
Henley
Royal Leamington Spa
Wellingborough
Warwick
Alcester
Southam
Daventry
Stratford-upon-Avon
Ettington
Evesham
Pershore
Chipping Campden
Shipston-on-Stour
Towcester
Banbury
Broadway
Moreton
Brackley
Milton Keynes
Winchcombe
Stow-on-the-Wold
Chipping Norton
Buckingham
Bletchley
West
OXFORD
South East
Bicester
BUCKINGHAM
Northleach
Woodstock
Burford
Blenheim Palace
Kidlington
R. Trent
Great Ouse
Derwent

1 Bear and Ragged Staff

Station Rd,
Bransford WR6 5JH
Tel.: (01886)833399 – Fax: (01886)833106
e-mail: mail@bear.uk.com **Website:** www.bear.uk.com

VISA MC AE

 **Fuller's London Pride, Hobson's Twisted Spire**

This traditional inn dates from 1861, when it was built as a tax collection house; it was originally part of a Warwick estate and its name comes from the symbol on the Warwickshire coat of arms. Set in a quiet country lane, it has spacious gardens and a front dominated by two lovely old oak trees. Huge blackboard bar menus offer everything from sandwiches to Thai style fishcakes, with plenty of pub classics like sausage and mash or fish and chips. Dishes like slow-braised shoulder of pork or roast rump of Malvern Hills grazed lamb are available in the more formal, linen-clad dining room, and fish specials are chalked up on a board. Before appearing on your plate, vegetables make the short journey from the back garden to the kitchen and, although other produce may come from further afield, they do try to keep ingredients as local as possible. There are steak nights on Fridays, roasts for Sunday lunch and weekend barbecues in the summer.

Closing times

Closed dinner 25 December and 1 January, in winter Monday and Sunday dinner

Prices

Meals: £ 15 (weekday lunch Tuesday-Saturday lunch) and à la carte £ 20/30

Typical Dishes

Warm chicken liver salad

Roast Malvern Hills lamb

Sticky toffee & sultana pudding

4½ mi southwest of Worcester by A 44 and A 4103; from Bransford follow signs to Powick. Parking.

2 The Royal Forester

Callow Hill DY14 9XW
Tel.: (01299)266286
e-mail: contact@royalforesterinn.co.uk
Website: www.royalforesterinn.co.uk

Timothy Taylor Landlord, Hobson's Town Crier, Wye Valley HPA

Situated right in the heart of the Wyre Forest this pub is aptly named and if it really dates back to 1411 as people believe, is one of the oldest in Worcestershire. A full refurbishment has brought it up-to-date and created a modern feel but it hasn't lost sight of its country origins and retains a relaxed, easy-going atmosphere. The dining room with its chunky wood tables and exposed stone walls is the most rustic in feel, while the bar is lighter and brighter, courtesy of the adjoining terrace. The appealing, down-to-earth menu features a concise, good value set selection or a more wide-ranging à la carte; particularly noteworthy are the local grilled steaks, while other dishes might include scallops with pea purée or linguine with wild mushrooms. The modern, comfortable bedrooms are cleverly designed after colourful foodstuffs; they include purple, green and blue themed rooms – 'Aubergine', 'Pear' and 'Blueberry' respectively.

Closing times
Open daily
Prices
Meals: £ 13 and à la carte £ 18/35
7 rooms: £ 55/79

Typical Dishes
Pan-seared scallops
Roast duck breast
Assiette of rhubarb

3 mi southwest of Bewdley.
Parking.

England • West Midlands • Hereford and Worcester

3 Bell & Cross

Holy Cross,
Clent DY9 9QL

Tel.: (01562)730319 – Fax: (01562)731733
Website: www.bellandcrossclent.co.uk

VISA

 **Kinver Edge, Enville Ale, Timothy Taylor Landlord**

Every inch of wall space seems to be filled with framed photos at this friendly little pub – little being the operative word, given the cosy feel in each of its rooms. Traditional-looking both outside and in, with its tiled floors, wheelback chairs and wooden tables; one of its snugs is a great place to settle down in for the evening – while the terrace and pretty garden are the natural choice on sunny days – and the servers are attentive wherever you sit. Cooking is tasty, balanced and well executed and you'll find that classic dishes such as lamb chops and roasted chicken share the menu with more modern and international offerings such as Peking duck rolls or veal Schnitzel Carbonara. Desserts will definitely take you back a few years with old favourites such as knickerbocker glory, rice pudding and trifle on the menu, and who can resist the temptation of treacle tart, when it's listed as being served with Granny's thick custard?

Closing times
Closed 25 December

Prices
Meals: à la carte £ 18/25

Typical Dishes
Duck rillettes
Grilled calves liver
Warm treacle tart & custard

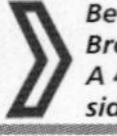

Between Stourbridge and Bromsgrove off northbound A 491; the pub is on the left hand side in Holy Cross. Parking.

4 The Colliers Arms

Tenbury Road,
Clows Top DY14 9HA

Tel.: (01299)832242
e-mail: thecolliersarms@aol.com **Website:** www.colliersarms.com

 **Hobson's Best Bitter, Bewdley Old School, Wye Valley Butty Bach, Three Tuns Cleric's Cure**

A young new owner may have taken over at the helm of The Colliers Arms but the pub is still very popular with the older generation, who obviously appreciate good quality, homecooked food. Several rooms offer differing atmospheres in which to dine; there's a snug little bar with a traditional feel to it, an open main bar with a log fire, furnished with polished wooden tables and decorated with some decidedly fishy wall paper, plus – the best place to sit – an airy dining room at the rear of the pub, with pleasant views of the garden. There's no danger of finding fashionable fusion dishes here: instead you'll find all the old favourites on the menu; traditional hearty British dishes like steak and chips, sausage and mash and steak and kidney pudding, as well as sandwiches and lighter snacks at lunch. The choice of food on the menu is dictated by the seasons and everything is fresh and homemade.

Closing times
Closed Sunday dinner

Prices
Meals: £ 14 (dinner Monday-Thursday) and à la carte £ 18/25

Typical Dishes
Pork & leek terrine
Pan-fried red snapper
Rhubarb crème brûlée

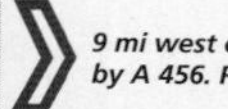
9 mi west of Kidderminster by A 456. Parking.

5 The Chequers

Kidderminster Rd,
Cutnall Green WR9 0PJ
Tel.: (01299)851292 – Fax: (01299)851744
Website: www.chequerscutnallgreen.co.uk

 **Wye Valley HPA, Sharp's Doom Bar, Timothy Taylor Landlord**

Don't be put off by this roadside pub's unremarkable exterior: it's obviously just a cover to stop the masses thronging here in their droves. Inside it's a different story - extremely characterful, with rustic style aplenty in the form of sandblasted beams, exposed brickwork and wood and tiled floors. There's a lounge bar with sofas and armchairs in which to make yourself comfortable and a restaurant with chunky dark wood tables, whilst the patio and garden area are popular in the spring and summer months. The large à la carte dinner menu offers modern dishes and is supplemented by daily specials. Cooking is flavoursome, with international leanings, so your chicken might come Yuk Sung style, your sea bream might be made into a Goan curry, and your chicken breast might come served with kumara potato and chorizo. The lunchtime menu offers lighter bites; from sandwiches and salads to pasta and panini.

Closing times
Closed 25 December, 26 December dinner and 1 January

Prices
Meals: à la carte £ 18/25

Typical Dishes
Parm ham & fresh fig salad
Grilled sea bass
Lemon curd cheesecake

3 mi north of Droitwich Spa on A 442. Parking.

6 The Butchers Arms

Lime St,
Eldersfield GL19 4NX
Tel.: (01452)840381
Website: www.thebutchersarms.net

 **Wye Valley Butty Bach, St Austell Tribute, Dorothy Goodbody, RCH Pitchfork**

Apart from the modern sign swinging outside and the pine picnic benches scattered across the neatly-kept lawn, this pub remains as traditional as ever and wouldn't look out of place on a historic film set. Two small rooms display original beams, part-oak flooring and a wood burning stove, while dried hops hang from the bar and knick-knacks and memorabilia adorn the walls. A few of the small wooden tables – some former sewing tables – are left for the local drinkers, while the rest are set for 20 or so diners, which isn't a bad number for a team of two. With only one person in the kitchen the menu is understandably quite concise but it changes regularly – sometimes even from service to service – and despite the lack of man-power, everything from the bread to the ice cream is homemade. Cooking sees refined pub dishes alongside a few more unusual items such as Bath Chaps (pig's cheeks); while vegetables arrive courtesy of a local villager.

Closing times

Closed 25-26 December, first week in January, Sunday dinner, Monday, and Tuesday lunch

Booking essential

Prices

Meals: à la carte £ 28/36

Typical Dishes
Braised Cornish squid
Gower seabass
Marmalade pudding

South of M50 between Junctions 1 and 2. Parking.

7 Plough and Harrow

Rhydd Rd, Guarlford WR13 6NY
Tel.: (01684)310453
e-mail: info@theploughandharrow.co.uk
Website: www.theploughandharrow.co.uk

 **Wadworth IPA and 6X**

This modernised country pub is run by a keen, friendly young couple with the help of their team of polite, chatty staff; adept at keeping things well under control, even when there's a rush on. And there might well be a rush on when you visit, since the tasty food on offer here is like all good pub food should be: unfussy in style and cooked with pride and care, using good quality produce; including plenty of fruit, herbs and vegetables from their own kitchen garden. Menus change seasonally, with simpler snacks and sandwiches available at lunchtime alongside dishes like chicken and gammon pie or steak and chips, while dinner dishes have more of a restaurant feel to them; perhaps terrine of ham hock and foie gras or salmon smoked blini to start, followed by breast of Gressingham duck or pan roast scallops. Sit by the open fire in the comfy, beamed bar, or, for a more formal feel, head past the sofa to the bright, split-level dining room.

Closing times
Closed 25 December, Sunday dinner and Monday

Prices
Meals: à la carte £ 20/35

Typical Dishes
Squid risotto with scallops
Breast of duck
Panna cotta

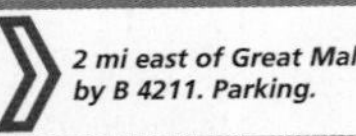
2 mi east of Great Malvern by B 4211. Parking.

8 The Wellington

Wellington,
Hereford HR4 8AT
Tel.: (01432)830367
e-mail: thewellington@hotmail.com **Website:** www.wellingtonpub.co.uk

 **Hobson's Best, Wye Valley HPA and Butty Bach**

Everyone wants to live the dream but not many succeed. The owner here is one of the lucky few. Arriving with no experience in either a kitchen or a pub environment, he is now the proud owner of a highly popular, much-loved neighbourhood pub – a real local's local – and has taught himself the culinary skills required. Located in the centre of the village, parking can be challenging but it's definitely worth searching for a spot so you can relax by the fire in the spacious open bar. With smartly laid scrubbed wooden tables and a pleasant conservatory leading out to the gardens, the dining room has a more formal feel, although the service remains laid-back throughout. The chefs use only local, traceable produce and the menu changes daily to reflect their highly seasonal ethos. Dishes feature fairly classical combinations and might include loin of speckle-faced Welsh lamb, pedigree Hereford sirloin steak or rare breed Welsh white pork.

Closing times

Closed 25 December, Sunday dinner and Monday lunch

Prices

Meals: à la carte £ 24/32

Typical Dishes

Hereford hop soufflé
Fillet of local venison
Lemon semifreddo

5 mi north by A 49. In village centre. Parking.

9 The Lough Pool at Sellack

Sellack,
Ross-on-Wye HR9 6LX
Tel.: (01989)730236 – Fax: (01981)570322
e-mail: david@loughpool.co.uk **Website:** www.loughpool.co.uk

Inspectors' favourites

Wye Valley Bitter, Butty Bach, Butcombe Bitter

Situated in a wonderfully rural spot down the country lanes of Hereford, this 16C black and white timbered inn is well off the beaten track. With a name like this you won't be surprised to find that opposite the pub is a pond, complete with ducks and weeping willows swaying gently in the breeze. Overlooking this beautiful view is the garden, so make time to sit with a real ale or Herefordshire cider and admire the view. With hop bines entwined around wooden beams, flag stone floors and roaring open fires, the atmosphere is truly rustic and, despite the comings and goings of various chefs, the food too has stayed true to its roots. Cooking is traditional and in good pub style, provides great value. With much of the produce being delivered from just down the road, ingredients are well sourced; the latest seasonal availability informing the daily menu – you might find crab salad, followed by loin of lamb, finished off with rhubarb posset.

Closing times

Closed 25 December, Sunday dinner and Monday (except bank holidays)

Prices

Meals: à la carte £ 21/28

Typical Dishes

Perroche goat's cheese salad
Rack of spring lamb
Duo of chocolate

3 ¼ mi northwest of Ross-on-Wye; turn right off A 49 (Hereford) and follow signs for Hoarwithy. Parking.

10 Mill Race

Walford,
Ross-on-Wye HR9 5QS
Tel.: (01989)562891
e-mail: enquiries@millrace.info **Website:** www.millrace.info

 **Wye Valley Ales and guest ales from Malvern Brewery and Wickwar Brewery**

Boasting a spacious interior and a large terrace with countryside views, this bright, modern pub is a relative newcomer to the scene. Built by a local tradesman it plays perfect host to variety of inspired events: the first Monday of each month sees a specials night – maybe French, Game or Creole – which features themed dishes, drinks and cocktails, while during the warmer months regular BBQs and a yearly Food Fayre take place. The constantly evolving menu has a sound seasonal British base and focuses on good quality food cooked simply and well. Dishes are tasty and uncomplicated, and feature carefully sourced, ethical produce – meat from farms that treat their animals humanely and fish from non-depleted stocks or sustainable sources – and on top of that they even convert their used fat into fuel. Reminiscent of the old market days, locals can exchange their home-grown fruit, vegetables or flowers in return for lunch. How satisfying.

Closing times
Open daily

Prices
Meals: à la carte £ 12/27

Typical Dishes
Braised duck leg
Confit pork belly
Orange & ginger pudding

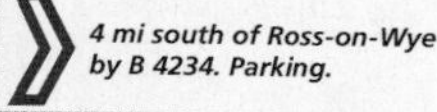
4 mi south of Ross-on-Wye by B 4234. Parking.

England • West Midlands • Hereford and Worcester

11 The Stagg Inn

Titley HR5 3RL
Tel.: (01544)230221 – Fax: (01544)231390
e-mail: reservations@thestagg.co.uk
Website: www.thestagg.co.uk

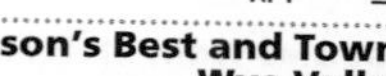

Hobson's Best and Town Crier, Ludlow Best and Gold, Wye Valley Butty Bach

The busy bar's beams at this characterful country dining pub are almost entirely covered by a collection of porcelain water jugs, and its three dining rooms with their dried hops and polished wood tables are similarly rustic in feel. Local produce is noticeably to the fore on the seasonally-changing menus, and includes the pub's own pigs and chickens as well as fruit and vegetables from the garden. Cooking is classically-based and served without pretence, allowing the flavours of the top quality ingredients to speak for themselves. Weekday bar snacks might include ploughman's and sandwiches, while dishes on the à la carte tend more towards choices like pigeon breast, fillet of Herefordshire beef or saddle of venison. Simply furnished bedrooms have a distinctly rural character, typified by the exposed beams; three are above the pub, the others are situated in the Grade II listed old vicarage a few minutes walk away in the village.

Closing times

Closed first 2 weeks in November, Sunday dinner and Monday

Booking essential

Prices

Meals: à la carte £ 20/30

6 rooms: £ 70/130

Typical Dishes

Warm pigeon salad

Fillet of Herefordshire beef

Rhubarb jelly & compote

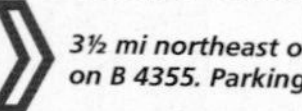

3½ mi northeast of Kington on B 4355. Parking.

12 Three Crowns Inn

Bleak Acre,
Ullingswick HR1 3JQ

 Tel.: (01432)820279 – Fax: (08700)515338
e-mail: info@threecrownsinn.com **Website:** www.threecrownsinn.com

Wye Valley, Butty Bach, Hobson's Best Bitter

A hallmark of this rural, family-run pub is its unfussy cooking: the chef-owner takes the finest of local ingredients and gives them Three Crowns treatment, producing robust, tasty dishes which are easy on the eye as well as on the pocket. The set blackboard lunchtime menu, located above the fire, offers classic dishes such as moules and frites, while the daily-changing à la carte might tempt you with starters such as roast woodcock with risotto of its liver, followed by confit duck or peppered sirloin of Herefordshire beef. Service is chatty and polite and the atmosphere is relaxed. Hops hang from low beams and there are seats both for drinkers and diners – the most popular being those by the open fire – while the more modern extension is used for dining during busier periods. A bedroom also housed in the extension is smart, with contemporary styling; the owners hope to add more soon.

Closing times

Closed 25-26 December and Monday

Prices

Meals: £ 15 (lunch) and à la carte £ 26

1 room: £ 95

Typical Dishes

Cheddar & spinach soufflé

Grilled Cornish Gurnard

Chocolate truffle tart

1¼ mi east of village on unsigned country lane. Parking.

13 The Bell Inn

Green Lane,
Yarpole HR6 0BD
Tel.: (01568)780359
Website: www.thebellinnyarpole.co.uk

 **Wye Valley Pale Ale, Timothy Taylor, Hooky Bitter**

Set in the charming village of Yarpole, between Ludlow and Leominster, this black and white timbered inn is mentioned in the Domesday Book, and, as you might hope, has a real sense of identity. Low beams and wonky timberwork are on display throughout the building and the dining room – a converted barn – still houses a cider press and mill wheel; outside picnic tables are strewn across the pleasant, neatly kept garden. Cooking is a mixture of British and French. The bar menu offers traditional classics, with dishes such as prawn cocktail, fish pie, sirloin steak or Hereford snails. The restaurant on the other hand, sees more modern influences, featuring maybe smoked salmon rillettes, Herefordshire rare beef salad or terrine of confit rabbit leg and foie gras; followed by roast fillet of black bream, slow roast leg of Brittany rabbit or Elwy Valley lamb chop with confit lamb breast. Service is skilled and you can guarantee a warm welcome.

Closing times

Closed Monday, and Sunday dinner (October to June)

Prices

Meals: à la carte £ 19/24

Typical Dishes

Home-cured salmon
Lamb belly & black pudding
Lemon tart

4 mi north of Leominster by B 4361 and minor road west. Parking.

14 The Roebuck Inn

Brimfield SY8 4NE
Tel.: (01584)711230
e-mail: info@theroebuckludlow.co.uk
Website: www.theroebuckinnludlow.co.uk

 **Banks Bitter, Pedigree**

The Roebuck Inn has seen several changes in owner in recent years, its fortunes rising up and down accordingly, but with new French chef-owner Olivier Bossut in charge, its star is once again on the up. It comes as no surprise to find dishes such as gateaux of crab in a saffron beurre blanc, terrine of piglet and foie gras, millefeuilles of green asparagus or cassoulet Toulousain on the menu, but French or otherwise, dishes are freshly cooked, seasonal and full of flavour. Meat comes from a butcher in nearby Ludlow, and ingredients are sourced locally. Located right in the middle of the village, and dating back to the 15C, this inn is every inch the classic country pub, with friendly staff and a relaxed, informal feel, and you can eat in either the stylishly furnished dining room or in the bar. If you want to stay a while and discover the Ludlow area, three bedrooms have a homely feel.

Closing times

Closed Sunday dinner

Booking essential

Prices

Meals: à la carte £ 17/36

3 rooms: £ 65/85

Typical Dishes
Lobster ravioli
Beef Wellington
Raspberry cup

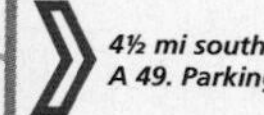

4½ mi south of Ludlow; signed off A 49. Parking.

15 The Feathers at Brockton

Brockton, Much Wenlock TF13 6JR

Tel.: (01746)785202

e-mail: feathersatbrockton@googlemail.com

Website: www.feathersatbrockton.co.uk

 **Hobson's Best, Woods Parish Ale**

This rustic 16C pub is situated on the edge of the village, not far from Much Wenlock, in an area popular with walkers. Take your pick from four dining areas: all are snug with warm, homely décor, open fires and lots of stripped wood, exposed beams and thick stone walls. It's a personally run place – he cooks; she looks after the bar – and the atmosphere is relaxing and unpretentious, with the focus firmly on the food. Having learnt his trade in the Big Smoke, chef-owner Chris returned to Shropshire to open The Feathers back in 2004 – and his tasty cooking has been attracting customers ever since. Mainly British and traditional in style, dishes are made using local produce and might include corn-fed chicken breast, shoulder of lamb or steak and ale pie, with a specials board expanding the selection further. Should you wish to prolong your stay at The Feathers, four comfortable, country style bedrooms are now available.

Closing times

Closed 25 December, 1 January, Monday, Tuesday lunch

Prices

Meals: £ 10 (Tuesday-Sunday dinner) and à la carte £ 15/25

4 rooms: £ 50/75

Typical Dishes

King prawns

Slow-cooked pork belly

Sticky toffee pudding

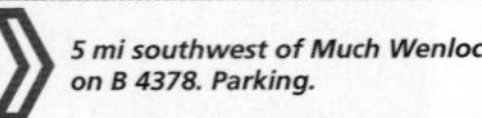

5 mi southwest of Much Wenlock on B 4378. Parking.

16 The Burlton Inn

Burlton SY4 5TB
Tel.: (01939)270284 – Fax: (01939)270928
e-mail: enquiries@burltoninn.com
Website: www.burltoninn.com

    VISA AE

 **Robinson's Unicorn, Robinson's Trouble & Strife, Hartley's XB**

Set on a busy road in a small village between Ellesmere and Shrewsbury, this traditional 18C whitewashed inn welcomes you with a colourful flower display. Having been taken over by its current owners in late 2008, it's undergoing a transformation; a landscaped garden and terrace are under construction and there are even more plans for improvement afoot. It's a characterful place with wooden beams and some soft seating by a wood burning stove. To one side there's a dining area but you can eat throughout – although it can get busy in the bar with local drinkers, especially on a Friday. Offering six choices per course, the menu features unfussy, classical cooking with a refined, contemporary touch. Dishes evolve with the seasons and produce is good quality and locally sourced; for lighter appetites the bar serves some tasty snacks including pork pies, pickles and cheese. The neat, wood-furnished bedrooms boast spacious bathrooms.

Closing times
Closed 25 December

Prices
Meals: £ 16 (dinner) and à la carte £ 17/28
6 rooms: £ 65/85

Typical Dishes
Pork belly & scallops
Chicken cassoulet
Honey panna cotta & hazelnut nougat

8 mi north of Shrewsbury on A 528. Parking.

17 The Sun Inn

Marton SY21 8JP
Tel.: (01938)561211
e-mail: suninnmarton@googlemail.com
Website: www.suninn.org.uk

VISA 

Hobson's Best, Six Bells Brewery monthly ales

Set in a quiet village in the Marches on the English-Welsh border, this warm and welcoming stone pub has a real countryside feel. It's very much a family affair, with father and son combo Peter and Dominic cooking up a storm in the kitchen, and wife Jean and daughter-in-law Sally providing smooth, efficient service out front. In the bar area a blackboard displays a list of daily specials, while in the restaurant – with its pastel violet coloured walls – there's a regularly changing modern British/ Mediterranean menu and a fresh fish board alongside. Cooking is straightforward, unfussy and unashamedly classical, using local, seasonal and organic ingredients where possible, including meat from the nearby farms. Dishes may include steak and kidney pudding, roast loin of lamb or wild boar steak, followed by pears in red wine or cappuccino brûlée. It can get busy, especially at weekends, so it's advisable to book in advance.

Closing times
Closed Sunday dinner (except last Sunday in the month), Monday, and Tuesday lunch

Prices
Meals: £ 13/16
and à la carte £ 15/33

Typical Dishes
Salmon brandade
Sauté of Guinea fowl
Raspberry & white chocolate parfait

8½ mi southeast of Welshpool on B 4386. Parking.

18 The Crown Country Inn

Munslow SY7 9ET
Tel.: (01584)841205
e-mail: info@crowncountryinn.co.uk
Website: www.crowncountryinn.co.uk

 **Hobson's Golden Glow, John Roberts XXX, Ludlow Brewery Boiling Well**

This is an honest-to-goodness pub, with a real sense of the countryside; its exposed beams, flagstone floors and inglenook fireplaces bearing witness to a longevity which includes time spent as a 'hundred house' for travelling magistrates. Its experienced owners have been here for nearly a decade, serving tasty food in the relaxed atmosphere of its snug bar and more formal restaurant. Their wide-ranging menu teems with dishes make from seasonal, locally sourced produce; it changes regularly but might include braised shoulder of local lamb, pavé of Hereford beef sirloin or the pub's own oak smoked Shropshire farm chicken breast. Local cheeses are listed in order of strength and flavour and there are often events such as the popular Pudding Club nights, where, as well as your main course, you get to devour half a dozen desserts. The three good value bedrooms are comfortable and individually styled with a pleasant country feel.

Closing times

Closed 25 December, Sunday dinner and Monday

Prices

Meals: à la carte £ 23/30

3 rooms: £ 55/90

Typical Dishes

Black pudding crostini
Slow-cooked belly pork
Warm spiced carrot cake

Between Much Wenlock and Craven Arms on B 4378. Parking.

England • West Midlands • Shropshire

19 The Fox

Pave Lane,
Chetwynd Aston, Newport TF10 9LQ
Tel.: (01952)815940 – Fax: (01952)815941
e-mail: fox@brunningandprice.co.uk **Website:** www.fox-newport.co.uk

 **Woods Shropshire Lad, Weetwood Cheshire Cat, Thwaites Original**

Despite being set in a small village, this spacious whitewashed pub attracts plenty of visitors – and it's easy to see why. Outside, chunky wooden furniture sits among pleasant gardens, while inside there's a large central bar surrounded by numerous characterful rooms of varying shapes and sizes. All are wood floored and adorned with an intriguing array of pictures and photographs but it's the bright barrel-ceilinged room that provides particular appeal. It does get busy, so it's advisable to book, or you could end up on the waiting list. Service is well-organised and friendly, although with no uniform, you could mistake some of the staff for customers. The extensive daily menu offers robust cooking, with light bites for the smaller appetite, as well as tasty, reliable classics including soups, salads, steaks and pies for the hungry. You have to get up and order at the bar but the hearty dishes that arrive soon reward your efforts.

Closing times
Open daily

Prices
Meals: à la carte £ 18/30

Typical Dishes
Potted salt beef
Braised shoulder of lamb
Chocolate & Shropshire stout cake

 *1½ mi south of Newport by A 41 (Wolverhampton rd). Parking.* 

20 Hundred House

Bridgnorth Rd,
Norton TF11 9EE
Tel.: (01952)580240 – Fax: (01952)580260
e-mail: reservations@hundredhouse.co.uk **Website:** www.hundredhouse.co.uk

   MC

 **Regularly changing ales such as Wem Brewery Shropshire Stout, Cherry Bomb, All Seasons Bitter**

Run for over twenty years by two generations of the Phillips family, this inn has a quirky style all of its own. History seems deeply ingrained into its web of rooms, with their tiled floors, open fires and oak panelling, and the dried herbs and hops hanging from ceilings add to the rustic flavour. Hearty food on the menus includes classics such as steak and kidney pie, venison casserole and sausage and mash, as well as dishes which take their influences from further afield, such as tapas, Thai green curry and Greek salad. Ingredients are sourced from local suppliers – and none more so than the inn's own beautiful herb and flower garden. The country style bedrooms offer comfort as well as character with features such as half testers and four posters; and if you enjoy swinging then you've come to the right place – thanks to the velvet covered seats artfully suspended from the beams in some of the rooms.

Closing times

Accommodation closed 25-26 December

Prices

Meals: à la carte £ 25/40

10 rooms: £ 61/133

Typical Dishes

Stilton stuffed mushrooms

Chicken curry

Pear & almond tart

7 mi south of Telford on A 442. Parking.

21 The Armoury

Victoria Quay,
Welsh Bridge, Shrewsbury SY1 1HH
Tel.: (01743)340525 – Fax: (01743)340526
e-mail: armoury@brunningandprice.co.uk **Website:** www.armoury-shrewsbury.co.uk

 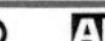

VISA MC AE

Thwaites, Weetwood Cheshire Cat, Three Tuns 1664, Cottage E-type, Shropshire Gold, Worfield OBJ, Goffs Jouster, Wem Rainbow Chaser

Situated just over the bridge from Shrewsbury's new Theatre Severn, this 18C former warehouse, by contrast, has a fascinating history. Built for military use, it's done service as a bakery and a World War II convalescent home, and even been moved brick by brick to this spot in sight of the old bridge, where it cries out for a bankside terrace to enjoy the summer sunshine. Inside, gilt-framed mirrors, engravings and Edwardiana cover the brick walls, yard upon yard of old books are rivalled only by row upon rows of malts and liqueurs behind the bar, and a huge ceiling and tall arched windows make the open-plan room feel light and spacious. Lots of big tables, with a hotch-potch of second-hand chairs, make it ideal for a big get-together: its great popularity means there's usually a buzzy atmosphere, and the daily changing menu of modern favourites offers something for everyone, from pan-fried snapper fillet to sausage and mash.

Closing times
Open daily

Prices
Meals: à la carte £ 19/32

Typical Dishes
Devilled mushrooms
Venison steak
Chocolate & orange Cointreau tart

By the Welsh Bridge. Frankwell car park over Welsh Bridge.

22 Hand and Cleaver

Butt Lane,
Ranton ST18 9JZ
Tel.: (01785)822367
e-mail: cathy@handandcleaver.co.uk **Website:** www.handandcleaver.co.uk

VISA MC AE

Black Sheep, Fuller's London Pride, Old Speckled Hen, Hancocks, Cottage Brewing Company

The trouble with running a pub as massive as the Hand and Cleaver is how on earth to fill it with customers. Despite its remote location away from the village centre, its owners are having no such problems and its reputation for good food and drink is drawing people in from near and far. Previously at The Buxhall Crown in Suffolk, the friendly couple have plenty of experience and, while he cooks up a storm in the kitchen, she makes sure everything flows smoothly out front. The pub dates from the mid 17C and boasts a snug bar, open fires and old beams; other elements of the décor, like the embossed plaster walls, Victorian-style lighting and wooden tables may make you feel as if you've stepped back into the '70s. The regularly changing menu features traditional dishes such as chicken liver pâté, fish and chips, chicken and leek pie or lamb chump, with tasty desserts like chocolate torte or bread and butter pudding with custard to follow.

Closing times
Closed Sunday dinner (in winter) and Monday (except bank holidays)

Prices
Meals: £ 15 (lunch) and à la carte £ 20/28

Typical Dishes
Pan-fried pigeon breast
Lamb chump
Malva pudding & cream

5 mi west of Stafford by minor roads. Frankwell car park opposite.

23 The Hand and Trumpet

Main Road, Wrinehill CW3 9BJ
Tel.: (01270)820048 – Fax: (01270)821911
e-mail: hand.and.trumpet@brunningandprice.co.uk
Website: www.hand-and-trumpet-wrinehill.co.uk

VISA MC

 **Deuchar's IPA, Salopian's Oracle, Hyde's Original, Wem's Cascade, Riverhead's Fools Ale, Weetwood's Cheshire Cat**

What better way to while away a summer's afternoon than sitting on the terrace of the Hand and Trumpet, overlooking the pleasant pond and tucking into a classic dish of sausage and mash or maybe a lighter offering, such fishcakes or salad of marinated lamb? The daily menus here offer plenty of choice and Veggies are also well catered for, with the likes of 'blue cheese and caramelised red onion bread and butter pudding' on the list. This sizeable pub is just as pleasant inside as out, with rug covered floorboards, open fires, bookshelves and all manner of pictures adorning the walls; and it's well worth the trip to the bar to watch your order being sucked into the intriguing pipe system and hurtled around the ceiling before plopping down into the kitchen. With plenty of room to spare, the tables are well-spaced – the larger ones often frequented by groups of local uni students. Good service is provided by a friendly, competent team.

Closing times
Closed 25 December

Prices
Meals: à la carte £ 19/28

Typical Dishes
Chicken, ham & liver terrine
Faggots & onion gravy
Sticky toffee pudding

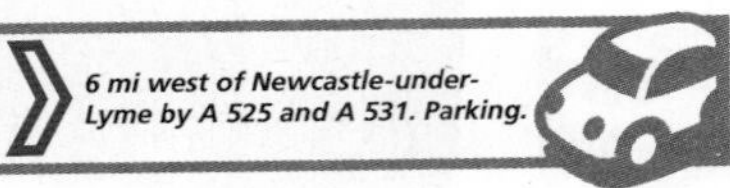
6 mi west of Newcastle-under-Lyme by A 525 and A 531. Parking.

24 The Baraset Barn

1 Pimlico Lane,
Alveston CV37 7RJ
Tel.: (01789)295510
e-mail: barasetbarn@lovelypubs.co.uk **Website:** www.lovelypubs.co.uk

 **Purity UBU**

A traditional-looking pub concealing a stylish, modern interior, the shimmering silvers and brushed velvet of its atmospheric lounge and intimate mezzanine blending well with its 200 year old flagstones, brick walls and wooden beams. The private dining room is a real feature and overlooks the main dining area, while the glass-fronted kitchen means that the chefs are on view hard at work. Perhaps a seat in the airy conservatory beckons or you fancy going al fresco on the contemporary continental-style terrace; this is an easy-going place with all day opening, and lingering lunches seem positively encouraged. Add a chirpy young team to the mix and you can see why they're popular – and all this before any mention of the food itself: cooking is assured and flavoursome and the modern menu offers something for everyone, from a simple Caesar salad, seared scallops or a sociable sharing plate to the more substantial steak or spit roast chicken.

Closing times
Closed Sunday dinner

Prices
Meals: £ 15 and à la carte £ 20/30

Typical Dishes
Devilled kidneys on toast
Roast duck with spiced orange sauce
Sticky toffee & date pudding

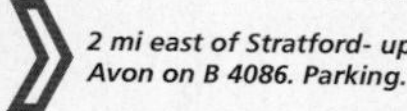

2 mi east of Stratford- upon-Avon on B 4086. Parking.

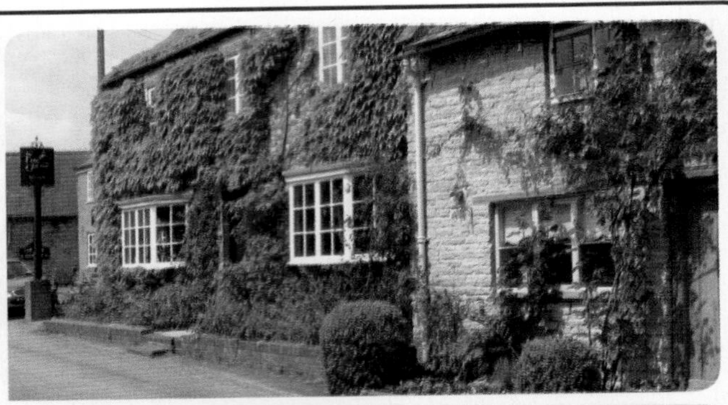

25 The Fox & Goose Inn

Front St, Armscote CV37 8DD
Tel.: (01608)682293 – Fax: (01608)682293
e-mail: mail@foxandgoosearmscote.co.uk
Website: www.foxandgoosearmscote.co.uk

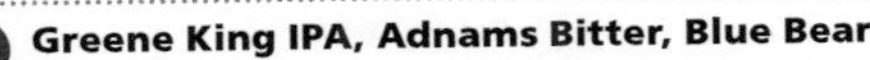

Greene King IPA, Adnams Bitter, Blue Bear Roar Spirit

Happily situated in the peaceful hamlet of Armscote, this creeper-clad, red brick inn has a more modern, slightly quirkier interior than its traditional outer appearance might suggest. The open-plan bar and dining room boast a log burner at their centre; there are cushions and candles – and even a stuffed fox chasing a goose along the mantelpiece. If you're here for a drink, try the locals snug, and if the temperature soars, head for the back garden and its decked terrace. Cooking is unfussy and flavoursome, the simple menu of classic dishes supplemented by an extensive blackboard menu of daily specials. Choices might include homemade beef and Butcombe ale pie or steak and chips and the friendly service fits the atmosphere perfectly. Four compact and fun bedrooms are decorated on a Cluedo theme, with bold colour schemes of scarlet, mustard, plum and blue, while claw foot baths with candles bring a touch of luxury to proceedings.

Closing times
Open daily

Prices
Meals: à la carte £ 15/50
4 rooms: £ 30/110

Typical Dishes
Pork & chicken terrine
Roast Loch Duart salmon
Rhubarb crumble

2½ mi north of Shipston-on-Stour by A 3400. Parking.

26 The King's Head

21 Bearley Rd,
Aston Cantlow B95 6HY
Tel.: (01789)488242 – Fax: (01789)488137
e-mail: reservations@thekh.co.uk **Website:** www.thekh.co.uk

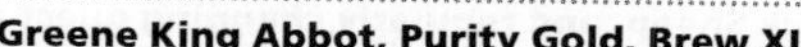 **Greene King Abbot, Purity Gold, Brew XI**

People purportedly travel to this pretty pub from quite a distance to enjoy the now revived duck suppers for which the pub was formerly famous. They are not its only claim to fame, however, since in 1557, Shakespeare's parents reputedly held their wedding reception here. Would the wedding banquet have involved the wild venison casserole, the pheasant or the saddle of rabbit? We can only speculate; although it's probably safe to say that they would not have feasted on the pork Yuk Sung or tomato risotto now also on offer. The abstract art hanging on the walls brings a contemporary touch to the restaurant, while the tables and cushion-clad chairs would not look out of place in a French farmhouse. With its low, heavily beamed ceiling, flag stoned floors and large stone fireplaces, the main lounge bar is equally as charming, while if it's privacy you're after, there are also several smaller nooks in which to make yourself cosy.

Closing times
Closed 25 December

Prices
Meals: £ 15 and à la carte £ 15/25

Typical Dishes
Baked goats cheese
Duck breast
Dark chocolate truffle cake

3 mi south of Henley-in-Arden off B 4089. Parking.

27 The Chequers Inn

91 Banbury Rd, Ettington CV37 7SR
Tel.: (01789)740387
e-mail: hello@the-chequers-ettington.co.uk
Website: www.the-chequers-ettington.co.uk

Black Sheep, and regularly changing guest ales such as Sharp's Doom Bar, Hardy & Hanson's Olde Trip

The signs outside scream country gastropub but to assume so would be off the mark; with its chandeliers, brushed velvet furniture and round-backed Regency chairs, this place is anything but formulaic; indeed its individual interior comes as a welcome surprise. The bar is a popular spot with villagers, no doubt pleased with the large selection of beers as well as their local's transformation from run down boozer to smart, contemporary inn. A further draw comes in the form of the food: tasty dishes such as slow braised belly pork with chorizo and white beans, or grilled sea bass fillets with sautéed fennel, sun blushed tomatoes and aubergine tapenade show the kitchen's ability to cleverly combine flavours; dishes come exactly as described on the menu, so a side dish is generally required. Local ingredients are well used, from the Stratford sourced meat to the mustard from Tewkesbury. Friendly service completes the package.

Closing times
Closed Sunday dinner and Monday

Prices
Meals: à la carte £ 18/27

Typical Dishes
Wood pigeon breast
Braised belly pork & beans
Trio of chocolate

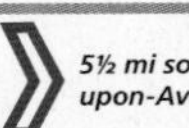

5½ mi southeast of Stratford-upon-Avon by A 422. Parking.

28 The Fox & Hounds Inn

Great Wolford CV36 5NQ
Tel.: (01608)674220
e-mail: enquiries@thefoxandhoundsinn.com
Website: www.thefoxandhoundsinn.com

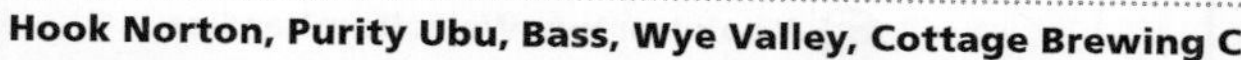

Hook Norton, Purity Ubu, Bass, Wye Valley, Cottage Brewing Co

A warm and welcoming family-run pub, where dried hops hang from the ceiling, a log burner nestles in the inglenook, flickering candles create a cosy atmosphere…and a stuffed fox watches your every move. Ivy-clad and set back from the road, its quintessential English character makes this the perfect Cotswolds stop-off when the fuel gauge in your bread basket reaches empty. Jamie, the chef, is passionate about growing his own vegetables, herbs and salad and sources as many of his ingredients as possible locally, so Dexter beef comes from the nearby village of Chastleton, venison hails from Todenham and seasonal game is gleaned from local shoots. The concise blackboard menu allows him to retain the freshness of the dishes whilst demonstrating his sound culinary understanding and his bold, wholesome cooking benefits from a pure style, entertaining no extraneous ingredients or flavours. Bedrooms are simple and neat, with a spacious feel.

Closing times

Closed 6-20 January for meals, Sunday dinner and Monday

Prices

Meals: à la carte £ 26/40

3 rooms: £ 50/80

Typical Dishes

Dexter beef Bresaola
Roe deer & cabbage
Rhubarb & ginger crumble

4 mi northeast of Moreton-in-Marsh by A 44. Parking.

29 The Halford Bridge

Fosse Way,
Halford CV36 5BN

Tel.: (01789)748217 – Fax: (01789)748159
e-mail: su@thehalfordbridge.co.uk **Website:** www.thehalfordbridge.co.uk

VISA MC AE

Hook Norton, Wells Bombardier

This imposing stone building set on the Fosse Way dates from 1567, its wide central archway a reminder of its former life as a stop off point for coach and horses travelling the famous Roman road. On sunny days, cross the cobbles to the enclosed courtyard. Head right for the atmospheric bar and lounge with its ornately carved furniture, or left for the dining room. Classic combinations are given a personal twist on the seasonally changing menu, so your steak might come with stilton stuffed vine tomatoes or duck breast might be served on a mushroom and lentil ragout. Service from local staff is everything it should be: enthusiastic, chatty and well organised. When it comes to the bedrooms, it seems the team here have gone a bit nuts; and as is the case with their nutty namesakes, the rooms vary greatly in shape and size. Most have wooden beams, which lend a characterful feel; choose one at the back to minimise noise from the road.

Closing times

Closed Sunday dinner

Prices

Meals: £ 14 (Monday-Thursday) and à la carte £ 16/25

10 rooms: £ 75

Typical Dishes

Garlic bread
Rib-eye steak
Sticky toffee pudding

9 mi north of Moreton in Marsh by A 429. Parking.

30 The Howard Arms

Lower Green,
Ilmington CV36 4LT

Tel.: (01608)682226 – Fax: (01608)682874
e-mail: info@howardarms.com **Website:** www.howardarms.com

Old Hooky Hook Norton, Purity Brewing Co, Pigbrook North Cotswold Brewery

This warm gold stone inn, situated on the green of a peaceful village, is the very essence of the English country pub. Outside there's a pleasant terrace and garden, while inside there's character aplenty, in the form of gleaming flag floors, wood beams and an inglenook fireplace. With a whole host of local suppliers, you can expect to find regional produce on your plate, including fruit and vegetables from Ebrington and herbs from the pub's own garden. Menus err towards the traditional and dishes might include duck liver and sage paté or asparagus and rocket risotto, followed by calves liver and bacon, tender Cotswold lamb neck fillet or steak and chips. Desserts could include warm strawberry jam Bakewell tart, lemon and lime posset or sticky toffee pudding. The original bedrooms are cosy, featuring antique furniture and designer fabrics, and one even has wooden beams. The new rooms in the extension to the rear are more contemporary.

Closing times

Closed 25 December dinner

Prices

Meals: à la carte £ 20/31

8 rooms: £ 85/140

Typical Dishes

Duck liver & sage paté
Beef & ale pie
Sticky toffee pudding

4 mi northwest of Shipston-on-Stour, in the centre of the village. Parking.

31 The Boot Inn

Old Warwick Rd,
Lapworth B94 6JU
Tel.: (01564)782464
e-mail: bootinn@hotmail.com **Website:** www.lovelypubs.co.uk

  MC AE

Fuller's London Pride, Old Speckled Hen, Hobgoblin

Make sure you book ahead if you want to eat at the Boot; it gets deservedly busy despite – or even perhaps because of - its village location, close to the junction of the Grand Union and Stratford-upon-Avon canals. The front pub area, with its central bar and surrounding warren of little nooks and crannies, has a cosy, rustic feel to it, whilst the large main dining room, with its wooden floor and stylish décor, is on a different level, both literally and metaphorically. On sunny days, the favoured seats are those in the garden, but wherever you sit, the welcome is a warm one, and the service from t-shirted staff is friendly and attentive. The modern menus contain a mix of classics that take you on a gastronomical tour around Europe and beyond, so you'll find plates of a Baltic or Iberian flavour to share, and dishes such as pie of the day or steak alongside pot au feu or crispy oriental duck salad.

Closing times
Open daily
Booking essential
Prices
Meals: à la carte £ 18/25

Typical Dishes
Smoked haddock gratin
Rump of lamb
Belgian waffles

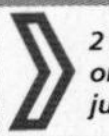

2 mi southeast of Hockley Heath on B 4439; on the left hand side just before the village. Parking.

32 **The Red Lion**

Long Compton CV36 5JS
Tel.: (01608)684221 – Fax: (01608)684968
e-mail: info@redlion-longcompton.co.uk
Website: www.redlion-longcompton.co.uk

Adnams Broadside, Hook Norton Old Hooky and Hooky Bitter

With its flag floors and log fires, this 18C former coaching inn retains the character of a country pub, and its stylish interior boasts a warm, modern feel. There are various rooms in which to dine – plus a well tended garden and terrace out the back for sunny days – and regular quiz nights and monthly live acoustic music attract a local crowd. The seasonal menu offers classic pub dishes like homemade steak and Hook Norton pie, pan-fried calves liver and fish and chips, with old favourites like rhubarb crumble or warm chocolate fudge cake for dessert. These are tasty, home-cooked dishes from the tried-and-tested school of cooking – so if you had something a little more adventurous in mind, try the daily specials board instead. Staff are pleasant and smartly attired; Cocoa, the chocolate Labrador, also gives a warm welcome. Bedrooms may be slightly on the small side, but are stylish and contemporary, with a good level of facilities.

Closing times
Open daily

Prices
Meals: £ 15 (dinner) and à la carte £ 25/32
5 rooms: £ 55/90

Typical Dishes
Smoked haddock
Steak & Hook Norton pie
Hazelnut cream & raspberry pavlova

5 mi north of Chipping Norton by A 3400. Parking.

35 The Crabmill

Claverdon,
Preston Bagot B95 5EE
Tel.: (01926)843342 – Fax: (01926)843989
e-mail: thecrabmill@lovelypubs.co.uk **Website:** www.thecrabmill.co.uk

 **Greene King Abbot Ale, Purity UBU, Tetleys**

This pub's beautifully timbered exterior hints at its rural character and the various rooms are a charming mix of old and new; ancient beams blending seamlessly with contemporary chocolate and pink décor. By day, the summer room sofas make a great spot for a casual lunch; by night no meals are served here, but it remains a relaxing lounge space, with plenty of papers and magazines to keep you occupied, should conversation idle. Table 6 is one of the most popular, table 1 will suit a group, while on summer days, only a seat on the summer terrace or in the garden will suffice. The modern Mediterranean menu offers generous portions of dishes such as lamb kofta, pork saltimbocca or braised shoulder of beef; specials often involve fish, and lunchtime means more than just sandwiches; with falafels, hummus and tzatziki with pitta bread, or slow cooked bolognaise alongside ploughman's and paninis. Polite service can struggle at busier times.

1 mi east of Henley-in-Arden on A 4189. Parking.

Closing times

Closed 25 December, dinner 26 December, 1 January and Sunday

Booking essential

Prices

Meals: £ 13 (dinner) and à la carte £ 25/30

Typical Dishes

Bubble & squeak
Sea bass fillets, crayfish spaghetti
Lemon posset

33 The Bell Inn

The Green,
Tanworth-in-Arden B94 5AL
Tel.: (01564)742212
e-mail: thebell@realcoolbars.com **Website:** www.thebellattanworthinarden.co.uk

Timothy Taylor Landlord, Black Sheep

With its squashy sofas and leather bar stools, The Bell's much modernised, boldly stylish interior has a cool and relaxed feel. Its open log fire and rich wood furniture and panelling help it to retain an essence of homeliness, however; and the Morris dancers occasionally seen shaking their hankies and sticks on the village green opposite add to the authentic villagey feel of the place, as do the small shop and the post office in the corner. The décor may be mostly modern, but the cooking is quite classic in style, with dishes like sausage and mash or braised lamb shank – and fish is a particular speciality. Theme nights and wine tasting evenings bring in a local crowd, and there are some comfy seats round the bar if you've just come for a drink. Overnight stays here are popular with those visiting the NEC. Opt for a front-facing, newer bedroom; all are individually decorated, with sleek, minimal styling and contemporary furniture.

Closing times
Closed Sunday dinner

Prices
Meals: £ 15 and à la carte £ 18/27

9 rooms: £ 50/120

Typical Dishes
Sauté chicken livers
Grilled seabass, creamed leeks
Local cheese board

4½ mi northwest of Henley-in-Arden by A 3400 and Tanworth Road; close to church. Parking.

34 The Bell Inn

Binton Rd,
Welford-on-Avon CV37 8EB
Tel.: (01789)750353 – Fax: (01789)750893
e-mail: info@thebellwelford.co.uk **Website:** www.thebellwelford.co.uk

VISA AE

Purity Gold & UBU, Hooky Bitter, Hobson's Best, Flowers Original (OB)

Visitors fanning out from Stratford strike lucky when they come across this part 17C redbrick inn. If it's the summer months, they can flop down at The Bell's enticingly attractive wood-furnished outside terrace with its array of hanging baskets. Or step inside, any time of year, and admire the flagged and beamed bar, glowing fire and rustic knick-knacks. Various other rooms mean there's space to breathe in here, with a range of tables, chairs and pews to stretch out at: the recently refurbished glass roofed dining room is maybe the most stylish place to eat. Local produce is very much to the fore, with local suppliers' names printed on the back of the menus. These offer a good balance of modern British and classic cuisine. They change a couple of times a year, and are supplemented by an extensive range of daily specials.

Closing times
Open daily

Prices
Meals: à la carte £ 21/30

Typical Dishes
Cherry tomato tarte Tatin
Sea bass, bloody Mary sauce
Sticky toffee pudding

4 mi west of Stratford-upon-Avon by B 439 and a lefthand turn south. Parking.

36 The White Horse

Kenilworth Road,
Balsall Common CV7 7DT
Tel.: (01676)533207 – Fax: (01676)532827
e-mail: info@thewhitehorseatbc.co.uk **Website:** www.thewhitehorseatbc.co.uk

 **Greene King IPA, Jennings Cumberland Ale, Wells Bombardier**

Modernity strikes the Midlands in the form of this monumental pub – part of the Metro Group – which, having undergone refurbishment, now boasts a spacious bar lounge with low-backed leather tub chairs, art-adorned walls and a distinctive feel. The L-shaped dining area is as good as divided in three; the conservatory part being the best in which to sit, unless the British weather is uncharacteristically fine, in which case head for either the decked front terrace or the rear paved one. The menu has a universal appeal, as attested to by the pub's popularity, and dishes are freshly prepared, with care and understanding. Meat comes from the Midland's finest; Aubrey Allen, with spit roast chickens from the pub's rotisserie particularly worth a go. Old favourites like fish pie and toad in the hole are here, as is the odd European flavour, with dishes such as lamb koftas or spaghetti. Portions are generous so two courses should suffice.

Closing times
Open daily

Prices
Meals: à la carte £ 18/25

Typical Dishes
Black pudding salad
Steak, Guinness & mushroom pudding
Apple crumble

5 mi northwest of Kenilworth by A 452. Parking.

37 The Malt Shovel

Barston Lane,
Barston B92 0JP
Tel.: (01675)443223 – Fax: (01675)443223
Website: www.themaltshovelatbarston.com

 **St Austell Tribute, Wells Bombardier**

It's not far from Solihull and the M42, yet this sizeable ivy-clad, cream-washed pub, feels a world away from hectic city life. To the rear there's a small pine-furnished patio and a huge garden strewn with picnic benches, where colourful shrubs and hanging baskets abound. This is the perfect place to sit on a warm summer's day, but inside it's just as pleasant, with a rustic bar boasting tiled sasso flooring, open fires and stripped pine tables, and the kitchen partly on display at one end. Here you'll find a wide-ranging menu of freshly prepared, seasonal dishes with a traditional base – and plenty of seafood on display. If you're after a more formal experience, then head to the stylish restaurant in the converted barn annexe, where you'll discover more elaborate set course dinner menu and daily fish specials. If you're celebrating there's a good selection of wines to consider, while the weekly changing ales keep the locals happy.

Closing times
Closed Sunday dinner

Prices
Meals: £ 25 (dinner) and à la carte £ 28

Typical Dishes
Seared scallops
Baked cod
Chocolate & almond bread & butter pudding

Off A 452 just south of Hampton-in-Arden; follow signs for Barston village. Parking.

38 The Orange Tree

Warwick Road,
Chadwick End B93 0BN
Tel.: (01564)785364 – Fax: (01564)782988
Website: www.lovelypubs.co.uk

 VISA

 **Greene King IPA, Old Hooky, Black Sheep**

Set in the small but affluent village of Chadwick End, this is a sizeable place – even without counting the neat lawned gardens and spacious terrace. Characterful country dining pub it is not: it's modern, contemporary and can get a tad on the loud side; and it does a pretty decent drinking trade too. The large bar is set over various levels, some with characterful wooden beams, all with comfy modern seating – and there's a dining room with chunky wooden tables, low backed chairs and leather banquettes. The same menu is served throughout, so you can choose your favourite spot and settle in. The wide-ranging menu has something for everyone, offering several dishes in a choice of sizes, as well as some sharing plates; there are salads, pizzas, pastas and grills, as well as the spit roast free range chicken with a choice of sauces, which is something of a speciality. Service is polite and friendly, if a little haphazard on occasion.

Closing times
Closed Sunday dinner
Booking essential

Prices
Meals: à la carte £ 18/24

Typical Dishes
Grilled gambas
Braised beef
Chocolate fondant

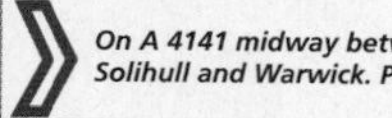

On A 4141 midway between Solihull and Warwick. Parking.

England's biggest county has a lot of room for the spectacular; it encapsulates the idea of desolate beauty. The bracing winds of the Dales whistle through glorious meadows and deep, winding valleys, while the vast moors are fringed with picturesque country towns like Thirsk, Helmsley and Pickering. Further south the charming Wolds roll towards the sea, enhanced by such Georgian gems as Beverley and Howden. Popular history sits easily here: York continues to enchant with its ancient walls and Gothic Minster, but, owing to its Brontë links, visitors descend on the cobbled street village of Haworth with as much enthusiasm. Steam railways criss-cross the region's bluff contours, while drivers get a more streamlined thrill on the Humber Bridge. Yorkshire's food and drink emporiums range from quaintly traditional landmarks like the country tearoom and fish and chip shops proudly proclaiming to be the best in England, to warm and characterful pubs serving heart-warming local specialities.

North East
North West
YORKSHIRE
Yorkshire Dales National Park
Peak District National Park
NORTH YORKSHIRE
Middleton-in-Teesdale
Appleby
Brough
Barnard Castle
Bishop Auckland
Newton Aycliffe
Stockton-on-Tees
Darlington
Bowes
Kirkby Stephen
Eaglescliffe
Scotch Corner
Richmond
Reeth
Swale
Leyburn
Hawes
Bedale
Thirsk
Ullswater
Patterdale
Shap
Orton
Tebay
Windermere
Kendal
Sedbergh
Whernside
Kirkby Lonsdale
Ingleton
Clapham
Lune
Lancaster
Settle
Threshfield
Wharfe
Ure
Ripon
Pateley Bridge
Fountains Abbey
Knaresborough
Gisburn
Skipton
Ilkley
Otley
Harewood
Ribble
Clitheroe
Colne
Keighley
Bingley
Blackburn
Padiham
Nelson
Burnley
BRADFORD
LEEDS
Accrington
Halifax
Garforth
Castleford
Darwen
Chorley
Rawtenstall
Todmorden
Brighouse
Rochdale
Dewsbury
Wakefield
Bury
Bolton
Oldham
Huddersfield
Holmfirth
Barnsley
Wigan
Leigh
MANCHESTER
Ashton-under-Lyne
St. Helens
Glossop
Stocksbridge
Conisbrough
Altrincham
Hyde
Stockport
High Peak
SHEFFIELD
Widnes
Knutsford
Whaley Bridge
Castleton
Frodsham
Northwich
Wilmslow
Chapel-en-le-Frith
Dronfield
Staveley
Macclesfield
Buxton
Baslow
Winsford
Chatsworth House
Tarporley
Middlewich
Congleton
Bakewell
Sandbach
Crewe
Little Moreton Hall
Clay Cross

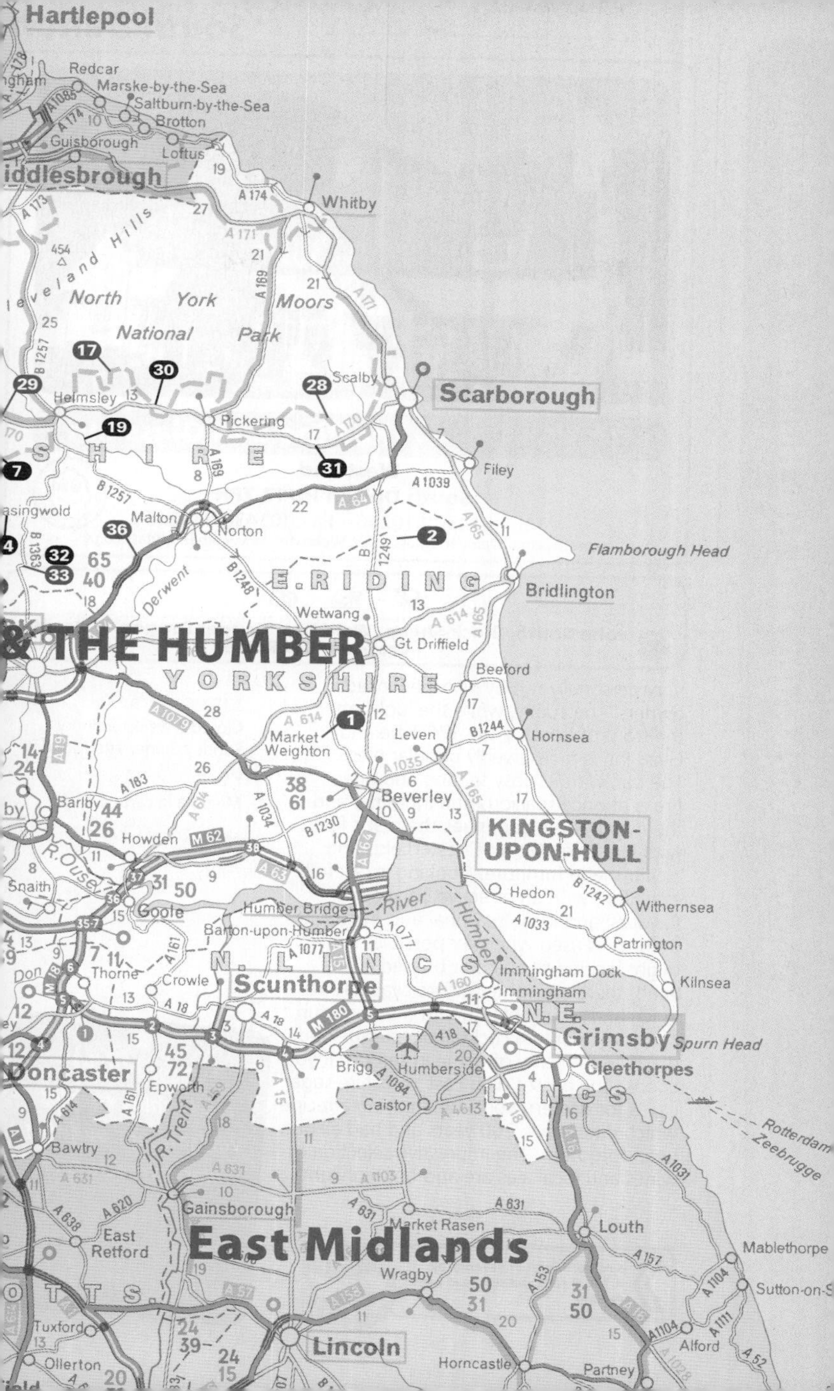

Hartlepool
Redcar
Marske-by-the-Sea
Saltburn-by-the-Sea
Brotton
Guisborough
Loftus
iddlesbrough
Whitby
Cleveland Hills
North York Moors
National Park
Scalby
Scarborough
Helmsley
Pickering
Filey
Malton
Norton
Flamborough Head
Bridlington
E. RIDING
Derwent
Wetwang
Gt. Driffield
& THE HUMBER
YORKSHIRE
Beeford
Market Weighton
Leven
Hornsea
Beverley
Barlby
Howden
KINGSTON-UPON-HULL
R. Ouse
Snaith
Goole
Humber Bridge
River Humber
Hedon
Withernsea
Barton-upon-Humber
Patrington
Thorne
Crowle
N. LINCS
Scunthorpe
Immingham Dock
Immingham
Kilnsea
N. E.
Grimsby
Spurn Head
Doncaster
Epworth
Brigg
Humberside
Cleethorpes
Caistor
LINCS
R. Trent
Bawtry
Rotterdam
Zeebrugge
Gainsborough
Market Rasen
Louth
East Retford
East Midlands
Mablethorpe
Wragby
Sutton-on-S
NOTTS.
Tuxford
Lincoln
Alford
Ollerton
Horncastle
Partney

1 The Pipe and Glass Inn

West End,
South Dalton HU17 7PN
Tel.: (01430)810246 – Fax: (01430)810246
e-mail: email@pipeandglass.co.uk **Website:** www.pipeandglass.co.uk

Inspectors' favourites

John Smith, Black Sheep, Wold Top, Copper Dragon, Daleside, Cropton, Old Rosie

Very personally run by its experienced owners – he cooks, while she looks after the front of house – the 17C Pipe and Glass Inn is a deservedly popular place. The bar, with its cosy seating and open fire is at once spacious and intimate, and the dining room continues the rustic feel, with low level leather Chesterfields and locally made furniture. Cooking is carefully executed, with an effective balance of flavours, and local, seasonal and traceable produce is used wherever possible. Dishes might include sea bass or braised crispy lamb; there are lighter dishes available at lunch and a daily blackboard menu of pub classics like prawn cocktail or sausage and mash, with plenty of game in season. If you choose the posset with East Yorkshire sugar cakes for dessert, you'll be enjoying a recipe which dates back 200 years and had all but been forgotten. The impressive selection of wines and local ales are another highlight.

Closing times

Closed 2 weeks January, Sunday dinner and Monday

Prices

Meals: à la carte £ 18/40

Typical Dishes

Wild rabbit rissoles
Venison suet pudding
Warm treacle tart

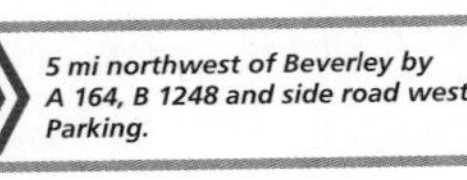

5 mi northwest of Beverley by A 164, B 1248 and side road west. Parking.

2 The Falling Stone

Main St,
Thwing YO25 3DS
Tel.: (01262)470403

 **John Smith Cask, Theakston XB, Woldtop Falling Stone, Courage Directors**

Named after a meteorite which dropped from the skies here many years ago, this brick built pub was taken over by new owners in 2007 – Peter is to be found behind the bar, while Ros takes care of front of house – and they have made it very much a part of village life, with regular quiz and theme nights. Go through the door on your right and you enter a small bar with an open fire and hunting themed pictures on the walls; take the left door for the comfortable, traditionally furnished lounge area – great for pre-dinner drinks – and a smart linen-clad restaurant. The same blackboard menu of classic pub dishes is served throughout and choices might include gammon and egg or pie and chips as well steaks and altogether more wholesome soups. This is a pub that takes its beer seriously and there's a fine selection of local ales from the Wold Brewery, including some very good bitter. Service is polite and friendly and the ambience relaxed.

Closing times
Closed Sunday dinner and Tuesday

Prices
Meals: £ 7/18 and à la carte £ 14/25

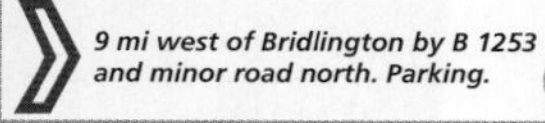
9 mi west of Bridlington by B 1253 and minor road north. Parking.

3 Crab and Lobster

Dishforth Rd,
Asenby YO7 3QL

Tel.: (01845)577286 – Fax: (01845)577109
e-mail: reservations@crabandlobster.co.uk **Website:** www.crabandlobster.com

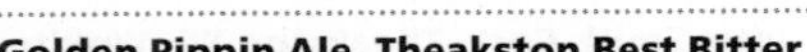
Golden Pippin Ale, Theakston Best Bitter

From the moment you set eyes on this pub, you'll realise it's no ordinary place. Thatched crabs and lobsters sit on the roof, old advertisements and lobster pots hang from the walls, and an old lampppost and thatched umbrellas stand proudly outside. Inside it's just as quirky, with charming exposed beams hung with knick-knacks aplenty and all kinds of characterful memorabilia strewn over every surface; and if that's not enough to keep you entertained, there are monthly jazz and theme nights too. The same menu is served in both the bar and dining room, and, unsurprisingly, features plenty of seafood. You'll find the likes of fish soup, scallops, fishcakes, oysters, fish pie and lobster, alongside traditional British dishes such as cheese soufflé, pork cheek confit and crusted loin of lamb. Split between an 18C Georgian Manor and log cabins, the stylish bedrooms are themed around famous hotels of the world; some boast private hot tubs.

Closing times
Open daily

Prices
Meals: £ 13/35
and à la carte £ 25/52

14 rooms: £ 100/230

Typical Dishes
Baked Queenies
Fish & chips
Sticky toffee & vanilla ice cream

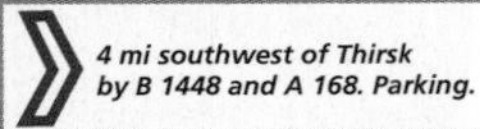
4 mi southwest of Thirsk by B 1448 and A 168. Parking.

4 George and Dragon Inn

Aysgarth DL8 3AD
Tel.: (01969)663358 – Fax: (01969)633773
e-mail: ganddinn@hotmail.com **Website:** www.ganddinn.com

Black Sheep Bitter, Golden Sheep, Theakston, John Smith Cask, Yorkshire Dales Brewery

Set in prime walking country, in the heart of the National Park and close to the breathtaking waterfalls of the River Ure, this 17C coaching inn makes the perfect base for exploring Wensleydale and its famous creamery. This is a proper pub in all senses of the word: there's not a games machine or plasma screen in sight and if you've made yourself comfy in the laid-back bar, you're welcome to settle in for the night, dinner and all. For a more structured experience there's a Victorian themed dining room, and the patio offers great views of Pen Hill when it's warm enough to sit outside. Lunch ranges from sandwiches and pub classics to a good value set three courses, so you might find anything from fishcakes to pan-fried salmon. Dinner offers more substantial seasonal dishes such as pigeon breast, lamb rump or pork in Parma ham. Bedrooms are individually styled, comfy and well priced. One boasts a four-poster, another, a whirlpool bath.

Closing times
Open daily

Prices
Meals: £ 13/26
and à la carte £ 18/30
7 rooms: £ 40/90

Typical Dishes
King scallops
Pan-fried sea bass fillets
Crème brûlée

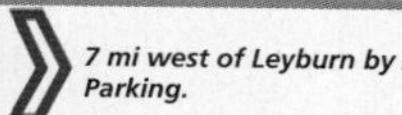
7 mi west of Leyburn by A 684.
Parking.

England • Yorkshire and The Humber • North Yorkshire

5 The Bull

Broughton BD23 3AE

Tel.: (01756)792065 – Fax: (01756)792065

e-mail: enquiries@ribblevalleyinns.com **Website:** www.thebullatbroughton.co.uk

 VISA MC

Hetton Pale Ale, Timothy Taylor Landlord

In 2009 The Bull became the fourth member of Ribble Valley Inns – but don't expect some sort of faceless corporate brand – this is the bourgeoning pub company set up by Nigel Haworth and Craig Bancroft, co-proprietors of Lancashire's celebrated Northcote. They have led the way in promoting the specialities of their region and The Bull is no different. You can expect real ales, local meats and cheeses, as well as traditional British dishes, rediscovered classics and the sort of puddings that make you feel proud and patriotic. The Bull is an appropriate moniker as this pub is big and solid looking. It's at the side of Broughton Hall and its extensive estate, as well as being close to the delightful market town of Skipton. Inside is made up of assorted snugs and spaces, with beams, stone floors and log fires. However cosy as it is in winter, it is an equally charming pub on a summer's day, thanks to its large rear terrace.

Closing times

Open daily

Prices

Meals: à la carte £ 20/30

Typical Dishes

Yorkshire pudding

Venison escalope & dock pudding

Frumenty

3 mi west of Skipton on A 69. In the grounds of Broughton Hall Country Park Estate. Parking.

6 The Red Lion

Burnsall BD23 6BU
Tel.: (01756)720204 – Fax: (01756)720292
e-mail: redlion@daelnet.co.uk **Website:** www.redlion.co.uk

Timothy Taylor, Theakston, Copper Dragon

At the heart of the small rural community of Burnsall, on the banks of the River Wharfe, lies this stone built, ivy-clad inn; a historical haven for diners, fresh from fishing, walking, hunting, touring or business. With reputedly haunted cellars dating from the 12C, and a panelled bar – formerly a Ferryman's inn dating from the 16C – there's certainly plenty of character imprinted in this inn's creaking beams. Two comfortable lounge areas are perfect for relaxing or for a spot of lunch, while the traditionally furnished restaurant is perfect for dinner. Lunchtimes might see sandwiches, meatballs and chickpea fritters on offer while an evening menu might include locally shot game casserole or free range calves liver. Bedrooms come in various shapes and sizes but the original rooms have the most character, with beams, sloping floors, uneven walls and antique furniture. The newer rooms, though less individual, also have good facilities.

Closing times
Open daily

Prices
Meals: £ 32 (dinner) and à la carte £ 20/35

25 rooms: £ 60/150

Typical Dishes
Warm lamb fillet salad
Roast cod loin
Bakewell tart & ice cream

7 mi north of Bolton Abbey by B 6160. Parking.

7 The Abbey Inn

Byland Abbey YO61 4BD
Tel.: (01347)868204 – Fax: (01347)868678
e-mail: abbeyinn@english-heritage.org.uk
Website: www.bylandabbeyinn.co.uk

Black Sheep, Timothy Taylor

With stones borrowed from the beautiful 12C Cistercian Abbey and evidence of a medieval hostelry underfoot, this delightful period inn is steeped in history. Set in a breathtaking location, it displays heritage colours, stone walls, flag flooring and historic documents aplenty, with intimate front rooms looking out to the Abbey, and a larger Victorian-Gothic themed room boasting a large glass roof. Cooking is seasonal and local, employing simple techniques to allow natural flavours to show through; it ranges from light bites and a set menu at lunch to a more substantial à la carte supplemented by specials in the evening. This may include tian of crab with pink grapefruit or tea-smoked venison with pickled rhubarb, followed by rack of Swaledale lamb or East Coast Whiting, with sweet Yorkshire or vanilla milk pudding for dessert. Charming bedrooms, two with Abbey views, boast spacious, luxurious bathrooms and Mousey Thompson furnishings.

6 mi southwest of Helmsley by A 170 and minor road south; opposite the ruins of Byland Abbey. Parking.

Closing times

Closed 24 December dinner, 25 December, 31 December dinner, 1 January, Sunday dinner, Monday and Tuesday

Booking essential

Prices

Meals: £ 16 (dinner) and à la carte £ 19/26

3 rooms: £ 69/149

Typical Dishes

Duck liver parfait
Pan-fried sea trout
Yorkshire trifle

8 Carlton Bore

Carlton Husthwaite,
YO7 2BW
Tel.: (01845)501265
e-mail: chefhessel@aol.com **Website:** www.carltonbore.co.uk

Golden Bore Bitter, John Smith's, Hambleton Ales, Timothy Taylor Landlord

Sister to the Old Bore in West Yorkshire, this spacious 17C inn is situated at the heart of a delightful stone and brick built village, with pleasant countryside views. The owner's experience shines through here, especially in the kitchen, where they have a passion for local ingredients and try hard to source only Yorkshire based produce. Suppliers are recognised in a list on the menu or next to the dishes which they have contributed to, and some are even depicted in caricatures on the pub walls. The à la carte is immensely appealing, featuring dishes such as monkfish fillet, trio of lamb or steak and kidney pudding topped with oysters, as well as pub classics like fish and chips and desserts like brioche bread and butter pudding. For those watching the pennies, the fixed price credit crunch menu is the sensible choice, but with three boar's heads watching over you and food like this, there's no shortage of reasons for you to pig out.

Closing times

Closed first 2 weeks in January, Monday and Tuesday

Prices

Meals: £ 15 (lunch) and à la carte £ 22/30

Typical Dishes

Blue Wensleydale fritters
Crispy belly pork
Rhubarb jelly & flackjacks

5 mi southeast of Thirsk off A 19. Parking.

9 Foresters Arms

Carlton-in-Coverdale DL8 4BB
Tel.: (01969)640272 – Fax: (01969)640272
e-mail: cjchambers100@hotmail.com
Website: www.forestersarms-carlton.co.uk

John Smith Cask, Black Sheep, Daleside, Wensleydale, Yorkshire Dales Brewing Co

Whether you've built up an appetite walking, grouse shooting or having fun fighting folly at the Forbidden Corner, the Foresters Arms will provide welcome sustenance and an open fire by which to warm yourself. Situated at the entrance of the rural village of Carlton, this small, stone-built pub has two characterful, picture-filled, flag-floored rooms in which to eat, plus a formal beamed dining room which is open in the evenings, and seats outside for sunny afternoons. The welcome and the service are friendly, and the keen owners have put the emphasis here firmly onto the food, with traditional home-cooked dishes, made wherever possible with locally sourced ingredients. Specials are chalked up on the blackboard by the bar and you can choose between dishes such as Roe deer steak, pheasant breast or seafood parcel. Three rooms offer a comfortable bed for the night; décor ranges from cottage-style to modern.

Closing times

Limited hours in winter

Prices

Meals: à la carte £ 15/20

3 rooms: £ 65/79

Typical Dishes

Black pudding salad
Smoked haddock potato cake
Apricot & almond cake

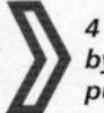

4 ½ mi southwest of Middleham by Coverdale rd. Parking next to pub in village car park.

10 Fox and Hounds

Carthorpe DL8 2LG
Tel.: (01845)567433 – Fax: (01845)567155
e-mail: helenjt36@btinternet.com
Website: www.foxandhoundscarthorpe.co.uk

 **Black Sheep Bitter, Worthington's beers**

If you like a bit of history with your main course, then this ivy-clad stone pub could be the place for you. Photos, curios and old farming equipment cover every available surface, and there's an old water pump and anvil on display – the pub having started life several centuries ago as the village smithy. Set close to the A1, it's been serving travellers for over 200 years, the last 26 of them under the watchful eye of the Fitzgerald/Taylor family. When it comes to eating, there's a huge array of choice, both on the daily specials and the à la carte. Husband and wife work together in the kitchen, preparing tasty dishes from well sourced local produce; fish from Hartlepool, meat from the butcher in Bedale, flour grown and milled in Yorkshire, and dairy products from the local village dairy – and if you fancy taking a little bit of Yorkshire home with you, organic flour, honey, and homemade jams and chutneys are for sale behind the bar.

Closing times
Closed first week in January and Monday

Prices
Meals: £ 16 (lunch Tuesday-Thursday & dinner daily) and à la carte £ 19/30

Typical Dishes
Ham hock terrine
Baked whole sea bass
Sticky ginger pudding

9 mi north of Ripon by minor road via Wath and Kirklington. Parking.

11 Ye Old Sun Inn

Main Street,
Colton LS24 8EP
Tel.: (01904)744261
e-mail: kelly.mccarthy@btconnect.com **Website:** www.yeoldsuninn.co.uk

Timothy Taylor Landlord and Golden Best, Black Sheep Bitter, York Criterion, Deuchar's IPA

The demise of many a local post office has highlighted their importance in the local community, but Ye Old Sun Inn is a good example of how significant a role the pub plays in local life. This family-run pub does it all: from selling homemade produce from their small deli to holding cookery demonstrations. They are also great ambassadors for local suppliers, several of whom are name-checked on the menu. The open fires and rustic feel make this a very popular place with the local community, although race days at the Knavesmire bring a regular invasion of interlopers. The menus change monthly and are as seasonal as ever. Highlights on the main menu are the home-smoked salmon, local asparagus and 'plate of Burdass lamb'; but there is also a separate list of 'pub classics' from 30-day aged steaks to local sausages.Those not from these parts can take advantage of the three very smart bedrooms in the recently acquired house next door.

Closing times
Closed 26 December, 3 weeks in January and Monday lunch

Prices
Meals: £ 17 (lunch) and à la carte £ 20/30

3 rooms: £ 75/120

Typical Dishes
Yorkshire tapas
Trio of Gressingham duck
Spotted Dick and custard

3 mi northeast of Tadcaster by A 659 and A 64. Parking.

12 The Tiger Inn

Coneythorpe HG5 0RY
Tel.: (01423)863632 – Fax: (01423)330439
e-mail: ifgill@btinternet.com
Website: www.tiger-inn.co.uk

 **Black Sheep Bitter, Timothy Taylor Landlord & Golden Best**

A cuddly toy tiger surveys proceedings from his elevated position at one end of the bar, but despite an interesting theory about a travelling circus, no one seems sure of the origins of this red brick pub's unusual name. Atypical in name, yet traditional in nature, its style comes from the classic school of pub furnishing, with green wood panels, pew seating and countryside prints on the walls. Its front rooms, whose windows overlook the green, are where the locals gather for a drink; there's a beamed room ideal for larger groups, plus more formal dining rooms at the rear. Cooking is robust and hearty; with a modern take on a classic British menu, and fairly-priced dishes might include fish pie, boiled salt beef, Yorkshire hotpot or roast saddle of rabbit. The sweetly-named 'Soup made this morning' tells you all you need to know about the food's freshness; there are sandwiches and nibbles, plus a blackboard menu of mostly fish specials.

Closing times
Open daily

Prices
Meals: £ 17 and à la carte £ 17

Typical Dishes
Whitebait
Slow-roast shoulder of lamb
Apple crumble

 *5 mi northeast of Knaresborough by A 59 and minor road north. Parking.* 

13 Wyvill Arms

Constable Burton DL8 5LH
Tel.: (01677)450581

John Smith, Theakston, Black Sheep

As you approach this pub you might recognise the building immediately behind it: a large Elizabethan stately home set in 300 acres of parkland landscaped by Capability Brown: well, that's if you're a fan of the 2006 film adaptation of Kenneth Grahame's Wind in the Willows anyway. To the rear of this ivy-clad, stone-built pub you'll find pleasant gardens and a small sitting area overlooking fields full of sheep; while inside classical décor and rustically-themed furnishings provide a warm, intimate feel. For dining, there's a choice of seating areas: a small open-fired bar, a stone-floored area with banquettes and a more formal room with high-backed leather chairs. There's plenty of choice on the menu too, which features local, traceable Yorkshire produce in carefully prepared, classical dishes. You'll find tasty mature steaks, daily fish specials; and Nigel's Yorkshire puddings are a must on Sundays. Bedrooms are simple but well-kept.

Closing times
Open daily

Prices
Meals: à la carte £ 24/36

3 rooms: £ 55/75

Typical Dishes
Breast of pigeon salad
Fillet of lamb in herb crust
Double lemon tart

3½ mi east of Leyburn on A 684. Parking.

14 The Durham Ox

Westway,
Crayke YO61 4TE
Tel.: (01347)821506 – Fax: (01347)823326
e-mail: enquiries@thedurhamox.com **Website:** www.thedurhamox.com

   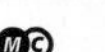 AE

 **Black Sheep, Timothy Taylor Landlord, Theakston's Bitter**

Set in a sleepy little hamlet, not far from Crayke Castle, the 300 year old Durham Ox is a bustling, family-run pub which boasts pleasant views over the vale of York and up towards the medieval church. You'll receive a warm welcome whether you to sit in the rustic flagstoned bar with its carved wooden panelling and vast inglenook fireplace, or the more formal beamed dining room; but when the weather's right, the rear courtyard is a the place to be. Exhibited around the country in the early 19C, the Durham Ox reached a weight of 270 stone at its peak. If you too, have the appetite of an ox, choose one of the hearty dishes from the regularly changing à la carte, which features plenty of fresh seafood, local meats and Crayke game as well as tasty chicken from the rotisserie. Set in converted farm cottages, the cosy bedrooms display original brickwork and quarry tiling; some are suites, some are set over two floors and some have jacuzzis.

Closing times
Closed 25 December dinner
Booking essential

Prices
Meals: à la carte £ 15/35
5 rooms: £ 80/150

Typical Dishes
Baked scallops
Sutton Bank rib-eye steak & frites
Steamed ginger pudding

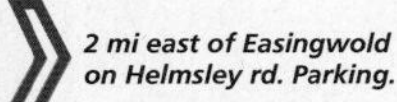

2 mi east of Easingwold on Helmsley rd. Parking.

15 The Travellers Rest

Dalton DL11 7HU
Tel.: (01833)621225
e-mail: annebabsa@aol.com

 **No cask ale offered**

A community needs a pub. Somewhere for locals to meet, to relax; to drink: perchance to dine. And the more remote the village it serves, the more important the pub. It may look fairly unassuming as you approach from Richmond, past various military shooting ranges, but The Traveller's Rest is one such pub. Anne greets her customers warmly and seemingly knows everyone by name; there is often a regular or three to be found in the bar – and the take away fish and chips nights go down a storm. If eating in, choose from the bar or one of two dining rooms; the first has quirky bookshelf wallpaper, while the second is more formal, with linen-clad tables. The menu is chalked up on blackboards and offers plenty of fresh, homemade dishes including the likes of fishcakes or Thai green curry as well as pub favourites like steak and chips. The homemade terrines are worth seeking out – while the duck with orange sauce remains a classic.

Closing times

Closed 25-26 December, 1 January, 1 week in November, dinner Sunday and Monday, lunch Monday-Saturday

Prices

Meals: à la carte £ 17/31

Typical Dishes

Pork & black pudding
King prawn stir fry
Raspberry & white chocolate cheesecake

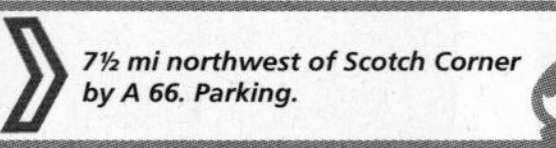

16 The Blue Lion

East Witton DL8 4SN
Tel.: (01969)624273 – Fax: (01969)624189
e-mail: enquiries@thebluelion.co.uk
Website: www.thebluelion.co.uk

  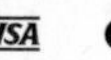

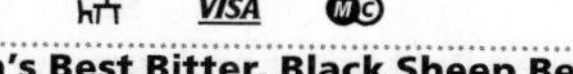

Theakston's Best Bitter, Black Sheep Best Bitter, Black Sheep Riggwelter

We all know a Red Lion but a Blue Lion? Well it's a little different and that's exactly what this pub is: a refreshing change from the status quo. The pleasant village of East Witton provides the perfect setting, but if you picked it up and moved it this pub would still exude charm and character aplenty. Solid stone floors, walls filled with countryside memorabilia, open fires and gentle candlelight provide a warm, friendly glow, while the delightful bar is stocked with real ales and a good selection of wines. With seasonality and traceability at their core, the tasty mix of classic and modern dishes changes daily, and the locally bagged game in particular is always a welcome sight. In a similar style to the bar, the bedrooms – split between the pub and the outbuildings – are warm, cosy and feature lots of wood. If you're after a true and honest pub then look no further, The Lion and its experienced owner definitely win the blue ribbon.

Closing times

Open daily

Booking essential

Prices

Meals: à la carte £ 26/35

15 rooms: £ 68/135

Typical Dishes

Baked goat's cheese

Cassoulet duck leg

Treacle sponge

3 mi southeast of Leyburn on A 6108. Parking.

17 The Plough Inn

Main Street, Fadmoor YO62 7HY
Tel.: (01751)431515 – Fax: (01751)432492
e-mail: enquiries@theploughfadmoor.co.uk
Website: www.ploughrestaurant.co.uk

 **Black Sheep Best Bitter and summer guest beer Gt Newsome Brewery Sleck Dust**

Set in a delightful location by the village green, the 18C Plough Inn sits on the edge of the North York Moors, midway between Pickering and Helmsley, and not far from Hutton-Le-Hole and the Ryedale Folk Museum. There's no lack of choice when it comes to where to eat; get here early to bag the snug, with its open fire, or pick from various cosy rooms and hidey holes, including the formal half-panelled dining room, or – if the weather's looking good – one of the outside picnic tables. Like the décor, the cooking is traditional in style, with freshly prepared dishes such as sausage and mash, fish and chips or steak and mushroom suet pudding, as well as classic puddings such as crème brûlée or treacle tart. Produce is sourced locally where possible, and the two course special menu is a steal. If you're into camping, then this is definitely the inn for you: dine in the pub, and your pitch in the site behind it comes for free.

Closing times
Closed 25 December and 1 January

Prices
Meals: à la carte £ 16/30

Typical Dishes
Baked figs with Brie & Parma ham
Pan-fried pork tenderloin
Iced mint chocolate parfait

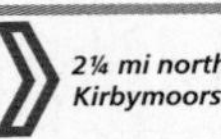
2¼ mi northwest of Kirbymoorside. Parking.

18 The General Tarleton Inn

Boroughbridge Rd,
Ferrensby HG5 0PZ

Tel.: (01423)340284 – Fax: (01423)340288
e-mail: gti@generaltarleton.co.uk **Website:** www.generaltarleton.co.uk

 **Black Sheep Bitter, Timothy Taylor Llandlord**

With four spacious rooms, a bright glass-roofed courtyard and al fresco dining either in the garden or on the lovely decking, you're spoilt for choice at this 18C coaching inn. One of the forerunners of today's gastropubs, it still leads the way, the menu featuring a strong seasonal, local base, with traceability and supplier relationships at its core. There's no longer a distinction between the brasserie and restaurant, so the same menu of tasty, warming dishes is served throughout. Several old favourites can always be found, maybe fish and chips or steak and ale pie, while other dishes could include crispy belly pork or seafood in a pastry bag (their speciality), followed by char-grilled haunch of venison or corn-fed Goosnargh duckling in gingerbread sauce; and for dessert, perhaps Yorkshire custard tart with Armagnac soaked prunes or pannacotta with green apple sorbet. Bedrooms are individually styled, luxurious and very comfortable.

Closing times
Open daily

Prices
Meals: à la carte £ 25/32
13 rooms: £ 75/150

Typical Dishes
Seafood in pastry parcel
Braised belly pork
Yorkshire curd tart

3 mi north of Knaresborough by A 6055. Parking.

19 The Star Inn

High St,
Harome YO62 5JE

Tel.: (01439)770397 – Fax: (01439)771833
e-mail: jpern@thestarinnatharome.co.uk **Website:** www.thestaratharome.co.uk

Inspectors' favourites

Hambleton Ales, Leeds Brewery, Theakston

Twinkling brightly in the firmament, this aptly named star's reputation precedes it, so you will need to book well ahead for one of its eight restaurant tables; or alternatively, arrive early to dine in the deliciously snug beamed bar. Cooking is a celebration of the pub's Yorkshire roots and dishes combine traditional Northern flavours with more up-to-date nuances, using ingredients sourced from local estates and farms. How unusual, yet how welcome it is to see words such as woof, hare, lovage and parkin on a menu. Dining in the restaurant allows access to the cosy, romantic coffee loft where you can enjoy complimentary cheese and crackers with your after dinner drink; there's a seriously compiled wine list and staff provide professional service. Luxuriously-appointed rooms have a stylish country feel and the gastronomic empire spawned by this beautiful 700 year old inn's success now includes a herb garden, a butcher's shop and a deli.

Closing times

Closed 1 January and Monday lunch

Booking essential

Prices

Meals: à la carte £ 30/45

15 rooms: £ 120/230

Typical Dishes

Foie gras 'Toad in the Hole'
Fillet of Whitby turbot
Yorkshire curd tartlet

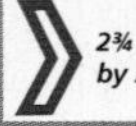

2¾ mi southeast of Helmsley by A 170. Parking.

20 The Angel Inn

Hetton BD23 6LT
Tel.: (01756)730263 – Fax: (01756)730363
e-mail: info@angelhetton.co.uk
Website: www.angelhetton.co.uk

 **Timothy Taylor Landlord, Hetton Pale Ale, Black Sheep Bitter**

There is many a chef and restaurateur around the country who owe their success to the formative years they spent at this iconic 18C Yorkshire institution. Don't be fooled by the relatively remote setting – you have to book ahead to get a table in the bar and even then it can be a bit of a scrum. It's jammed with character and charm but the long serving staff all ably anticipate their customers' needs. Those will food allergies will welcome the effort put in on the menu to identify those dishes that contain nuts, dairy or are gluten free. It is also flexible and uses plenty of local bounty; there is something for everyone, at prices that are sensible and the cooking is eminently satisfying. There is also a more formal dining room available. Wine is a huge draw here – there is an enormous selection by the glass and the cave is well worth a visit. You'll find the luxuriously appointed bedrooms in a converted stone farm building.

Closing times
Closed 25 December and 1 week in January
Booking essential

Prices
Meals: à la carte £ 28/34
5 rooms: £ 130/155

Typical Dishes
Angel's little moneybag
Goosnargh duck breast
Dark chocolate fondant

5¾ mi north of Skipton by B 6265.
Parking.

21 The Charles Bathurst Inn

Langthwaite DL11 6EN
Tel.: (01748)884567 – Fax: (01748)884599
e-mail: info@cbinn.co.uk
Website: www.cbinn.co.uk

   MC

Timothy Taylor Landlord, Theakston Best Bitter, Black Sheep Best Bitter & Riggwelter

This characterful 18C hostelry is named after a local land and lead mine owner – a former resident – who was the son of Oliver Cromwell's physician. Sitting on the edge of the Pennine way, high in the hills of Arkengarthdale, it boasts commanding views over the surrounding countryside and is so remotely set, that the only sound you'll hear by day is the 'clink' of the locals throwing quoits and at night, the hoot of an owl. Inside you're greeted by open fires, various timbered snugs and a spacious dining room that exudes rustic charm aplenty, with old monochrome photos and sepia lithographs on display. Unusually inscribed on a mirror, the daily menu offers refined yet hearty classical British dishes, with the likes of broccoli and stilton soup or asparagus and Wensleydale tart, followed by plenty of local meats; maybe fillet of beef on oxtail terrine or pork with apple and celeriac boulangère. Bedrooms are spacious and extremely comfy.

Closing times
Closed 25 December

Prices
Meals: à la carte £ 18/30
19 rooms: £ 98/123

Typical Dishes
C B salad
Supreme Guinea fowl
Lemon cheesecake

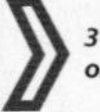
3¼ mi northwest of Reeth on Langthwaite rd. Parking.

22 The Sandpiper Inn

Market Pl,
Leyburn DL8 5AT

Tel.: (01969)622206 – Fax: (01969)625367
e-mail: hsandpiper99@aol.com **Website:** www.sandpiperinn.co.uk

Black Sheep, Copper Dragon Brewery, Dent Brewery

This charming 16C inn sits just off the square, right in the heart of the busy market town of Leyburn and its experienced owners seem to know exactly what their customers want, be they here to drink or to dine. If you're after a tipple, there are some great beers on offer, a good selection of wines by the glass and a terrific range of malt whiskies. If you're eating, you can sit in the traditional bar or rustic dining room; frequently changing blackboard menus display a range of homemade dishes made from the finest local produce, with details of provenance proudly displayed on the walls. Choose perhaps from poached Yorkshire asparagus, caramelised belly pork, delicious local lamb or mature well-hung beef. Lunchtimes are a simpler affair with maybe some local gammon and eggs, as well as the ever popular fresh fish finger sandwich. If you're here at the weekend, make sure to book ahead. The two pleasant bedrooms have a homely feel.

Closing times
Closed 25-26 December, 1 January, Monday, and Tuesday in winter

Prices
Meals: à la carte £ 21/33
2 rooms: £ 65/80

Typical Dishes
Pigeon and squash risotto
Slow-cooked Dales lamb
Assiette of desserts

In town centre. Limited parking available in the Market Place.

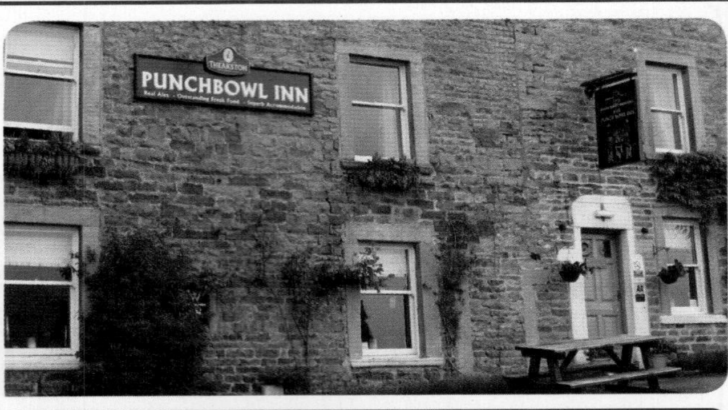

23 The Punch Bowl Inn

Low Row DL11 6PF

Tel.: (01748)886233 – Fax: (01748)886945

e-mail: info@pbinn.co.uk

Website: www.pbinn.co.uk

Theakston's Best Bitter, Black Sheep Best Bitter & Riggwelter, Timothy Taylor Landlord

In the heart of Swaledale, with splendid views over the countryside, the 17C stone built Punch Bowl Inn has always been a popular stopping off point for walkers - and never more so than now. Having been thoroughly modernised, it reopened at the end of 2006 under the capable ownership of the proprietors of the nearby CB Inn, who, in their appreciation for abbreviation, now refer to it the PB Inn. Modernised it may have been, but with open fires, solid wood floors and a bar crafted by Robert 'Mousey' Thompson, it's retained a wealth of rustic charm, and the atmosphere is one of relaxed informality, with customers seemingly blissed out on endorphins from all that fresh Yorkshire air and exercise. As at the CB, menus are writ large on mirrors above the fire, and have a strong sense of the seasons, so expect tasty stew and sticky toffee pudding in the winter and salads in the summer. Bedrooms are stylish, spacious and supremely comfortable.

Closing times

Closed 25 December

Prices

Meals: à la carte £ 18/25

11 rooms: £ 98/120

Typical Dishes

Roast butternut squash salad

Local aged rump steak

Yorkshire parkin

In the middle of hamlet. Parking.

24 The Dawnay Arms

Newton-on-Ouse YO30 2BR

Tel.: (01347)848345

e-mail: dine@thedawnayatnewton.co.uk
Website: www.thedawnayatnewton.co.uk

 **Timothy Taylor Golden Best, Tetleys Cask, Hambleton Best, Black Sheep, Copper Dragon Golden Pippin**

Having been the subject of a hefty conversion in 2007, this capacious 18C inn – named after the last owners of nearby Beningbrough Hall - boasts a handsome rustic style, thoroughly in tune with its rural surroundings. It's got the low beamed ceilings and the roaring fires. It's got the walls filled with countryside art and the solid stone floors. It's got the locally-crafted chunky wood tables. All that, and a stuffed armadillo too. A native Yorkshireman cooks up tasty, good value dishes in the kitchen, with everything fresh, homemade and seasonal; the lunch menu offers sandwiches and pub classics like shepherd's pie alongside fish stew or slow roast rump of lamb, while the dinner menu might tempt you with confit pork belly or ballotine of chicken. If you don't fancy eating in the bar, try the more formal rear dining room; it looks out over the terrace and gardens and down to the River Ouse, where the occasional guest arrives by boat.

Closing times

Closed 1 January, Sunday dinner and Monday (except bank holidays)

Prices

Meals: £ 15/16
and à la carte £ 20/35

Typical Dishes

Homemade black pudding
Local wild rabbit pie
Custard tart & rhubarb

 *8 mi northwest of York by A 19 and minor road west. Parking.* 

25 The Black Swan

Oldstead YO61 4BL
Tel.: (01347)868387
e-mail: enquiries@blackswanoldstead.co.uk
Website: www.blackswanoldstead.co.uk

 **Black Sheep Best Bitter, Copper Dragon Best Bitter**

All too often nowadays, village pubs – traditionally at the hub of village life – are taken over by out-of-towners. Not so The Black Swan; owned and run by a family who have lived and farmed in Oldstead for generations. Originally a 16C house, it's been lovingly converted and features a cosy downstairs bar with open fire and oak fittings by the famous 'Mousey' Thompson. Food is served mainly in the spacious upstairs dining room and in a smaller, slightly more formal room. Everything, including the black pudding, is homemade and the seasonal produce is locally sourced whenever possible. Dishes might include slow-roasted belly pork, pan-fried red mullet or braised shin of beef and Black Sheep ale pie; there are simpler dishes for children and a decent selection of real ales and local beers. With all this – and laudably low prices – it's no wonder the locals are flocking in. Bedrooms are currently being refurbished.

Closing times

Closed 2 weeks in mid January and Monday lunch

Prices

Meals: £ 16 and à la carte £ 21/28

Typical Dishes

Homemade black pudding

Rump of beef two ways

Custard tart with rhubarb

6 mi southwest of Helmsley by A 170 and minor road via Byland Abbey. Parking.

26 The Golden Lion

6 West End,
Osmotherley DL6 3AA
Tel.: (01609)883526
Website: www.goldenlionosmotherley.co.uk

Timothy Taylor Best, Jennings Salamander, North York Dales Brewery

The Golden Lion has probably done more to invigorate walkers than sunshine and a following wind. It's situated in the delightful and historic village of Osmotherley and represents the starting line for those about to set off on the Lyke Wake walk or at least those who have, at some stage, contemplated the walk. There's nothing fancy-pants about this place and that's the beauty of it – just a rustic, warm interior with open fires, great beers and staff who make you feel instantly at ease. The food also fits neatly into these surroundings. There's a bit of French, a little Italian with some pasta dishes but, above all, food that satisfies, whether that's a nice piece of fresh roasted halibut or a local mature steak accompanied by a pint in front of the fire. In contrast, the three bedrooms are quite modern in their style but, most importantly, have that one thing that overnighters demand before all else – a decent shower.

Closing times
Closed 25 December, lunch Monday and Tuesday

Prices
Meals: à la carte £ 20/24
3 rooms: £ 60/90

Typical Dishes
Fresh crab mayonnaise
Smoked haddock fishcakae
Prune, apple & walnut cake

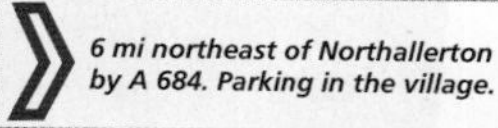

6 mi northeast of Northallerton by A 684. Parking in the village.

27 The Crown Inn

Roecliffe YO51 9LY
Tel.: (01423)322300 – Fax: (01423)322033
e-mail: info@crowninnroecliffe.com **Website:** www.crowninnroecliffe.com

Theakston's, Sharp's Doom Bar, Nellie Dean, Swing Low, Black Sheep, Caledonian IPA

Recently refurbished, this 16C coaching inn's cosy inner boasts a solid stone floor, wooden beams and open fires; the bar is lined with local pictures and foodie photos and a butcher's block is piled high with countryside magazines through which to flick. Sourcing is given its rightful significance by the Crown's kitchen and the food served here has a broad Yorkshire burr; the result being distinctive, reliable, no nonsense bar meals such as winter vegetable broth, homemade game pie, braised pork neck and locally handmade pork sausages. For a more formal experience, head for a linen-laid table in the elegant dining room where you can sample classical, carefully-crafted cooking in the form of confit of beef shin and roasted marrowbone, wild venison or Scarborough lemon sole. Menus are supplemented by daily-changing blackboard specials - the fish are particularly tasty. Bedrooms are currently being refurbished.

Closing times
Closed Sunday dinner

Prices
Meals: £ 19/22
and à la carte £ 25/45

Typical Dishes
Home-smoked salmon
Rump of beef Béarnaise
Handmade Yorkshire cheese

1 mi west of Boroughbridge by minor road. Parking.

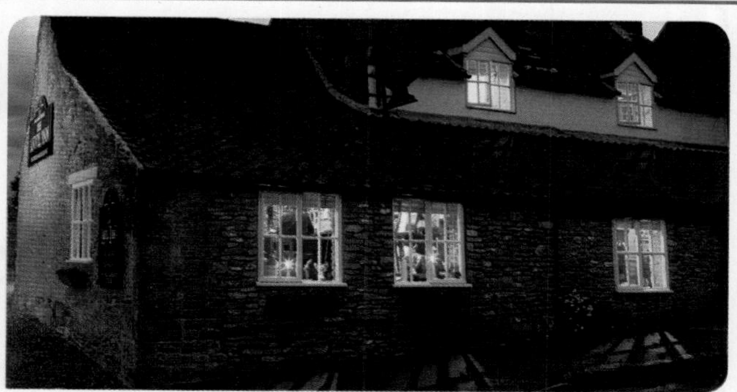

28 The Anvil Inn

Main St, Sawdon YO13 9DY
Tel.: (01723)859896
e-mail: theanvilinnsawdon@btinternet.com
Website: www.theanvilinnsawdon.co.uk

 **Copper Dragon Best Bitter, Wold Top Falling Stone**

As its name suggests, this charming Yorkshire inn with views over Dalby Dale was formerly a smithy; its workshop in use as recently as twenty-five years ago. Much of the associated paraphernalia remains in what is now the bar, including bellows, various tools, the open forge and, naturally, the original anvil. In marked contrast, but blending in seamlessly, is the boldly coloured, contemporary sitting room; a delightful spot for a pre-dinner drink. Cooking is classical in essence, but the odd international influence creeps in too, so expect crispy duck and pancakes alongside Shetland mussels or slow roasted daube of beef. Local chef Mark prides himself on the use of locally sourced produce; eggs come from the pub's own hens and the local Stillington pork is a firm favourite. There are only seven tables in the intimate restaurant, so be sure to book ahead; particularly for Sunday lunch, which has become something of an institution.

Closing times
Closed 25-26 December, 1 January, Sunday dinner and Monday

Prices
Meals: à la carte £ 19/28

Typical Dishes
Baked sardines
Yorkshire lamb loin
Fresh mint panna cotta

12 mi southwest of Scarborough by A 170 to Brompton and minor road north. Parking.

29 The Hare Inn

Scawton YO7 2HG
Tel.: (01845)597769
e-mail: info@thehareinn.co.uk
Website: www.thehareinn.co.uk

 **Black Sheep Bitter, Timothy Taylor Landlord**

The appeal of many a pub lies in its far-flung setting and The Hare's location couldn't be more remote – it nestles in the depths of the North Yorkshire Moors, close to Rievaulx Abbey and Sutton Bank, which, as many gliders know, is where you'll find some of the country's best views. But The Hare is more than just a hideaway – it's also got plenty of character, with parts of the pub dating back to the 13C. For some, it even resembles a smart scout hut and would certainly win a badge for hospitality – you're guaranteed a warm welcome, from the two black Labradors as well as the owner. The food is equally pleasing, whether that's the local asparagus, whole roast sea bass, sweet new season lamb or 'proper' puddings like lemon posset. It's also sufficiently local – meat comes from Masham and poultry from Pateley Bridge – to add to the sense of place. It gets pretty jam packed at weekends so a little patience is sometimes required.

Closing times
Closed Sunday dinner and Monday

Prices
Meals: à la carte £ 20/30

Typical Dishes
Ham hock terrine
Masham lamb
Chocolate cappuccino mousse

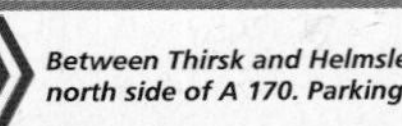

Between Thirsk and Helmsley off north side of A 170. Parking.

30 Fox and Hounds

Main St,
Sinnington YO62 6SQ
Tel.: (01751)431577 – Fax: (01751)432791
e-mail: foxhoundsinn@easynet.co.uk **Website:** www.thefoxandhoundsinn.co.uk

 **Copper Dragon Best Bitter, Black Sheep Special**

It's easy to see why this handsome and sturdy stone pub, dating from the 18C, is something of a local institution: it has much charm, is run smoothly and offers something for everyone. If you fancy staying overnight, then book ahead as the bedrooms get snapped up quickly. It's fairly substantial inside and comes divided into a number of areas; if you want to chat to the good burghers of Sinnington then sit in the bar but there's also a dining room at the rear. The menu is all about flexibility, with virtually all the starters available in larger sizes for main courses. Local specialities remains the popular choice, whether that's the Bleikers smoked salmon, the scallops with black pudding or the Swaledale 'Old Peculiar' cheese soufflé; those who have a more international inclination can choose maybe coriander crab cakes. There is something reassuring about the main courses, which could include slow-cooked shoulder of lamb or fish pie.

Closing times
Closed 25-26 December

Prices
Meals: à la carte £ 20/30
10 rooms: £ 49/120

Typical Dishes
Old Peculiar cheese soufflé
Brisket of beef Bourguignon
Lemon tart

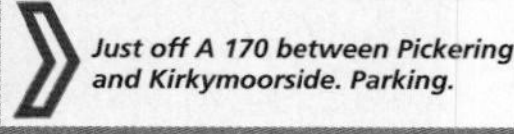

Just off A 170 between Pickering and Kirkymoorside. Parking.

31 Coachman Inn

Pickering Road West,
Snainton YO13 9PL

Tel.: (01723)859231 – Fax: (01723)850008
e-mail: james@coachmaninn.co.uk **Website:** www.coachmaninn.co.uk

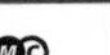

 **Woldtop Brewery; Wold Gold and Wolds Way (summer only)**

This very substantial, but undeniably pretty, Grade II listed Georgian former coaching inn exudes charm and warmth. It may be just off the busy main coastal road but it benefits from a delightful garden to the side and not only has an elegant dining room – all polished tables, gleaming glassware and sparkling cutlery – but also boasts a cosy sitting room, a traditional and characterful bar and spacious, individually styled bedrooms. Extra warmth comes from the owners who run it with indisputable care and enthusiasm; father makes the puddings, the daughter cooks and mother does everything. You can feel there is also genuine passion about food here; they'll use local sirloin steak to make your lunchtime sandwich and there is also a strong element of tradition – Beef Wellington is a menu favourite and how often do you see steak Diane these days? Other local specials include Whitby scampi and Brompton sausages.

Closing times

Closed 25 December, 1 January, Monday and lunch Tuesday

Prices

Meals: à la carte £ 22/35

3 rooms: £ 50/75

Typical Dishes

Crispy duck salad

Braised beef on onion mash

Bread & butter pudding

½ mi west by A 170 on B 1258. Parking.

The Blackwell Ox Inn

32 The Blackwell Ox Inn

Huby Rd,
Sutton-on-the-Forest YO61 1DT
Tel.: (01347)810328 – Fax: (01347)812738
e-mail: info@blackwelloxinn.co.uk **Website:** www.blackwelloxinn.co.uk

 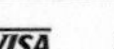

 **Timothy Taylor Landlord, Black Sheep Bitter, John Smith's Cask, Copper Dragon IPA**

It may be named after an intimidating six foot Teeswater ox but, unlike its namesake, this early 19C brick-built pub is never short of a warm welcome. Inside, boldly painted walls give it a slightly modern edge, while cosy sofas in the snug open-fired bar provide a homely feel; follow it through to the restaurant and you'll find inviting linen-laid tables, a concise lunch/early evening set menu and more extensive à la carte. Cooking is hearty, straightforward and satisfying, so you're likely to find old favourites such as beer-battered fish or rib-eye steak, alongside dishes of a more Gallic persuasion, maybe lamb rillettes or smoked salmon batons with horseradish crème fraîche. There's also the odd more ambitious offering, so your calves liver might arrive with an English mustard pancake, as well as white onion and lavender jam. Bedrooms are finished to a high standard; some feature four-posters, some boast Victorian roll-top baths.

Closing times
Closed 25 December, 1 January and Sunday dinner

Prices
Meals: £ 14 and à la carte £ 14/30
7 rooms: £ 65/110

Typical Dishes
Confit belly pork
Blackened red snapper
Chocolate bread & butter pudding

8 mi north of York by B 1363. Parking.

Sutton-on-the-Forest

33 Rose & Crown

Main St,
Sutton-on-the-Forest YO61 1DP

Tel.: (01347)811333 – Fax: (01347)811333
e-mail: mail@rosecrown.co.uk **Website:** www.rosecrown.co.uk

   AE

Black Sheep Best, York Brewery Yorkshire Terrier

The Rose and Crown sits in the main thoroughfare of a pretty little village, just 10 minutes drive from York. The small, cosy front bar creates a welcoming and intimate atmosphere and the dining room and conservatory add to the overall charm. There is a bewildering array of menus available, from 'early bird' to 'light bites', from the à la carte to a list of 'classics' – but don't be frightened off. What this means is that you may have to spend a little more time leafing through them but you'll almost certainly find something that appeals – to your appetite and your pocket – whether that's the sirloin of Yorkshire beef, pork cutlet with black pudding, ham hock terrine or just a Caesar salad. Local cheeses go into the potato cakes; the piccalilli is homemade and the haddock uses a local York beer for its batter. Perhaps the pub's best feature is the enclosed rear garden which comes with a super terrace and an impressively sized gazebo.

Closing times

Closed first week in January, Sunday dinner and Monday

Booking essential

Prices

Meals: £ 20 and à la carte £ 25/35

Typical Dishes

Seared king scallops

Roast breast of chicken

Dark chocolate fondant

On B 1363 north of York. Parking.

34 **The Stone House Inn**

Thruscross HG3 4AH
Tel.: (01943)880325
e-mail: john.mcewan@mac.com
Website: www.stonehouseinn.co.uk

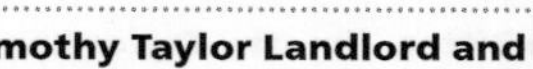

Unless you're a seasoned walker you are unlikely to stumble across this 300 year old coaching inn, as it's set high up in the remote Yorkshire dales and is very exposed. Surrounded by countryside vistas, it retains many of its original features, including wooden beams, exposed stone walls and flagged floors; with a pair of welcoming fires making even the bleakest day seem brighter. It's ideal for the family, with the friendly staff accommodating your needs, from help with highchairs to handing out activity packs. A family man himself, the owner cleverly recruited his two young children, Rosie and Ashley, to help compile the kids menu, and what could be better than a menu for children, designed by children? For older guests, the wide-ranging main menu features everything from salads and curries to British pub classics – all made from local, seasonal produce – whilst the specials display dishes of a more ambitious nature.

Closing times
Open daily
Prices
Meals: à la carte £ 12/27

Typical Dishes
Smoked mackerel pâté
Steak & ale pie
Treacle tart

10 mi west of Harrogate by A 59 and minor road north. Parking.

35 The Bruce Arms

Main St,
West Tanfield HG4 5JJ

Tel.: (01677)470325 – Fax: (01677)470925
e-mail: info@bruce-arms.co.uk **Website:** www.bruce-arms.co.uk

VISA  AE

Black Sheep Bitter, Timothy Taylor Landlord, Worthington

Set on a roundabout in the heart of the pretty village of West Tanfield, this traditional 200 year old stone-built pub may not have the most attractive of façades, but you'd be wise not to judge a book by its cover, as what it may lack in appearance, it certainly makes up for in its food. Husband and wife team Russell and Rosie have really hit the right note with the cooking, sourcing quality ingredients from local suppliers wherever possible. Dishes are mainly modern British and arrive neatly presented. You might find degustation of Tanfield rabbit with green pistachio nut crust, salad of pheasant with pasta and hazelnut cream or pan fried scallops with cauliflower puree, pancetta and curried salt; followed by fillet of turbot meuniere with brown shrimp risotto and chanterelle cream, or rolled medallions of lamb saddle with berbere spiced lamb rillette and aubergine puree. Upstairs, the pine-furnished bedrooms are simple but comfy.

Closing times

Closed Sunday dinner

Prices

Meals: £ 27 and à la carte £ 16/27

3 rooms: £ 50/80

Typical Dishes

Quail terrine

Fillet of beef & marrow

Rum baba pineapple & coconut

Between Masham and Ripon on A 6108. Parking.

36 The Stone Trough Inn

Kirkham Abbey,
Whitwell-on-the-Hill YO60 7JS
Tel.: (01653)618713 – Fax: (01653)618819
e-mail: info@stonetroughinn.co.uk **Website:** www.stonetroughinn.co.uk

  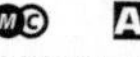

 **Timothy Taylor Landlord**

Set in the Howardian Hills, overlooking the River Derwent and the ruins of Kirkham Abbey, this attractive stone pub is named after what was thought to be a stone trough outside its door – but was later revealed to be the base of a cross erected by a French knight in 1120, in memory of his son. It's a building of real size and dominance, with various beamed rooms and charming snugs scattered about, a large press still in situ and open fires aplenty. You'll find locals in the games room and when weather allows, sun-worshippers on the terrace. Cooking is straightforward, hearty and filling, with a strong classical base. Menus display a mix of local and more cosmopolitan dishes, so you might find potted shrimps or chicken liver pâté, honey-glazed ham hock, rabbit pie or loin of venison; finished off with Eton Mess or heartwarming treacle tart. Produce is local, seasonal and home-grown; and specials are chalked up on the blackboard daily.

Closing times
Open daily

Prices
Meals: à la carte £ 20

Typical Dishes
Pigeon breast
Pork & sage sausage & mash
Banoffee pie

5 mi southwest of Malton off A 64; follow signs for Kirkham Priory. Parking.

37 The Milestone

84 Green Lane,
Sheffield S3 8SE
Tel.: (0114)2728327
e-mail: info@the-milestone.co.uk **Website:** www.the-milestone.co.uk

 **3 weekly changing beers from the following breweries Bradfield, Thornbridge, Kelham Island, Wentworth**

That the owners of The Milestone can boast their own herd of free range pigs speaks volumes about their approach to food: passionate about organic, locally sourced produce, they consider the quality of their ingredients to be the key to their success and don't believe in buying in things like bread, pasta and puddings, since they can make them in-house. The mid 18C pub, a one-time alehouse for the local steelworkers, is well and truly hidden away in the backstreets of the industrial area of the city. Some of the hearty dishes on the 'gastro' menu – like the stewed organic chicken, lamb burger, and beef bourguignon – have become classics, but the emphasis here is on evolution and seasonality, so what's on offer changes frequently. While downstairs is spacious, with understated décor, simple wood tables and banquettes, the beamed first floor room provides a more formal dining space, with a menu to match. Eager, chatty service throughout.

Closing times
Closed 25-26 December

Prices
Meals: £ 17/20
and à la carte £ 17/24

Typical Dishes
Salt cod cheek & chorizo salad
Braised ox cheek
Yorkshire cheeses

Between A 61 and River Don. Parking in Green Lane and Ball Street.

38 The Cricket Inn

Penny Lane,
Totley S17 3AZ
Tel.: (0114)2365256
e-mail: simon@relaxeatanddrink.co.uk **Website:** www.cricketinn.co.uk

 **Thornbridge Brewery - Lord Marples, Kipling, Jaipur**

Pleasant bird song and the satisfying thwack of leather on willow are among the only sounds to be heard from the garden of this characterful stone pub. Set in a valley, about six miles outside of Sheffield, this bustling inn is a million miles from hectic city life. Cooking is hearty, robust and very satisfying, and dishes can arrive on anything from slates to wooden boards. The extensive menu covers everything from bar snacks, platters and pies through to grills and roasts, with a variety of cheeses, pudding, cakes and pastries to follow. With much of the produce being sourced locally it has a strong Yorkshire base, and speciality dishes such as 'Stump' – a regional and aptly named side dish of mashed root vegetables – can often be found. The menu also suggests an ideal beer to accompany each starter and main course, most of which are supplied by the local Thornbridge brewery. Make sure you arrive early, as bookings aren't accepted.

Closing times
Closed 25 December

Prices
Meals: £ 12 and à la carte £ 18/26

Typical Dishes
Homemade Scotch egg
Jack Baker's fish pie
Vanilla panna cotta

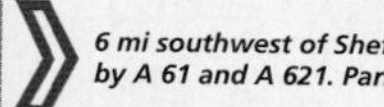
6 mi southwest of Sheffield by A 61 and A 621. Parking.

39 The Fleece

152-154 Main St,
Addingham LS29 0LY
Tel.: (01943)830491
e-mail: thefleece@mac.com **Website:** www.thefleeceaddingham.co.uk

  AE

Timothy Taylor Landlord, Black Sheep Bitter, Tetley's Cask Bitter, Copper Dragon Golden Pippin

Set on the main street of the village of Addingham, this large, ivy-clad inn is a popular meeting place for locals who congregate to drink and discuss the day's events in its small public bar. Often equally as busy is the larger lounge and dining area; decorated with countryside pictures and knick-knacks, and whose beamed ceilings and stone floors and walls bear testament to the building's 18C genesis. The large blackboard menus displayed on the walls change frequently according to what's fresh and what's in season. Homely dishes with Yorkshire roots, such as locally sourced steak and meat pies offer lots of comfort appeal but the wide-ranging menus also include more contemporary dishes too. Service from friendly local staff remains efficient and polite, even when there's a rush on, and the hugely generous portions that they place in front of you present an enjoyable challenge you find you just have to conquer.

Closing times
Open daily

Prices
Meals: à la carte £ 18/26

Typical Dishes
King scallops in streaky bacon
Wild rabbit suet pudding
Fleece chocolate tower

In the centre of Addingham on the busy through road. Parking.

40 Shibden Mill Inn

Shibden Mill Fold,
Halifax HX3 7UL

Tel.: (01422)365840 – Fax: (01422)362971
e-mail: enquiries@shibdenmillinn.com **Website:** www.shibdenmillinn.com

VISA MC AE

Theakston XB, Shibden Bitter, Black Sheep Bitter, Moorhouse's beers

"The mill wheel has long been silent… The old order has changed and what was once a central place of business, is now one of pleasure, beer and boats." (J. Lister, 1911). Set in the valley, overlooking the Red Beck stream, this whitewashed inn started life as early 14C corn mill, was later used for spinning, and in 1890, was sold to a brewing company. Today, you'll find a charming open-fired bar full of nooks, crannies and locals, and a rustic upstairs restaurant with recently exposed original oak beams. If you're looking to eat, there's plenty of choice, with dishes ranging from the traditional – maybe home cured corned beef hash, roasted rib-eye or treacle tart – to the more modern, such as crab trifle with lemon cocktail, scallops with bacon crème caramel or butternut squash fondant. For something a little different, come on a gourmet dinner evening or experimental guinea pig night. Individually appointed bedrooms are comfy and cosy.

Closing times
Open daily

Prices
Meals: à la carte £ 20/31
11 rooms: £ 79/143

Typical Dishes
Wild mushroom ravioli
Daube of beef, truffled mash
Custard tart

2¼ mi northeast by A 58 and Kell Lane (turning left at Stump Cross Pub), on Blake Hill Rd. Parking.

41 Olive Branch

Manchester Rd,
Marsden HD7 6LU
Tel.: (01484)844487

e-mail: mail@olivebranch.uk.com Website: www.olivebranch.uk.com

 **Greenfield Ales Delph Donkey and Monkey Business**

Set on a busy main road this stone-built drovers inn houses many small and characterful rooms, each adorned with food-themed pictures, sepia photos, old menus and more. Most tables are set for dining and there's a chatty, bustling atmosphere, while for the warmer weather, a decked terrace and secluded garden are hidden round the back. The large menu displays an even split between meat and seafood, ranging from pigeon and venison, to sea bass and monkfish; with daily specials displayed on large yellow post-it notes around the bar. Taking on a traditional style, cooking is robust, hearty and straightforward, and uses local produce wherever possible. Service is friendly, if sometimes lacking a little in direction. Bedrooms are modern, comfortable and unique; Serengeti displays wooden statues and printed fabrics, while Duck features ornamental fowl and a bath time friend. Be prepared to have your breakfast order ready when you check in.

 *1 mi northeast on A 62. Parking.* 

Closing times

Closed 26 December, first 2 weeks in January and Monday-Saturday lunch

Prices

Meals: £ 19 (weekday dinner) and à la carte £ 26/40

3 rooms: £ 55/70

Typical Dishes

Trio of duck
Assiette of seafood
Selection of European cheeses

42 The Old Bore

Oldham Rd,
Rishworth HX6 4QU
Tel.: (01422)822291
e-mail: chefhessel@aol.com **Website:** www.oldbore.co.uk

 **Black Sheep Best, Golden Bore Brass Monkey**

A surprisingly short distance from the M62, this personally run pub is wonderfully inviting, not least because of its delightful side terrace, popular in hot weather. In the colder months, a comfy red leather seat by the open fire in the bar is best, surrounded by hunting print walls full of knick knacks and pewter tankards hanging from the beams. Two main dining rooms are very smartly dressed and food here takes a similarly luxurious approach, with truffles, foie gras and other high quality local ingredients carefully employed to create classical British dishes. The main à la carte changes on a monthly basis; choices might include home smoked sea trout, English snails and black pudding, cod tikka, rabbit saddle or roast partridge, while for those concerned about the coffers, the daily set menu offers a less pricey alternative. Regular events such as cookery demonstrations and jazz evenings pull in the crowds. The Old Bore? Far from it.

Closing times
Closed first 2 weeks in January, Monday and Tuesday

Prices
Meals: £ 15 and à la carte £ 25/35

Typical Dishes
Scallops & belly pork
Duo of lamb
Belgian chocolate brownie

6 mi southwest of Halifax by A 58 and A 672. Parking.

43 The Millbank

Mill Bank,
Sowerby Bridge HX6 3DY
Tel.: (01422)825588
e-mail: eat@themillbank.com **Website:** www.themillbank.com

  MC

 **Timothy Taylor Landlord and guest beers Copper Dragon, Burton Ale**

The Millbank was in the vanguard of the modernised-pub-with-good-food movement and continues to pull in the punters, who create quite a buzz. It's split between a small bar and a dining room but it's the food that's the draw here. The conservatory extension to the dining room is the place to sit if you want to admire the views which stretch over the Ryburn Valley. Local artists' work adds to the contemporary feel of the place and uniformed staff provide courteous, if at times slightly impersonal, service. The menu is quite an extensive document but prices are good when one considers the quality of the ingredients and the skill and understanding with which they are used. The cooking can be considered either restaurant style food with a rustic edge or sophisticated pub grub. What you can expect is plenty of choice and something that all pubs should have – a section marked 'British Classics'.

Closing times

Closed first week in January and Monday

Booking essential

Prices

Meals: à la carte £ 20/32

Typical Dishes

Spiced duck confit pie

Yorkshire venison steak

Apple jelly with lemon cream

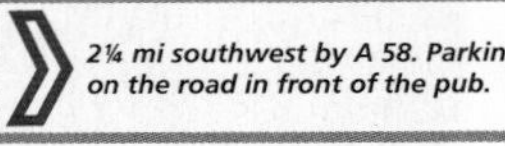

44 Woodman Inn

Thunder Bridge HD8 0PX

Tel.: (01484)605778 – Fax: (01484)604110
e-mail: thewoodman@connectfree.co.uk
Website: www.woodman-inn.co.uk

Timothy Taylor Best and Landlord, Black Sheep

If you're following one of the many footpaths that pass close to the Southern Pennines, make sure you stop off at this small hamlet, in the quiet wooded valley. Built from local Yorkshire stone, this traditional 19C inn boasts a wood-faced bar – complete with convivial locals – a leather furnished lounge and more formal linen-laid restaurant. The latter is only open in the evenings and is great for special occasions but stay in the bar for a more atmospheric day-to-day affair; service is polite and efficient, wherever you sit. The extensive menus change in line with the seasons and have a distinctive British bias. Lunch sees hearty classics served in generous portions, while the evening dishes take on a more complex, ambitious approach; you might find rack of lamb, pan-fried sea bream or twice cooked pork belly, with specials displayed on a blackboard. Located in a row of nearby weaver's cottages, bedrooms are simple and well-kept.

Closing times
Closed 25 December dinner

Prices
Meals: £ 16/19
and à la carte £ 29

12 rooms: £ 48/74

Typical Dishes
Bang bang king prawn skewers
Pan-fried sea bream
Tasting selection

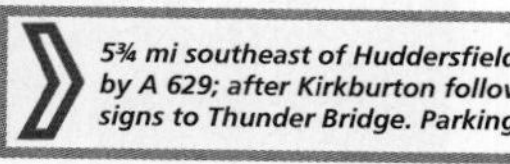

5¾ mi southeast of Huddersfield by A 629; after Kirkburton follow signs to Thunder Bridge. Parking.

45 The Fox and Hounds

Hall Park Road, Walton LS23 7DQ
Tel.: (01937)842192
e-mail: basil@thefoxandhoundswalton.com
Website: www.thefoxandhoundswalton.com

  AE

Timothy Taylor Landlord, Black Sheep and regular guest ale

Tucked away in the centre of a sleepy little West Yorkshire village east of Wetherby, this characterful stone pub has two rooms set for dining, plus a cosy snug – home to Basil, the stuffed fox, in his basket – which also has tables set aside for local drinkers. Pleasant country décor takes in low beamed ceilings and framed countryside prints; the table mats are adorned with hunting cartoons and a fish tank on the bar provides a relaxing diversion as you sup your pint. The chef may be Mexican, but the menu tends towards classic British dishes, with more adventurous offerings available on the specials board. Cooking is hearty and robust and makes good use of local produce; the wide choice further extended by an early evening menu of pub favourites. The atmosphere is friendly and service is chatty and knowledgeable; look out for owner Alan who doubles as local Conservative councillor, and local girl Maggie who's been here for 25 years.

Closing times
Open daily
Booking essential

Prices
Meals: £ 18 (lunch) and à la carte £ 17/30

Typical Dishes
Homemade black pudding
Pork shoulder
Jam roly-poly

3 mi east of Wetherby by minor road; between A 659 and B 1224. Parking.

Scotland may be small, but its variety is immense. The vivacity of Glasgow can seem a thousand miles from the vast peatland wilderness of Caithness and Sutherland's Flow Country; the arty vibe of Georgian Edinburgh a world away from the remote and tranquil Ardnamurchan peninsula. And how many people link Scotland to its beaches? But wide golden sands trim the Atlantic at South Harris, and the coastline of the Highlands boasts empty islands and turquoise waters. Meantime, Fife's coast draws golf fans to St Andrews and the more secretive delights of the East Neuk, an area of fishing villages and stone harbours. Wherever you travel, the scent of a dramatic history prevails in the shape of castles, cathedrals and rugged lochside monuments to the heroes of old. Food and drink embraces the traditional, too, typified by Aberdeen's famous Malt Whisky Trail. And what better than Highland game, fresh fish from the Tweed or haggis, neeps and tatties to complement a grand Scottish hike…

Lewis
Stornoway
St. Kilda
Tarbert
North Uist
Lochmaddy
Uig
Dunvegan
Portree
South Uist
Lochboisdale
Skye
Kyle of Lochalsh
Barra
Castlebay
Sea of the Hebrides
Rhum
Mallaig
Coll
Tiree
Tobermory
Fort William
Ben Nevis
1344
Mull
Craignure
Oban
Loch Linnhe
Fionnphort
Firth of Lorn
Colonsay
Lochgilphead
Islay
Port Askaig
Jura
Port Ellen
Kintyre
Campbeltown
Malin Head
HEBRIDES
The Minch
Lochinver
Tongue
Lairg
Ullapool
Dornoch
Dingwall
HIGHLANDS
Nairn
Inverness
Loch Ness
Aviemore
Newtonmore
Cairngorm Mountains
1309
SCOTLAND
Grampian
R. Tay
Crianlarich
Crieff
Perth
Stirling
Kinross
Falkirk
Dunoon
Dumbarton
Greenock
Rothesay
GLASGOW
EDINBURGH
Brodick
Arran
Ardrossan
Firth of Clyde
Hamilton
Kilmarnock
Lanark
Peebles
Ayr
Moffat
Hawick
Cairnryan
Stranraer
Dumfries
Kirkcudbright
Solway Firth
Carlisle
Workington
Whitehaven
Keswick
North West
Windermere
Kendal
Man
Peel
Ramsey
Douglas
Dunnet
Brora
Tain
Giant's Causeway
North Channel
Buncrana
Lough Foyle
Portrush
Coleraine
Ballycastle
Antrim Glens
Letterkenny
Londonderry / Derry
Strabane
Donegal
Northern Ireland
Ballymena
Larne
Omagh
Bundoran
Sligo
Enniskillen
Lough Neagh
Lisburn
BELFAST
Bangor
Armagh
Boyle
Monaghan
Newry
Newcastle
Ireland
Dundalk
Longford
Liverpool
1
4
5
8
11
12
13
14
15
16
17
18
19
20
22
138
112
59
41
47
212
53
102
86
167
73
48
154

Yell
Unst
Shetland
Hillswick
Sandness
Mainland
Lerwick
Sumburgh
Bergen
Aberdeen
Stromness
Westray
Rousay
Sanday
Stronsay
Kirkwall
Firth
Aberdeen
Wick
NORTH SEA
MER DU NORD
Banff
Fraserburgh
Keith
Peterhead
1
Stromness
Lerwick
Aberdeen
Stonehaven
Montrose
Arbroath
Berwick
Berwick-upon-Tweed
Coldstream
North East
Blyth
Tynemouth
South Shields
Sunderland
Bergen
Stavanger
Haugesund
Kristiansand
Gateshead
Hartlepool
Middlesbrough
Whitby

1 Cock and Bull

Ellon Rd,
Blairton, Balmedie AB23 8XY
Tel.: (01358)743249 – Fax: (01358)742466
e-mail: info@thecockandbull.co.uk **Website:** www.thecockandbull.co.uk

 VISA MC AE D

Deuchar's 80 and IPA and guest ales

A quirky, atmospheric pub visible from the adjacent A90 and with a sense of fun befitting of its name; check out the mural on the men's toilet door and the profusion of knick-knacks throughout. There's a choice of three rooms in which to dine – between them providing enough space for the many punters this pub attracts: a cosy lounge with open fire and low leather sofas, a more formal dining room and an open, airy conservatory. Wherever you sit, the menu's the same, and there's plenty of choice. Make sure you've built up an appetite before stopping off because we're talking big, hearty portions of honest, manly food, with nothing too fancy or fiddly: think black pudding, slow roast pork belly or chargrilled Aberdeenshire steak. There's a freshly made burger every day – maybe venison or beef; they are rightly famous for their fish and chips and prices are the right side of reasonable, particularly at lunchtime.

Closing times
Open daily

Prices
Meals: à la carte £ 20/35

Typical Dishes
Arbroath smokie
Stuffed pork belly
Apple & toffee cheesecake

6 mi north of Aberdeen by A 90. Parking.

2 The Steading

(at Lochside Lodge and Roundhouse restaurant), Kirriemuir DD8 5JJ
Tel.: (01575)560340 – Fax: (01575)560251
e-mail: enquiries@lochsidelodge.com **Website:** www.lochsidelodge.com

 **Inveralmond Brewery**

Set in a peaceful location beside Lintrathen Loch at the foot of a picturesque glen, this stone-built pub started life as a simple farm outbuilding. Now however, it's home to a spacious dining room decorated with old farm tools and whisky tins, and a small leather furnished bar that's ideal for pre or post-dinner drinks. The kitchen is shared with the adjacent fine dining restaurant and the chef uses good ingredients to craft everything from familiar classics to more original offerings. The homemade bread, ice creams and desserts are delicious and if you fancy taking part of your experience home with you, the chef's jams, sauces and chutneys are for sale. Smart bedrooms are divided between the hayloft and courtyard; the former boasting new bathrooms, the latter offering more space. Situated close to the Cairngorms National Park and a multitude of estates, it provides a great stop-off point for walkers, game shooters and fishermen alike.

Closing times

Closed 25-27 December, first 3 weeks in January, 2 weeks in early October, Sunday and Monday

Prices

Meals: £ 13/25

Typical Dishes

Terrine of pork & black pudding
Slow-roasted belly pork
Lemon & chilli panna cotta

8 mi west of Kirriemuir by B 951. Parking.

3 Drovers

Memus DD8 3TY
Tel.: (01307)860322 – Fax: (01307)860300
e-mail: info@the-drovers.com **Website:** www.the-drovers.com

VISA MC AE

Greene King IPA, Inveralmond Breweries Ossian

Set in a lovely location on the fringes of a peaceful hamlet, this remote Highland inn is actually a converted crofter's cottage. To find it, you'll either need your sat nav or a passenger who's adept at reading maps; but when you do, you'll be rewarded with 360° views of the surrounding countryside. The snug bar reminds you that you're in prime cattle country – its sage coloured walls filled with highland cow prints, mounted cow heads and a superb collection of highland cow horns, as well as a welcoming open fire. Cheery service from a local team helps to set the tone and there's also a more formal dining room if that's what you're after. Following the style of the pub, dishes are hearty and warming, with plenty of comfort food on offer, such as braised pork belly, mashed potato and liver. They have a steady stream of regulars, so price plays an important role too, with the weekly changing four-choice set menu providing good value.

Closing times
Open daily

Prices
Meals: £ 25/30
and à la carte £ 20/30

Typical Dishes
Haggis, neeps & tatties
Pork belly & cider gravy
Sticky toffee pudding

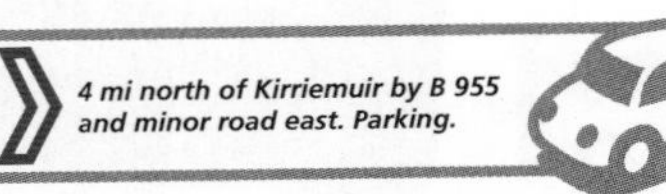
4 mi north of Kirriemuir by B 955 and minor road east. Parking.

4 The Oyster Inn

Connel PA37 1PJ

Tel.: (01631)710666 – Fax: (01631)710042

e-mail: stay@oysterinn.co.uk **Website:** www.oysterinn.co.uk

VISA MC AE

Deuchar's IPA

With views over the Falls of Lora and across to the mountains, this brightly coloured inn has it all: a bar, restaurant and bedrooms. Steeped in history, the 18C Ferryman's Bar got its name from serving nearby ferry passengers, although it was better known as the Glue Pot because people used to get 'stuck' waiting for the return boat. A map of the highlands and islands is posted to the ceiling and memorabilia adorns the walls; touch a glue pot to bring you luck. It's always bustling, especially in the summer, although stone walls and cosy log fires make it just as appealing in the winter. Cooking is good, honest and simple, with dishes ranging from burgers and lasagne to haggis and seafood crêpes. If you sit inside there's often local entertainment such as the fiddle or accordion, while outside there are pleasant views from the terrace. Bedrooms boast pine furniture, colourful prints and contemporary throws; budget bunk rooms available.

Closing times

Open daily

Prices

Meals: à la carte £ 20/40

16 rooms: £ 23/59

Typical Dishes

Seafood chowder

Grilled langoustines

Cranachan

5 mi north of Oban by A 85.
Parking.

5 Tayvallich Inn

Tayvallich PA31 8PL
Tel.: (01546)870282 – Fax: (01546)830116
e-mail: info@tayvallichinn.co.uk
Website: www.tayvallichinn.co.uk

    AE

 **Loch Fyne Ales**

With boats bobbing gently in a sheltered harbour and only a single lane track for access, it's easy to see the appeal of this sleepy waterside location. Popular with boaters – a set familiar to the owners, who formerly ran a charter yacht business – the village hosts two maritime festivals a year: the 'Weekend' in July and the 'Regatta' in August. On these occasions you'll find the pub deserted, as everyone follows Glen and Lynn to the beach for a BBQ. The rest of the year, however, you'll do well to head for the inn, with its slate walls, pine furniture and large wood burner; the adjacent dining room providing a calmer, more peaceful scene. The short main menu ranges from burgers and pies to seafood and steak, whilst the large daily specials board almost doubles your choice of dishes. Cooking is straightforward and uses the freshest local produce, relying heavily on the latest catch in summer and on locally shot game in the winter.

Closing times

Closed 25-26 December, mid-Jan to mid-Feb, and Monday-Tuesday (November to Easter)

Prices

Meals: à la carte £ 17/30

Typical Dishes

Scallops with chilli & lime

Salmon fillet, mustard glaze

Amarretto crème brûlée

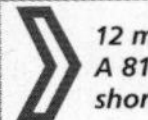

12 mi west of Lochgilphead by A 816, B 841 and B 8025; on west shore of Loch Sween. Parking.

6 The Cobbles Inn

7 Bowmont St,
Kelso TD57JH
Tel.: (01573)223548 – Fax: (01573)223548
e-mail: info@thecobblesinn.co.uk **Website:** www.thecobblesinn.co.uk

 **Stewart Brewing, Broughton Ales, Hadrian & Border Brewery**

At the point where the rivers Teviot and Tweed converge, you'll find the quaint market town of Kelso and, off its cobbled market square, this characterful 19C coaching inn. Run by a husband and wife team, it offers the choice of a snug bar with real open fire and some good local ales or a pleasant dining room with tartan carpet; if you really want to get in with the locals come on a Friday night and you'll find the folk club holding their weekly jam session here. The daily changing menu is appealing and displays a strong seasonal base, with smartly presented dishes ranging from scotch eggs to steaks, wild mushrooms to lamb's liver. Ingredients are always fresh, tasty and sourced from the larder of Scotland: you'll find daily delivered Eyemouth fish, fantastic local meats, superb Hawick cheeses and some excellent soft fruits. What's more, it's good value, especially when you choose from the lunchtime and early evening set menus.

Closing times

Closed Sunday dinner and Monday

Prices

Meals: £ 17 (Sunday lunch) and à la carte £ 19/30

Typical Dishes

Wild wood pigeon on haggis

Duo of Border lamb

Normandy apple flan

On-street parking and free public car park at the rear.

7 The Wheatsheaf

Main Street, Swinton TD11 3JJ
Tel.: (01890)860257 – Fax: (01890)860688
e-mail: reception@wheatsheaf-swinton.co.uk
Website: www.wheatsheaf-swinton.co.uk

 **Stewart's IPA**

Set in the heart of the village overlooking the green, this substantial stone inn is far from your typical pub. Inside, numerous sofa-filled rooms are interlinked with two small dining areas – one boasting smart linen-laid tables and high-backed leather chairs; the other an attractive pine-clad ceiling and matching pine furniture. The hands-on owners are extremely passionate about their food but drinkers are equally as welcome. Midday presents two choices: a bar menu of light pub classics such as fishcakes and beef cobbler, or a lunch menu which steps things up a gear and offers the likes of chicken liver parfait or grilled salmon with risotto; dinner expands upon the latter, offering a larger selection of restaurant-style dishes. Well-presented plates feature flavoursome local produce, with seafood from Eyemouth and meat from the surrounding border farms. Upstairs and in the annexe, bedrooms are spacious, cosy and well equipped.

Closing times
Closed 25-26 and 31 December and 2nd week in January

Prices
Meals: à la carte £ 18/38
10 rooms: £ 65/112

Typical Dishes
Breast of woodpigeon
Peppered loin of venison
Hot sticky ginger & pear pudding

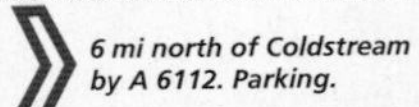
6 mi north of Coldstream by A 6112. Parking.

8 The Sorn Inn

35 Main St,
Sorn KA5 6HU
Tel.: (01290)551305 – Fax: (01290)553470
e-mail: craig@sorninn.com **Website:** www.sorninn.com

No real ales offered

It may not look much from the outside but this simple whitewashed inn proves that you should never judge a book by its cover. It's very much a family affair; the father checking you in to one of the neat bedrooms and the son preparing your meals. The first clues as to the quality of the food are the framed menus in reception informing you of the latest dishes and the presence of the chefs' Holy Bible 'Larousse' on the shelf. Move through to the snug bar and you'll be presented with a choice of robust dishes including homemade pastas, fresh fish and some great quality, locally sourced steaks that are cooked to perfection – order an extra portion of the tasty onion rings to go with it. For more refined cooking with a slight Mediterranean edge, head for the dining room, where'll you find carefully and knowledgeably executed dishes such as chump of lamb with couscous or fish fricassée with tomato pasta. The same care is taken at breakfast.

Closing times
Closed Sunday dinner and Monday

Prices
Meals: £ 19/24
and à la carte £ 20/29
4 rooms: £ 40/95

Typical Dishes
Duo of wild mallard
Loin of venison
Chocolate & almond financier

2 mi east of Catrine by B 713.
Parking.

9 The Kings Wark

36 The Shore,
Leith EH6 6QU
Tel.: (0131)5549260
e-mail: lesleyandmike@gmail.com **Website:** www.kingswark.com

Deuchar's IPA, Caley 80/-, Harvistons Bitter & Twisted and Schiehallion

Often described as a 'silver thread in a ribbon of green', the Water of Leith flows from Pentland Hills to Leith Harbour, where, on the quayside, you'll find this brightly coloured pub. Built in 1434 as a royal armoury and store for King James I's wine and provisions, it also found use as a naval yard and later, a royal palace, before being completely rebuilt following a fire. It's a proper old-fashioned pub and hugely characterful inside, displaying scrubbed floorboards, wooden beams, exposed stone walls and heavily embossed wallpaper. In a similarly classical vein, the hand-written bar menu lists hearty, rustic dishes including the likes of stews and roast meats, with a few Mediterranean flavours also present. If you're after something a touch more substantial both in content and price, head for the area to the right of the main room, where you'll find the restaurant menu and a blackboard of freshly prepared, locally sourced specials.

Closing times
Open daily
Prices
Meals: à la carte £ 15/26

Typical Dishes
Tea-smoked beef brisket
Fillet of sea-trout
Lemon posset

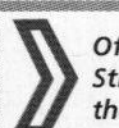

Off the south side of Bernard Street, A 199. Parking across the street on the shore.

10 The Ship on the Shore

24-26 Shore,
Leith EH6 6QN
Tel.: (0131)5550409
e-mail: shipontheshore@btconnect.com **Website:** www.theshipontheshore.co.uk

  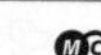 MC AE

 **No real ales offered**

With its neat blue façade inset with ship's navigation lights and modelled on the Royal Yacht Britannia, this period building on the quayside looks like it's ready to set sail. Inside, the walls are papered with European maritime charts, scrubbed wooden floors mimic a ship's deck and it's filled with nautical bric à brac; including a rack of oars hanging from the ceiling. Regulars propping up the bar and a friendly service team buzzing around help to create a relaxed, informal atmosphere. The kitchen follows a philosophy of 'sustainable Scottish seafood served simply with style', and 99% of the menu is just this. With so many popular classics on offer, the main menu stays the same, while numerous blackboards list the freshest daily specials; you will find everything from Cullen Skink and pints of prawns through to Orkney scallops and whole roast sea bass. For those partial to more land-based fare, there's the odd meat dish on offer too.

Closing times
Closed 24-26 December

Prices
Meals: à la carte £ 20/35

Typical Dishes
Steamed Torridon mussels
Dressed Scrabster brown crab
Chocolate gingerbread pudding

On east side of river. On-street parking.

11 Babbity Bowster

16-18 Blackfriars St,
Glasgow G1 1PE
Tel.: (0141)5525055 – Fax: (0141)5527774
e-mail: babbity@btinternet.com

   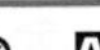

Deuchar's IPA, Kelburn Misty Law and regularly changing guest ales

If you're wondering about the name, 'babbity' means to 'bob', a 'bowster' is the wheelshaft of a watermill, and the 'babbity bowster' is an old country dance which used to be performed at the end of every Scottish ball. Located on the edge of the Merchant City in the heart of Glasgow, this double-fronted Georgian building has become part of local tradition itself, and one glance at the fiercely Scottish décor, regional memorabilia and framed musical score of the aforementioned dance, tells you why. The cheery owner really does go that extra mile, although it's hard not to be satisfied when you're surrounded by such a fine selection of local ales and whiskies. Cooking is firmly rooted in tradition, with straightforward, seasonal dishes including all the old Scottish favourites such as cullen skink, neeps and tatties. In the upstairs restaurant, dishes are more elaborate and arrive with generous portions of veg and dauphinoise potatoes.

Closing times
Closed 25 December and 1 January

Prices
Meals: à la carte £ 15/23

Typical Dishes
Cullen skink
Confit de canard
Clootie dumpling

In city centre north of the Central railway station. Parking for hotel guests only.

12 Summer Isles (Bar)

Achiltibuie IV26 2YG
Tel.: (01854)622282 – Fax: (01854)622251
e-mail: info@summerisleshotel.com
Website: www.summerisleshotel.com

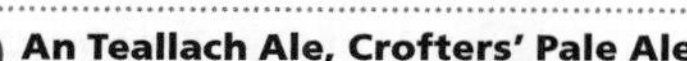

An Teallach Ale, Crofters' Pale Ale

This bar is attached to the Summer Isles hotel, but access is only from the outside – not through the hotel. Polished wood tables in its modern front room are set for dining; the rear room is where you head if you're after a drink and a natter with the locals or to catch up with the news or the sport on the telly. Since these are its only two rooms, the pub can get full quite quickly; on sunny days, the lawned outside dining area creates a pleasant third alternative. As one might expect, given the pub's location, menus are seafood orientated, with only the freshest and wettest sea creatures available for your degustation; they offer snacks and some traditional pub dishes as well, with daily specials also competing for your attention in the evening. Bedrooms are split between the main house and various converted outbuildings; all are individually styled and comfortable with good facilities and quality furnishings.

Closing times
Closed November to late-March Monday and Tuesday

Prices
Meals: à la carte £ 20/30
13 rooms: £ 85/200

Typical Dishes
Smoked mackerel pâté
Seafood platter
Banoffee pie

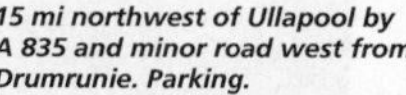

15 mi northwest of Ullapool by A 835 and minor road west from Drumrunie. Parking.

13 Applecross Inn

Shore St,
Applecross IV54 8LR
Tel.: (01520)744262
e-mail: applecrossinn@btconnect.com **Website:** www.applecrossinn.uk.com

Isle of Skye Brewing Co

Set between the mountains of the mainland and the Isle of Skye, the Applecross Peninsula provides a haven from the world outside. Its Gaelic name 'a Chomraich' means 'The Sanctuary'; and it really is. It seems miraculous that this charming Highland inn can get so busy, as access to this tiny fishing village is either via a 24 mile coastal track or steep zigzagging mountain pass; albeit accompanied by panoramic views over the Kintail Mountains and Outer Hebrides. Menus offer local, seasonal produce, and with stunning views over the water to the distant hills of Skye, you might even be able to see where some of the ingredients come from. Fresh seafood arrives regularly from Applecross Bay and venison from the nearby estate, so you may find squat lobster cocktail or dressed crab salad, followed by king scallops with bacon or venison sausages. Located in a row of old fishermen's cottages, bedrooms are smart and comfy; all boast sea views.

Closing times

Closed 1 January,
25 December for meals

Booking essential

Prices

Meals: à la carte £ 15/30

7 rooms: £ 100/110

Typical Dishes

Squat lobster

Prawns in lemon & garlic

Homemade sticky toffee pudding

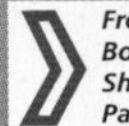
From Kishorn via Belach nam Bo (Alpine Pass) or round by Shieldaig and along the coast. Parking.

14 Badachro Inn

Badachro IV21 2AA
Tel.: (01445)741255 – Fax: (01445)741319
e-mail: lesley@badachroinn.com
Website: www.badachroinn.com

An Teallach Ales, Caledonian 80/-

This rustic Highland pub occupies a superbly sheltered spot in a secluded little inlet on the south shore of Loch Gairloch. The decked terrace and conservatory dining room boast great views out over Badachro Bay towards the Outer Hebrides, while picturesque hills and mountains rise up behind the inn. There are two private moorings in the bay for those arriving by boat and you can watch the local fishermen landing their daily catches of prawns and salmon on the nearby jetty; some of which is destined for the pub. On busier days you may have to sit inside but it's no real hardship as the beamed, open-fired bar, its walls adorned with local maritime charts, provides a cosy, welcoming atmosphere. Choose between two menus; one featuring light snacks such as paninis and jacket potatoes, the other offering simple but more substantial pub and restaurant-style fare. Ingredients are locally sourced, with a particular emphasis on fresh seafood.

Closing times
Closed 25-26 December

Prices
Meals: à la carte £ 20

Typical Dishes
Crab salad
Gairloch langoustines
Chocolate & coffee truffle pot

6 mi south of Gairloch by A 832 and B 8056. Parking and 2 moorings for boats.

15 Cawdor Tavern

The Lane,
Cawdor IV12 5XP
Tel.: (01667)404777 – Fax: (01667)454584
e-mail: enquiries@cawdortavern.info **Website:** www.cawdortavern.info

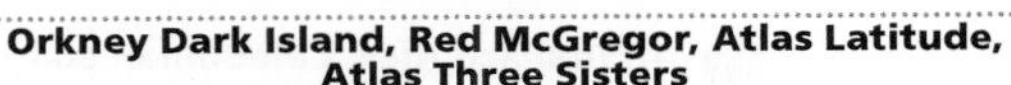

Orkney Dark Island, Red McGregor, Atlas Latitude, Atlas Three Sisters

All hail, Macbeth! Hail to thee, Thane of Cawdor! All hail, Macbeth, that shalt be king hereafter! Macbeth may have died several centuries before it was built, but the next door castle is well-known for its role in Shakespeare's tragedy, and this smart whitewashed pub was once its joiners' workshop. It's an immensely charming place, with a rustic, lived-in feel, and is very passionately run by the hands-on owner – who, having purchased both the Orkney and Atlas breweries, isn't short an award winning ale or two when it comes to stocking the bar. Exposed beams and wooden-panelling abound, and it's hard to choose between the lovely open-fired bar, characterful lounge and traditional restaurant. The wide-ranging menu is fit for king and offers a good selection of frequently changing, classically based dishes. You might find trio of Scottish black pudding, haggis and white pudding, followed by Highland venison with bramble and juniper jus.

5 mi south of Nairn by B 9090.
Parking.

Closing times

Closed 25 December and 1 January

Booking essential Saturday-Sunday

Prices

Meals: à la carte £ 17/25

Typical Dishes

Scallops on black pudding

Chicken breast with haggis

Chocolate truffle tart

16 **Kylesku**

Kylesku IV27 4HW
Tel.: (01971)502231
e-mail: info@kyleskuhotel.co.uk
Website: www.kyleskuhotel.co.uk

Bottles: Skye : Red Cuillin, Black Cuillin; Black Isle : Red Kite, Yellowhammer; Cairngorm Wildcat, Hebridean Gold

This former coaching inn is situated in a peaceful village on the shores of two sea-lochs, in the heart of Scotland's first 'Global Geopark', an area of great geological value. Whether you choose to sit in the bar or outside, there are fabulous panoramic views over Loch Glendhu to the mountains beyond, with similarly impressive outlooks from most of the homely bedrooms. In the bar, two blackboards display the day's menu: one, a seasonal à la carte, the other, a list of daily specials. As you would hope, specialities come in the form of local meat and game – lamb, beef and wild venison from the Highlands – and fresh seafood, which is landed daily on the slipway beside the Hotel; this may include haddock, scallops, crab, lobster or langoustines. With both hot and cold smoking taking place on site, salmon also features highly. After you've eaten lunch, head down to the waters edge, where you can catch a boat trip to the nearby seal colony.

Closing times

Closed mid-October to end February

Prices

Meals: £ 29 (dinner) and à la carte £ 18/27

8 rooms: £ 60/94

Typical Dishes

Venison terrine

Grilled langoustines

Bread & butter pudding

32mi north of Ullapool by A835, A837 and A894. Public car park in the village 50m walk.

17 Loch Ness Inn

Lewiston IV63 6UW
Tel.: (01456)450991
e-mail: info@staylochness.co.uk
Website: www.staylochness.co.uk

Cairngorm Trade Winds, Black Cuillin

Apart from the name and its proximity to the famous loch, there's nothing inside to suggest a link to either Scotland or the mythical monster; making it an honest local pub rather than just a typical tartan-clad tourist attraction. With its neat, tidy exterior and smart wood-furnished rear terrace, you'd never guess that it had stood derelict for seven years; especially when you're rubbing shoulders with numerous groups of locals in the buzzing Brewery bar. Next door, the dining area consists of two spacious rooms featuring exposed stone walls, black slate floors and new timbered beams, enhanced by modern lighting and contemporary artwork on the walls. At lunchtime you'll find a small blackboard menu of honest pub classics, and at dinner, more restaurant-style dishes such as risotto or confit of duck. Named after local lochs and glens, the individually styled bedrooms – with solar panels of their roofs –have a Scottish country feel.

Closing times
Open daily

Prices
Meals: à la carte £ 17/30
12 rooms: £ 57/99

Typical Dishes
Applecross Bay prawns
Roast duck breast & pork belly
Chocolate crème brûlée

14 mi southwest of Inverness by A 82. Parking.

18 Plockton

41 Harbour St,
Plockton IV52 8TN

Tel.: (01599)544274 – Fax: (01599)544475
e-mail: info@plocktonhotel.co.uk **Website:** www.plocktonhotel.co.uk

VISA MC AE

Deuchar's IPA, Plockton Brewery Crags Ale, Skye Brewery Hebridean Gold

Set on the waterfront overlooking Loch Carron, this building started life as two small cottages before being transformed into an inn. Boasting an unusual black exterior, it stands out among the other whitewashed buildings in this small National Trust village; and not just based on its appearance. It's been owned by the Pearson family for over 20 years and has a really welcoming feel – the friendly staff chatting away to both locals and visitors alike. The bar's the centre of activity but there's a small terrace and restaurant if you fancy something a bit quieter. Their speciality is seafood but you'll also find Highland meats and plenty of locally grown Scottish produce; dishes could include Plockton smokies or squat lobster tails to start, followed by seafood bake, casserole of Highland venison or roast monkfish in streaky bacon. Bedrooms are split between the pub and a nearby annexe; those to the front boast great bay views.

Closing times
Open daily

Prices
Meals: à la carte £ 15/40
15 rooms: £ 55/120

Typical Dishes
Plockton smokies
Chargrilled Plockton prawns
Homemade raspberry cranachan

5 mi north of Kyle of Lochalsh. Parking 50 yards away in village car park.

19 Stein Inn

MacLeod Terr,
Stein, Waternish IV55 8GA
Tel.: (01470)592362
e-mail: angus.teresa@steininn.co.uk **Website:** www.stein-inn.co.uk

 VISA MC

Deuchars IPA, Trade Winds, Reeling Dock, Red & Black Cuillin, Skye Ale, Sheepshagger Northern Light, Dark Island

Set on the Waternish Peninsula, towards the northwest end of the island, this whitewashed building dates back to 1790 and beyond, and is the oldest inn on Skye. With large black lettering on the side wall stating its purpose, it's easy to find by car – although seafarers are just as welcome, as this tiny fishing village provides visitor moorings. A characterful wood panelled bar and traditional stone-walled lounge with open fire form the heart of the pub but there's also a quieter dining room, and benches outside for the warmer months. At lunchtime you'll find the likes of fresh crab sandwiches, ploughman's with Scottish cheeses and maybe even a haggis toastie; while dinner – again formed around the latest local produce – is more substantial, and might include Skye scallops, local venison or Scottish salmon. Bedrooms are simple and well-kept; and with no TV, you're free to watch the comings and goings of picturesque Loch Bay instead.

Closing times

Open daily

Prices

Meals: à la carte £ 16/25

5 rooms: £ 37/100

Typical Dishes

Scallops in oatmeal
Venison steak
Homemade fruit crumble

22 mi west of Portree by A 87, A 850 and B 886; on the shore of Loch Bay. Parking.

20 An Lochan Country Inn

Glendevon FK14 7JY
Tel.: (01259)781252 – Fax: (01259)781526
e-mail: tormaukin@anlochan.co.uk
Website: www.anlochan.co.uk

Bitter and Twisted, Thrappledouser, Luckie Ale

This 18C drovers' inn is nestled in the Ochil hills and the drive to reach it is rather breathtaking. It is a great base for hiking, and with Gleneagles just up the road, is also a nifty place to stay if you're here for the golf. Cosy up out of the cold in the beamed bar, with its rustic stone floors and roaring log fire; there's a fantastic choice in beer and whisky, including a beer brewed in Glasgow. The sourcing of quality Perthshire ingredients is of paramount importance to the enthusiastic team, and they aim to acquire everything from within a 25 mile radius: Highland beef comes, appropriately, from a chap called Angus and lamb from a man named Jim. Mary and Shonna hand dive for scallops and the excellently named Winston Churchill, whose red-laced boots grace the menu, stalks the venison. Bread is made on the premises and the well-priced set menu is an attractive option. Traditional, cosy bedrooms feature a flicker of tartan.

Closing times
Open daily

Prices
Meals: £ 13/20
and à la carte £ 20/30

13 rooms: £ 85/100

Typical Dishes
Wild boar terrine
Lamb with lentils
Baileys crème brûlée

22 mi southwest of Perth by M 90 to Junction 7, A 91 and A 823. Parking.

21 The Anglers Inn

Main Road,
Guildtown PH2 6BS
Tel.: (01821)640329
e-mail: info@theanglersinn.co.uk **Website:** www.theanglersinn.co.uk

Inspectors' favourites

 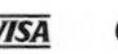   

Locally brewed ales - changing weekly

Situated in a tiny hamlet in the heart of Perthshire, not far from Scone Palace where the Scottish Kings were crowned, this whitewashed pub is surrounded by soft fruit farms and distant views of the Cairngorm and Trossach Mountains. Whilst it doesn't look much from the outside (it could be any of a hundred Scottish country roadside inns), this pub is different, in fact, it's hardly a pub at all; the plain décor, laminate flooring and high-backed chairs are for diners only and you must head to the public bar next door if you are after a relaxing drink. The good value restaurant-style menu is ambitious, displaying a fairly classical French base and some good combinations. Traditional fish and chips is a bestseller but with well-prepared fresh ingredients and careful cooking, you can't go wrong with any dish. Rooms are clean and simple; for hunters and fishermen freezers are available to keep any game or fish fresh.

Closing times
Closed Monday
(January-May)

Prices
Meals: £ 15 (lunch)
and à la carte £ 22/40

5 rooms: £ 50/100

Typical Dishes
Anglers fish cakes
Chargrilled rib-eye steak
Rhubarb crème brûlée

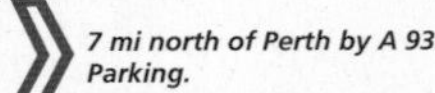
*7 mi north of Perth by A 93.
Parking.*

22 **The Strathardle Inn**

Kirkmichael PH10 7NS
Tel.: (01250)881224 – Fax: (01250)881373
e-mail: strathardleinn@btconnect.com
Website: www.strathardleinn.co.uk

Thrappledouser, Houston Peter's Well, Orkney Brewery Dark Island

As you leave the village of Kirkmichael, heading south towards Blairgowrie on the A924, you pass by this 18C drover's inn, opposite the river. Stop off instead and experience the warm welcome extended by the owners; they hail from Yorkshire originally but are now deeply rooted in this beautiful part of Scotland – a fact that reveals itself in their judicious use of seasonal produce sourced from the surrounding countryside. Cooking is robust and technically sound, with a Scottish twist. The concise lunch menu offers pub favourites like fish and chips, while dinner might feature local venison, smoked salmon or sirloin steak highlander and can be taken in either the bar or the dining room – both of which boast open fires. Bedrooms are simple and modern. Sit in the stillness of the guest lounge to find out what the area has to offer: walking, fishing, a leisurely game of golf; or something more energetic like shooting, cycling or climbing.

Closing times

Closed 2 weeks in January

Prices

Meals: à la carte £ 19/22

8 rooms: £ 50/70

Between Pitlochry and Blairgowrie on A 924. Parking.

Typical Dishes

Smoked salmon
Venison steak
Homemade Baileys cheesecake

It's nearly six hundred years since Owen Glyndawr escaped the clutches of the English to become a national hero, and in all that time the Welsh passion for unity has bound the country together like a scarlet-shirted scrum. It may be only 170 miles from north to south, but Wales contains great swathes of beauty, such as the dark and craggy heights of Snowdonia's ninety mountain peaks, the rolling sandstone bluffs of the Brecon Beacons, and Pembrokeshire's tantalising golden beaches. Bottle-nosed dolphins love it here too, arriving each summer at New Quay in Cardigan Bay. Highlights abound: formidable Harlech Castle dominates its coast, and Bala Lake has a railway that steams along its gentle shores. Hay-on-Wye's four pubs and eighteen bookshops turn perceptions on their head, and Welsh cuisine is causing a surprise or two as well: the country teems with great raw ingredients now employed to their utmost potential, from the humblest cockle to the slenderest slice of succulent lamb.

/BAILE ÁTHA CLIATH
Douglas (I. of Man)
Liverpool
Mostyn
Belfast
Dublin
LIVERPOOL
Liverpool Bay
Southport
St. Anne's
Ainsdale
Formby
Ormskirk
Skelmersdale
Wigan
Chorley
Bolton
Bury
Leyland
Darwen
St. Helens
Warrington
Widnes
Runcorn
Leigh
Altrincham
Bootle
Wallasey
Hoylake
Birkenhead
Bebington
Ellesmere Port
North West
Northwich
Winsford
Frodsham
Chester
Tarporley
Middlewich
Sandbach
Crewe
Nantwich
Newcastle-under-Lyme
Audlem
Market Drayton
Eccleshall
Whitchurch
Wrexham
Wrecsam
Ruabon
Ellesmere
Wem
Hodnet
Crudgington
Telford
WREKIN
Ironbridge
Shrewsbury
SHROPSHIRE
West Midlands
Minsterley
Stretton
Bridgnorth
Montgomery
Newtown
Welshpool
Y Trallwng
Caersws
Llanfyllin
Llynclys
Oswestry
Berwyn
Llangollen
Corwen
Holyhead/
Caergybi
Holy Island
Isle of Anglesey
ANGLESEY
Amlwch
Llanerchymedd
Llangefni
Rhosneigr
Menai Bridge
Newborough
Beaumaris
Great Ormes Head
Llandudno
Colwyn Bay/
Bae Colwyn
Rhyl
Prestatyn
Mostyn
Holywell
Flint/Fflint
Queensferry
Mold/
Yr Wyddgrug
Conwy
Bangor
Penmaenmawr
Llanfairfechan
Abergele
St. Asaph
Denbigh/
Dinbych
Ruthin/
Rhuthun
Bethesda
Carnedd Llewelyn
Capel Curig
Llanrwst
Betws-y-Coed
Pentrefoelas
Cerrigydrudion
Caernarfon
Caernarfon Bay
Llanberis
Snowdon
Snowdonia
Beddgelert
Blaenau Ffestiniog
Ffestiniog
Porthmadog
Criccieth
Penrhyndeudraeth
Nefyn
Lleyn Peninsula
Pwllheli
Abersoch
Aberdaron
GWYNEDD
Snowdonia National Park
Harlech
Bala
Dee
Dolgellau
Barmouth
Cader Idris
Mallwyd
Tywyn
Aberdovey
Machynlleth
WALES
Bay

WALES
CEREDIGION
CARMARTHENSHIRE
PEMBROKESHIRE
POWYS
HEREFORD
South West
BRISTOL CHANNEL
Carmarthen Bay
St. Bride's Bay
Pembrokeshire Coast National Park
Brecon Beacons National Park
Black Mountain
Strumble Head
St. David's Head
St. Govan's Head
Worms Head
Lundy
Rosslare
Cork
Severn Estuary
Aberaeron
Llanrhystud
New Quay
Aberporth
Cardigan/ Aberteifi
Newport
Fishguard/ Abergwaun
St. David's
Haverfordwest/ Hwlffordd
Milford Haven/ Aberdaugleddau
Pembroke Dock/ Doc Penfro
Pembroke
Tenby/ Dinbych-y-pysgod
Saundersfoot
Narberth
Whitland
St. Clears/ Sanclêr
Carmarthen Caerfyrddin
Newcastle Emlyn
Crymych
Llandysul
Synod Inn
Lampeter
Tregaron
Llandovery Llanymddyfri
Llanwrtyd-Wells
Llandeilo
Llangadog
Sennybridge
Brecon/ Aberhonddu
Rhayader Rhaeadr
Llandrindod Wells
Builth Wells/ Llanfair-ym-Muallt
Knighton
Presteigne
Kington
Hay-on-Wye
Talgarth
Crickhowell
Abergavenny/ Y Fenni
Monmouth/ Trefynwy
Pontrilas
Ross on Wye
Hereford
Leominster
Ludlow
Kidderminster
Bewdley
Stourport
Tenbury Wells
Worcester
Bromyard
Great Malvern
Upton
Ledbury
Newtown
Gloucester
Newnham
Coleford
Lydney
Chepstow
Usk
Raglan
Pontypool
Cwmbran
Abertillery
Blaenavon
Brynmawr
Ebbw Vale/ Glyn Ebwy
Tredegar
Merthyr Tydfil
Hirwaun
Aberdare/ Aberdar
Mountain Ash/ Aberpennar
Rhondda
Pontypridd
Bargoed
Bedwas
Risca
Caerphilly
NEWPORT/ CASNEWYDD
CARDIFF/ CAERDYDD
Penarth
Barry/ Barri
Cowbridge
Bridgend/ Pen-y-bont
Porthcawl
Maesteg
Port Talbot
Neath/ Castell-nedd
Swansea/ Abertawe
The Mumbles
Port-Eynon
Rhossili
Llanelli
Burry Port
Kidwelly
Cross Hands
Ammanford
Pontarddulais
Pontardawe
Pendine
Severn Bridge
Chipping Sodbury
Dursley
Malmesbury
Avonmouth
Portishead
Clevedon
Congresbury
Weston-Super-Mare
BRISTOL
Keynsham
Bath
Corsham
Bradford-on-Avon
Trowbridge
Frome
Beckington
Shepton Mallet
Wells
Glastonbury
Burnham
Bridgwater
Watchet
Williton
Dunster
Minehead
Porlock
Exmoor
Lynmouth
Lynton
Combe Martin
Ilfracombe
Croyde
Braunton
Barnstaple
Simonsbath

1 The White Eagle

Rhoscolyn LL65 2NJ
Tel.: (01407)860267 – Fax: (01407)861623
e-mail: white.eagle@timpson.com **Website:** www.white-eagle.co.uk

 **Cobblers, Thornbridge Brewery, Weetwood Eastgate Ale**

Set in a small coastal hamlet on the peninsula, The White Eagle boasts great sea views from its spacious decked terrace. From the outside it may look more like a restaurant but swing a right through the door and you'll find locals playing on slot machines in a cosy open-fired bar, where enlarged postcards of the area fill the walls. It's rightly popular, so you might have to wait for a table; fill your time by wandering around the open-plan dining room with glass feature wall and display of the owners' business history – they also own Timpson Shoe Repairs. The monthly menu offers something for everyone, from sandwiches and salads to pub classics and more sophisticated fare. Dishes arrive well-presented, in a contemporary style, whether it's traditional battered haddock, chips and peas or more modern pan-fried salmon with prawn and chorizo butter. Daily fish specials, regular pie or sausage weeks and weekend beer festivals also feature.

Closing times
Closed 25 December

Prices
Meals: à la carte £ 20/27

Typical Dishes
Black pudding fritters
Pan-fried salmon
Bara Brith & butter pudding

5 mi south of Holyhead by B 4545 and minor road south. Parking.

2 The New Conway

53 Conway Rd,
Cardiff CF11 9NW
Tel.: (029)20224373
Website: www.theconway.co.uk

    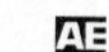

 **Greene King IPA, Light Headed, Otter Bitter, Otley, Fee Fi Fo Fum and rotating guest ales**

Known locally as the Chelsea of Cardiff, all this residential area just north of the city lacked was a decent neighbourhood pub. Having been shown some sorely needed love, the New (improved) Conway now fits the bill rather nicely. Still very much a place for local drinkers, you are welcome here for everything from a pint and a bowl of chips whilst you watch the Six Nations, through to a three course meal and a bottle of wine from the well-priced list. A makeover has given the pub a light, modern feel, with comfy sofas by the fire and shelves crammed with books and board games. Although prone to the odd over-elaboration, their approach to food is, in the main, pleasingly simple: using fresh, seasonal and local produce to create tasty pub classics like steak and chips, toad in the hole or apple and raisin crumble. Having chosen from the daily changing blackboard menu, place your order at the bar; service is friendly and efficient.

Closing times
Open daily

Prices
Meals: à la carte £ 15/30

Typical Dishes
Smoked mackerel pâté
Braised ox cheek
Conway Mocha experience

 *Parking in neighbouring roads.* 

3 Y Polyn

Nantgaredig SA32 7LH
Tel.: (01267)290000
e-mail: ypolyn@hotmail.com **Website:** www.ypolyn.co.uk

 **Ffos-y-Ffin Ale, Deuchar's IPA, Tomos Watkins Cwrw Haf**

With a wealth of experience shared between the owners, you can be sure that they know what they're doing here. Set in a great corner location on a rural road, next to a stream and with views across the surrounding fields, this pub attracts diners from far and wide. The whole place feels like a modern, rustic style dining room and despite the casual attire of the servers, most guests dress to the nines. Cooking is classical but with a modern element and, as you would expect, is hearty, tasty and uses local produce wherever possible. The simpler lunch selection is priced accordingly, while in the evening the choice expands under a set menu, each dish arriving with a complimentary side of veg; some main courses do attract a supplement. There's a sensibly priced wine list and the host enjoys making recommendations. In the hallway, co-owner and restaurant consultant Simon Wright's articles are on display and copies of his book are for sale.

Closing times
Closed 25-26 December, 1 January, Sunday dinner, and Monday

Prices
Meals: £ 13/29
and à la carte £ 20/32

Typical Dishes
Pork rillettes & beetroot chutney
Lamb hotpot
Treacle tart & vanilla ice cream

5 mi east of Carmarthen on A 40; from Nantgaredig 1 mi south by B 4310 on B 4300. Parking.

4 The Angel

Salem SA197LY
Tel.: (01558)823394
e-mail: rodpeterson@btconnect.com **Website:** www.angelsalem.co.uk

 **Brains S A and changing guest beer**

Atypical appearance-wise for a village pub and seemingly situated in the middle of nowhere, The Angel Inn is nonetheless a heavenly haven for hungry punters. Its inviting bar lounge offers comfy sofas and open fires, while a meal in its Edwardian style dining room comes with linen-laid tables. Great care and pride is taken with the cooking, which falls mostly into the traditional category, with dishes such as pressed ham hock, roast fillet of Welsh beef and Swansea Bay sea bass. Words like sushi, wasabi, spaghetti and tiramisu also crop up on the menu, and there are some unusual combinations, too, in dishes such as the salmon with Welsh rarebit, poached egg and asparagus. Whilst the dinner menu comes at a set cost, dishes on the shorter lunch menu are individually priced. The blackboard displays simpler pub classics like lamb's liver and bacon; there's homemade fudge served with your coffee and homemade chutneys come with the cheese.

Closing times
Closed 1 week in spring, Sunday dinner, Monday, Tuesday lunch

Prices
Meals: à la carte £ 20/35

Typical Dishes
Smoked salmon tortellini
Steamed Welsh lamb pudding
Earl Grey crème brûlée

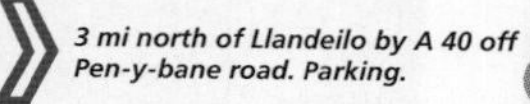
3 mi north of Llandeilo by A 40 off Pen-y-bane road. Parking.

5 Harbourmaster

Quay Parade, Aberaeron SA46 0BA
Tel.: (01545)570755
e-mail: info@harbour-master.com
Website: www.harbour-master.com

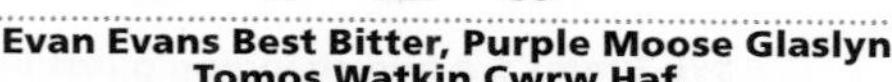
Evan Evans Best Bitter, Purple Moose Glaslyn, Tomos Watkin Cwrw Haf

Having bought and expanded into the old Sea Aquarium next door, The Harbourmaster reopened in Easter 2008 after a major refit and refurbishment. Its bedrooms all have bright colours to reflect being by the sea and are named after boats built in the harbour. The room where the bar counter once stood has now been restyled as the restaurant, complete with nautical pictures, and offers an appealing menu where Welsh Black beef and lamb, and assorted local seafood are permanent fixtures. Those wanting more relaxed surroundings should try the bar, with its large U shaped counter and views into the kitchen. Here the offerings are more pub-like in design. The choice between fishcakes, Caesar salad, oatcakes with Welsh cheeses or venison sausages with parsnip mash and gravy will probably be made easier by the day's weather. Brunch is also available for those spending the day at a more leisurely pace.

Closing times
Closed 25 December, Monday lunch (October-May)

Prices
Meals: £ 18 (lunch) and à la carte £ 20/35

13 rooms: £ 50/250

Typical Dishes
Smoked haddock & cockle chowder
Cum Ystwyth sirloin
Chocolate fondant

In town centre overlooking the harbour. Parking on the harbour road.

6 Pen-y-Bryn

Pen-y-Bryn Rd, Upper Colwyn Bay, Colwyn Bay LL29 6DD
Tel.: (01492)533360
e-mail: pen.y.bryn@brunningandprice.co.uk
Website: www.penybryn-colwynbay.co.uk

  VISA MC AE

 **Thwaites Original, Flowers Original, Great Orme Best, and guest ales - Timothy Taylor Landlord, Conwy Castle, Black Sheep Best, Phoenix & Arizona**

You might need to take your sat nav with you, as even when you've located the right residential street, you could easily pass Pen-y-Bryn by. Looking more like a medical centre than a place to dine, it boasts impressive panoramic views over Colwyn Bay, especially from the garden and terrace. Inside it's spacious and open plan: walls are crammed with pictures, etchings, cartoons and bookcases, whilst old bottles and pottery adorn the beams. Despite the oak floors, old furniture and open fires, it has a modern, laid-back feel; the large tables making it ideal for family outings or gatherings with friends. The extensive daily menu offers plenty of choice, with a good list of sandwiches and light bites, as well as a generous selection of the usual three courses; dishes range from a classical ploughman's to more adventurous fare such as pheasant. During 'Beer and Bangers' weeks a second menu boasts 12 varieties of sausage and over 20 beers.

Closing times
Open daily

Prices
Meals: à la carte £ 19/26

Typical Dishes
Smoked haddock fish cakes
Braised shoulder of Welsh lamb
Sticky toffee pudding

1 mi southwest of Colwyn Bay by B 5113. Parking.

7 The Groes Inn

Tyn-y-Groes LL32 8TN
Tel.: (01492)650545 – Fax: (01492)650855
e-mail: reception@groesinn.com
Website: www.groesinn.com

 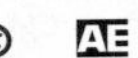 

Located in the foothills of Snowdonia, with the estuary in front and the mountains behind, the setting couldn't be more beautiful. Flowers greet you at the door and the characterful beamed interior is filled with pictures, copperware and china; all bathed in the glow of firelight. If it's nooks and crannies you're after, there are several small rooms encircling the comfy bar, as well as an airy conservatory and an intimate dining room. The bar menu features local Welsh and British dishes in neatly presented, generous portions, while at dinner, the restaurant steps things up a gear, offering more adventurous dishes. The blackboard specials feature plenty of fish from the nearby waters, and there's usually lamb reared on the salt marshes and game from the local estates. Wash this down with a pint from the local Orme Brewery and then head for a tastefully-styled bedroom or the log cabin; all have views and some boast terraces or balconies.

Closing times
Open daily

Prices
Meals: à la carte £ 25/35
14 rooms: £ 85/157

Typical Dishes
Ham hock terrine
Fillet steaks
Groes pancake, homemade ice cream

3 mi south of Conwy on B 5106.
Parking.

8 Glasfryn

Raikes Lane,
Sychdyn, Mold CH7 6LR

Tel.: (01352)750500 – Fax: (01352)751923
e-mail: glasfryn@bandp.co.uk **Website:** www.glasfryn-mold.co.uk

 VISA  AE

 **Facers, Snowdonia Ale, Timothy Taylor Landlord, Flowers Original, Thwaites, Cheshire Cat**

An early example of Arts and Crafts architecture, this glazed red-brick building was intended to be a judges' residence for the courts opposite, but, never used, was later turned into a farm before falling into disrepair. Set next to the monstrous Theatr Clwyd, it too is a sizeable place; the open-plan interior able to cater for a few hundred at every sitting, with some tables seating up to 20 at a time. The friendly team cope well with the numbers, both on the floor and when you order at the large central bar; where you can watch your order whizz past in the vacuum tube system on its way to the kitchen. Menus offer plenty of choice, from pub classics such as fish and chips, to culinary classics such as plaice Véronique; with some lighter dishes like Mediterranean vegetable linguine alongside. Portions are generous, prices are sensible and service is surprisingly swift. The garden and terrace boast pleasant views over the town below.

Closing times
Closed 25 December

Prices
Meals: à la carte £ 18/31

Typical Dishes
Smoked duck with chutney
Braised pheasant
Banana & pecan meringue

 *1 mi north by A 5119 on Civic Centre rd. Parking.* 

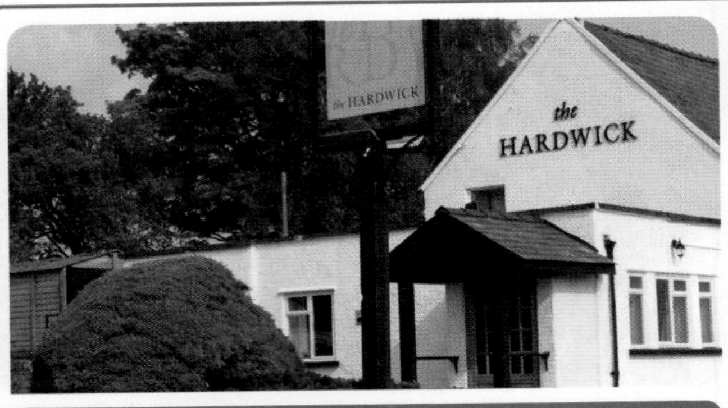

9 The Hardwick

Old Raglan Rd,
Abergavenny NP7 9AA
Tel.: (01873)854220
e-mail: info@thehardwick.co.uk **Website:** www.thehardwick.co.uk

Inspectors' favourites

 **Rhymney Best, Hobby Horse, Otley Brewery**

To pass by this simple, whitewashed pub would be a culinary crime, but with its unassuming exterior, could be all too easily done. Having won the BBC's 'Great British Menu', chef Stephen Terry has become somewhat of a local celebrity, but he takes it in his stride and can often be found chatting away to the locals. With wooden tables arranged on slate floors the pub is simply furnished but this helps to frame the fabulous mountain views that can be seen from the tables by the windows. The philosophy here is simplicity and the use of local produce is paramount, so much so that Stephen can often be found not on the phone, but on the farm when placing his orders. Menus are lengthy and feature both British and Mediterranean influences, ranging from eggs Benedict and duck hash to rare breed middle white pork and roast skate wings. Some dishes come with a choice of portion size and there's a good value set menu at lunch. Booking is essential.

Closing times

Closed 25-26 December, Sunday dinner and Monday (except bank holidays)

Booking essential

Prices

Meals: £ 21 (lunch) and à la carte £ 29/40

Typical Dishes

Welsh rarebit
Roast hake
Amalfi lemon meringue pie

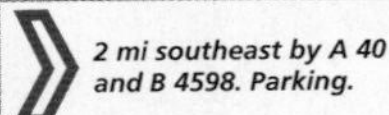

2 mi southeast by A 40 and B 4598. Parking.

10 Raglan Arms

Llandenny NP15 1DL
Tel.: (01291)690800 – Fax: (01291)690155
e-mail: raglanarms@aol.com
Website: www.raglanarms.com

 **Wye Valley Butty Bach, Breconshire Brewery**

It may look like a row of stone cottages, and once offered hospitality of an entirely different kind when it functioned as the local brothel, but The Raglan Arms is very much the village pub. With fireside leather sofas, simply laid scrubbed pine tables and vases filled with fresh flowers, it offers a wholesome cosiness; dining happens mostly in the front of the room, while drinkers tend to congregate in the conservatory at the back. Menus change slightly at each service and are short and to the point. The kitchen is clearly serious about food, using local produce wherever possible and employing a range of cooking styles. Dishes could include home cured bresaola, imam bayildi with mint and crème fraîche, goujons of lemon sole or linguine with cambozola, while dessert might mean a panna cotta or some homemade ice cream and sorbets. There is always a sandwich available at lunch, and main courses offer particularly good value for money.

Closing times
Closed 25-26 December, most bank holidays, Sunday dinner and Monday

Prices
Meals: à la carte £ 22/31

Typical Dishes
Tian of crab with mango
Trio of duck
Sauternes custard with prunes

4¼ mi northeast of Usk by A 472 off B 4235. Parking.

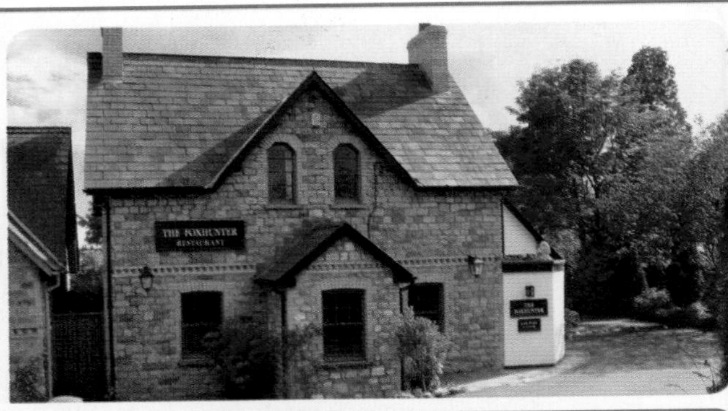

11 The Foxhunter

Nant-y-Derry NP7 9DD
Tel.: (01873)881101
e-mail: info@thefoxhunter.com
Website: www.thefoxhunter.com

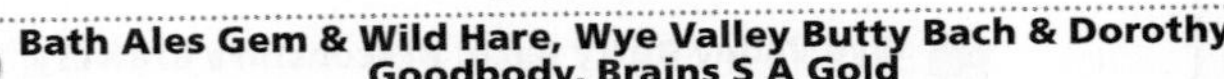

Bath Ales Gem & Wild Hare, Wye Valley Butty Bach & Dorothy Goodbody, Brains S A Gold

Owner Matt Tebbutt's skill in the kitchen has long been recognised in this area of Wales; thanks to his television work, word has now spread, making this former station master's house a popular destination for gastronomes. Inside, the feel is fresh and bright, with food prints on the walls, flagstone floors and wood burning stoves. The simply laid tables are set out in rather regimented rows in the main dining room; sit instead by the fireside in the cosy central space. The short menus change at each service and feature dishes which range in style from classic British to fusion; perhaps Longhorn sirloin, mozzarella and beef tomato, or sashimi of tuna with warm pepperonata salad. Portions are large and hearty and come served with tasty homemade bread; the wine list is impressive, with plenty of range in price. Want to learn more about food? Go foraging with a guide in local woodland, before enjoying the fruits of your labour in the pub.

Closing times
Closed 25-26 December, 1 January, Sunday dinner, Monday

Prices
Meals: £ 25 (lunch) and à la carte £ 29/36

Typical Dishes
Wild garlic soup
Loch Fyne scallops
Elderflower posset

6½ mi south of Abergavenny by A 4042 and minor rd. Parking.

12 The Bell at Skenfrith

Skenfrith NP7 8UH

Tel.: (01600)750235 – Fax: (01600)750525

e-mail: enquiries@skenfrith.co.uk

Website: www.skenfrith.co.uk

 **Kingstone Gold, Monmouth, Wye Valley Bitter, Stoke Lacey**

Nestling in a verdant valley, in view of the Black Mountains and the River Monnow, The Bell offers uncomplicated warmth: a seat in a comfy sofa by the inglenook, candles and meadow flowers on the tables and friendly, unobtrusive service. The weekly changing menu features classics styled in a modern manner: there is almost always a salad using ingredients from the pub's organic garden; other dishes might include Wye Valley smoked salmon, a vegetable risotto, or a carpaccio of Brecon beef. Cooking is clean and fresh and lets the ingredients speak for themselves; the local suppliers of the produce invariably credited on the menu. The fruits of the vine are also taken seriously here; there is a large selection of wines by the glass and an impressive choice of champagnes. Bedrooms are understated in their elegance, with super-comfy beds, fluffy towels and personalised toiletries. Heckham Peckham, with mezzanine bathroom, is the best.

Closing times

Closed last week in January, first week February, Tuesday (November-Easter)

Booking essential

Prices

Meals: £ 23 (Sunday lunch) £29 (dinner and à la carte £ 20/29

11 rooms: £ 75/220

Typical Dishes

Pan-seared King scallops

Roast middle neck of Welsh lamb

Rhubarb Eton Mess

11 mi west of Ross-on-Wye by A 49 on B 4521. Parking.

13 The Felin Fach Griffin

Felin Fach,
Brecon LD3 0UB
Tel.: (01874)620111
e-mail: enquiries@eatdrinksleep.ltd.uk **Website:** www.felinfachgriffin.co.uk

VISA MC

Wye Valley Butty Bach, Hereford Pale Ale, Breconshire Brewery Cribyn or Red Dragon

Like its sister operation, The Gurnard's Head, this pub is rather unique. A terracotta-coloured former farmhouse set in picturesque countryside, the atmosphere here is so laid back it's almost horizontal. With visitors aged from 1-100 and from all walks of life, it has an almost bohemian atmosphere and, without much work, could easily become your home from home. Bright paintwork, a mixture of classical and modern art, and magazines scattered about the place provide a very 'lived in' feel; so it'll strike you as perfectly natural to head to one of the super-comfy bedrooms after your meal. The young staff are adept at interacting with customers but just as importantly, have a good knowledge of what they are serving. Dishes like tasty roast salmon, local venison or wild sea bass are attractively presented and a cut above your usual pub grub, with amuse bouches served at dinner, delicious soda bread and homemade chocolates.

Closing times
Closed 25 December and a week in January

Prices
Meals: £ 19/28
and à la carte £ 30/38

7 rooms: £ 70/150

Typical Dishes
Tartare of smoked salmon
Rump of Herdwick lamb
Selection of British cheeses

4¾ mi northeast of Brecon by B 4602 off A 470. Parking.

14 The Bear

High St,
Crickhowell NP8 1BW

Tel.: (01873)810408 – Fax: (01873)811696
e-mail: bearhotel@aol.com **Website:** www.bearhotel.co.uk

VISA MC AE

 **Bass, Revd James, Rumney, Thwaites**

They were one of the first providers of hospitality for travellers, yet, over the years, many coaching inns have sadly fallen by the wayside. Standing proudly on the main street of this small town, its hanging baskets creating a riot of colour, the well-maintained Bear thankfully bucks the trend. Stepping through the front door into its hugely characterful lounge bar, with its shiny brass and open fireplaces, you can well believe that it has been here since 1432. Diners can sit here or in the more formal restaurant; the latter may be more romantic but the former is undoubtedly the more appealing. The menu offers tasty, tried-and-tested dishes such as prawn cocktail, Welsh rarebit fish and chips or lasagne. The 'specials' add interest and a young cheery team provide swift and assured service, even when busy. Bedrooms have been recently updated; the most characterful are in the main house and feature beams, four-posters and fireplaces.

Closing times
Closed 25 December

Prices
Meals: à la carte £ 17/25
34 rooms: £ 70/153

Typical Dishes
Welsh rarebit
Shank of Welsh lamb
Bread & butter pudding

 *In the town centre. Parking.* 

Crickhowell

15 Nantyffin Cider Mill Inn

Brecon Rd,
Crickhowell NP8 1SG
Tel.: (01873)810775 – Fax: (01873)810986
e-mail: info@cidermill.co.uk **Website:** www.cidermill.co.uk

 **Brains - Reverend James and S.A.**

Situated on the main road, just across from the River Usk, sits this converted 16C cider mill, with its salmon pink tinge. Its enthusiastic owners fly the flag for Welsh produce, with short, simple menus which feature predominantly Mediterranean influences. The à la carte focuses on meat dishes, with choices like the ever popular confit of lamb; there's a blackboard menu of fish specials, with the likes of scallops and mussels, while the set price 'Drovers' Menu' features old favourites such as shepherd's pie, honey-roast gammon and rhubarb crumble. Most people dine in the homely bar, with its wood burning stoves at either end. The spacious adjoining barn, open Friday and Saturday evenings and Sunday lunch – and home to the original cider press – has a completely different feel, with clothed tables, wicker chairs and skylights. Real ales, and of course cider, are available on tap, while the short wine list offers plenty for under £30.

Closing times
Closed Monday (except bank holidays), Sunday dinner (October to Easter)

Prices
Meals: £ 17 (lunch) and à la carte £ 22/30

Typical Dishes
Smoked chicken ravioli
Confit of Welsh mountain lamb
Sticky toffee pudding

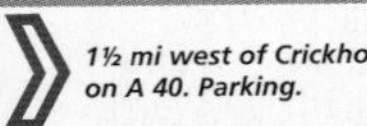
1½ mi west of Crickhowell on A 40. Parking.

16 Old Black Lion

26 Lion St,
Hay-on-Wye HR3 5AD
Tel.: (01497)820841 – Fax: (01497)822960
e-mail: info@oldblacklion.co.uk **Website:** www.oldblacklion.co.uk

  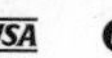  AE

 **Reverend James, Wye Valley, Butty Bach**

Sitting comfortably in the ancient market town of Hay-on-Wye, this traditional part-13C pub stands on the site of the old town gates and would once have provided refuge for travellers passing through from Ireland to England. Although its visitors have now changed – here for the antique and bookshops, as well as the annual literary festival – the pub has not, and it still retains much of its old world charm: inside you'll find low beams and scrubbed wooden tables set amongst brightly coloured walls. The food here is tasty and honest, and arrives in hearty portions; starters and desserts present some good choices, while for main course there's a seemingly endless list of dishes, with even more favourites chalked up on the board – maybe duck on parsnip purée or herb crusted lamb. Just across from the pub, the newly refurbished bedrooms boast rich colours and modern bathrooms, while those in the main building display antique furnishings.

Closing times
Closed 25 December

Prices
Meals: à la carte £ 21/31
10 rooms: £ 48/95

Typical Dishes
Baked crab & Caerphilly cheese
Rack of lamb
Bread & butter pudding

In the town centre. Parking.

17 Three Tuns

4 Broad St,
Hay-on-Wye HR3 5DB

Tel.: (01497)821855 – Fax: (01497)821955
e-mail: info@three-tuns.com **Website:** www.three-tuns.com

 **Wye Valley Butty Bach**

After being devastated by fire in 2005, the future of this Grade II listed pub – thought to be the oldest surviving building in Hay-on-Wye – was left hanging in the balance. Thankfully though, two dedicated locals picked up the pieces and brought it back to life, managing to save many of the original features, including cruck truss beams, a period dog-leg staircase and large inglenook fireplace. Downstairs the bar leads through to cosy sofas set beneath a big glass roof, and onwards to the terrace; find a seat, study the blackboard menu of wholesome classics, then head to the bar to order. The deep-fried cod in local Wye Valley Butty Bach beer-batter is a firm favourite – but if you'd rather have your cod crab-crusted and accompanied by tagliatelli, head upstairs, where you'll discover friendly table service and a more formal atmosphere. Portions are good and hearty, and the tasty homemade puddings and ice creams are no exception.

Closing times

Closed 25-26 December, Sunday dinner, Monday and Tuesday

Prices

Meals: à la carte £ 20/28

Typical Dishes

Crab cakes
Butty Bach battered cod
Treacle tart & vanilla ice cream

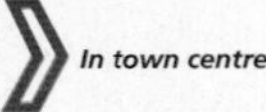

In town centre.

18 **The Talkhouse**

Pontdolgoch SY17 5JE
Tel.: (01686)688919
e-mail: info@talkhouse.co.uk
Website: www.talkhouse.co.uk

 **No real ales offered**

Run by an experienced husband and wife team along the lines of a classic French bistro, The Talkhouse has the look and feel of a small house. There's a comfy lounge strewn with books and magazines, with old black and white photos of the village on the wall, and a cosy bar with seats around the fire for the drinkers. The colourful rear garden, with its gazebo and terrace, is the owners' pride and joy and the best tables in the house are those in the back room which overlook it. Cooking has a very masculine feel to it, with hearty portions and bold flavours; the menu is chalked up on a blackboard and changes daily. Dishes might include stuffed chicken breasts, Welsh lamb rump or pan-fried fish; desserts are read out at the end and might include cheesecake, sticky toffee pudding, ice cream and some local cheeses. Bedrooms follow the cottagey style of the pub, with antique pine furniture and colourful furnishings; Myfanwy is the best.

Closing times

Closed 1-14 November, 24-26 December, Monday-Tuesday (except residents), Wednesday-Thursday lunch

Booking essential

Prices

Meals: à la carte £ 22/30

3 rooms: £ 70/125

Typical Dishes

Ham hock & parsely terrine

Stuffed chicken breast

Vanilla panna cotta

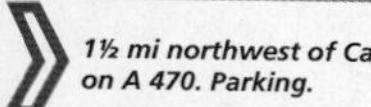

1½ mi northwest of Caersws on A 470. Parking.

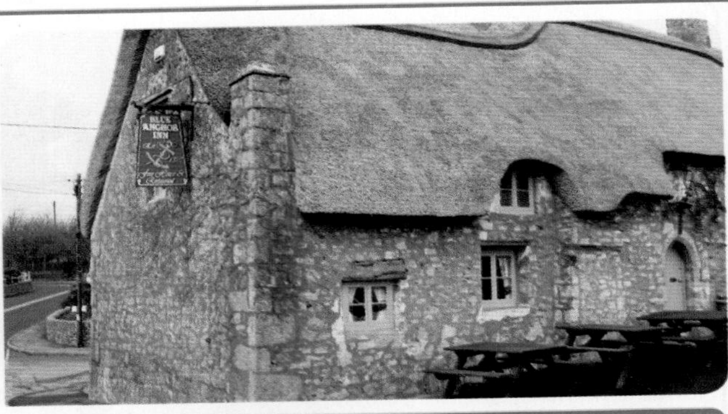

19 The Blue Anchor Inn

East Aberthaw CF62 3DD
Tel.: (01446)750329
e-mail: colemanjeremyj@googlemail.com
Website: www.blueanchoraberthaw.com

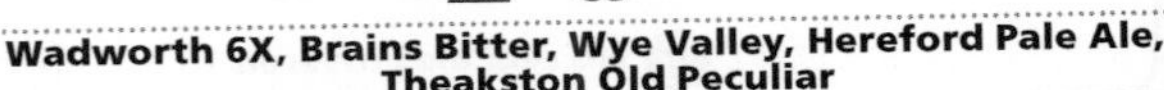

Wadworth 6X, Brains Bitter, Wye Valley, Hereford Pale Ale, Theakston Old Peculiar

The name of this pub dates back to 1380, when East Aberthaw was a bustling trading port and the ships that moored in Aberthaw Bay would leave with their anchors covered in a distinctive blue mud. Inside the stone walls and thatched roof of this medieval pub, you'll find low beamed ceilings and exposed brick walls, along with an inglenook fireplace and nooks and crannies aplenty. You enter into a slate-floored, drinkers-only bar and dimly lit dining area but the real surprise is the vast upstairs restaurant which is open for dinner and Sunday lunch. Cooking is traditional and wholesome, with smart, straightforward presentation and plenty of flavoursome combinations. At lunchtime you'll find simpler dishes such as grilled gammon or beef and ale stew alongside the usual baguettes, jackets and salads; while in the evening, the à la carte provides more interest, and could include pan-seared wood pigeon, local venison or pan-roasted pheasant.

Closing times
Closed Sunday dinner

Prices
Meals: à la carte £ 16/28

Typical Dishes
Pan-seared wood pigeon
Roast oriental pork belly
Lemon mousse

Turn at the cement factory and follow the road for approximately 1 mile. Parking opposite the pub.

20 Pant-yr-Ochain

Old Wrexham Rd, Gresford LL12 8TY
Tel.: (01978)853525 – Fax: (01978)853505
e-mail: pant.yr.ochain@brunningandprice.co.uk
Website: www.brunningandprice.co.uk

Flowers Original, Timothy Taylor Landlord, Weetwood Cheshire Cat, Purple Moose Glas Lyn

It can be safely said that this isn't your usual 21C pub – or even a typical English inn, for that matter – but that's because essentially, it's a classic country manor house. With the previous owners' coat of arms on display and Tudor wattle and daub walls behind the 16C inglenook fireplace, it's definitely steeped in history. Outside, mature gardens and well manicured lawns stretch down to a small lake; and on a warm summer's day, lunch on the terrace or lawn is hard to beat. On colder days, follow the polished quarry tile floors to the large central bar, and choose one of the numerous rooms surrounding it; some with ancient beams and exposed brick walls, all with nooks and crannies aplenty. The daily changing menu offers hearty, wholesome dishes, ranging from pub classics like lamb's liver through to more interesting hake with crab butter. It's a popular place, so arrive early but leave the kids at home because it's over 12s only.

Closing times
Closed 25 December
Booking essential

Prices
Meals: à la carte £ 19/28

Typical Dishes
Scallops & carrot pureé
Steak & game suet pudding
Vanilla panna cotta

3½ mi northeast of Wrexham by A 483 on B 5445; then 1 mi south of Gresford. Parking.

21 The Hand at Llanarmon

Llanarmon Dyffryn Ceiriog LL20 7LD
Tel.: (01691)600666 – Fax: (01691)600262
e-mail: reception@thehandhotel.co.uk
Website: www.thehandhotel.co.uk

 VISA MC

Weetwoods' Eastgate and Cheshire Cat, Stonehouse Station Bitter, Brains Revd James

It's hard to be sure whether the carved wooden hand is commanding you to halt your progress through this delightful village or beckoning you to venture inside the inn; either way, you'd be wise to obey. Set at the crossroads of two old drovers' roads, The Hand has been providing hospitality for several centuries and its current owners are continuing the tradition with flair, providing a warm welcome and hearty meals to travellers through this lush valley. Rustic charm abounds in the form of stone walls, open fires and ancient beams; there' s a cosy bar, a spacious dining room, a pool room and quite a collection of taxidermy. The daily changing menu offers loads of choice, with plenty of wholesome pub classics like steak and kidney pie or slow braised lamb shank. Portions are generous and cooking is fresh and flavoursome. Cosy bedrooms have hill views and recently modernised bathrooms – plus a decanter of sherry for a late night tipple.

Closing times
Open daily
Prices
Meals: £ 18 (Sunday) and à la carte £ 20/32
13 rooms: £ 44/120

Typical Dishes
Smoked cod risotto
Ceiriog Valley lamb
Chocolate & chilli panna cotta

At the head of Ceiriog Valley northwest of Oswestry. Parking.

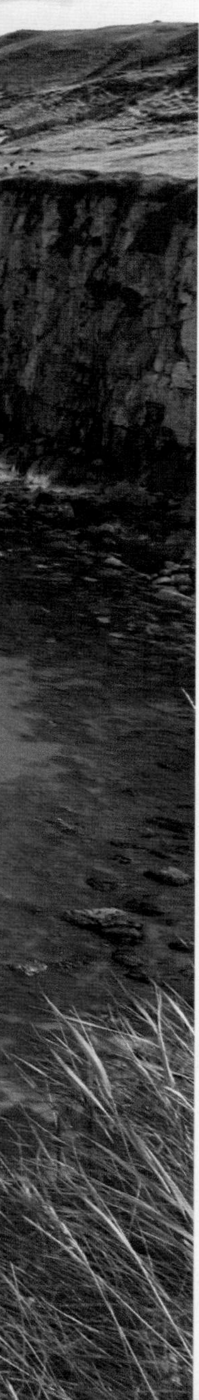

The presiding image of Northern Ireland for outsiders is buzzing Belfast, lying defiantly between mountain and coast. Its City Hall and Queen's University retain the power to impress, and it was within its mighty shipyards that the Titanic first saw the light of day. But the rest of the Six Counties demands attention, too. The forty thousand stone columns of the Giant's Causeway step out into the Irish Sea, part of a grand coastline, though Antrim can also boast nine scenic inland glens. County Down's rolling hills culminate in the alluring slopes of Slieve Donard in the magical Mourne Mountains, while Armagh's Orchard County is a riot of pink in springtime. Fermanagh's glassy, silent lakelands are a tranquil attraction, rivalled for their serenity by the heather-clad Sperrin Mountains, towering over Tyrone and Derry. On top of all this is the cultural lure of boisterous oyster festivals and authentic horse fairs, while farmers' markets are now prominent all across the province.

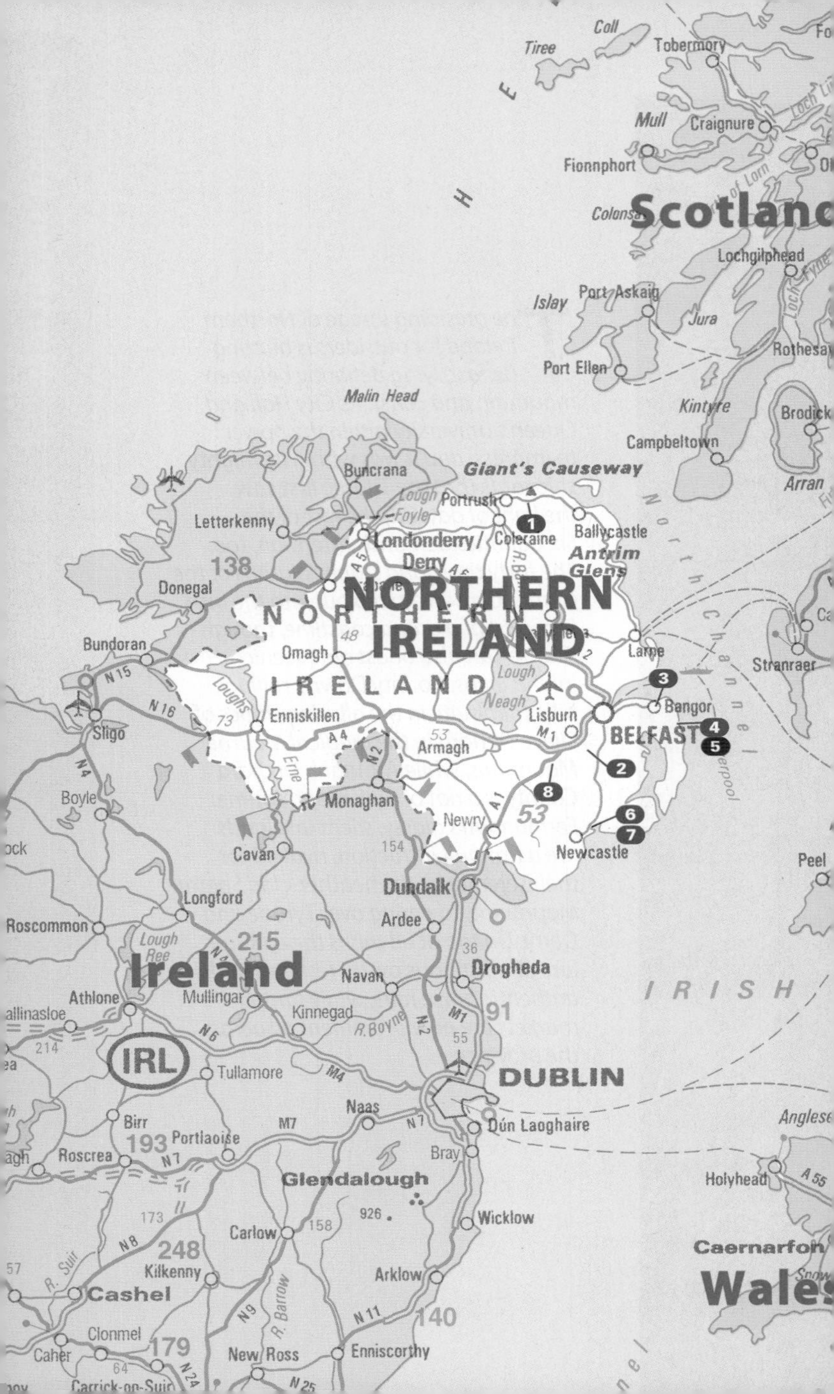

Coll
Tiree
Tobermory
Mull
Craignure
Fionnphort
Colonsay
Scotland
Lochgilphead
Islay
Port Askaig
Jura
Port Ellen
Rothesay
Kintyre
Brodick
Campbeltown
Arran
Malin Head
Giant's Causeway
Buncrana
Lough Foyle
Portrush
Letterkenny
Londonderry / Derry
Coleraine
Ballycastle
Antrim Glens
138
Donegal
NORTHERN IRELAND
Bundoran
Omagh
Larne
Stranraer
N 15
N 16
Loughs
Erne
Lough Neagh
Sligo
Enniskillen
Lisburn
Bangor
BELFAST
Armagh
Boyle
Monaghan
Newry
Cavan
Newcastle
Peel
Dundalk
Longford
Ardee
Roscommon
Lough Ree
215
Ireland
Drogheda
Navan
Athlone
Mullingar
Kinnegad
R. Boyne
91
IRISH
IRL
Tullamore
DUBLIN
Naas
Birr
Dún Laoghaire
193
Portlaoise
Anglesey
Roscrea
Bray
Holyhead
Glendalough
Wicklow
Carlow
Caernarfon
248
Kilkenny
Arklow
Wales
Cashel
140
Clonmel
Caher
179
New Ross
Enniscorthy
Carrick-on-Suir

1 The Distillers Arms

140 Main St,
Bushmills BT57 8QE
Tel.: (028)20731044 – Fax: (028)20731516
e-mail: gary1369@aol.com **Website:** www.distillersarms.com

 **No real ales offered**

A designated conservation area with over 90 listed buildings lining its streets, Bushmills, famous for its whiskey, has its own unique feel – this spacious pub playing its part in the character of this busy town. Set close to the most acclaimed whisky distillery in Ireland – and once home to its owners – The Distillers Arms has recently been taken over by a local boy, Gary, who is breathing new life into the place. Greys, aubergines and bold modern prints vie for attention in the charming dining room, with exposed stone walls and open fires adding a pleasant touch. The menu encompasses all countries and cuisines, with plenty of tried-and-tested combinations and seasonal Irish produce; expect local beef, fish from Donegal, Braemar farm ice cream and a chef's special every day. The philosophy is simple: "Are the ingredients fresh and would I like to eat it?" If the answer is 'yes', then onto the menu it goes; and at a good price too.

Closing times
Closed 24-26 December, 11-12 July, Monday in winter

Prices
Meals: à la carte £ 15/28

Typical Dishes
Chicken liver parfait
Saddle of rabbit in Parma ham
Steamed marmalade pudding

Close to the Bushmills whiskey distillery. Parking.

2 The Pheasant

410 Upper Ballynahinch Rd, Annahilt BT26 6NR
Tel.: (028)92638056 – Fax: (028)92638026
e-mail: info@thepheasantrestaurant.co.uk
Website: www.thepheasantrestaurant.co.uk

Set in the heart of County Down, The Pheasant – sister to The Plough at Hillsborough – is a sizeable yellow-washed inn with a typical Irish feel; right through from the traditional signs and Guinness posters, to the warm welcome and relaxed atmosphere. There's a gothic style to the place, which features stained glass, hunting murals and ornaments aplenty; the traditional open-fired bar making a great place to sit when it's cold, and the patio providing an ideal spot in the warmer months. Cooking uses local, seasonal produce, with seafood the speciality in summer, and pheasant from the nearby estate in winter, along with wood pigeon, partridge and venison. Children are well catered for, with a selection of freshly prepared dishes just for them, as well a selection toys, colouring books and climbing frames to keep them amused. It's a popular place, so if you're out for an occasion, it might be wise to book the snug or Gamekeepers Loft.

Closing times
Closed 25-26 December, 12-13 July

Prices
Meals: £ 13 (lunch) £20 (dinner) and à la carte £ 20/28

Typical Dishes
Warm beef salad
Venison & pheasant sausages
Trio of Irish cheeses

1 mi north of Annahilt on Lisburn rd. Parking.

3 **Coyle's**

44 High St,
Bangor BT20 5AZ
Tel.: (028)91270362 – Fax: (028)91270362
Website: www.coylesbistro.co.uk

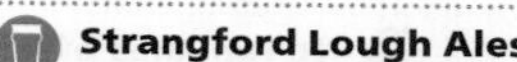
Strangford Lough Ales

In the popular seaside resort of Bangor, you'll find Coyle's, a black painted pub that's, well, typically Irish. If you're looking for a quiet drink and a good meal then this is the place to come; there are no rowdy groups or noisy sports fans, just couples out for a dinner à deux, sat alongside families and friends catching up on the latest gossip. There's a choice of laid-back wood-furnished bistro with small bar area or smarter first floor restaurant – and two different menus; both highlighting a selection of low fat dishes. On the bar menu you'll find the likes of macaroni cheese, fishcakes or steak, and more international flavours such as chilli and ginger chicken; not forgetting several tasty vegetarian options. The bistro menu steps things up a gear; you might find smoked salmon and blini gâteau or devilled lamb's kidneys with pancetta, followed by scallops with spinach risotto or red pepper crusted pork with gnocchi Romana.

Closing times
Closed 25 December

Prices
Meals: à la carte £ 23/32

Typical Dishes
Coconut braised duck leg
Chicken & lentil hot pot
Pear & almond tart

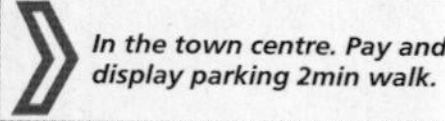
In the town centre. Pay and display parking 2min walk.

Donaghadee

4

Grace Neill's

33 High St,
Donaghadee BT21 0AH
Tel.: (028)91884595 – Fax: (028)91889631
e-mail: info@graceneills.com **Website:** www.graceneills.com

   AE

 **No real ales offered**

It first opened as The King's Arms in 1611 and, 400 years later, the oldest pub in Ireland is still going strong. Renamed in the 1900s after a former landlady who would welcome every visitor with a kiss, this characterful pub welcomes you back in time; pass by the patio and you'll find beamed snugs displaying antique bottles and old pictures – the place where smugglers once gathered to plot and scheme. Crafted from locally sourced produce, the extensive main menu offers largely classical dishes; you might find Portavogie prawn cocktail or Strangford Lough mussels, followed by homemade burgers, chef's choice sausages or beef and Guinness pie. For those working to a timetable, there's an express menu available at lunchtime; and every meal is supplemented by a list of daily fish and seafood specials. There's live music at the weekends but if you prefer to provide the entertainment yourself, a guitar and tin whistle are kept behind the bar.

Closing times
Closed 25 December

Prices
Meals: à la carte £ 23/35

Typical Dishes
Goat's cheese puff
Seabass fillets with chilli butter
Passion fruit & raspberry cheesecake

In town centre. Parking.

5 **Pier 36**

36 The Parade,
Donaghadee BT21 0HE
Tel.: (028)91884466 – Fax: (028)91884636
e-mail: info@pier36.co.uk **Website:** www.pier36.co.uk

 **No real ales offered**

You couldn't pick a better location for the family business than on the waterfront of this picturesque harbour, opposite the local lighthouse. And it's not just the location that's welcoming – the hospitality is second to none too – the owners having thought of everything, even providing reading glasses for those who have forgotten theirs. It's a spacious place, with a traditional open-fired bar and modern dining room, and plenty going on, including Jazz Wednesdays, Motown Fridays and regular steak or seafood nights. Extensive menus feature good value Light Lunch and Tea Time Tasters in the week, and tempting breakfasts at weekends. Dishes range from the traditional to the more modern, displaying some international influences and plenty of fresh local seafood; you might find a sharing seafood tower, followed by Finnebrogue rump of venison, with as many as 12 desserts – plus ice creams – to finish. Simple, comfy bedrooms boast sea views.

Closing times
Closed 25 December

Prices
Meals: £ 13 (Monday-Saturday until 6.30pm) and à la carte £ 20/35

7 rooms: £ 50/90

Typical Dishes
Seared scallops and bacon
Finnebrogue venison
Apple sponge & custard

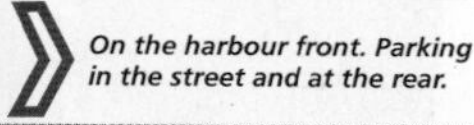
On the harbour front. Parking in the street and at the rear.

6 Buck's Head Inn

77-79 Main St,
Dundrum BT33 0LU
Tel.: (028)43751868
e-mail: buckshead1@aol.com **Website:** www.bucksheadrestaurant.com

 **No real ales offered**

Situated in the historic village of Dundrum, best known for its ruined Norman castle, this mustard-coloured inn looks every inch the traditional pub from the front, with its window boxes and big gold signage. In contrast, the restaurant area overlooking the walled garden to the rear – open in the evening only – has a much more contemporary appearance. Lunch is served in the bar, as is high tea; a popular early evening choice with walkers fresh from Dundrum Bay or the Mourne Mountains, happy to warm themselves by the open fire and admire the oil paintings for sale on the walls. Seafood is the speciality on the modern, internationally-influenced menus, where Dundrum Bay mussels might come au naturel and oysters might come Thai style, while chicken might come as simple chicken supreme or spicy, with a noodle salad. The long-established owners take the wine list seriously and it's well worth investigating.

Closing times
Closed 24-25 December, Monday (October-April)

Prices
Meals: £ 29 (dinner) and à la carte £ 16/28

Typical Dishes
Seafood chowder
Rump of Mourne lamb
Pecan meringue

In the village. Parking in the street.

7 **Mourne Seafood Bar**

10 Main St,
Dundrum BT33 0LU
Tel.: (028)43751377
e-mail: bob@mourneseafood.com **Website:** www.mourneseafood.com

    AE

 **Belfast Ale, Clotworthy Dobbin**

Standing over the road from the popular Buck's Head Inn, this rather untypical seafood bar was previously the current owner's home, and the name plaque 'Downshire Manor' can still be found on the front. He also runs an oyster and mussel farm in Carlingford Lough, source of many dishes here, while other produce is brought in from the local boats. The owner is keen for people to try 'bi-catch' species rather than fish under pressure such as cod, and this simple, casual bar is a great place to give it a go: prices are reasonable and fair. There's a core menu: meanwhile, waiters take time to explain the six or seven daily blackboard specials. Wet fish is available to buy and chef is happy to suggest the best way to cook if asked. It's not just seafood on the menu here: locally reared chicken and steaks also make an appearance. An excellent local reputation is building, so, if it's summertime, do make sure you book first.

Closing times

Closed Monday-Wednesday (October to April)

Booking essential in summer

Prices

Meals: £ 25 (Saturday dinner) and à la carte £ 17/27

Typical Dishes
Crab claws in garlic butter
Monkfish
Lemon meringue pie

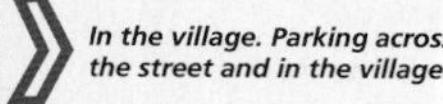
In the village. Parking across the street and in the village.

8 The Plough Inn

3 The Square,
Hillsborough BT26 6AG
Tel.: (028)92682985 – Fax: (028)92682472
e-mail: pattersonderek@hotmail.co.uk

 **Hilden Real Ale selection and guest bitters**

With its lush forest and 40 acre lake, impressive 17C castle and steep streets lined with antique shops, picturesque Hillsborough has plenty to offer; including the locally acclaimed Plough Inn. It's very personally run and having been trading since 1752, is well established within the local community. A former coaching inn, it appears from the outside to be a normal pub – inside, however, you might not recognise it as such, as it's almost three separate establishments in one. There's a traditional dark wood bar serving classical pub dishes, with a similarly styled dining room – renowned for its seafood and steaks – this is where you'll find the regulars and older folk. Upstairs, there's a stylish bistro offering a modern, international menu that's popular with the younger groups; while next door you'll find families in the all day café-cum-weekend nightclub – and there's a choice of terraces too.

Closing times

Closed 25-26 December

Prices

Meals: £ 15/25
and à la carte £ 15/28

Typical Dishes

Seared wood pigeon risotto
Blonde veal
Trio of desserts

At the top of the hill in the square. Parking.

It's reckoned that Ireland offers forty luminous shades of green, and of course an even more famous shade of black liquid refreshment. But it's not all wondrous hills and down-home pubs. The country does other visitor-friendly phenomena just as idyllically: witness the limestone-layered Burren, cut-through by meandering streams, lakes and labyrinthine caves; or the fabulous Cliffs of Moher, unchanged for millennia, looming for mile after mile over the wild Atlantic waves. The cities burst with life: Dublin is now one of Europe's coolest capitals, and free-spirited Cork enjoys a rich cultural heritage. Kilkenny mixes a renowned medieval flavour with a taste for excellent pubs; Galway, one of Ireland's prettiest cities, is enhanced by an easy, boho vibe. Best of all, perhaps, is to sit along the quayside of a fishing village in the esteemed company of a bowl of steaming fresh mussels or gleaming oysters and the taste of a distinctive micro-brewery beer (well, makes a change from stout…).

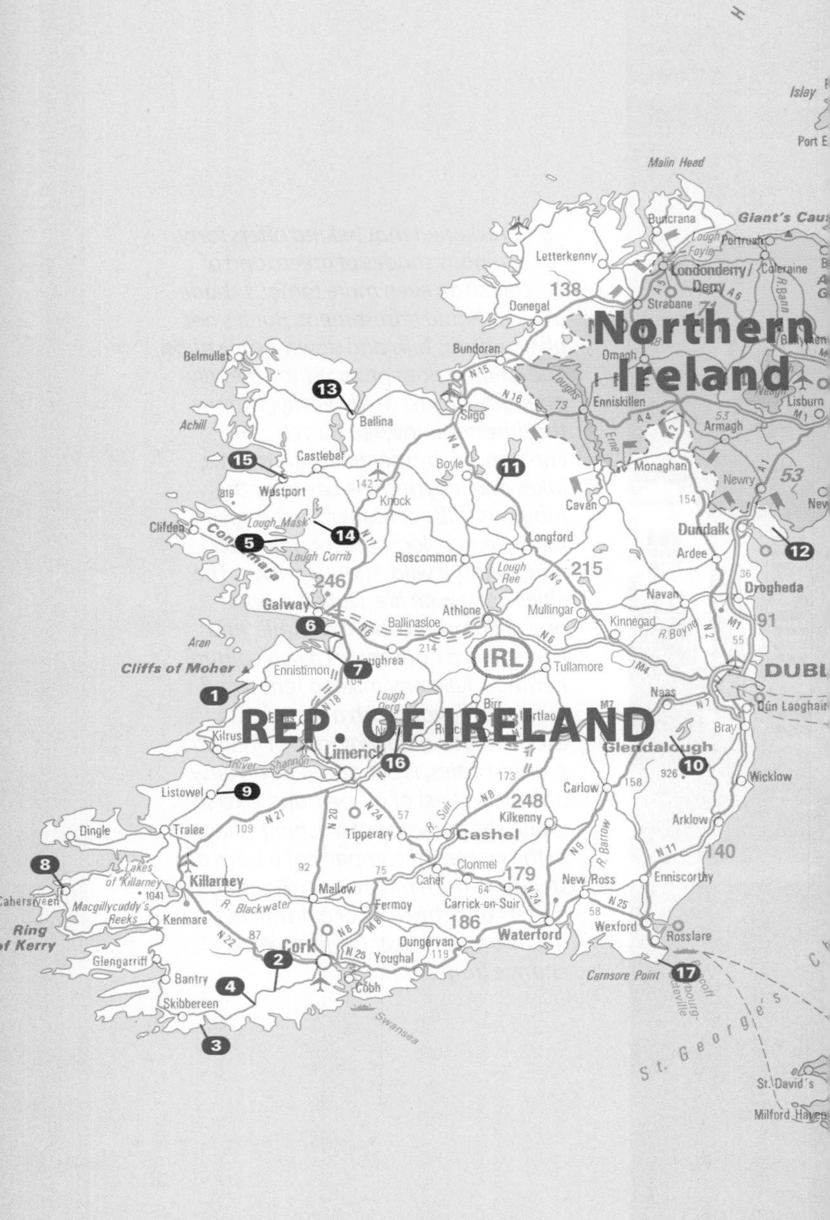

Northern Ireland
REP. OF IRELAND
IRL
Malin Head
Giant's Causeway
Buncrana
Portrush
Coleraine
Letterkenny
Londonderry/Derry
Strabane
Donegal
Omagh
Bundoran
Enniskillen
Lisburn
Armagh
Belmullet
Ballina
Sligo
Achill
Castlebar
Boyle
Monaghan
Westport
Knock
Cavan
Newry
Clifden
Lough Mask
Connemara
Lough Corrib
Longford
Dundalk
Roscommon
Lough Ree
Ardee
Drogheda
Galway
Athlone
Mullingar
Navan
Ballinasloe
Kinnegad
R. Boyne
Aran
Loughrea
Tullamore
Cliffs of Moher
Ennistimon
DUBLIN
Lough Derg
Birr
Naas
Dún Laoghaire
Bray
Kilrush
River Shannon
Limerick
Glendalough
Wicklow
Listowel
Carlow
Dingle
Tralee
Tipperary
Cashel
Kilkenny
Arklow
Lakes of Killarney
Killarney
Clonmel
Caher
R. Barrow
Enniscorthy
Cahersiveen
Macgillycuddy's Reeks
Mallow
Fermoy
New Ross
Ring of Kerry
Kenmare
R. Blackwater
Carrick-on-Suir
Wexford
Rosslare
Cork
Dungarvan
Waterford
Glengarriff
Youghal
Bantry
Cobh
Carnsore Point
Skibbereen
Swansea
St. George's Channel
St. David's
Milford Haven
Islay

1 Vaughan's Anchor Inn

Main Street,
Liscannor

Tel.: (065)7081548 – Fax: (065)7081548
e-mail: info@vaughans.ie **Website:** www.vaughans.ie

No real ales offered

There aren't many pubs where you can sit and sip a pint of the black stuff, have a natter over a seafood platter and then pick up your groceries. One such place is to be found in the picturesque fishing village of Liscannor, along the rugged road to the much-visited Cliffs of Moher. This is a proper pub; lively and full of traditional character, from its bay window full of nautical bric à brac to its long bar spanning almost three rooms and its collection of football banners and scarves. Family-run, it has built up a fine reputation over the last three decades, and chef Denis' seafood-based menus are a big part of the reason why. Eat at simple wooden tables in the cosy, old-style bar or in the newer but equally informal restaurant; typical pub favourites are on offer at lunch, with more adventurous, elaborate meals – from oysters and lobster to duck and foie gras – served in the evening. Bedrooms are too modest for us to recommend.

Closing times
Closed 25 December

Prices
Meals: à la carte € 22/35

Typical Dishes
Black pudding & duck egg
Roasted rump of lamb
Chocolate fondant

2 km from Lahinch by coast road, on main route to Cliffs of Moher. Parking.

2 Poacher's Inn

Clonakilty Rd, Bandon
Tel.: (023)8841159
e-mail: mclaughlinbc@hotmail.com

VISA 

Smithwicks

You've a passion for cooking but you work in recruitment, so what do you do? If you're Barry McLaughlin, you take the bull by the horns and persuade the owner of a nearby restaurant to let you work in the kitchens on a Saturday. You enjoy it so much that you resign from the day job and enrol on a cookery course…fast forward five years and you're successfully running your own pub in your home town of Bandon; the strong local following attracted by a winning combination of smart, comfortable surroundings and wholesome, homecooked food. Sandwiches, fish pies, steaks and the like make up the simple menu available in the cosy bar, supplemented by a daily changing blackboard menu of ten or more – mostly fish – specials. Fresh, local seafood is also very much the order of the day in the intimate upstairs restaurant, where cheery, attentive service keeps things ticking along nicely, and the good value Sunday lunch is particularly popular.

Closing times
Closed 25 December, Good Friday

Prices
Meals: à la carte € 22/36

Typical Dishes
Hot crab claws
Seafood pie
Spiced plum crème brûlée

 *2 km southwest on N 71. Parking.* 

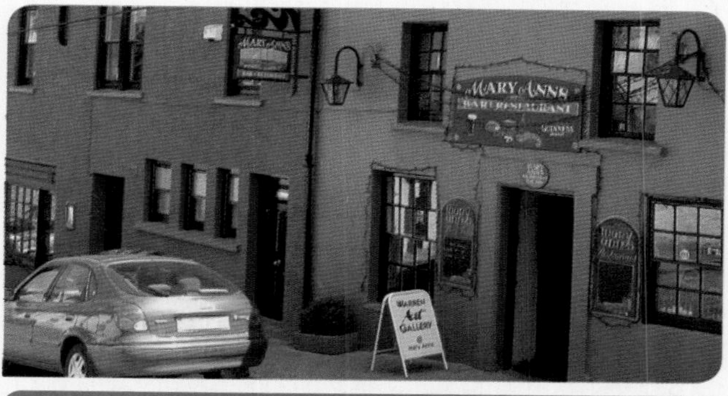

3 Mary Ann's

Main St, Castletownshend
Tel.: (028)36146 – Fax: (028)36920
e-mail: maryanns@eircom.net
Website: www.westcorkweek.com/maryanns/

  VISA MC

 **No real ales offered**

Don't go searching round this pub for someone called Mary Ann – it's actually named after a previous owner – the current ones have been here since 1988 and go by the names of Fergus and Patricia. Eat at simple wooden tables in the bar or head upstairs to dine on tablecloths; in the summer, it's the huge outside terrace which accommodates the crowds, when the pub gets busy with sailors stopping for the night in the harbour. Not too many pubs can boast their own art gallery, but this one can, and it attracts visitors up this steep, narrow street from far and wide. Called The Warren Gallery, it houses the owner's collection of modern Irish art, mostly bought at auction on his travels around the country. The food served here may not quite qualify as a work of art, but it's extremely tasty and there's plenty of it; portions are huge, with masses of vegetables, and the emphasis is firmly on fresh fish and seafood.

Closing times

Closed 25-27 December, Monday in winter

Prices

Meals: à la carte € 25/45

Typical Dishes

Baked avocado & crabmeat
Scallops Mary Ann
Strawberry meringue roulade

Between Rosscarbery and Skibbereen south of N 71. Parking in the main street.

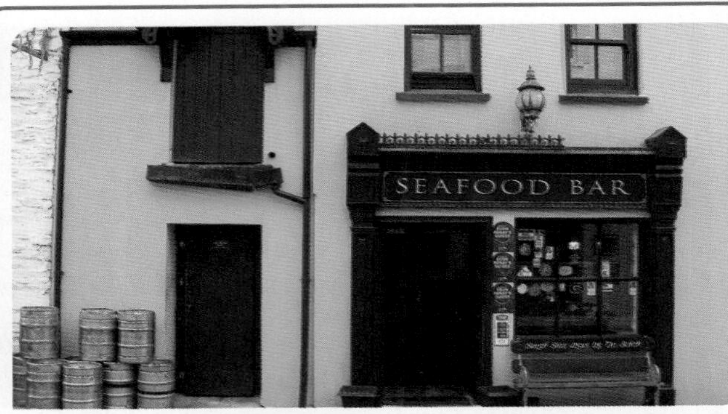

4 **An Súgan**

41 Wolfe Tone St,
Clonakilty
Tel.: (023)8833719 – Fax: (023)8833825
e-mail: ansugan4@eircom.net **Website:** www.ansugan.com

 VISA

 **No real ales offered**

Personally run by a capable family team, this salmon-pink pub with its traditional shop front, is everything you could ask for. Offering charm aplenty and a real sense of history, it has established itself as something of a local institution, and along with the regulars, you'll find plenty of visitors in the four characterful dining rooms. The logo – depicting a fish, a lobster and several shellfish – provides a good idea of what to expect from the cooking. Menus are based around the daily arrival of fresh fish and seafood from a local supplier, so you'll discover an all day selection of light dishes such as moules marinierè, seafood salad or salmon and potato cakes, followed by more substantial offerings in the evening; maybe coquille of seafood, prawn farcies or salmon in filo pastry. Less fishy plates might include chicken liver pâté or roasted lamb shanks, while specials might involve stuffed crab claws, black sole or whole lobster.

Closing times
Closed 25-26 December and Good Friday

Prices
Meals: à la carte € 25/45

Typical Dishes
Fresh crab claws
Súgan seafood basket
Queen of puddings

 *East of town centre. Parking n the street.* 

5 **John J Burke**

Mount Gable House, Clonbur

Tel.: (094)9546175

e-mail: tibhurca@eircom.net **Website:** www.burkes-clonbur.com

 **No real ales offered**

Four generations of the Burke family have presided over this popular pub, each keeping it true to tradition, much like the unspoilt village of Clonbur in which it resides. The big open bar has a cavernous feel, with high ceilings and walls filled with knick-knacks; keep an eye out for the miniature football figures painted in the different counties' colours, lined up their current standings above the bar. If the weather's inclement, you might choose to sit by the open fire in the rear restaurant; on a sunny day it's best to be out on the terrace, with its view over the garden and of the distant Mount Gable. Light meals are available at lunchtimes, with an à la carte of more hearty meat or fish dishes in the evenings. There's a pool room for those handy with a cue, but if armchair sports are more your thing then head for the snug – once an old shop – to catch the all important scores on the flat screen. Upstairs simple bedrooms await.

Closing times

Closed 25 December and Good Friday

Prices

Meals: à la carte € 30/38

4 rooms: € 35/70

Typical Dishes

Seafood chowder

Honey glazed bacon & cabbage

Homemade apple tart

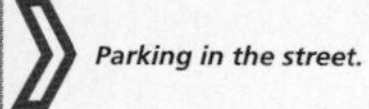

Parking in the street.

6 Moran's Oyster Cottage

The Weir,
Kilcolgan

Tel.: (091)796113 – Fax: (091)796150

e-mail: moranstheweir@eircom.net **Website:** www.moransoystercottage.com

Inspectors' favourites

 VISA  AE

 **Smithwicks**

Situated in a tiny hamlet, and accessed via country lanes, unless you'd heard of this inn, you'd never know it was there. Chances are, though, if you're in this part of the world, you most definitely will have heard of it, as its reputation for all things edible and from the sea tends to precede it – and the pictures on the walls show in whose famous footsteps you follow. In the summer, the place gets packed out; and don't be too surprised if you see the odd coach driving up here, for the place is now virtually a tourist attraction. What's the big deal? Well, it makes for a very pleasant spot on a sunny day, watching the swans glide by, and with its 18C origins, thatched roof and cosy front bar, it certainly has plenty of character. It's well-run and the service is friendly, but primarily people come here for the oysters. The seafood is fresh and simply prepared, and includes smoked salmon, crabs, prawns – and oysters. Always oysters.

Closing times

Closed 24-26 December and Good Friday

Prices

Meals: à la carte € 25/40

Typical Dishes

Native oysters
Lobster with salad
Baileys cheesecake

5min from the village of Clarinbridge. Parking in road.

7 Keogh's Bar

Main St,
Kinvarra

Tel.: (091)637145 – Fax: (091)637028
e-mail: mikeogh@eircom.net **Website:** www.kinvara.com/keogh

 **No real ales offered**

Dying for a drink or a bite to eat? In your rush to park the car and cross the threshold of this red-hued pub, be careful which door you take, for picking the wrong one could mean that you end up communing with a different sort of spirit entirely in next door's funeral parlour. Assuming you've chosen the correct entrance, you'll find yourself in a traditional Irish bar: there's a small front lounge decorated with old memorabilia and photos of local Gaelic football teams, a separate bar busy with locals, and a dining area furnished with simple wooden tables, where most folks sit to eat. Gateway to the Burren, Kinvara is a pretty fishing village on the Galway coast, so as is to be expected, there's plenty of seafood on the menu, but they also offer traditional hearty dishes such as roast beef and lamb or lasagne, as well as paninis for those with smaller appetites, and a range of classic desserts such as bread and butter pudding.

Closing times
Open daily

Prices
Meals: à la carte € 18/27

Typical Dishes
Smoked salmon salad
Baked fillet of cod
Homemade apple pie

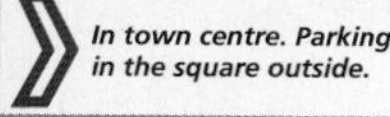

In town centre. Parking in the square outside.

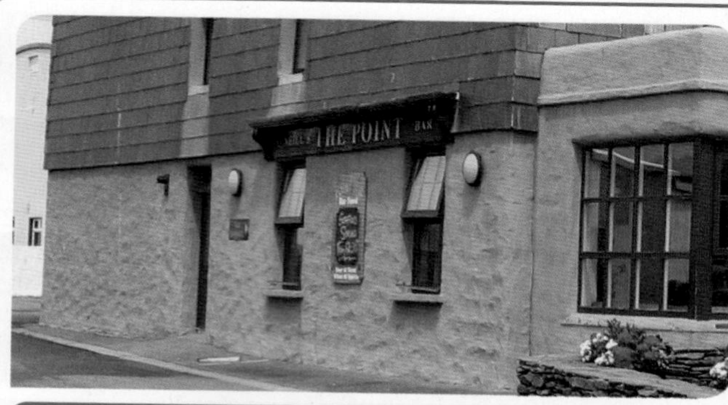

8 O'Neill's (The Point) Seafood Bar

Renard Point,
Cahersiveen
Tel.: (066)9472165 – Fax: (066)9472165
e-mail: oneillsthepoint@eircom.net

 **No real ales offered**

Located down on the western edge of the Iveragh Peninsula, where the car ferry leaves for Valencia Island, The Point is one of those places people return to time and time again. One of the reasons behind this enthusiasm would have to be the friendly nature of the pub's owners. Their welcome is so warm, it's positively toasty, and having been at the reins for two decades now, they've certainly learnt more than just the basics when it comes to pleasing their customers. The concise seafood menu serves up whatever is freshest and wettest that day; perhaps some lobster, monkfish, squid or shrimp – and of course salmon, as one would expect opposite a smoked salmon factory. The lunchtime menu is shorter, but somewhat cheaper; they don't accept credit cards and there are no desserts but there is a short wine list and the Irish coffee goes down a treat. Simply furnished, the bar is decorated with maritime memorabilia and a Leeds United shield.

Closing times
Closed March-October

Prices
Meals: à la carte € 28/38

Typical Dishes
Hot crab claws with chilli
Pan-fried hake in garlic
Irish Coffee

West of Cahirsiveen: follow the signs for the ferry. Parking.

9 Allo's Bar

41 Church St,
Listowel
Tel.: (068)22880 – Fax: (068)22803
e-mail: allos@eircom.net

VISA MC AE

No real ales offered but a large selection of Irish whiskies

Right in the heart of Listowel, famous for its annual literary and horse-racing festivals, sits this characterful pub, brightly painted in shades of yellow and orange. Step inside and it's as if you've entered a time warp; jugs hang from the ceiling, old adverts for tobacco and whiskey dot the walls, and rows of books line the shelves. There's a small snug at the front, and you can eat either in the bar, with its very long counter, or more formally next door in the restaurant, above cherry wood floorboards reputed to have come from the London Stock Exchange. Lunchtime sees a simple menu of snacks and nibbles on offer, while there's a full à la carte of traditional Irish meat and fish dishes in the evening as well as themed evenings every Thursday. Antique-furnished bedrooms are reached via a steep, narrow staircase; room 1 boasts a four poster bed and roll top bath, while 2 and 3 offer a comfortable night's slumber in a sleigh bed.

Closing times
Closed Sunday-Monday and bank holidays

Booking essential

Prices
Meals: à la carte € 20/45

3 rooms: € 60/100

Typical Dishes
Courgette fritters
Baked fillet of hake
Tarte au citron

In the town centre, off north corner of the Square. Parking in front on street and at rear.

10 Ballymore Inn

Ballymore Eustace

Tel.: (045)864585 – Fax: (045)864747

e-mail: theballymoreinn@eircom.net **Website:** www.ballymoreinn.com

 **No real ales offered**

Set in a small village in horse breeding country, close to the Aga Khan's stud, this pub's claim to fame is that Clint Eastwood and Larry Hagman have popped in on their way to the races. To the rear, there's a large bar that screens sporting events and hosts live music, while to the front is a spacious dining area with red leather banquettes, mosaic flooring and a Parisian brasserie feel. Lunchtime sees salads, homemade pizzas and main courses such as stir fry, risotto and chicken curry, with a few more substantial dishes appearing at dinner. The owner is keen to promote small artisan producers, so you'll find organic veg, meat from quality assured farms and farmhouse cheeses on your plate. Portions are generous but you don't want to miss the tasty bread to start or the homemade tarts and pastries to finish. The pleasant staff always go the extra mile and service is stepped up a gear at weekends with a receptionist and sommelier.

Closing times

Closed 25 December and Good Friday

Prices

Meals: € 22/30 and à la carte € 34/58

Typical Dishes

Connemara ham

Duncannon cod

Plum & almond tart

9 km south of Naas by R 411. Parking.

11 The Oarsman

Bridge St,
Carrick-on-Shannon
Tel.: (071)9621733 – Fax: (071)9621734
e-mail: info@theoarsman.com **Website:** www.theoarsman.com

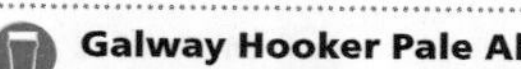
Galway Hooker Pale Ale

If you're cruising on down to Carrick-on-Shannon, the boating capital of inland Ireland, or maybe angling for a fish in one of its many surrounding lakes, make time to pay a visit to the suitably named Oarsman. Owned and run by the Maher family, who have been involved in the hospitality industry for generations, it's set on a busy street in the town centre; a friendly, characterful place with a lively local feel. Its double-fronted windows are filled with county flags and bric à brac, and the old-fashioned charm continues inside, with dark wood panelled walls filled with photos, mirrors and ornaments. Menus offer a mix of snacks, salads, soups and sandwiches as well as popular pub favourites, daily blackboard specials and more restaurant-style dishes, all made with produce gleaned from the local landscape. Swift, efficient service from polite and chatty staff is the other key ingredient in a pleasant lunch or evening out.

Closing times
Closed 25 December, Good Friday, Sunday and Monday (except bank holidays)

Prices
Meals: € 20/35
and à la carte € 18/22

Typical Dishes
Seared Kilkeel scallops
Sautéed monkfish tail
Vanilla crème brûlée

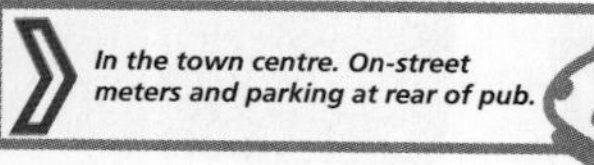
In the town centre. On-street meters and parking at rear of pub.

Republic of Ireland • Leitrim

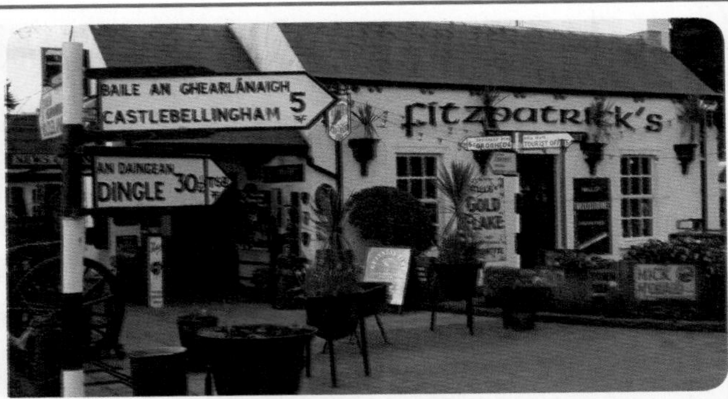

12 Fitzpatricks

Rockmarshall, Jenkinstown

Tel.: (042)9376193 – Fax: (042)9376274

e-mail: admin@fitzpatricks-restaurant.ie

Website: www.fitzpatricks-restaurant.com

 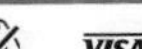 

 **McArdles**

At the foot of the Cooley Mountains on the coast road to the peninsula, you'll find this classical whitewashed pub overlooking Dundalk Bay. To call it characterful would be an understatement: this is a place where you can take in the whole Irish experience without even leaving the building. The car park and gardens are filled with colourful flowers set in old collectibles such as bicycles, boots and even a bed; while inside there's memorabilia aplenty and a fascinating collection of old chamber pots and Victorian toiletries in the bathrooms. There's a drinkers-only area frequented by the locals and a beautiful bar with polished brass rails. The extensive menu features hearty, flavoursome portions of traditionally prepared dishes, such as chowder, chicken wings and home battered scampi. Local seafood and steaks are something of a speciality, while more adventurous offerings can be found in the restaurant, which opens later in the week.

Closing times

Closed Monday in winter (except bank holidays)

Prices

Meals: € 25 (dinner) and à la carte € 30/43

Typical Dishes

Seafood chowder

Corned beef with mustard sauce

Baked rice pudding

9 km northeast of Dundalk following N 52 on R 173. Parking.

13 Crockets on the Quay

The Quay,
Ballina

Tel.: (096)75930 – Fax: (096)70069
e-mail: info@crocketsonthequay.ie **Website:** www.crocketsonthequay.ie

   AE

 **Smithwicks**

Despite appearances – it's housed in a bright orange building outside the town – this is a proper Irish pub, with a spacious, dimly lit and atmospheric interior; wooden floors, beams and a huge central bar. There's a more modern, relaxed area to the rear, where turned down televisions keep you up to date with the sports scores, and the adjacent, stone built former boat house is home to the more formal restaurant, where the same menu is served. Fresh, hearty cooking uses quality ingredients and there's plenty of choice on the menu, with pub favourites like fish and chips and fillet of Irish beef alongside dishes such as pan-fried hake fillet, roast breast of Barbary duck and warm Connemara smoked salmon. There's a terrace out front with a view over the river, staff are ultra-friendly and the place well run. Modest bedrooms offer simple comforts; choose six, seven or eight, as they are above the restaurant and therefore the quietest.

Closing times
Closed 25 December, Good Friday, and lunch Monday-Saturday

Prices
Meals: € 35/45
and à la carte € 23/39
8 rooms: € 45/80

Typical Dishes
Steamed Achill mussels marinière
Fried fillet of sea bream
Warm banana bread

On the northeast edge of town by N 59 besides the River Moy. Parking.

14 **JJ Gannons**

Main St,
Ballinrobe

Tel.: (094)9541008 – Fax: (094)9520018
e-mail: info@jjgannons.com **Website:** www.jjgannons.com

  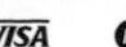

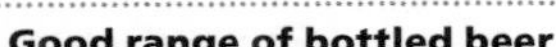
Good range of bottled beer

Situated on the busy one way system, in the very centre of town, the traditionally-fronted JJ Gannons started life in 1838 and, having been numerous things over the years, including a grain store, a garage and even a funeral parlour, is now a modern pub, owned and run by a third generation of Gannons. It boasts a stylish, seductively-lit front bar with wood floors, exposed stone and white and chocolate bucket chairs and banquettes. There's a dimly-lit chill out area, a small terrace and a smart, spacious rear restaurant which lets in plenty of natural light. A fantastic selection of wines by the glass complements an interesting menu of modern classics available in both the bar and the restaurant, and the informal service matches the laid back ambience. Bedrooms are comfortable and modern, with bright colour schemes, flat screen TVs, dark wood furniture and sleek bathrooms.

Closing times
Closed 25 December and Good Friday

Prices
Meals: € 12/45
and à la carte € 12/45

10 rooms: € 69/200

Typical Dishes
Wild mushroom bruschetta
Venison Wellington
Bread & butter pudding

In the centre of town on the one-way system. Parking.

15 **Sheebeen**

Rosbeg,
Westport
Tel.: (098)26528 – Fax: (098)24396
e-mail: info@croninssheebeen.com **Website:** www.croninssheebeen.com

 **No real ales offered**

This attractive whitewashed, thatched pub is situated to the west of town, looking out over Clew Bay and in the shadow of famed mountain, Croagh Patrick. According to legend, this was where St. Patrick fasted for 40 days and 40 nights before banishing all the snakes from Ireland, and thousands of Catholics make a pilgrimage up the mountain every year on the last Sunday in July; some barefoot, and some on their knees as a penance. Fasting not your thing? Cooking here is fresh and simple – everything is homemade, including the bread - with the more interesting dishes to be found among the large selection of daily specials. Try the local fish and seafood, which is accurately prepared and full of flavour – perhaps cod terrine, smoked salmon mousse, lobster, sea trout or John Dory. Live music nights take place every Friday and Saturday; but during the week, don't be surprised to hear Peggy Lee blasting out of the system instead.

Closing times
Closed Monday-Friday
(1 November to 16 March)

Prices
Meals: à la carte € 22/40

Typical Dishes
Honey roast ham terrine
Pan-fried king scallops
Blueberry & almond tart

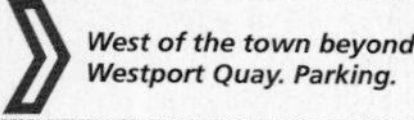
West of the town beyond Westport Quay. Parking.

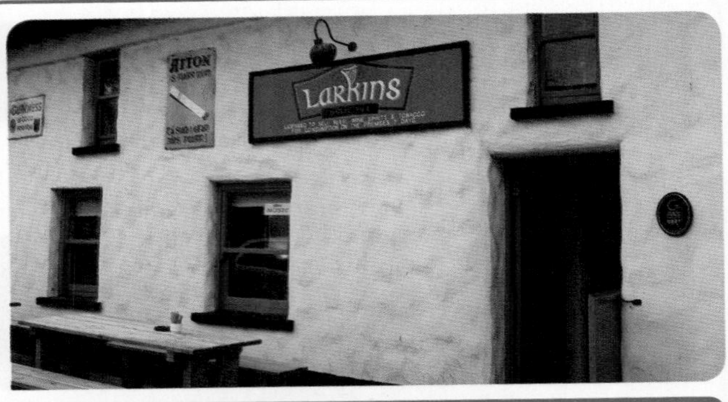

16 Larkins

Garrykennedy

Tel.: (067)23232 – Fax: (067)23933

e-mail: info@larkinspub.com **Website:** www.larkinspub.com

No real ales offered

This thatched, whitewashed inn at the end of the lane looks barely big enough to swing the proverbial pussycat, leave alone house a whole troop of Irish dancers, but Larkins is actually a lot larger on the inside than it appears from the out, and plenty big enough to accommodate the local live music groups who entertain from Wednesday to Sunday. Whitewashed walls covered with old pictures and classic adverts spark off nostalgia, as do the cabinets behind the bar full of old food packets and tins. There is a simple lunch menu and a longer evening version, both of which offer wholesome, hearty cooking served in portions which will satisfy the healthiest of appetites. Homemade soda bread is served at the start of your meal, and you can choose from dishes ranging from steak burger and stew to sea bass and salmon, via seafood chowder and spicy chicken salad. The rear garden and dining room overlook the shores of Lough Derg.

Closing times

Closed 25 December, Good Friday, and Monday-Friday lunch (November-April)

Prices

Meals: à la carte € 32/38

Typical Dishes

Steamed Atlantic mussels

Honey roast duckling

Selection of Tipperary cheese

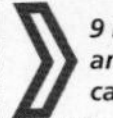

9 km west of Nenagh by R 494 and minor road north. Free public car park opposite.

17 The Lobster Pot

Carne
Tel.: (053)9131110 – Fax: (053)9131401

VISA MC

Smithwicks

A long-standing family owned pub, the Lobster Pot is a veritable Wexford institution. Its success is in part due to the fact that it has a vision and clearly sticks to it; a vision so fantastically full of all things fishy that you can't help but feel that the Carne should change its name to Pesce just to fit in. We're talking platefuls of Wexford cockles and mussels, smoked salmon or mackerel, crab, prawns, or simply the finest, freshest oysters available. This is cuisine that's been washed in with the tide; cooked precisely, served without pretence – and delicious washed down with a pint of Guinness. You can bet you won't be the only one to have heard about the place, though, so to guarantee your appetite is sated, aim to arrive early – preferably when they open. Grab a seat out front or in one of four semi-divided snugs; the nautical knick-knacks which clutter the walls will keep you occupied until someone arrives to take your order.

Closing times

Closed 25-26 December, 17 January to 10 February, Good Friday and Monday (except bank holidays)

Prices

Meals: à la carte € 35/50

Typical Dishes

Baked crab Mornay
Grilled Dover sole
Homemade pear & almond tart

South of Rosslare Harbour. Parking.

A

B

C

D

Index of Pubs and Inns

O

P

Q

R

S

T

V

W

Y

eating out in pubs

Michelin Maps & Guides

*Michelin Maps & Guides
Hannay House,
39 Clarendon Rd
Watford WD17 1JA
Tel: (01923) 205247
Fax: (01923) 205241
www.ViaMichelin.com
eatingoutinpubs-gbirl@
uk.michelin.com*

Manufacture française des pneumatiques Michelin

*Société en commandite par actions au capital de 304 000 000 EUR.
Place des Carmes-Déchaux
63 Clermont-Ferrand (France)
R.C.S. Clermont-Fd B 855 200 507*

*Dépôt légal Septembre 2009
Printed in France 07-09*

Typesetting:

*NORD COMPO, Villeneuve-d'Ascq (France)
Printing and binding:
CANALE, Turin (Italy)*

Photography

*Project manager: Alain Leprince
Agence ACSI – A Chacun Son Image
242, bd. Voltaire– 75011 Paris*

Location Photographs:

Jérôme Berquez, Frédéric Chales, Ludivine Boizard, Jean-Louis Chauveau/ACSI

Thanks to:

The Nags Head, Great Missenden, The Punchbowl Inn, Crosthwaite and The Talbot, Iwerne Minster for the cover images.

*P12: P. Adams/Getty images
P14: P. Adams/Getty images
P15: C. Labonne/Michelin
P46: Travel Ink/Getty images
P112: C. Eymenier/Michelin
P202: P. Thompson/Getty images
P202: P.Adams/Getty images
P244: © English Heritage
P358: S. Allen/Getty images
P470: I. Pompe/Hemis.fr
P512: I. Pompe/Hemis.fr
P562: O. Forir/Michelin
P588: D. Noton /NPL/Jacana
P614: O. Forir/Michelin
P626: O. Forir/Michelin*

YOUR OPINION MATTERS!

To help us constantly improve this guide, please fill in this questionnaire and return to:

Eating out in Pubs 2010
Michelin Maps & Guides,
Hannay House, 39 Clarendon Road,
Watford, WD17 1JA, UK

First name: ....

Surname: ....

Address: ....

Profession: ....

< 25 years old ☐ 25-34 years old ☐

35-50 years old ☐ > 50 years ☐

1. How often do you use the Internet to look for information on pubs?

Never ☐
Occasionally (once a month) ☐
Regularly (once a week) ☐
Very frequently (more than once a week) ☐

2. Have you ever bought Michelin guides?

☐ Yes ☐ No

3. If yes, which one(s)?

Eating out in Pubs ☐
The Michelin Guide Great Britain & Ireland ☐
The Green Guide (please specify titles) ☐

....

Other (please specify titles) ☐

....

4. If you have previously bought Eating out in Pubs, what made you purchase this new one?

....

....

5. If you buy the Michelin Guide Great Britain & Ireland, how often do you buy it?

Every year ☐
Every 2 years ☐
Every 3 years ☐
Every 4 years or more ☐

ABOUT EATING OUT IN PUBS :

6. Did you buy this guide:

For holidays? ☐
For a weekend/short break? ☐
For business purposes? ☐
As a gift? ☐
For everyday use ☐

7. **How do you rate these different elements of this guide?**

NB: **1. Very Poor** **2. Poor** **3. Average** **4. Good** **5. Very Good**

	1	2	3	4	5
Selection of pubs	☐	☐	☐	☐	☐
Number of pubs in London	☐	☐	☐	☐	☐
Geographical spread of pubs	☐	☐	☐	☐	☐
Menu Prices	☐	☐	☐	☐	☐
Practical information (services, menus)	☐	☐	☐	☐	☐
Photos	☐	☐	☐	☐	☐
Description of the pubs	☐	☐	☐	☐	☐
Cover	☐	☐	☐	☐	☐
The format & size of the guide	☐	☐	☐	☐	☐
Guide Price	☐	☐	☐	☐	☐

8. **How easily could you find the information you were looking for ?**

....

....

9. **Please rate the guide out of 20 ..../20**

10. **Which aspects could we improve?**

....

....

....

....

....

....

11. **Was there a pub you particularly liked or a choice you didn't agree with? Perhaps you have a favourite address of your own that you would like to tell us about? Please send us your remarks and suggestions.**

....

....

....

....

....

....

....

....

....

....

The information you provide will be collected and processed by Manufacture Francaise des Pneumatiques Michelin. If you do not wish the information to be made available to other companies in the Michelin group, please tick the box ☐

By the terms of the French "Informatique et Liberté" act 6th January 1978, you are entitled to access, modify, rectify and delete information relating to you. To exercise this right, you should contact:

Manufacture Francaise des Pneumatiques Michelin
46 avenue de Breteuil
75324 Paris Cedex 07
France